encyclopedia of
ASTRONOMY
GILBERT E. SATTERTHWAITE
F.R.A.S., F.G.S.

HAMLYN
LONDON · NEW YORK · SYDNEY · TORONTO

TO MY FIRST TUTOR
Dr A. F. O'D. ALEXANDER

© Gilbert Elliott Satterthwaite 1970
ISBN 0 600 41106 0

Published by
THE HAMLYN PUBLISHING GROUP LIMITED
LONDON · NEW YORK · SYDNEY · TORONTO
Hamlyn House, Feltham, Middlesex, England
Second Impression 1973
Printed in the United States of America

FOREWORD

BY PATRICK MOORE O.B.E., F.R.A.S.

There was a period, not many decades ago, when astronomy was regarded as a subject far removed from everyday life. Its practical applications in navigation and timekeeping were recognised, but otherwise it remained a study very much on its own.

The situation today is very different. It is no longer possible to give a clear-cut distinction between astronomy and other branches of science—such as chemistry, physics, and even biology. Moreover, we are living in the Space Age, and with the launching of the first manned vehicles to the Moon our whole outlook has changed; it has ceased to be 'isolationist', even though we must always bear in mind the fact that our rockets can take us only to the very local parts of the universe.

All these developments have led to a surge of interest in astronomy, which may well be partially—though certainly not wholly—due to the spectacular advances in space research. One result is that the trickle of astronomical literature has become a raging torrent. Books of all kinds have appeared, of varying scope and (it must be admitted) of varying standard. Most of them cater for a particular kind of reader; either the professional astronomer, whose work is basically mathematical and who is concerned chiefly with stellar research, or else the amateur, whose interests are concentrated upon the Moon and planets.

To write about astronomy, one must be an astronomer, and one must have the ability to impart knowledge, which requires literary skill. These facts are not always appreciated. I welcome Mr. Satterthwaite's book particularly because it has a wide scope, and because he is exceptionally well qualified to write it. He has been a professional astronomer at the Royal Greenwich Observatory, and resigned his post there only to take up an important appointment connected with scientific literature. He is also a well-known observer of the planet Jupiter, a field which has always been traditional to amateurs. Therefore, he has an insight into all the three essentials for compiling a standard reference-book.

What he has done, and done very successfully, is to produce a work which will be of great use to professional astronomers, to science students, and to amateurs. The decision to arrange the topics in alphabetical order has been a wise one, since it makes for quick and easy checking.

The range of modern astronomy is wider than many people suppose. Nobody can hope to cover it all at specialist level. The research astrophysicist will hardly ever bother to turn his telescope toward the Moon or a planet; conversely, the amateur who is chiefly interested in (say) the changing features on Jupiter will have scant knowledge of the spectra of remote galaxies. The field of the solar observer is just as specialized. We have the radio astronomers, who have come so much to the fore; we have investigations into the ultra-violet and X-radiations from space; we have the instrument-makers, without whom no research could be carried on. Neither must we forget what has always been termed 'positional astronomy', which is at the root of timekeeping and navigation, and with which Mr. Satterthwaite was himself so closely connected during his years at the Royal Greenwich Observatory.

In view of his experience as a professional astronomer and as an amateur observer, and with his strong literary connections, Mr. Satterthwaite has been well able to combine all this knowledge into a comprehensive text. Various dictionaries of astronomy have appeared in the past, but not in this form; the present book is more than a dictionary. It is a work of reference which will be useful to all astronomers, and I have no doubt that it will remain a standard text for many years to come.

ACKNOWLEDGMENTS

I have dedicated this book to Dr Alexander in gratitude for his patient help and the example of his own astronomical work. I hope that it will not be judged too unworthy a tribute.

I also wish to record my sincere gratitude to my family: to my parents, for their early encouragement and lasting support; and to my wife and children, who have constantly striven to provide an environment conducive to the writing of this book and have been shamefully neglected in return.

I would also like to thank Patrick Moore, not only for his generous Foreword, but also for his friendship, guidance and support for 22 years; my debt to him is very great.

It would be impossible to pay adequate tribute here to all the others who have helped me during the preparation of this book, or even to list them. Nevertheless I wish to thank them all most sincerely, for their help and encouragement, for the pleasure of their company and the stimulus of their conversation.

There are some to whom thanks are due, but for whose help this book could never have been completed: to Mrs Patricia Wigmore and Miss Gail Roden, who between them typed much of the copy; to Miss Jean Elliot, who spent many hours reading proofs; and to Mr Donald Beale and Mr Patrick Moore, for much help with the illustrations.

I am grateful to the Councils of the Royal Astronomical Society and the British Astronomical Association for permission to reproduce material from their publications, and to the Controller of Her Majesty's Stationery Office for permission to reproduce data from *The Astronomical Ephemeris*.

For illustrations used in the plates I am greatly indebted to Mr W. M. Baxter (Plates 1a; 2d; 3a–f); Dr G. Fielder (6e); Cdr H. R. Hatfield (6a, b, g); Dr E. M. Lindsay (15f; 20a–c; 21e); Dr R. McLean (16f); Mr P. A. Moore (9c, d; 17b; 25d; 26b; 28d; 32c); Dr W. H. Steavenson (13e; 14a, d; 20e); Allison Studios, Armagh (24d); Cambridge University Press (15c, d; 20d); Faber & Faber Limited (9c, d; 13d; 14b, c); Gauthier–Villars, S.A.R.L. (9b); Grubb–Parsons Limited (31b); the Hutchinson Group (10d; 12g; 13b, e; 14a, d; 17a, c; 28c); John Murray Limited (13c); the Ronan Picture Library (32a); VEB Carl Zeiss, Jena (24c); National Aeronautics and Space Administration, Washington (5b, c, e; 6d, f; 7b, c; 8a–e; 10f, g); National Geographic Society, Washington (2a); The Royal Society (17c); The Science Museum, London (21a, b; 25a–c, e; 26c); U.S. Navy (2e); Press Department, U.S.S.R. Embassy in London (7a); and the Directors of the following observatories: Armagh (15f); Boyden (20a–c; 21e); Harvard College (23b); Heidelberg (16e); Kodaikanal (2f); Lick (2c; 4a–c; 9e, f; 10c, e; 22d; 31a); Lowell (12d, e; 13f; 15a, b, e); McDonald (10b; 14c; 16d; 30b); Meudon (1c, d; 14b); Mount Wilson and Palomar (1e; 5a, d; 6c; 9a; 10a; 12a–c; 13a; 14e; 17d; 18a–e; 19a–d; 21c; 22a, b; 23a, c–f; 24a, b; 29a, b; 30c, d; 31d); Radio Astronomy Section, Cavendish Laboratory, Cambridge (32b, d); Pic-du-Midi (6e); Radcliffe (22c); Royal Greenwich Observatory (1b; 16a–c; 27a–c, e; 28a, b; 29d, e); Royal Observatory, Edinburgh (22e); Yerkes (2b; 21d; 30a).

G. E. S.

INTRODUCTION

'That's one small step for Man; one giant leap for Mankind.' Neil Armstrong's historic words marked the culmination of more than a decade of scientific and technological effort. During that time—sometimes termed the 'Space Age'—this book has been written. During that time I have seen astronomy (in the broadest sense) develop from a rather remote subject, popularly regarded as of interest only to a minority of fanatical enthusiasts and absent-minded professors, to a stimulating and exciting subject which is constantly in the news. This is not solely due to the newsworthy space programmes; the recent Earth-based discoveries of the quasars and pulsars, for instance, both caught the public's imagination.

In this book I have made no attempt to chronicle the epoch-making achievements in space, but I have sought to provide details of the fundamental astronomical background to them.

If the events leading up to the writing of this book can be said to have a beginning, it was probably the day in 1946 when my father won a book token at a fancy dress ball. My twelfth birthday being imminent, that token was partly expended on a book for me. I chose *The Angry Planet* by the late John Keir Cross, which told the story of an imaginary journey to Mars. Intrigued by this work of fiction, I was stimulated to read more factual texts and later to attend evening classes. Ever since I have been held captive by this most fascinating of studies.

Probably the strongest stimulus for this book came from my own evening-class students, who by their interest and questioning convinced me of the need for a comprehensive text at this level, arranged in encyclopaedic format.

The arrangement is quite straightforward, but a little preliminary study of it will facilitate future reference to the text. As far as possible the main word of the entry governs its position, and duplicate entries are avoided. Thus chromatic aberration is treated only under **Aberration, chromatic.**

Articles describing various aspects of a single body are grouped together: thus the entry **Mars** is followed by a further nine entries describing that planet and its satellites. I hope that this will be found helpful by those readers who wish to study a particular body in detail.

Undefined terms occurring in the text in **bold type** themselves appear as separate entries in the book. Where an entry is part of a broader topic, cross-reference is made in the form 'See . . .'. Thus, the entry **Barred spiral galaxy** includes the cross-reference '(See **Galactic structure**)'.

Reference to other entries on related topics is made by 'See also . . .'. Thus the entry **Apogee** concludes with the cross-reference '(See also **Perigee**)'.

Certain entries provide an index to a group of related shorter entries, e.g. **Constellation names and abbreviations; Mars—surface features of; Moon—principal surface features of; Star catalogues.**

It would be impossible to list and keep up to date even the principal space missions. I make no excuse for tabulating details of some of the early ones, however, believing that they record an important epoch in astronomical history.

I also believe strongly in the value of an historical approach to the study of astronomy. I have therefore included numerous biographical notes on distinguished astronomers of the past, both amateur and professional, and have tried to show the parts they played in the development of the science. This inevitably raises a difficult question —whether or not to include similar notes on contemporary astronomers. In general I support the view that it is better to leave posterity to judge the relative importance of their work, but there are some whose names are already so frequently cited in contemporary reports that some reference to them is essential. I have kept such entries as few and as brief as possible; the list is very subjective and no reflection is implied on those who have not been included.

The compilation of a book of this size and scope is an enormous task, and has occupied my spare time for several years. If the result helps others to derive as much enjoyment from the heavens as I have had, however, I shall feel amply rewarded.

GILBERT E. SATTERTHWAITE,
Orpington, Kent

A

Å. The accepted abbreviation for the **Ångström unit,** *q.v.*

A.A. Abbreviation for **Annuaire Astronomique,** *q.v.*

A.E. Abbreviation for **The Astronomical Ephemeris** and **The American Ephemeris,** *q.v.*

AGK. Abbreviation for the *Astronomische Gesellschaft Katalog,* published in Leipzig in 1890. (See **Astronomische Gesellschaft catalogues.**)

AGK 2. Abbreviation for the *Zweiter Katalog der Astronomische Gesellschaft,* containing the positions of some 183,000 stars (epoch 1950·0) and published in Hamburg in 1951. (See **Astronomische Gesellschaft catalogues.**)

A.N. Usual abbreviation of the **Almanaque Náutico,** *q.v.*

A STARS Stars of spectral class *A*; they are white stars with surface temperatures of 8,000–11,000° K. *Sirius* is a notable example.

A.U. The usual abbreviation for the **Astronomical Unit,** *q.v.*

ABERRATION, CHROMATIC A lens defect arising from the fact that the refractive index of any type of glass varies with wavelength, and consequently light of different colours is brought to different foci; thus a simple converging lens will focus light of shorter wavelength (e.g. blue) closer to itself than light of longer wavelength (e.g. red)—see Fig. 1.

This defect can be reduced in compound lenses; by choosing differently constituted glasses of suitable refractive indices for the components of a doublet, one can ensure that the light of two selected wavelengths is brought to a common focus. This is termed an **achromatic lens.**

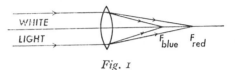

Fig. 1

Achromatic telescope objectives usually employ suitable curvatures and types of glass to reduce both chromatic and **spherical aberration** (*q.v.*).

ABERRATION OF LIGHT A phenomenon which arises from the fact that light travels with a velocity which is finite compared with the orbital velocity of the Earth; it results in an apparent displacement of the star's position.

Aberration can best be illustrated by imagining an observer standing in the rain. The rain is assumed to be falling vertically. Whilst the observer remains stationary the rain will appear to him to be falling vertically, but, as soon as he moves, the rain, although still falling vertically, will appear to him to be falling diagonally towards him. The rain's apparent motion will be towards the observer, whatever the direction in which he moves.

Similarly, during the time taken by the light from a star to travel to Earth the Earth will move on in its orbit, and the star will consequently appear to be displaced towards the point in the heavens towards which the Earth is moving at that instant.

The effect can be analysed by the use

of the parallelogram of velocities, as shown in Fig. 2, in which O is the location of the observer, OX the direction of the Earth's orbital motion at the time and

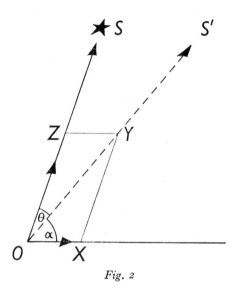

Fig. 2

OZ the true direction of the star S. The apparent direction of the star is then given by the diagonal OY; the observer will thus see the star in the position S'. The angular displacement of the star, θ, can be determined by means of the formula

$$\theta = \frac{v}{c} \sin \alpha,$$

where α is the angle between the apparent direction of the star and the direction of the Earth's motion (this angle is sometimes termed the 'Earth's Way'), v is the orbital velocity of the Earth and c is the velocity of light.

The constant $\frac{v}{c}$ is termed the constant of aberration, and has a value of $20''.47$.

The phenomenon of aberration was discovered by Bradley from his observations of the star γ Dra.

ABERRATION, PLANETARY As light travels at a finite velocity, the light of an observed body in the solar system will

have left the body some seconds previously, during which time the body will have moved on in its orbit; in order to obtain the accurate position of the body at the instant of observation it is therefore necessary to correct the observed place for the motion of the body during the light-time.

Hence, if a planet's position is measured at time T, and the light-time is t, the measured place will be correct for the time $(T-t)$; to obtain the place at time T the measured R.A. and Dec. must be corrected by the addition of the factors $t\Delta\alpha$ and $t\Delta\delta$ respectively, where $\Delta\alpha$ and $\Delta\delta$ are the rates of change of R.A. and Dec. for the planet concerned, at the epoch of observation. This is termed correcting for planetary aberration.

ABERRATION, SPHERICAL A defect of simple lenses whereby light rays transmitted by various zones of the lens are not brought to a common focus; in the case of a simple converging lens, rays transmitted by the outer zones of the lens are brought to a nearer focus (F_A) than rays transmitted by the central zones of the lens (brought to a focus at F_B)—see Fig. 3.

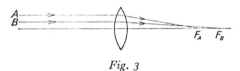

Fig. 3

This defect can be substantially reduced in the case of compound lenses, by the careful selection of the curvatures employed for the surfaces of the components. (See also **Aberration, chromatic.**)

ABSOLUTE MAGNITUDE A measure of the actual luminosity of a star, after allowing for its distance from the Earth. (See **Magnitude, absolute.**)

ABSOLUTE ZERO The lowest temperature possible, at which all molecular motion would cease and it is therefore unattainable, although extremely close up-proaches to it have been made in labora-tory experiments. It is the basepoint of the Kelvin scale of absolute temperature measurement. It is equivalent to $-273.15°$ on the Centigrade scale.

ABSORPTION, GALACTIC It is known that there are vast tenuous clouds of non-radiating gas and dust concentrated in the galactic plane, which absorb radiation incident upon them from more distant stars, thus reducing their apparent magni-tude to the terrestrial observer. In places these clouds can be 'seen' as dark obscura-tions against bright star fields—the 'ab-sorption nebulae'. It is obvious from counts of the numbers of stars of each magnitude that the absorbing matter is present throughout interstellar space, 'dimming' the more distant stars and galaxies very considerably, although it is much more concentrated in the galactic plane.

It has been shown that particles below a certain critical size will not scatter light of all wavelengths equally, but will scatter short-wavelength light (e.g. blue) much more than long-wavelength light (e.g. red); this phenomenon, termed *selective absorp-tion*, is detectable in the spectra of distant stars, whose light is reddened by an amount dependant upon the distance of the star and its galactic latitude. This effect is termed 'space-reddening'.

ABSORPTION LINES The dark lines of the **absorption spectrum**.

ABSORPTION OF LIGHT It was shown by Kirchhoff in 1860 that a body will absorb radiation of the same wavelength as that which it emits; this fact gives rise to the formation of the absorption spec-trum, when radiation from a very hot source passes through a cooler layer of the same substance.

ABSORPTION SPECTRUM The 'dark-line' spectrum produced by a body having a hot, gaseous layer through which light

from an even hotter source below is passed, the radiation from the hotter source being absorbed by the relatively cool gases of the upper layer. The forma-tion of the absorption spectrum depends upon the fact, discovered by Kirchhoff, that a body will absorb radiation of the same wavelength as that which it emits itself.

ACCRETION It has long been recognized that 'space' is not empty, but contains molecules of 'interstellar gas' (largely hydrogen) at a very low density. A star passing through this tenuous medium will gather some of these molecules to itself by its gravitational attraction, and thus increase in mass; this process is known as accretion.

It has been extensively studied by con-temporary theorists, notably Lyttleton, Bondi and Hoyle, who have shown that it is an important factor in stellar evolu-tion, and may well be the primary cause of the development of very massive stars.

Theories have also been developed, again principally by Lyttleton, that the formation of comets is due to the accretion of interstellar gas and dust as the solar system travels in its orbit around the galactic centre.

ACHERNAR The star α Eri, at the mouth of the great river depicted in the ancient star maps. It is a bluish-white star, spectral type $B5$, and has an apparent magnitude of 0.5; it is the ninth brightest star in the heavens.

ACHILLIS PONS Martian surface fea-ture, approximate position Ω 30°, $\Phi + 45°$. A lightish band running between the Mare Acidalium and Niliachus Lacus, con-necting Cydonia and Tempe.

ACHROMAT A lens corrected for chro-matic aberration. (See **Lens, achromatic**.)

ACHROMATIC LENS A lens corrected for chromatic aberration, also known as an *achromat*. (See **Lens, achromatic**.)

ACRUX The star α Cru, at the foot of the Southern Cross, pointing towards the south pole of the heavens. It is a nice double, both components being bluish-white stars of spectral type $B1$, of magnitudes 1·6 and 2·1, giving a combined visual apparent magnitude of 0·8. Both components are spectroscopic binaries. Their separation is 5″, position angle 118°.

ACTINIDE ELEMENTS Name sometimes given to the series of rare-earth-type elements having atomic numbers from 89 to 102 inclusive; the name derives from the first element in the series—actinium. (See **Chemical elements.**)

ADAMS, John Couch (1819–1892) Generally reckoned to be Britain's greatest mathematical astronomer since Newton. Born in Cornwall, Adams became interested in astronomy in early boyhood. He became an undergraduate of St. John's College, Cambridge, in 1839; in 1843 he was Senior Wrangler and Smith's Prizeman, and was elected a Fellow of his college. By this time he was already interested in the anomalies in the motion of Uranus, and analysed these in an effort to prove the existence of a trans-Uranian planet. As is well-known, Adams produced the first position for Neptune, although due to an unfortunate series of mischances the planet was first located using a position calculated by Le Verrier; happily, and rightly, Adams is now regarded as jointly responsible with Le Verrier for the discovery of the planet.

Among the many astronomical investigations that Adams conducted were a redetermination of the Moon's parallax; an explanation of the secular variation in the Moon's motion; an analysis of the motion of the November meteor shower (the Leonids), etc., etc., as well as many purely mathematical exercises. Following the cessation of his Fellowship of St. John's in 1852, Adams became a Fellow of Pembroke College, Cambridge, in 1853—a status he retained for the rest of his life. In 1858 he was appointed Professor of Mathematics in the University of St. Andrews, but was destined to lecture there for only one year, for within a few months he became Lowndean Professor of Astronomy and Geometry at Cambridge. In 1861 he became Director of the Cambridge Observatory.

Adams received Honorary Degrees from the Universities of Oxford, Edinburgh, Dublin and Bologna, as well as Cambridge; he was awarded the Copley Medal of the Royal Society in 1848. He was twice elected President of the Royal Astronomical Society, in 1851–1853 and 1874–1876, and was awarded its Gold Medal in 1866. In 1881 he was invited to succeed Airy as Astronomer Royal, but declined (he was already 62 years of age); in 1884 he represented Great Britain at the International Prime Meridian Conference in Washington. (See also **Neptune—discovery of.**)

ADAMS, Walter S. (1876–1956) One of the greatest in the great tradition of American practical astronomers. Adams was actually born in the Lebanon, of American parentage, but was educated mostly in the United States and spent his entire working career there. He was a protégé of Hale, who appointed him to the staff of the Yerkes Observatory in 1901 and in 1904 invited him to join the staff of the Mount Wilson Observatory, then being formed, as Assistant Astronomer. Adams became Assistant Director of the Mount Wilson Observatory in 1910 and Director in 1923—a position he held until his retirement in 1946. He remained active in a research capacity throughout his retirement, and died in the middle of his eightieth year. He was thus associated with Mount Wilson throughout the first half-century of its history; probably no-one contributed more to its development, save perhaps Hale himself.

Much of Adams' early work was concerned with radial velocities of stars, and he was one of the pioneers of the determination of stellar parallaxes by spectroscopic means. He made many notable contributions to stellar spectroscopy, and to spectroscopic studies of other bodies, including novæ and the atmospheres of the planets.

In addition to his great observing work Adams was also a first-class administrator, and guided the Mount Wilson Observatory through a period of great importance and expansion as well as making a notable contribution to the development of astrophysical research on an international scale. He received a multitude of honours, both in the United States and throughout the world. He was President of the Astronomical Society of the Pacific (1923) and of the American Astronomical Society (1931–1934); he was a Foreign Member of The Royal Society, and an Associate of the Royal Astronomical Society as early as 1914. He was awarded the Gold Medal of the R.A.S. in 1917, and served as Vice-President of the International Astronomical Union (1935–1949).

ADASTRÆ Proposed name of satellite XII of Jupiter, *q.v.*

ADHARA The star ε CMa, a blue-white star of spectral type *B2* and magnitude 1·4; there is an eighth-magnitude companion at 7ʺ5 separation, position angle 160°.

ADONIS Minor planet with a highly eccentric orbit ($e = 0·779$), discovered by the Belgian observer E. Delporte on 1936 February 12. Adonis passed the Earth at a distance of only a million miles *en route* to its perihelion well inside the orbit of Venus; its orbit was difficult to determine with accuracy, owing to the short apparition, rapid motion and eccentric orbit, and it is extremely unlikely that it will be recovered and positively identified at a future return.

ÆOLIS Martian surface feature, approximate position $\Omega\,215°$, $\Phi - 5°$. A well-defined light area in the equatorial region of the planet, bordered by the Mare Cimmerium to the south, Laestrygonum Sinus and Laestrygon to the east, Cer-

berus to the north and Pambotis Lacus and Cyclopia in the west. It is crossed by Antæus, from Læstrygonum Sinus to Pambotis Lacus.

ÆRIA Martian surface feature, approximate position $\Omega\,310°$, $\Phi + 10°$. Large ochre area adjoining the western border of the Syrtis Major. Separated from Arabia in the west by the long, straight canal Phison.

AEROLITE The most common form of meteorite, consisting largely of stony material. (See **Meteorite.**)

ÆTHERIA Martian surface feature, approximate position $\Omega\,230°$, $\Phi + 40°$. Lightish area in the north temperate region, north-west of Elysium.

ÆTHIOPIS Martian surface feature, approximate position $\Omega\,230°$, $\Phi + 10°$. Lightish area in the north tropical region, south-west of Elysium and north of the western end of the Mare Cimmerium.

AGATHODÆMON Martian surface feature, approximate position $\Omega\,70°$, $\Phi - 10°$. Prominent canal connecting Auroræ Sinus and Tithonius Lacus; forms the north-east boundary of Thaumasia.

AGE OF CELESTIAL BODIES The age of the Earth, as a solid planet, is believed from geological investigations to be of the order of 4,000 million years; from calculations based upon its present composition and radiative output the age of the Sun is estimated to be of much the same order.

From the dynamics of star clusters and binary systems astrophysicists have established the age of the universe as a whole at about 10,000 million years. If one accepts that the expanding nature of the universe indicates that the evolutionary theory is correct, it is possible to calculate the time that must have elapsed since the primordial 'explosion' postulated by that theory; estimates of this vary between 8,000 and 13,000 million years, which is in excellent agreement with the estimates made by astrophysical methods.

AGENA The star β Cen, magnitude 0·61; also known as *Hadar*.

AINSLIE, M. A. (1869–1951) An Instructor Captain in the Royal Navy, Maurice Ainslie was one of the most notable English amateur astronomers of this century. A bearded giant of a man, his commanding figure tended to belie the kindliness of his nature; one of his most valuable attributes was his constant interest in encouraging others new to astronomy.

He was a pillar of the British Astronomical Association, of which he was a member from 1906 until his death; he served as President of the Association (1928–1930). An expert optician, he was largely responsible for the formation of the Instruments and Methods of Observation Section of the Association in 1917, and was its first Director, which post he held until 1932.

Ainslie was a thorough and competent observer, his principal interests being the planets Jupiter and Saturn. He was Director of the Saturn Section of the B.A.A. for two important periods in its history (1930–1933; 1939–1945). Perhaps his most notable achievement as an observer was his observations from Blackheath of an unpredicted occultation of the star B.D. $+21°1714$ by the ring system of Saturn; the occultation was also observed by John Knight at Rye. Ainslie observed the star, undimmed, through Cassini's Division, and throughout almost the whole of its passage behind Ring A, although greatly dimmed. This historic observation proved both the translucency of the ring and that Cassini's Division is, in fact, a true gap.

(See also **Saturn—rings of.**)

AIRGLOW Faint light originating in the Earth's upper atmosphere and contributing to the faint luminosity of the night sky. It is probably due to the liberation of energy gathered during the day from the solar radiation and stored in the ionosphere; in addition to the basic airglow there is a further emission, the *twilight airglow*, observed after sunset when the upper atmospheric layers are still illuminated by the Sun.

(See also **Night sky, illumination of.**)

AIRY, Sir George Biddell (1801–1892) The seventh Astronomer Royal, believed by many to be the greatest of the distinguished incumbents of that office. Throughout his long working life Airy dominated not only British astronomy, but also the British scientific scene generally.

Airy was born in Alnwick, Northumberland, and educated privately in south-east England; it was obvious from his earliest years that he possessed a natural gift for mathematics, and thanks to the encouragement and help of numerous friends he obtained a place at Trinity College, Cambridge. One of his mentors at this crucial stage of his career was the Ipswich engineer Ransome, an association which was to prove of great benefit to Airy in his re-equipping of the Royal Observatory in later years.

Airy had a brilliant career at Cambridge; he graduated in 1823 as Senior Wrangler in the Mathematical Tripos, and was Smith's Prizeman; in 1824 he was elected a Fellow of Trinity College, and in 1826 he obtained his Master's degree and was appointed Lucasian Professor of Mathematics, thus achieving at the age of twenty-five a position once occupied by Newton. During his tenure of this chair Airy delivered a notable series of public lectures on Experimental Philosophy.

In 1828 Airy was appointed Plumian Professor of Astronomy and Superintendent of the Cambridge Observatory. Airy's first achievement in his new post was to reorganize completely the system of meridian observations and their reduction and analysis. In 1833 he presented a paper to the Royal Society on a long-period inequality in the motions of Venus and the Earth; for this important piece of analysis the Royal Astronomical Society awarded him its Gold Medal.

In 1835, following the resignation of the ailing Pond, Airy was appointed H.M. Astronomer Royal. He thus succeeded to the Directorship of the Royal Observatory at Greenwich at one of the lowest ebbs in its history; what was needed to bring the establishment back again to the forefront of astronomical research was a man of great strength of character and determination. These were among Airy's strongest qualities, and he took immediate steps to revitalize the Observatory. A stern taskmaster, he planned the expected output of each member of the staff for each day, down to the last detail, and expected his instructions to be carried out to the letter.

Airy introduced new procedures for the fundamental work of the Observatory, based upon the new system he had developed at Cambridge. He also undertook the mammoth task of analysing the meridian observations of the Moon and planets made during the period 1750–1830. The Royal Astronomical Society awarded Airy a second Gold Medal in recognition of his publication of the reduced and analysed observations of the planets, and a Testimonial in respect of the lunar observations.

Despite his preoccupation with his own astronomical researches and the administration of the Royal Observatory, Airy was constantly consulted by governmental and industrial concerns, both at home and abroad, on an incredibly wide range of scientific matters, and he gave carefully considered advice to each, and spent many hours of each week sitting on committees. He also organized three eclipse expeditions and two to observe the transits of Venus in 1874 and 1882.

Airy was responsible for the creation of a magnetic and meteorological observatory as a department of the Royal Observatory in 1840. The first embryonic time service was instituted by him in 1853 with the erection of a time-ball at Deal, released at one o'clock daily by means of an electric signal from the Royal Observatory clock. From 1865 time-signals were distributed throughout the country by means of the telegraph system operated by the railway companies. Greenwich Mean Time was adopted as the legal time of Great Britain in 1880.

Airy had proved himself an engineer of no mean ability during his years at Cambridge, and he was ever awake to the need to add new instruments to the Royal Observatory's equipment in order to play a leading part in new fields of research. Most of the instruments he added were designed by himself.

The first equatorial instrument erected at Greenwich was a 7-in. refractor erected in 1837, the gift of the Rev. R. Sheepshanks. The 'Great Equatorial' was erected in 1858; this instrument, a fine 12¾-in. refractor with objective by Merz, was driven by a sophisticated water-clock invented by Airy.

In 1847 Airy's **altazimuth** was erected for the purpose of obtaining extra-meridian positional observations of the Moon, and in 1851 the famous **Airy Transit Circle** commenced observations. Both these instruments were made to Airy's designs by his old friend Ransome, of the firm of Ransome and May of Ipswich.

In 1873 Airy created a new department of the Observatory, devoted to the study of the Sun, and in 1874 instituted astrophysical observations with the addition of a spectroscope to the Great Equatorial.

Airy retired from the Royal Observatory on 1881 August 15 at the age of 80, and was succeeded as Astronomer Royal by his Chief Assistant, W. H. M. Christie. He had served as Astronomer Royal for exactly 46 years. He lived in retirement in a house in Greenwich Park, within sight of the Observatory he had directed with such distinction for so long.

Lack of space prevents enumeration of Airy's many other contributions to science. It was said of him by one of his most distinguished successors, Sir Harold Spencer Jones, that he 'seemed to combine all the great qualities of his predecessors. He had Flamsteed's methodical habits; Halley's interest in the lunar theory; Bradley's devotion to the making of star catalogues; Maskelyne's promptitude in publishing and his keen interest in practical navigation, and Pond's refinement of observation.'

Airy received many honours, from his own country and from several foreign ones. He was created a Companion of the Most Honourable Order of the Bath (C.B.) in 1871, and elevated to knighthood as a Knight Commander of the same order (K.C.B.) in the following year. In 1875 he was presented with the Honorary Freedom of the City of London. He was an Honorary Fellow of Trinity College, Cambridge, and received honorary degrees from the Universities of Cambridge, Oxford and Edinburgh.

Elected a Fellow of the Royal Society in 1836, Airy served as its President in 1871–1873; he was awarded the Copley Medal of the Society in 1831 and the Royal Medal in 1845. He was a Fellow of the Royal Astronomical Society for 64 years, and a member of its Council for an unbroken period of 56 years. He was its elected President on no less than five occasions, a unique distinction; elected President for the periods 1835–1837, 1849–1851, 1853–1855 and 1863–1864, he was also elected to fill the vacancy left by the death of Baily, in 1844–1845.

After ten years of retirement, throughout most of which he remained both physically and mentally fit, Airy died on 1892 January 2 following an operation. Though strict and autocratic, he is remembered as a great man in every way, and as one of the greatest scientists England has ever produced.

AIRY DISK The 'spurious disk' at the centre of the in-focus image produced of a point-source by a telescope objective, due to **diffraction**.

AIRY TRANSIT CIRCLE The most famous meridian instrument of all time, and by a handsome margin the most productive.

Designed by Airy, this was one of the first instruments to combine the function of the previously separate transit instrument and mural circle; it was constructed by Messrs Ransome & May of Ipswich, with an object glass by Simms, and was erected at the Royal Observatory, Greenwich, in 1850. In view of the importance its position was later to attain, the considerations behind the choice of the actual site selected seem, in retrospect, somewhat casual. As an economy measure it was decided to mount the new instrument between two existing piers which had previously supported the vertical circles by Jones and Troughton. This decision was to cause great problems in later years in correcting for instrumental errors, the western (Jones' circle) pier being constructed of Portland Stone and the eastern (Troughton's circle) of granite.

The resulting meridian of the instrument was some 19 feet east of the previous Greenwich meridian, established by Bradley.

The first observation with the new transit circle was made during the night of 1851 January 4/5 by Thomas Ellis; it continued in constant use, with only minor modifications, for more than 103 years, a quite unparalleled record. In 1854 the instrument became the first meridian circle to provide electrical registration of transits in Right Ascension, by means of the impersonal micrometer.

In 1880 Greenwich Mean Time—then controlled by transit observations made by the 'Airy T.C.'—was adopted as the national standard time throughout Great Britain. In 1884 an international conference held in Washington adopted the meridian of the Airy T.C. at Greenwich as the Prime Meridian of longitude.

With this great instrument positional observations of the Sun, Moon, planets and major asteroids were made almost without a break until 1954; in addition no less than ten major fundamental and reference-star catalogues were compiled with its aid and published between 1860 and 1930. [Plate 27(b).]

The provision at Greenwich of the new Reversible Transit Circle in 1936 was intended to permit Airy's ageing instrument, once described by Newcomb as 'the most serviceable meridian instrument ever constructed', to be retired; the advent of the Second World War, however, and the subsequent removal of the Royal Observatory to Herstmonceux, conspired to keep it in useful service for a further twenty years. Only with the transfer of the Meridian Department of the Royal Observatory to Herstmonceux was the active life of the instrument concluded. The last observation—of the Sun—was made by the present writer on 1954 March 30.

The useful functions of the instrument were not yet concluded, however; today it remains *in situ*, and will be preserved so as a permanent reference mark to the Prime Meridian. The buildings of the Royal Observatory, for nearly three centuries the leading observatory for fundamental astronomy, are now used as an astronomical annexe to the National Maritime Museum. Many of the instruments used there during its great history are preserved for posterity in their original surroundings, a permanent reminder of the great Greenwich tradition; of all of them, the Airy Transit Circle is surely the finest memorial to that great heritage.

AITKEN, Robert G. (1864–1949) Famous American astronomer, a former Director of the Lick Observatory and one of the few great double-star observers. With the collaboration of W. J. Hussey he carried out a gargantuan programme of observations with the 36-in. refractor at Lick which resulted in the publication, in 1932, of the so-called 'Aitken Catalogue'—the *New General Catalogue of Double Stars.* This catalogue contains data for 17,180 pairs, and is the standard work of reference for double stars north of Dec. $-30°$.

In the nomenclature of double-star discoverers the single letter 'A' is used for Aitken's many discoveries; his name is

further commemorated in the recognized abbreviation for the Aitken Catalogue (ADS).

Among his many honours was the Gold Medal of the Royal Astronomical Society which he was awarded in 1932, in which year he also delivered the George Darwin Lecture to the Society.

AITKEN CATALOGUE The **New General Catalogue of Double Stars** compiled by R. G. Aitken (*q.v.*).

AL NA'IR The star α Gru, magnitude 2·2, spectral type *B5.*

ALBATEGNIUS Lunar surface feature co-ordinates $\xi + 067$, $\eta - 197$. A superb walled plain, 80 miles in diameter, in the heart of the southern mountainous region. It is almost diamond-shaped, and the broad, rugged walls, which rise to 14,000 ft in places, are broken in the south-east by the well-defined crater-ring Klein, some 20 miles in diameter and with a central mountain.

Albategnius has a beautifully conical central mountain, and there are a number of small rings and other features on its floor. Albategnius forms a prominent pair with Hipparchus.

ALBEDO Strictly, the ratio between the amount of light falling upon a tiny element of a surface and the total amount of light reflected by the element in all directions. The diffusion of reflected light may vary for different parts of a surface, and hence a mean albedo for the surface is very difficult to determine.

For astronomical purposes the albedo is taken to be the fraction of the total amount of incident light reflected by a sphere, assuming that the sphere is illuminated only by parallel light rays. In the case of bodies in the solar system, illuminated only by the very distant Sun, this is, for all practical purposes, the case.

The albedo is an important factor in considerations of the nature of the surface of astronomical bodies, and comparisons

9

with the reflectivity of known substances are of considerable assistance in such studies.

The albedos of the principal bodies in the solar system are:

Mercury	0·06	Saturn	0·76
Venus	0·76	Uranus	0·93
Mars	0·16	Neptune	0·84
Jupiter	0·73	Pluto	0·14 (estimated)
Earth	0·36	Moon	0·07

ALBIREO The star β Cyg, the faintest of the five stars which make up the so-called 'Northern Cross', and the star said to represent the eye of the flying swan in the ancient constellation figure.

Albireo is also one of the most beautiful double stars in the heavens; the primary is a beautiful golden-yellow (spectral type *K*0) star of magnitude 3·2, its companion is a bluish-green (*A*0) star of magnitude 5·4, at a separation of 35″ (position angle 54°).

ALCOR The star 80 UMa, sometimes designated ζ² UMa; a binary companion of ζ¹ UMa (*Mizar*), at a separation of 15″, position angle 150°. The magnitude being 4·0 the pair make an easy naked-eye double.

ALCYONE The star η Tau, a blue-white star of spectral type *B*5, magnitude 3·0, which is the dominant member of the **Pleiades** cluster.

ALDEBARAN The star α Tau, a red giant of spectral type *K*5, magnitude 0·8, said by the ancients to be the bloodshot eye of the bull, Taurus. It has a faint companion of the thirteenth magnitude at a distance of 31″, position angle 110°.

It is the focal point of the **Hyades** cluster, although it is not itself a member of the cluster.

ALGOL The star β Per. This star had long been known to be variable, but it was the young deaf-mute, John Goodricke, who in 1782 analysed the regular variations in its brightness and suggested

that they were due to a pair of stars in binary motion, the fainter one from time to time eclipsing the brighter.

The behaviour of this star has been recorded for many years, and an accurate light-curve produced (Fig. 4); from a study of this light-curve a great deal of information about the systems can be deduced. *Algol* is of spectral class *B8*.

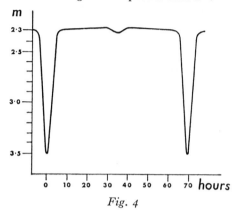

Fig. 4

The maximum apparent magnitude of this star is about 2·3; it remains at this brightness for about 25 hours, when it suddenly plunges, in about 5 hours, to a minimum magnitude of about 3·5; as soon as this minimum is reached the brightness increases, again in some 5 hours, to its former level. It remains at maximum for about a day, then there is a slight drop to a secondary minimum, then it remains at maximum for another day, the period of the total cycle being 69 hours, about 2·87 days.

The fact that the minima occur at equal intervals tells us that the bodies move either in a circular orbit or in an elliptical orbit with its major axis in the line of sight. The pointed minima indicate that the eclipses are partial, and the disparity between the minima indicates that one star is much brighter than the other. The dimensions of the bodies and their orbits can be determined with some precision by mathematical analysis of the light-curve.

(See also **Binary systems**.)

ALIDADE The Arabic name used for the sighting arm of a number of ancient instruments; it became adopted for the index arm of a quadrant or mural arc, to which in more recent times a telescope has been attached.

The ancient term is also sometimes used to denote the upper parts of the piers of a meridian circle, which bear the modern equivalent of the alidade of the ancient quadrant—the circle-reading microscopes.

ALL-SKY CAMERA A device for photographing the whole of the visible heavens simultaneously, particularly useful for recording auroral displays, etc.

It consists of a base upon which a convex mirror is mounted horizontally; a camera (or, more usually, a cine-camera) is supported above the mirror and directed vertically downwards so as to photograph the reflection of the heavens in the mirror.

ALMAGEST The volume in which Ptolemy recorded his astronomical theories. It was originally entitled *The Mathematical Collection*, but later became known as *The Great Astronomer* and then as *The Greatest* ($\mu\epsilon\gamma\iota\sigma\tau\eta$—pronounced 'megisty'); the Arabian astronomers prefaced this with the Arabic definite article 'al' and it thus became known as the *Almagest*, by which title it has been known ever since.

ALMANACS Annual volumes containing ephemerides of the Sun, Moon, planets, planetary satellites, minor planets, etc. The first publication of this type was *The Nautical Almanac*, prepared by the Nautical Almanac Office of the Royal Greenwich Observatory from 1767–1959.

The Nautical Almanac Office of the Navy Department of the U.S.A. was founded in 1849 and is now located at the U.S. Naval Observatory, Washington. It produced *The American Ephemeris* from 1855–1959 inclusive.

Following detailed discussions sponsored by the International Astronomical Union to increase international co-operation in the production of ephemerides, and to decrease duplication of effort, these two great publications were unified from 1960 onwards, the work of production being shared by the two Nautical Almanac Offices. The unified volume is entitled *The Astronomical Ephemeris* in the U.K., in the U.S.A. the name *The American Ephemeris* is retained.

There are three other important national Almanacs; these are the *Connaissance des Temps*, produced by the Bureau des Longitudes, Paris; the *Astronomicheskii Ephegodnik*, produced by the Institute of Theoretical Astronomy of the Academy of Sciences of the U.S.S.R., Leningrad (usually known to western astronomers as the *Annuaire Astronomique*); and the *Almanaque Náutico*, produced by the Instituto y Observatorio de Marina, San Fernando. A former major almanac was the *Berliner Astronomisches Jahrbuch* published by the Astronomisches Rechen-Institut, Heidelberg, until 1959. Germany adopted the unified *Astronomical Ephemeris* from 1960.

A number of other countries also produce annual almanacs.

Also of considerable importance are the annual handbooks for observers, notably the *Handbook of the British Astronomical Association* and *The Observer's Handbook* published by the Royal Astronomical Society of Canada.

ALMANAQUE NÁUTICO The Spanish equivalent of *The Astronomical Ephemeris*, produced by the Instituto y Observatorio de Marina, San Fernando, Spain. Usually abbreviated to A.N.

ALMUCANTAR The small circle through a star parallel to the horizon—i.e. of constant zenith distance and altitude. (See **Celestial sphere.**)

ALNILAM The star ϵ Ori, the central star of Orion's belt, a blue-white star of type *Bo*, magnitude 1·7.

ALNITAK The star ζ Ori, the eastern-most of the trio forming Orion's belt; the area to the south of this star is very nebulous, and includes the great absorption nebula, 'The Horsehead'.

ALPETRAGIUS Lunar surface feature, co-ordinates ξ−075, η−276. One of the most perfectly formed craters on the surface of the Moon, situated on the eastern side of the rampart connecting Arzachel and Alphonsus, on the western edge of the Mare Nubium. Of perfect circular form, it is 27 miles in diameter; the sharp walls have broad inner slopes and rise to 12,000 ft in the west. There is a huge central mountain.

ALPHONSUS Lunar surface feature, co-ordinates ξ−048, η−233. The central member of a great meridional trio with Ptolemæus and Arzachel. A perfectly circular walled plain, 70 miles in diameter, with broad rugged and terraced walls with peaks rising to 7,000 ft. The south-western and north-eastern walls are cut by a number of parallel valleys.

There is an elongated central mountain massif, running north–south from the centre of the floor to the southern rampart; the highest peak is at the northern end. There are a number of dark spots on the floor, notably those beneath the east, south-west and north-west ramparts. [Plates 5(a, e); 8(b, c, d).]

A number of observations of temporary red coloration in this formation, apparently due to the release of carbon gases of some kind, have been obtained during the past few years; these occurrences have not yet been satisfactorily explained.

ALTAI MOUNTAINS A prominent range of lunar mountains, running from the eastern wall of Piccolomini (ξ+440, η−490) to a point north-east of Catharina (ξ+340, η−270), a distance of more than 300 miles.

The range marks, in fact, a fault line in the surface crust; the surface to the east is practically level with the mountain

peaks, which rise some 6,000 ft. above the surface to the west. There is one peak of 13,000 ft.

ALTAIR The star α Aql, the principal star of the great constellation of the Eagle; it is a white star of spectral type A7, magnitude 0·8.

ALTAZIMUTH MOUNTING A telescope mounting having movements in altitude and azimuth. It has the disadvantage for astronomical purposes that to 'guide' the telescope so as to retain a celestial object in the centre of the field—i.e. to move it in a direction counter to the diurnal rotation of the Earth—involves imparting a motion in two planes simultaneously, which is almost impossible to achieve successfully. It has therefore been almost entirely superseded by the **equatorial mounting**. (See **Mountings, telescope**.)

ALTITUDE The angular elevation of a body above the observer's horizon. (See **Celestial sphere**.)

AMALTHEA Satellite V of Jupiter, *q.v.*

AMAZONIS Martian surface feature, approximate position Ω 140°, Φ 0°. Vast ochre desert in the equatorial regions of the planet, to the north of Memnonia and the Mare Sirenum.

AMBROSIA Martian surface feature, approximate position Ω 90°, Φ−40°. Canal in Thaumasia running due south from the Solis Lacus.

AMENTHES Martian surface feature, approximate position Ω 250°, Φ+5°. Bright patch between Æthiopis and Libya, adjoining the north-western end of the Mare Cimmerium and the tip of the Syrtis Minor.

AMERICAN EPHEMERIS *The American Ephemeris and Nautical Almanac*, produced by the Nautical Almanac Office of the U.S. Navy Department set up in 1849. The first issue was that for the year 1855. Since 1893 the Nautical Almanac Office has been located at the U.S. Naval Observatory in Washington. From 1960 it has been produced jointly with the British publication *The Astronomical Ephemeris*.

AMMONIA An invisible alkaline gas which is highly soluble in water and has a characteristic pungent odour. It is a simple compound of nitrogen and hydrogen —formula NH_3. It liquefies at $-33\cdot4°$ C. and freezes at $-78°$ C. It is an important constituent of the atmospheres of the major planets.

AMOR Minor planet no. 1221, discovered in 1932 by E. Delporte, the Belgian observer. Amor's orbit has a very high eccentricity (0·448), but despite this Delporte was able to determine the orbit accurately and recovered the asteroid at its next favourable apparition, in 1940.

In 1932 March Amor was at its least possible distance from the Earth, a little over 10 million miles. Its orbit approached that of the minor planet Eros very closely, and it has been suggested that the two bodies have a common origin.

The orbit of Amor is such that at a perihelic opposition there would actually be three passages through opposition— one three months before its perihelion, as the Earth overtakes the asteroid, a second at perihelion with the asteroid overtaking the Earth, and a third one three months after perihelion as the Earth again overtakes the asteroid.

ANASTIGMAT A lens so designed as to minimize the effect of **astigmatism.**

ANAXAGORAS Lunar surface feature, co-ordinates $\xi-050$, $\eta+959$. Well-formed and very bright crater in the north polar region, 32 miles in diameter. It has steep, terraced walls rising 10,000 ft above the interior, and a rugged central peak. It is the centre of a bright ray system.

ANAXIMANDER Lunar surface feature, co-ordinates $\xi-313$, $\eta+914$. A prominent ring formation close to the north-east limb, 54 miles in diameter. The walls rise over 6,000 ft, and to nearly 10,000 ft in the south-west.

ANDROMEDA (Mythological character. *Genitive* Andromedae, *I.A.U. abbreviation* And.) A northern constellation reaching midnight culmination in early October. It contains numerous stars of fourth magnitude and fainter, but only three second-magnitude (α, β, γ) and one third-magnitude star (δ). The three bright stars form a row, easily found because α And is one of the four corner stars in what is generally known as the 'Great Square of Pegasus'.

γ And is a magnificent double, with gold and blue components of magnitudes 3·0 and 5·0 respectively, some 10″ apart. R And is an interesting long-period variable, its magnitude ranging from 5·6 to 14·9 over a period of 410 days.

There are two more very interesting objects in the constellation—the great spiral galaxy (M 31), visible to the unaided eye as a faint misty patch close to ν And, and N.G.C. 7662, a bright, bluish planetary nebula.

ANDROMEDA, GREAT NEBULA IN Although known by this name for many years this object is not in fact a nebula at all, but a spiral galaxy of type Sb. It is a very fine specimen of its class, having a bright, well-defined nucleus and two very long spiral arms; these contain much bright nebulosity and obscuring dust, and both encircle the nucleus more than four times. [Plate 17(d).]

The earliest record of the Andromeda galaxy is of an observation made in the tenth century by a Persian astronomer named Al-Sûfi. The galaxy is visible to the unaided eye in good conditions, as a faint misty patch of light close to the star ν And; it has an apparent magnitude of 4·3. Its approximate position is R.A. 0 hr 40·0 min, Dec. $+41°$ 0′ (Epoch 1950·0).

It was included in Messier's catalogue (1781) as M 31, and is also designated N.G.C. 224. It was first listed as a nebula resolvable into stars by Sir William Herschel in 1786. There are two satellite galaxies, both ellipticals: they are designated N.G.C. 221 (M 32) and N.G.C. 205. All three are members of the local group.

Hubble discovered Cepheid variables in the Andromeda galaxy in 1923, and deduced a distance for the galaxy of about 750,000 light years; later determinations indicated a distance of about 900,000 l.y. These calculations had assumed, however, that the Cepheids discovered by Hubble were of Population II, but it was shown by Baade in 1952 that they were in fact the more luminous, Population I type. This indicated that the distance-scale in use for the distant galaxies was erroneous, and should be increased by a factor of more than 2; the Andromeda galaxy is, in fact, some 2,000,000 l.y. distant.

ANDROMEDIDS A meteor shower occurring on about Nov. 30, usually known as the Bielids from their association with Biela's Comet. The radiant is close to the star γ And.

ÅNGSTRÖM UNIT A unit of length used to express wavelengths of light. It is named after Anders J. Ångström (1814–1874), a Swedish pioneer spectroscopist. Using a grating spectrometer Ångström produced a map of the solar spectrum in 1868 which was used as the standard of reference for wavelengths for many years. The usual abbreviation is Å.

It is equal to 10^{-10} metres, i.e. $1/10,000,000$ mm or $1/10,000$ μ.

The zero of the scale of wavelength measurement was adopted by the International Union for Solar Research in 1907 as the wavelength of the red cadmium line in the solar spectrum, at 6438·4696 Å; this was also adopted by the International Astronomical Union, formed in 1922.

ANGULAR DIAMETER The angle subtended at the observer by the diameter of a distant body; the diameters of astronomical bodies are necessarily measured, and frequently expressed, in this form; if their distance is known, however, the linear diameter can easily be calculated from the angular diameter.

ANGULAR DISTANCE The apparent separation between two heavenly bodies, expressed in angular measure. It is most commonly used to indicate the distance of a planet from the Sun, Moon or a bright star.

ANNUAIRE ASTRONOMIQUE The name used by western astronomers for the **Astronomicheskii Ephegodnik**, *q.v.*

ANNUAL EQUATION An inequality in the Moon's motion caused by the variation in the Earth–Moon distance during a year. (See **Moon—motion of.**)

ANNUAL VARIATION The rate of change of position of a star, in both Right Ascension and Declination, due to the luni–solar precession and the proper motion of the star.

The annual variation in R.A. and Dec. are normally tabulated for each star included in a catalogue of star places.

ANNULAR ECLIPSE A solar eclipse in which the relative positions of the Sun, Moon and Earth are such that the vertex of the shadow-cone of the Moon fails to reach the surface of the Earth; as a result of this at the maximum phase a peripheral ring, or *annulus*, of the Sun is visible around the perimeter of the Moon. (See **Eclipse, solar.**)

ANOMALISTIC MONTH The interval between successive passages of the Moon through perigee; it is equal to 27·5546 mean solar days.

ANOMALISTIC YEAR The interval between successive passages of the Earth through perihelion. Owing to the eastward revolution of the apsides of the Earth's orbit due to precession—amounting to 11".25 per annum—the anomalistic year is longer than the tropical year by nearly 25 minutes; it is equal to about 365·2596 mean solar days.

ANSAE The extremities of the rings of Saturn as viewed from the Earth.

ANTAPEX, SOLAR The point on the celestial sphere away from which the Sun (and the entire solar system with it) appears to be moving. It is determined from a study of stellar proper motions, stars on average appearing to converge on the antapex. Its exact position is difficult to determine accurately, but it lies in the constellation Columba at about R.A. 6 hr, Dec. −30°. It is, of course, the diametrically opposite point to the **solar apex,** *q.v.*

(See also **Solar motion.**)

ANTARES The star α Sco, said to represent the heart of the Scorpion. It is a red supergiant of spectral type $M1$, and has an apparent magnitude of 0·9. It has a diameter approximately 285 times that of the Sun. There is a faint companion, magnitude 6·8, at position angle 275°, separation 3".2.

ANTARIAN STARS Archaic term used to denote stars in spectral class M, after the type-star *Antares* (class $M0$). (See **Stars—spectral classification of.**)

ANTLIA (Originally Antlia Pneumatica, the Air Pump. *Genitive* Antliae, *I.A.U. abbreviation* Ant.) A small southern constellation slightly north of Vela, whose brightest stars are three of the fourth magnitude.

ANTONIADI, Eugène M. (1870–1944) Probably the most able observer of Mars ever, Antoniadi certainly shares with Phillips the distinction of being the leading planetary observer of his generation. Born in Constantinople of Greek parentage he emigrated to France at the age of

twenty-three and remained there for the rest of his life, becoming a naturalized Frenchman in 1928.

He was interested in astronomy from boyhood, and was making useful observations of the Sun, Mars, Jupiter and Saturn during his teens; it was obvious from the start that he was not only a superb observer but also a most gifted artist—his planetary drawings and maps are superb specimens of skilled draughtsmanship. He worked for some years with the great Camille Flammarion at Juvisy, but from 1909 was allowed to use the great 32¾-in. refractor at Meudon and from that time onward this was his principal instrument.

At Juvisy he became a most experienced and skilful observer of Mars, and was to specialize in the study of that planet for the rest of his life. He was a founder member of the British Astronomical Association in 1890, and contributed to the first reports of its Mars Section; in 1896 he was appointed Director of the Section, which he led with great distinction for the next twenty-one years. His own knowledge and skill were supplemented by a superb organizing and analytical ability, with the result that Mars Section operated through that period with an enthusiasm, professionalism and success that it has never been able to attain since. The ten reports of the Section that Antoniadi produced are his most appropriate memorial. His book *La Planète Mars* was published in Paris in 1930.

Antoniadi was also a regular observer of the inner planets. His map of the surface markings of Mercury is still regarded as definitive; his book on Mercury (*La Planète Mercure et la Rotation des Satellites*, Paris, 1934) was the only book on the subject for about twenty years. He conducted extensive research into ancient Greek and Egyptian astronomy, and was also an archaeologist of note. He was awarded the Croix de Chevalier de la Légion d'Honneur for service to France during the First World War; during the Second World War he broadcast weekly on astronomical topics, though suffering from an incurable disease and within a few weeks of his death.

ANTONIADI SCALE The recommended system, devised by E. M. Antoniadi, for observers to record the **seeing** conditions in which their observations are made:
  I. Perfect seeing, without a quiver;
 II. Slight undulations, with moments of calm lasting several seconds;
III. Moderate seeing, with larger air tremors;
 IV. Poor seeing, with constant troublesome undulations;
  V. Very bad seeing, scarcely allowing the making of a rough sketch.

AONIUS SINUS Martian surface feature, approximate position Ω 105°, Φ − 45°. Dark condensation on south-western border of Thaumasia, connected to the Solis Lacus by Bathys.

APASTRON Farthest point in the relative orbit of one component of a binary system from the other star.
(See also **Periastron.**)

APENNINES Perhaps the most magnificent range of mountains on the Moon. They commence at the eastern border of the Mare Serenitatis, at ξ + 100, η + 473, and curve south and eastwards, forming the south-western border of the Mare Imbrium, to end at a point about ξ + 240, η + 260, close to the superb formation Eratosthenes.

The range forms the northern boundary of a triangular area of mountainous terrain; it contains many peaks of more than 15,000 ft. The highest is Mt. Huyghens (at ξ − 044, η + 345), which rises more than 18,000 ft above the Mare Imbrium.

The Apennines are a fine sight when on the terminator at about First Quarter; they can sometimes be seen as an arc of light curving into the unilluminated hemisphere, as the rising Sun catches their lofty peaks.

APEX, SOLAR The point on the celestial sphere towards which the Sun (and with it the entire solar system) appears to be moving, at a velocity of about 13 miles per second.

The solar apex is determined by a study of stellar proper motions, stars on average tending to diverge from the apex. The exact position of the apex is difficult to determine with certainty; it lies in the constellation Hercules at approximately R.A. 18 hr, Dec. + 30°.
(See also **Solar motion.**)

APHELION That point in the orbit of a planet which is farthest from the Sun.
(See also **Perihelion.**)

APLANATIC LENS A lens which, for a stated object distance, produces an image free from both **spherical aberration** and **coma**; in the case of an astronomical telescope objective the object distance is infinite and the image is formed in the prime focal plane, and an aplanatic O.G. is designed to produce the aberration-free image in this plane.

APOGEE The farthest point from the Earth in the orbit of another planetary body.
(See also **Perigee.**)

APOJOVE Farthest point from Jupiter in the orbit of another body; usually applied to Jovian satellites.
(See also **Perijove.**)

APOLLO Name given to **Mercury** (*q.v.*) when seen as a morning star by the ancient Greeks.

APOLLO Minor planet having a highly eccentric orbit, discovered by the German astronomer Reinmuth on 1932 April 27. Apollo was the first asteroid discovered to have an orbit extending inside those of the Earth and Venus, and passed within two million miles of the Earth. Owing to the consequent rapid motion, and to the high eccentricity and few observations obtainable during the short apparition, the orbit could not be determined with high precision and Apollo is unlikely to be rediscovered and positively identified at future returns.

APOLLO Name given to the American project to land astronauts on the surface of the Moon. The *Apollo* space vehicles will each carry a crew of three and will be placed in a selenocentric 'parking orbit'; they will carry a 'lunar excursion module' in which two members of the crew will be carried down to the surface and subsequently returned to the parent craft for the return to Earth.

APOSATURNIUM Farthest point from Saturn in the orbit of another body; usually applied to satellites of Saturn.
(See also **Perisaturnium.**)

APPARENT DIAMETER The diameter of an object as observed, usually applied to the disk of a planet or satellite. It is usually expressed in angular measure (the *angular diameter*); the linear diameter can be calculated from the angular diameter for any object whose distance from the Earth is known.

The apparent diameter of a bright object observed against a dark sky is less than the true diameter, due to **irradiation**, *q.v.*

APPARENT MAGNITUDE A numerical index to the brightness of a star relative to the other stars, taking no account of their differing distances and therefore not an indication of its true luminosity. (See **Magnitude, apparent.**)

APPARENT PLACE The position of a star on the celestial sphere, as seen by the observer and referred to the true equator and equinox of the moment of observation. It is normally measured in Right Ascension and Declination.

The apparent place is the position obtained by a meridian-circle observation, after correction for atmospheric refraction. (See also **Star places.**)

APPARITION Name given to each period during which a planet is observ-able; thus an apparition of Mars extends for a few months either side of each opposition, although some apparitions are more favourable than others, depending upon the distance and direction of the planet at opposition and the location of the observer.

APPULSE The *apparent* close approach of two heavenly bodies whose directions converge, although they may be at very different distances from the Earth and consequently not close to each other at all. An appulse may be regarded as a close approach of two bodies as they are observed on the celestial sphere; as all positional measurements are made in the celestial sphere their apparent co-ordinates will be very similar.

Thus, for example, Jupiter and the Moon may be seen in appulse, although the former is some 1,900 times the distance of the latter.

APSE Alternative form of **apsis**, *q.v.*

APSIDES, LINE OF The line joining the apsides of a planet or satellite. (See **Apsis.**)

APSIS One of the two points in the orbit of a planet or satellite about its primary where the **radius vector** of the body is at its maximum or minimum. Thus, the apsides of the Earth are its aphelion and perihelion.

APUS (The Bird of Paradise. *Genitive* Apodis, *I.A.U. abbreviation* Aps.) A southern circumpolar constellation between Triangulum Australis and the South Pole, containing five fourth-magnitude stars and a few fainter ones.

AQUARIDS Name given to meteor showers having their radiants in Aquarius. There are two principal showers, identified by the bright star nearest the radiant, the **Delta Aquarids** and the **Eta Aquarids**, *q.v.*

AQUARIUS (The Water-bearer. *Genitive* Aquarii, *I.A.U. abbreviation* Aqr.) A zodiacal constellation lying immediately south of the equator between Capricornus and Pisces and reaching midnight culmination in late August and early September. It is a large constellation, containing four third-magnitude stars (α, β, δ and ζ Aqr), a number of the fourth magnitude, and many fainter ones. There are several double and variable stars, notably R Aqr—a long-period variable whose magnitude varies over the range 6·0–11·0 in a period of 380 days. Close to ν Aqr is N.G.C. 7009, 'The Saturn Nebula'—a very bright, bluish planetary nebula resembling the planet Saturn, and about 5° north of β Aqr is M 2 (N.G.C. 7089), a splendid globular cluster.

AQUILA (The Eagle. *Genitive* Aquilae, *I.A.U. abbreviation* Aql.) An equatorial constellation reaching midnight culmination in mid-July. A large portion of the Milky Way crosses this constellation, which is rich in stars. The brightest star is *Altair* (α Aql), a fine *A7*-type star of magnitude 0·8.

Among the variables in this constellation are two notable Cepheids, U and η Aql, and a long-period variable, R Aql, which varies between 5·8 and 12·0 in a period of 310 days.

ARA (The Altar. *Genitive* Arae, *I.A.U. abbreviation* Ara.) A Southern circumpolar constellation containing a fair number of stars in its small area, including five of the third magnitude.

ARABIA Martian surface feature, approximate position Ω 330°, Φ + 20°. Ochre tract in the north temperate region, bounded by the canali Phison to the east and Euphrates to the west; the Ismenius Lacus is at the north-west corner.

ARAXES Martian surface feature, approximate position Ω 115°, Φ − 25°. Canal joining the Phœnicis Lacus and the eastern end of the Mare Sirenum, forming part of the north-western boundary of Thaumasia.

ARCADIA Martian surface feature, approximate position Ω 100°, Φ + 45°. Lightish area in the north temperate region, north-east from Amazonis.

ARCHIMEDES Lunar surface feature, co-ordinates $\xi - 060$, $\eta + 497$. A superb walled plain at the south-western edge of the Mare Imbrium, with sharp terraced walls rising to 7,000 ft in places and a very smooth floor. The diameter is about 50 miles.

ARCTURIAN STARS Archaic term for stars of spectral class K, after the type-star *Arcturus* (type *K1*). (See **Stars—spectral classification of**.)

ARCTURUS The star α Boo, the fourth brightest in the sky, having an apparent magnitude of − 0·1. It is an orange giant of type *K2* with a diameter approximately 23 times that of the Sun. It is a high-velocity star with some peculiarities in its spectrum. It is the second brightest star visible from the latitude of Great Britain.

AREOCENTRIC CO-ORDINATES A system of co-ordinates for the measurement of the relative positions of the surface features of Mars, referred to the centre of the spheroid. Although Mars is an oblate spheroid the polar compression is only 1/211 and there is therefore little significant difference between areocentric and **areographic co-ordinates**, *q.v.*

AREOGRAPHIC CO-ORDINATES The system of co-ordinates used to record the relative positions of Martian surface features, referred to the mean surface of the planet. As the polar compression of the Martian spheroid is very small, only 1/211, there is little significant difference between areocentric and areographic co-ordinates. The areographic latitude and longitude are usually indicated by Φ and Ω, respectively.

(See also **Martian surface features, Planetocentric co-ordinates, Planetographic co-ordinates.**)

AREOGRAPHY The physical study of the planet Mars—from 'Ares', the equivalent in Greek mythology of the Roman god of war 'Mars'.

ARES The Greek name for the god known as 'Mars' in Roman mythology—the god of war. Hence **areography**, *q.v.*

ARGELANDER, F. W. A. (**1799–1875**) Distinguished German astronomer who is remembered for his production of the classic catalogue of places and magnitudes for all the stars in the northern hemisphere down to the ninth magnitude—the famous *Bonner Durchmusterung* (usually abbreviated to B.D.). This colossal programme was carried out with a small but superb instrument made by Fraunhofer—an equatorially mounted comet-seeking refractor with a $3\frac{1}{2}$-in. $f/7$ objective and a Kellner $\times 10$ eyepiece. The B.D. was published in 1863.

ARGO NAVIS (The Ship 'Argo'). This former constellation is now divided into three separate constellations—**Carina, Vela** and **Puppis**, *q.v.* A single series of **Bayer letters** is shared by the three constellations, however.

ARGYRE I Martian surface feature, approximate position $\Omega\,40°$, $\Phi-50°$. Large well-formed ochre area to the south of the Mare Erythræum.

ARGYRE II Martian surface feature, approximate position $\Omega\,65°$, $\Phi-65°$. Large light ochre region adjoining the Mare Australe; south-west of Argyre I.

ARIADÆUS Lunar surface feature, co-ordinates $\xi+297$, $\eta+080$. A well-defined, bright crater, 9 miles in diameter, on the south-western border of the Mare Tranquillitatis; there is a smaller crater,

Ariadæus A, adjoining to the west. Just to the north is part of the wall of an ancient ruined ring formation, from which the giant Ariadæus Rille runs eastwards.

ARIADÆUS RILLE Lunar surface feature. This great cleft, discovered by Schröter in 1792, commences at a point just north of Ariadæus ($\xi+293$, $\eta+095$) and runs, slightly north of east, for more than 150 miles to a point just west of Hyginus ($\xi+140$, $\eta+140$). There are a number of minor branch rilles, one of which connects with the great Hyginus cleft.

The rille is only 2–3 miles wide, and like the other lunar rilles appears to be quite shallow. It is crossed by a series of prominent ridges, which have the effect of dividing it into a series of aligned but separate trenches.

ARIEL Satellite I of Uranus, *q.v.*

ARIES (The Ram. *Genitive* Arietis, *I.A.U. abbreviation* Ari.) A northern zodiacal constellation adjoining Taurus, and reaching midnight culmination in late October. Contains a number of faint stars but only three brighter than the fourth magnitude, of which the brightest is *Hamal* (α Ari).

Something over 2,000 years ago the vernal equinox was situated in this constellation, hence its being called the 'First Point of Aries', but due to precession during the intervening period it is now located at the far end of Pisces.

ARISTARCHUS Lunar surface feature, co-ordinates $\xi-676$, $\eta+402$. A well-defined crater ring near the north-eastern limb, in the Oceanus Procellarum; 29 miles in diameter. Aristarchus is the most brilliant object on the Moon, and is also the centre of a ray system. [Plate 6(e).]

Its outline is polygonal rather than circular, and the floor is crossed by a number of dark bands radiating from the central mountain.

Aristarchus forms a pair with the much darker Herodotus.

ARISTILLUS Lunar surface feature, co-ordinates $\xi + 018$, $\eta + 557$. A prominent, elliptical formation in the western part of the Mare Imbrium, north-west of Archimedes. The terraced walls rise to 11,000 ft in places, and there is a fine central mountain with three peaks. The diameter is 35 miles. Dusky bands, radial to the central mountain, have been observed on the crater floor.

ARISTOTELES Lunar surface feature, co-ordinates $\xi + 191$, $\eta + 768$. A fine walled plain, 60 miles in diameter, on the southern border of the Mare Frigoris. Forms a splendid pair with Eudoxus. The walls are terraced and much broken, and rise to more than 10,000 ft in places.

ARMAGH OBSERVATORY The principal observatory in Northern Ireland. It shares in the administration of the Boyden Observatory in South Africa, where it is part-owner of the 'ADH' 32-in. Schmidt–Cassegrain telescope with the Dunsink and Harvard Observatories. Much of its current research is devoted to Southern-Hemisphere star-fields, using plates obtained at Boyden.

The Armagh Observatory was founded by Lord Rokeby, formerly Archbishop Robinson, in 1790; the first Director was Rev. Dr James Hamilton. Among his successors of note were Dr Romney Robinson (Director for 59 years), J. L. E. Dreyer, compiler of the famous **New General Catalogue,** and Canon W. F. A. Ellison. The present Director, the seventh holder of the office, is Dr E. M. Lindsay, a leading astrophysicist and an expert on the Magellanic Clouds. Armagh is the oldest British observatory still operational on its original site.

A planetarium has recently been established in the grounds of the observatory, which will be the first in Ireland. [Plate 24(d).] It will be run on a non-profit basis and its programmes will be devised on an entirely instructional basis.

ARMILLARY SPHERE A medieval instrument, usually constructed in brass or other metal, used to solve problems of spherical astronomy, such as the conversion of the observed altitude and azimuth of an object to celestial latitude and longitude or Right Ascension and Declination. [Plate 25(b).]

ARNON Martian surface feature, approximate position $\Omega\,335°$, $\Phi + 48°$. Broad, dusky band running due north from Ismenius Lacus.

ARTIFICIAL HORIZON A device enabling altitudes to be measured on land, where no true horizon is visible as it is at sea. It consists of a shallow trough containing mercury, forming a truly horizontal mirror; a sextant, theodolite or similar instrument can then be used to measure the angle between the object under observation and its reflected image in the mercury trough; half this angle is the required altitude.

ARZACHEL Lunar surface feature, co-ordinates $\xi - 035$, $\eta - 316$. A magnificent formation, 60 miles in diameter, with broad, very rugged walls rising to 13,000 ft in the west. There is a complex central mountain massif.

Arzachel is the southernmost member of a superb meridional chain, of which the other two members are Ptolemæus and Alphonsus.

ASCENDING NODE The node at which the body concerned crosses the Ecliptic from south to north.

ASCENSIONAL DIFFERENCE The difference between the **Right Ascension** of a celestial object and its **oblique ascension.**

ASHEN LIGHT Phenomenon sometimes observed on the planet Venus when close to inferior conjunction, in which not only the thin, bright crescent but also the remainder of the disk is seen, the latter illuminated by a faint, luminous glow.

The appearance is very similar to the phenomenon of **earthshine** on the Moon, but is due to an entirely different cause—almost certainly electrical disturbance in the ionosphere of Venus.

ASTEROID Alternative term for a **minor planet**, *q.v.*

ASTIGMATISM A defect of optical systems, encountered when incident light meets the refracting or reflecting element obliquely. Its effect is that rays from different parts of the element are not brought to one focal point, but are focused in two focal lines, one in the plane of the

solely for astronomical photography; it is normally mounted, alone or in a battery of astrographs of different specifications, on a clock-driven equatorial mounting.

ASTROGRAPHIC CATALOGUE A photographic catalogue of the heavens made from plates obtained with a number of specially designed astrographic refractors at eighteen observatories throughout the world, as a result of the *Carte du Ciel* project inaugurated at a conference in Paris in 1887 and now controlled by a Commission of the International Astronomical Union. (See **Astrographic telescope; Carte du Ciel.**)

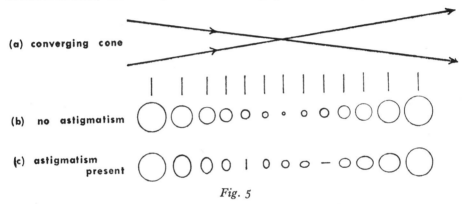

(a) converging cone

(b) no astigmatism

(c) astigmatism present

Fig. 5

optical axis and the other perpendicular to it. This is demonstrated in Fig. 5, in which the shape of sections through a converging cone (a) is shown when astigmatism is not present (b) and is present (c).

Astigmatism can be corrected by the use of cylindrical lenses where the nature of the optical system permits. Alternatively an objective can be so designed as to minimize the astigmatism—termed an **anastigmat**.

ASTROBIOLOGY The study of the possibilities of environments found elsewhere in the universe being capable of supporting life in some form.

ASTROGRAPH A telescope designed

ASTROGRAPHIC CHART A partially completed photographic atlas of the heavens produced as part of the **Carte du Ciel** project, *q.v.*

ASTROGRAPHIC PLATE A plate obtained with one of the astrographic refractors specially designed for the *Carte de Ciel* project. (See **Astrographic telescope; Carte du Ciel.**)

ASTROGRAPHIC TELESCOPE Generally, a photographic telescope used to obtain plates of star fields, usually for astrometric purposes. Specifically, the term is normally reserved for the series of special photographic refractors designed for the *Carte du Ciel* project. These were based upon a prototype developed by the brothers Paul and Prosper Henry of Paris. Similar instruments were ordered for the eighteen observatories who had agreed to co-operate in the project. Some of the instruments for European observatories were ordered from the brothers Henry, and no less than six were made by Howard Grubb of Dublin, including those for Greenwich, Oxford and the Cape.

The instruments were equatorially mounted refractors of 13-in aperture and 135-in focal length. The objectives were doublets colour-corrected for 4,000–4,800 Å and designed to be free from coma. The plates covered an area of slightly more than 2° square on a scale of 1' to 1 mm—very convenient for measuring.

Although the ambitious *Carte du Ciel* project was never completed, the astrographic telescopes have made substantial contributions to stellar astronomy—especially the determination of proper motions. (See also **Carte du Ciel**.)

ASTROLABE An instrument for the measurement of the altitudes of heavenly bodies. In medieval times astrolabes were constructed in brass or other metals, and consisted of a vertical graduated circle, with an *alidade* pivoted at its centre; the circle was suspended from a small ring-handle. The instrument was held up to the eye, and the alidade rotated until the object under observation was sighted along it; the altitude of the object could then be read off from the circle. [Plate 25(a).]

The term astrolabe is sometimes used to describe a more complex medieval instrument, the **armillary sphere**. (See also **Prismatic astrolabe**.)

ASTROLOGY The study of the alleged influences of the heavenly bodies upon human affairs, developed by the ancient Chaldeans, Greeks and Egyptians. It has no scientific basis and little reason for a place in contemporary society. It must, however, be remembered that much of the early development of astronomical knowledge arose from the ancients' study of astrology and from the accompanying observations.

ASTROMETRY The measurement of precise positions of celestial objects on photographic plates specially taken for the purpose.

The positions obtained may be *absolute* positions, related to reference stars whose positions are known with high precision from meridian-circle observations, or *differential* positions, mainly from sets of plates exposed at widely separated epochs. Differential positions are used principally for the determination of stellar parallaxes and proper motions. (See also **Plate constants; Plate scale; Standard co-ordinates**.)

ASTRONAUTICS The study of all aspects of controlled locomotion in space, including *inter alia* the problems and techniques of rocket propulsion, artificial earth satellites, instrumented lunar and planetary probe vehicles, navigation and survival in space and, ultimately, travel to and landings upon the Moon and planets.

ASTRONOMER ROYAL The office of H.M. Astronomer Royal is as old as the Royal Observatory, which is the oldest scientific institution in Great Britain; the two were, in fact, founded together. The office has always carried with it the Directorship of the Royal Observatory, and is the highest position in astronomy attainable in the British Commonwealth. It is therefore occupied only by astronomers in the front rank in world standing, who have already earned for themselves the highest possible reputations as scholars and scientific administrators. The history of the Royal Observatory demonstrates that most of the Astronomers Royal have been theorists of the highest ability and that all of them have been great observers, and have instituted and analysed observational programmes that have been major landmarks in the history of astronomy.

In 1675 King Charles II issued a Royal Warrant for the foundation of the Royal Observatory at Greenwich, and another appointing the Rev. John Flamsteed as 'our astronomical observator' with the

Table 1. H.M. Astronomers Royal

Astronomer Royal	lived	served as A.R.
1. Rev. John FLAMSTEED	1646–1719	1675–1719
2. Edmond HALLEY	1656–1742	1719–1742
3. James BRADLEY	1693–1762	1742–1762
4. Rev. Nathaniel BLISS	1700–1764	1762–1764
5. Rev. Nevil MASKELYNE	1732–1811	1764–1811
6. John POND	1767–1836	1811–1835
7. Sir George AIRY	1801–1892	1835–1881
8. Sir William CHRISTIE	1845–1922	1881–1910
9. Sir Frank DYSON	1868–1939	1910–1933
10. Sir Harold SPENCER JONES	1890–1960	1933–1955
11. Sir Richard WOOLLEY	b. 1906	1956–

title of Astronomer Royal and the princely salary of £100 per annum—out of which he was expected to provide his own instruments and assistance, save for one 'silly, surly labourer'.

Thus was created an office which has since been occupied by most of the greatest astronomers this country has ever produced; brief details of the men and their achievements are given under their own names in other parts of this book. Read in conjunction with the story of the Royal Observatory they demonstrate that in astronomy, at least, this country not only was but has been for three centuries, and still remains, a leading nation.

The distinguished holders of the office of H.M. Astronomer Royal are listed in the accompanying table; it will be noted that they are both long-lived and long-serving, for with the exception of Bliss none of the first ten served for less than

twenty years; their average term of office is 28 years—even taking into account the non-existence of 'retiring ages' in former times this is a remarkable record, especially for a post at the very top of a scientific discipline. Yet the cares of the office cannot be said to affect longevity, the average lifetime of the past Astronomers Royal being practically 75 years!

(See also **Royal Greenwich Observatory; Royal Observatory, Greenwich**.)

ASTRONOMER ROYAL FOR IRELAND Popular misnomer for the title **Royal Astronomer for Ireland**, *q.v.*

ASTRONOMER ROYAL FOR SCOTLAND A post created by Royal Warrant in 1834 to provide a Director for the Royal Observatory in Edinburgh. This position had previously been held by the Regius Professor of Practical Astronomy in the

Table 2. H.M. Astronomers Royal for Scotland

Astronomer Royal for Scotland	lived	served
1. Thomas HENDERSON	1798–1844	1834–1844
2. Charles PIAZZI SMYTH	1819–1900	1845–1889
3. Ralph COPELAND	1837–1905	1889–1905
4. Frank Watson DYSON	1868–1939	1905–1910
5. Ralph Allen SAMPSON	1866–1939	1911–1937
6. William Michael Herbert GREAVES	1897–1955	1938–1955
7. Hermann Alexander BRÜCK	b. 1905	1957–

University of Edinburgh, and in fact constituted the only duties associated with this sinecure Professorship. This link with the University has been preserved, and to this day the Astronomer Royal for Scotland has held the Chair of Astronomy in the University—no longer a sinecure!

Although it has always been a small establishment the Royal Observatory of Edinburgh has made many notable contributions to the development of astronomy and astrophysics, and its seven Directors have all been practical astronomers of great distinction. They are listed in Table 2.

(See also: **Royal Observatory, Edinburgh**.)

ASTRONOMICAL EPHEMERIS The United Kingdom edition of the annual volume produced jointly by the Nautical Almanac offices of the U.K. and U.S.A.; it replaces **The Nautical Almanac**, *q.v.* The first issue of the new 'A.E.' was that for 1960.

ASTRONOMICAL PUBLICATIONS The publication of astronomical work has evolved in a pattern similar to that of most scientific disciplines. In addition to monographs and symposia, published in the main by commercial publishing houses, there are a great many serial publications produced by learned societies, observatories and (in a few cases) commercial presses throughout the world; it is in these journals that most of the results of astronomical research work are reported.

The compilation of even a highly select list would be quite beyond the scope of the present book; readers requiring information about published books are advised to consult their municipal librarian. The specialist serial publications are listed in the *World List of Scientific Publications* (4th edn., 3 vols., Butterworth, London, 1963–1965), which also gives details of library holdings.

ASTRONOMICAL TRIANGLE A spherical triangle on the **celestial sphere**; its sides will be arcs of great circles.

ASTRONOMICAL TWILIGHT The periods during which the depression of the Sun's centre below the theoretical horizon is between 12° and 18°. (See **Twilight**.)

ASTRONOMICAL UNIT One of the fundamental units of distance measurement in astronomy; it is defined as the geometrical mean distance of the Earth from the Sun. It is computed from the known equatorial mean radius of the Earth, and the mean equatorial horizontal parallax of the Sun. Adopting 8″.79 as the best determination of the solar parallax, 1 Astronomical Unit (usually abbreviated to A.U.) is equal to 92,957,209 miles.

(See also **Parallax, solar**.)

ASTRONOMICHESKII EPHEGODNIK The Russian equivalent of *The Astronomical Ephemeris*, produced by the Institute of Theoretical Astronomy of the Academy of Sciences of the U.S.S.R., Leningrad. Usually known to western astronomers as the *Annuaire Astronomique* and abbreviated to A.A.

ASTRONOMISCHE GESELLSCHAFT CATALOGUES A catalogue of star positions, epoch 1875·0, obtained with meridian circles at a number of observatories was published in Leipzig in 1890 as the *Astronomische Gesellschaft Katalog*, known as AGK.

A revision was carried out by the observatories at Bonn and Hamburg (Bergedorf), the positions being determined photographically. The catalogue contains the positions of about 183,000 stars for the epoch 1950·0, and was published in 1951 as the *Zweiter Katalog der Astronomische Gesellschaft*, known as the AGK 2.

A further revision, to be known as the AGK 3, is now in course of preparation, from which it is hoped to determine proper motions for the stars listed.

ASTRONOMISCHES JAHRBUCH The *Berliner Astronomisches Jahrbuch*, published since 1776, the German equivalent of *The Astronomical Ephemeris*. It ceased publication in 1959, consequent upon the unification, from 1960, of *The Nautical Almanac* and *The American Ephemeris* as *The Astronomical Ephemeris*.

ASTRONOMISCHES RECHEN-INSTITUT

The astronomical computing centre for Germany, situated in Heidelberg and currently directed by the eminent mathematical astronomer Dr. Auguste Kopff. Formerly responsible for the preparation of the *Berliner Astronomische Jahrbuch*, now discontinued, the Astronomisches Rechen-Institut is now the recognized centre for the preparation of fundamental position catalogues. Since 1960 it has been responsible for the production of the annual volume *Apparent Places of Fundamental Stars* under the auspices of the International Astronomical Union. The stars listed therein are those of the FK 3 catalogue produced by the Rechen-Institut, now engaged on the preparation of the FK 4.

ASTRONOMY

'Astronomy' is, strictly speaking, a general term embracing all aspects of the study of the heavens. It therefore includes practical, theoretical and historical studies of classical astronomy (concerned mainly with the positions, dimensions and motions of the heavenly bodies); astrophysics; cosmochemistry; astrobiology; cosmology. It also overlaps geophysics in such subjects as aurorae; atmospheric physics; solar–terrestrial relationships and cosmic rays.

ASTROPHYSICS

The study of the physical properties of astronomical bodies. It is a comparatively new branch of astronomy that has developed as a result of the application of photography, spectroscopy and photometry to astronomical observation. It has provided great opportunities for the theorist to play a part in increasing our knowledge of the heavens, and thus paved the way for the almost incredible advances made in cosmological theory in the past few years.

ATLANTIS

Martian surface feature, approximate position Ω 185°, $\Phi - 35°$. A small lightish area adjoining the southeast end of the Mare Cimmerium.

ATLAS

Lunar surface feature, co-ordinates $\xi + 481$, $\eta + 727$. A prominent crater, 55 miles in diameter, close to the northwest limb. Forms a pair with Hercules. The terraced walls rise to 11,000 ft in the north. There are six small mountains in a ring in the centre of the floor, the remains of a ruined ring. There are three large dark areas on the floor which are variable in extent.

ATLAS CŒLESTIS

An atlas of the northern sky based upon the observations made by the first Astronomer Royal, John Flamsteed. It was published in 1729, nine years after Flamsteed's death. The associated catalogue, *Historia Cœlestis Brittanica*, had been published in 1725.

The charts of the *Atlas Cœlestis* are beautifully drawn, accurate positions of nearly three thousand stars being elaborated by representations of the ancient constellation figures.

(See also **Flamsteed, Rev. John.**)

ATLAS COELI SKALNATÉ PLESO

The **Skalnaté Pleso Atlas** and catalogue, *q.v.*

ATMOSPHERE

The gaseous envelope surrounding a planet and retained by its gravitational field.

ATMOSPHERE

The unit of atmospheric pressure. One atmosphere (abbreviated as 1 atm) is defined to be the pressure exerted by a column of mercury of prescribed density, 760 mm high. It corresponds to 1,013,250 dynes per square centimetre, or 14·69595 pounds per square inch.

ATMOSPHERE, TERRESTRIAL

The atmospheric mantle of the Earth extends for some hundreds of miles above its surface, but the air density decreases very rapidly with height—about 90 per cent of the total weight of the atmosphere lies below a height of 10 miles, and 99·9 per cent below a height of 30 miles; the upper atmosphere is, therefore, extremely tenuous.

The air we breathe largely consists of a mixture of oxygen and nitrogen; in fact 99·97 per cent of dry air at the surface comprises only three gases: nitrogen (78·09%), oxygen (20·95%) and argon (0·93%). The remaining 0·03 per cent comprises very small proportions of carbon dioxide, neon, helium, methane, krypton, hydrogen, nitrous oxide, carbon monoxide, xenon, ozone and radon. The air at the surface actually contains, on average, about 1·2 per cent water vapour.

The atmosphere consists of a number of well-defined strata in which the gradient of air temperature to height differs considerably; this is shown in Fig. 6.

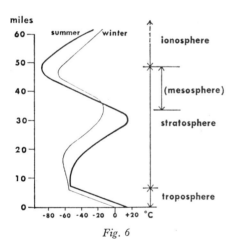

Fig. 6

The lower stratum of the atmosphere is termed the *troposphere*; this extends to a height of about seven miles. In the troposphere the air temperature decreases steadily with height, at very roughly 10° C per mile. The upper surface of the troposphere is termed the *tropopause*; the temperature here is of the order of −50° C.

Above the tropopause is the *stratosphere*; up to a height of about twelve miles the temperature remains fairly constant, but above that height it increases with height until it reaches a maximum of between −10° and +20° C at about 33 miles. Above this it decreases with height again, reaching a minimum of about −70° C at about 48 miles. Above this height lies the **ionosphere** (*q.v.*), in which the temperature once again increases with height.

Some workers term the upper part of the stratosphere, above 33 miles, the *mesosphere*.

ATMOSPHERIC PHYSICS The study of the physical properties of the Earth's atmosphere, by means of observations made by radio and radar techniques, with balloon- and rocket-borne equipment, etc.

ATOM For long regarded as the fundamental particle of matter, the atom is now known to be divisible and is therefore better described as the smallest stable unit of a given element. Each chemical element has an atom of distinct and unique structure.

The principal constituent parts of an atom are a nucleus comprising (mainly) protons and neutrons, and a number of electrons distributed in the space surrounding the nucleus. Neutrons possess no electrical charge, whereas each proton has a unit, positive, charge. Each electron has a unit, negative, charge, and as atoms in their normal state contain equal numbers of protons and electrons their charges balance out and the atom as a whole is electrically neutral. Protons and neutrons are the 'heavy' particles in the atom, both having a mass of about $1·7 \times 10^{-24}$ gm, although neutrons are slightly heavier than protons. Electrons are less than one thousandth of this weight (about $9·1 \times 10^{-28}$ gm), and it follows, therefore, that by far the greater part of the weight of an atom is concentrated in its nucleus.

It is conventional to envisage the electrons as orbiting, planet-like, around the nucleus; this is in fact an oversimplification, but as the actual motion of electrons can only be defined mathematically, in terms of quantum theory, it provides a convenient picture of atomic structure for the non-mathematician and we shall utilize it here.

On this basis the simplest atom, that of hydrogen, can be visualized as a nucleus consisting of a single proton with a single electron in orbit around it. The second simplest atom is that of helium; this consists of a nucleus comprising two neutrons and two protons, and two orbiting elec-

to a shell farther out; the atom is then said to be 'excited'. Similarly, if an electron transfers from an outer to an inner shell energy will be radiated.

Atoms whose outer shell contains the maximum possible number of electrons, or nearly so, prove to be fairly inert; on the other hand, atoms whose outer shell contains only one or two electrons prove to be chemically active. The atoms with only one electron in their outer shells, and which are all very active elements,

Table 3.   The ten lightest atoms

Element	Symbol	Atomic number	Atomic weight (approx.)	No of particles in nucleus		No. of electrons		
				(neutrons)	(protons)	(Shell 1)	(Shell 2)	(Shell 3)
Hydrogen	H	1	1	0	1	1	0	0
Helium	He	2	4	2	2	2	0	0
Lithium	Li	3	7	4	3	2	1	0
Beryllium	Be	4	9	5	4	2	2	0
Boron	B	5	10	5	5	2	2	1
Carbon	C	6	12	6	6	2	2	2
Nitrogen	N	7	14	7	7	2	2	3
Oxygen	O	8	16	8	8	2	2	4
Fluorine	F	9	19	10	9	2	2	5
Neon	Ne	10	20	10	10	2	2	6

trons. The latter are orbiting quite separately, but both remain at the same mean distance from the nucleus; they may therefore be described as orbiting in a common (spherical) 'shell'.

As we proceed to more complex atoms we find that their electrons are orbiting in a series of concentric shells. There is a maximum number of electrons that each may contain; thus, the first or innermost shell cannot contain more than two electrons; the second shell may also contain a maximum of two, the third up to eight, and so on. Basic information about the ten lightest atoms is given in Table 3.

An electron is free to move along any path, provided that it stays within its shell. Absorption of energy from outside the atom will cause an electron to transfer

are hydrogen, lithium, sodium, potassium, rubidium, caesium and francium.

Atoms are also made chemically very active when they are ionized; that is to say, deprived of one or more of their outer electrons. (See **Ionization**.)

ATOMIC CLOCK A device utilizing the natural resonance frequency of the caesium atom to make extremely precise measurements of time intervals; it is still in the process of development and is at present used as a check on the stability of quartz clocks, rather than as a replacement for them.

ATOMIC NUMBER The number of electrons orbiting about the nucleus of an atom; this is also equal to the number of protons in the nucleus. Elements are frequently classified by their atomic numbers.

(See also **Chemical elements.**)

ATOMIC WEIGHT The relative weight of one atom of an element. It is usually expressed on a scale where the atomic weight of the oxygen atom is taken to be 16·000.

There are two scales commonly in use, and it is therefore important to specify which is used. The *physical atomic weight* of a substance is the weight of an atom of its most commonly occurring isotope; the *chemical atomic weight* is the mean weight of an atom, taking into account the actual weights of all its known isotopes in their natural abundance. In general, physical atomic weights (which are used throughout this book) are greater than the corresponding chemical atomic weights by a factor of 1·000275.

(See also **Chemical elements.**)

AURIGA (The Charioteer. *Genitive* Aurigae, *I.A.U. abbreviation* Aur.) A large northern constellation reaching midnight culmination in early December. It is in the galactic plane, and so is crossed by part of the Milky Way and contains a number of interesting stars and clusters.

It is a striking constellation to the naked eye, α, β, η, ι and θ Aur making a great irregular hexagon with β Tau. The dominant star, *Capella* (α Aur), is a splendid example of spectral class *Go*, magnitude 0·1.

14 Aur is a multiple star, an easy double (magnitudes 5·0 and 7·2, separation 14″·5) with an eleventh-magnitude companion 11″·1 away.

θ Aur is a fine double, magnitude 2·7, 7·2; separation 2″·8.

ε Aur is a spectroscopic binary with a period of a little over 27 years.

M38 (N.G.C. 1912) is a beautiful open cluster, just south of σ Aur, and there are two more splendid open clusters in this constellation, M36 (N.G.C. 1960) and M37 (N.G.C. 2099), mid-way between θ Aur and β Tau and about 4° apart.

AURORA Sometimes known as the *polar lights*, the aurora is an illumination of the night sky observed mainly in sub-polar regions; often brilliant, usually beautiful, coloured and changing. The aurora is caused by streams of charged particles emitted by the Sun; on approaching the Earth they are attracted towards the magnetic poles. On entering the ionosphere they cause a gaseous discharge which produces the illumination.

The aurorae are seen overhead in the *auroral zones*; these are bands of latitude centred on latitudes 67° N and S. They can, however, be seen from great distances as an illuminated sky just above the horizon; the effect is very like the dawn-glow, hence the name *Aurora Borealis* (Northern Dawn) being used by Gassendi in 1621 to describe it. This name has been used ever since, and led to the southern equivalent being dubbed *Aurora Australis* (Southern Dawn) by Captain Cook in 1773.

The aurorae are usually beautifully coloured, red and green being the colours most often seen, and are often 'flickering' or 'rippling' as well as changing their form. A very common form is a great horizontal arc, with rays radiating from its upper edge; sometimes the arc brightens and then breaks up into a series of bands, resembling great folded and rippling curtains of colour hanging in the sky. Many magnificent displays have been observed and described by members of polar expeditions, for in the auroral zones they may be seen almost continuously. Only when there are particularly brilliant displays can they be seen from lower latitudes. [Plate 17(c)]

Originating as they do from solar radiation, it is only to be expected that there is a strong positive correlation between brilliant auroral displays and the cycle of solar activity; there is however a delay, the auroral maximum occurring 1–2 years after sunspot maximum.

AURORA AUSTRALIS The 'polar lights' visible from the auroral zone of the southern hemisphere; the name is believed to have been first used by Captain Cook in 1773. (See **Aurora**.)

AURORA BOREALIS The 'polar lights' visible in the auroral zone of the northern hemisphere; the term is believed to have been first used by Gassendi in 1621. (See **Aurora**.)

AURORÆ SINUS Martian surface feature, approximate position Ω 50°, $\Phi - 15°$. Very dark area in the south tropical region, north-west of the Mare Erythræum and adjoining the eastern end of Thaumasia. A number of canali radiate from this feature, including Agathodæmon to the west; Bætis, Ganges and Jamuna to the north; Aromatum Promontorium to the east.

AURORAL LINE Name frequently given to the green line of atomic oxygen of wavelength 5577 Å, which is very prominent in the spectrum of aurorae (where it was discovered before being produced in the laboratory).

AURORAL SPECTRUM The first spectroscopic study of the aurora was made by Ångström in 1867. He detected a prominent green emission line at about 5580 Å, and several more bands in the blue and red. The recording and analysis of auroral emission spectra is extremely difficult, however, due to the very low intensity of the radiation, and the often transient nature of particular displays, rendering long exposures impossible. Considerable ingenuity has been exercised in recent years to produce very fast high-resolution spectrographs specially for auroral work.

The most prominent line, originally discovered by Ångström, was not identified for many years; it was finally shown to be the 'forbidden line' at 5577 Å due to ionized oxygen. There are prominent lines due to molecular nitrogen, and the H_α and H_β lines of hydrogen have been detected in the spectra of the 'quiet' auroral arcs.

The red colour which is often a major feature of auroral displays is believed to be due to enhancement of the red oxygen lines.

AURORAL ZONES Those regions of the Earth where aurorae are most frequently observed; they are centred on about magnetic latitude 67° in both north and south hemispheres.

AUSONIA Martian surface feature, approximate position Ω 250°, $\Phi - 40°$. Large ochre area in the south temperate region of the planet, east of Hellas. Bounded in the north by the Mare Tyrrhenum and Euripus II, in the west by Euripus I, in the south by Promethei Sinus and Typhis Fretum and in the east by Xanthus. Sometimes termed Ausonia Australis (see **Trinacria**).

AUSTRALITE A form of silicaceous meteorite first discovered in Australia; the name now preferred is **Tektite**, *q.v.*

AUTOLYCUS Lunar surface feature, co-ordinates $\xi + 022$, $\eta + 510$. A prominent elliptical crater, 24 miles in diameter, south of the larger Aristillus with which it forms a pair. The floor is depressed, and the broad, terraced walls rise to some 9,000 ft.

There are a number of ridges radial to this formation, observable only under a low angle of illumination. There is also a very faint ray system.

AUTUMNAL EQUINOX The date on which the Sun lies in the direction of the First Point of Libra; also the name given to this point, which is a point of intersection of the Ecliptic and the celestial equator.

The Sun reaches the autumnal equinox on or about September 23; this date should strictly be termed the northern hemisphere autumnal equinox, it being spring in the southern hemisphere at the time.

(See also **Sun—apparent motion of.**)

AXIS OF ROTATION An imaginary line about which a body—e.g. a planet—is considered to rotate; its ends are termed the poles of rotation.

AXIS OF SYMMETRY An imaginary line about which a figure is symmetrical—e.g. the major axis of an ellipse. In the case of a solid figure, it is a possible axis of rotation of the corresponding two-dimensional figure; i.e., in the case of an ellipsoid, it is the major or minor axis of the corresponding ellipse.

AXIS, OPTICAL The central axis of an optical system. (See **Optical axis**.)

AZIMUTH The azimuth of a celestial object is the angular separation between the vertical circle through the object and the plane of the meridian. Thus it is the arc of the horizon intercepted by these two planes. It is normally measured westwards from the north point, from 0°–360°, but it sometimes measured from 0°–180° east or west of the north point, and sometimes from the south point. It is therefore essential to state the method used when listing azimuths.

(See also **Celestial sphere**.)

AZIMUTH ERROR OF A TRANSIT INSTRUMENT The angle by which the east–west (mechanical) axis of a transit instrument departs from being perpendicular to the plane of the meridian. (See **Transit-circle—errors of**.)

AZIMUTH STARS Bright circumpolar stars whose positions and proper motions are known with great accuracy and whose apparent place can therefore be assumed; observations of a number of these stars during a night's observing with a transit circle enable the azimuth error of the instrument to be determined.

B

B STARS Stars of spectral class *B*; they are bluish-white stars of surface temperatures around 12,000°K and are sometimes known as 'helium' or 'Orion-type' stars.

BAADE, W. H. Walter (1893–1960) One of the most distinguished observational astronomers of modern times, Baade was born in Germany but joined the staff of the Mount Wilson Observatory in 1931 and remained there until his retirement in 1958.

Baade's main preoccupation was with the types of star to be found in nearby galaxies and in globular clusters, and in 1944 he succeeded in resolving the nucleus of the great nebula in Andromeda (M 31) into its component stars, using the 100-in. reflector hitherto thought incapable of this feat.

These studies led to Baade's magnum opus, the postulation of the existence of the two **stellar populations**; Baade's work paved the way for the tremendous investigation into the problems of stellar evolution which has taken place in the last twenty years.

BÆTIS Martian surface feature, approximate position Ω 62°, $\Phi - 7°$. Prominent canal radiating north-westwards from Auroræ Sinus, culminating in the dark, prominent Juventæ Fons.

BAILLY Lunar surface feature, co-ordinates $\xi - 360$, $\eta - 920$; one of the largest of ring-formations on the Moon, having a diameter of 183 miles. Unfortunately, Bailly lies on the south-eastern limb and can only be observed at certain librations and under very favourable conditions. The walls are broken up by many small craters and rise to 14,000 ft. in places. There is a wealth of detail on the floor, including a prominent ridge running north–south and a particularly prominent pair of secondary craters (A and B). Bailly A is obviously a comparatively recent formation, as it breaks up not only the wall of Bailly itself but also that of B. Bailly B, now sometimes designated Hare, is an extraordinarily deep ring, being only about 40 miles in diameter but with a depressed interior over 14,000 ft. below the crest of its wall.

Bailly is named after the eighteenth-century French astronomer.

BAILY, Francis (1774-1844) A leading amateur astronomer and a Member of the Council of the Royal Astronomical Society, remembered for his observations of the total solar eclipses of 1836 and 1842, and for his explanation of the phenomenon now known as **Bailey's Beads.** [Plate 2(c).]

Baily also repeated, on behalf of the R.A.S., Cavendish's experiment to determine the mass of the Earth; his result gave a mean density for the Earth of 5·67 times the density of water—within 3 per cent of the value adopted today.

BAILY'S BEADS A phenomenon observed at second and third contacts in eclipses of the Sun. As the last tiny crescent of the Sun disappears behind the occulting Moon (or just before the first thin crescent reappears), it will be broken up into a chain of blobs of light, formed by the passage of the light rays between the high mountains on the Moon's limb. One or two of the 'beads' may disappear and be replaced by others, but the life of the entire phenomenon is very short. At times when the Moon's apparent disk is barely large enough to cover that of the Sun, and the eclipse is almost annular, the beads may be seen to extend almost all round the limb of the Moon, and may appear to 'travel' round from the ingress to the egress side.

The phenomenon was first described by Francis Baily following his observations at the total eclipses of 1836 and 1842, and was consequently dubbed with his name.

BALMER SPECTRUM One of the series of lines in the spectrum of hydrogen due to transitions between various energy levels. The wavelengths of the lines in the Balmer series are rather longer than those of the Lyman spectrum. (See **Hydrogen—spectrum of**.)

BALTIA Martian surface feature, approximate position Ω 50°, Φ + 60°. Ochre area in northern polar region, adjoining the north-western border of the Mare Acidalium.

BARLOW LENS A negative (diverging) lens which, placed between a telescope objective (or mirror) and the eyepiece, has the effect of increasing the focal length of the objective.

Use of a Barlow lens increases the range of magnifications which can be obtained with a given set of eyepieces, and permits greatly improved definition in many cases —especially in such combinations as a Newtonian reflector with a Huyghenian eyepiece.

BARNARD, E. E. (1857–1923) One of the greatest of American observational astronomers, Barnard was a superb visual observer; his drawings of the major planets, made with the great refractors at the Lick and Yerkes Observatories, are well known even today.

He was also a pioneer of photographic astronomy; he photographed the great nebula in Orion and the surrounding nebulosity using only a cheap magic-lantern lens, and made the first photographic discovery of a comet, in 1892.

Also in 1892, observing visually with the 36-in. refractor at Lick, Barnard discovered Satellite V of Jupiter.

BARNARD'S STAR The star BD + 4° 3561, situated in Ophiuchus (R.A. 17 hr 53 min, Dec. + 4° 25′). It has the largest known proper motion (10″.27 per annum) and is the fourth nearest star (its distance, 6·0 light years, exceeds only that of the triple star α/*Proxima* Centauri). It has a magnitude of 9·5 and is suspected of being a close binary with a period of 1·1 years.

From a study of variations in its proper motion P. van de Kamp has confirmed that it has a non-luminous companion only 1·6 times the mass of Jupiter—the only known case of a distant star having a planet of similar size to those in the solar system.

BARRED SPIRAL GALAXY A form of spiral galaxy which differs from the more common form in that the spiral arms do not commence at the nucleus but at the ends of a vast 'bar' centred on the nucleus. They were first classified by Hubble in 1936. The fundamental reason for their different structure from conventional spirals is not known, but they have been assumed to follow a parallel sequence of evolution by both Hubble and later theorists. (See **Galactic structure**.)

BATHYS Martian surface feature, approximate position Ω 105°, Φ − 40°. Canal radiating south-westward from Solis Lacus, joining the border of Thaumasia at Aonius Sinus.

BAYER LETTERS John Bayer was a Bavarian lawyer who lived from 1572–1605, who published in 1603 a star atlas entitled *Uranometria*; this recorded the positions and magnitudes of the 777 stars in Tycho Brahe's catalogue of 1602, and also of about 500 additional ones. The *Uranometria* was particularly valuable in that it provided a notation for the brighter stars which formed the basis of that used ever since.

The Bayer Letters are the letters of the Greek alphabet which, in conjunction with the genitive form of the constellation name, Bayer allocated to the brightest stars in each constellation (e.g. α Canis Majoris;

β Geminorum). The order of allocation was based upon the imagined configuration of the constellation figure, and not, as might be supposed, upon the relative brightness of the stars in it. (See also **Flamsteed number.**)

BEER, Wilhelm (1797–1850) A Berlin banker, and collaborator with J. H. von Mädler in the production of the deservedly famous *Mappa Selenographica*—then the most detailed and accurate lunar map in existence—and of the companion descriptive volume *Der Mond*. Beer and Mädler also collaborated in the production of the first systematic chart of the surface detail of Mars.

Little was heard of Beer after Mädler's departure for Dorpat in 1840. He was, incidentally, a brother of the composer Meyerbeer.

BELLATRIX The equatorial star γ Ori, marking Orion's left shoulder in the ancient delineation of the constellation. A bluish-white star of spectral type *B2* and apparent magnitude +1·7.

BELT Name used to denote planetary surface markings having the form of dark or dusky latitudinal bands. (See **Planetary surface features.**)

BERTHON DYNAMOMETER A measuring instrument devised for the determination of the diameters of small objects. The instrument consists of two machined metal straight-edges, inclined to one another by a small angle and rigidly fixed together; the object to be measured is inserted into the gap between them and slid into a position of contact with both straight-edges; its diameter can then be read off directly on a scale engraved on one of the straight-edges (see Fig. 7).

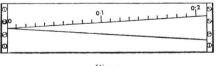

Fig. 7

The instrument is of some use to the astronomer, as it can be used to measure (by visual estimation) the diameter of the **exit pupil** of a telescope eyepiece.

BESSEL, Friedrich W. (1784–1846) One of the best known mathematical astronomers who ever lived; deservedly so, since few have contributed so much to our knowledge of the subject, or devised so many methods for furthering this knowledge.

Still the most commonly used method of interpolation in astronomical ephemerides is that due to Bessel, and the calculations of the circumstances of an eclipse or occultation are based upon the Besselian elements.

Bessel was active at a time when the development of positional astronomy was all-important, and his revisions of the calculating procedures then in use were therefore of incalculable value. He drew up a basic form for the reduction of positional observations, and improved the calculation of the corrections involved— those for aberration, precession, nutation and refraction; he also stressed the importance of correcting for the observer's personal equation and for the systematic errors of the instrument used.

It was Bessel who examined the departure of the movements of Uranus from those predicted, and concluded that this must be due to the presence of another planet beyond Uranus; he thus provided the stimulus for the work of Adams and Le Verrier which led to the discovery of Neptune.

It was also Bessel who deduced that fluctuations in the proper motion of *Sirius* and *Procyon* were due to their being binary systems, each having a faint, but fairly massive, companion, hitherto undetected; both companions have in fact been discovered visually, although years after Bessel's death in both cases.

Although an unparalleled mathematician, Bessel's work was not confined to the stimulation of observers or the analysis of their work; he was himself no mean observer, and was in fact the first person to use ? heliometer—the 6¼-in. instrument made by Fraunhofer for the Königsberg Observatory where Bessel worked—with which he measured many stellar parallaxes, notably that of 61 Cyg.

BESSEL Lunar surface feature, co-ordinates $\xi + 286$, $\eta + 370$, named after the great German astronomer-mathematician. Although only 12 miles in diameter, Bessel is especially prominent owing to its isolated position on the floor of the Mare Serenitatis. This deep crater of perfect form is further accentuated by its location on the bright ray from Menelaus which covers the Mare. The walls rise about 3,500 ft. above the surface of the Mare, but some 5,500 ft. above the crater's interior.

BESSELIAN ELEMENTS The quantities required to be substituted in equations developed by F. W. Bessel in order to calculate the circumstances of phenomena such as occultations, eclipses, etc.

BESSELIAN INTERPOLATION A means of obtaining, with considerable accuracy, intermediate values of a tabulated function from the values given. (See **Interpolation**.)

BETA TAURIDS A daylight meteor shower, discovered by radar, occurring at the end of June. The radiant is situated near β Tau. The shower probably has a common origin with Encke's Comet, and consequently with the night-time **Taurids** shower.

BETELGEUSE The equatorial star α Ori, marking the right shoulder of Orion in the ancient constellation figure. An orange-red giant of spectral type Mo, Betelgeuse is an irregular variable; its magnitude varies between $+0.1$ and $+1.2$ over a basic period of about $5\frac{3}{4}$ years, but also fluctuates throughout this time in a completely irregular manner. Interferometer measurements made with the 100-in. reflector at Mount Wilson Observatory indicate that the diameter of Betelgeuse is about 300 million miles—just about large enough to contain the orbit of Mars.

BIELA'S COMET A faint comet discovered by Biela in 1826, and found to be a periodic comet which had been observed previously in 1772 and 1805. The period is a comparatively short one, 6·6 years. The comet appeared quite normal at its return in 1832, but was apparently not observed in 1838; in 1846 it was seen, but its shape had undergone a considerable change. The comet had become very elongated, being described at the time as 'pear-shaped'; within ten days it separated into two distinct parts. The new double comet was observed over two months, by which time the components were some 175,000 miles apart. The twin comets returned, as expected, in 1852, but were by now about a million and a half miles apart; they have not been seen since, although passages of the Earth through the orbit of Biela's Comet in November have coincided with some magnificent meteor showers; the meteor stream concerned (the Andromedids) is therefore often known as the Bielids. [Plate 15(c, d).] (See also **Comets—disruption of.**)

BIELIDS A meteor shower occurring on about November 30 from a radiant near γ And; the stream has been shown to be associated with **Biela's Comet**. The shower is more properly known as the Andromedids. It has given rise to some magnificent displays in the past, but has been very weak in recent years.

BIFILAR MICROMETER An alternative name for the modern form of the filar micrometer. (See **Micrometer, filar**.)

BIG DIPPER Term used in the United States to describe that part of Ursa Major known elsewhere as *The Plough*, formed by the seven stars α, β, γ, δ, ϵ, ζ and η UMa.

BINARY SYSTEM A system in which two stars are in orbital motion around a

Table 4.   Some typical binary systems

Star	Apparent magnitude of components m_1	m_2	Period (years)	Semi-major axis (A.U.)	Distance of system (parsecs)	Total mass ($\times$ mass of Sun)
δ Equ	5·3	5·4	5·7	4·1	15·2	2·1
42 CBr	5·2	5·2	25·9	11·4	17·2	2·2
α CMi (*Procyon*)	0·5	13·5	40·2	14·5	3·4	1·9
α CMa (*Sirius*)	−1·6	8·4	49·9	20·2	2·6	3·2
α Cen	0·3	1·7	80·1	23·7	1·3	2·1
α Gem (*Castor*)	2·0	2·8	380	79	13·5	3·4

common centre of gravity, and are therefore physically interdependent. The earliest known binary systems were discovered by means of repeated visual observations over a long period; the relative motions of the component stars may also, however, be detected by the use of the **spectroscope**, the **interferometer** and the **photometer**.

Basic data for some typical binaries is given in Table 4. *Castor* is in fact a noteworthy multiple star, being composed of three spectroscopic binary systems.

Orbit. Each component of a binary system describes an elliptical orbit around the centre of gravity of the system; the orbits are similar in form, but of different size, that of the less massive component being the larger. Figure 8 (a) shows the actual orbits of *Sirius* and *Sirius B* during the period 1900–1945; their apparent motion in the sky, including the proper motion ·of the system, is shown for the same period in Fig. 8 (b). In this figure *Sirius* is represented by ○, *Sirius B* by ● and the proper motion of the system by →. The ratio of the sizes of the orbits is inversely proportional to the ratio of their masses. The orbit determined by observation is the **relative orbit**—the apparent orbit of the fainter component around the brighter. The relative orbit of *Sirius B* for 1900–1945, drawn to the same scale as Fig. 8 (a), is shown in Fig. 9. This is similar in shape to the actual orbits of the component stars, but is larger than either, its major axis being equal to the sum of the major axes of the component orbits.

Except in the rare cases where the plane of the relative orbit is perpendicular to the line of sight, the positions actually observed represent the projection of the relative orbit upon the celestial sphere. This apparent orbit can however be simply connected to the true relative orbit.

Seven elements define the orbit of a binary star: a, the semi-major axis of the relative orbit; e, its eccentricity; i, the inclination of the plane of the orbit from the perpendicular to the line of sight; Ω, the position angle of the node of the orbital plane and the plane perpendicular to the line of sight; ω the angular separation, in the orbital plane, between the node and periastron; T, the date of periastron passage; P, the orbital revolution period. Some authorities tabulate n, the mean motion, instead of P; in such cases P can be calculated by use of the relation $P = 360°/n$.

The periods of most visual binaries are between 20 and 100 years; some are even longer, and a few short-period systems are known with periods of only a few months. Many very long-period binaries are known but have not yet been observed over a large enough part of a revolution for their orbital elements to be accurately determined. The periods of spectroscopic and eclipsing binaries are much shorter.

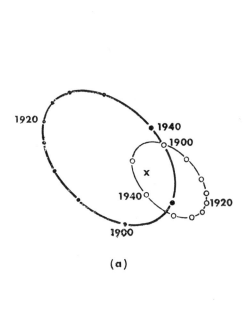

(a)

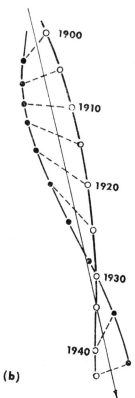

(b)

Fig. 8

Binary orbits usually have high eccentricities, averaging about 0·5; there is a tendency for the longer-period binaries to have higher orbital eccentricities.

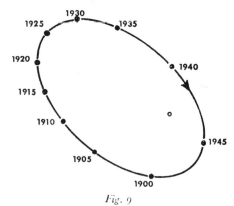

Fig. 9

Mass. One of the most important aspects of binary star observations is that, for those binary systems whose parallax has been accurately determined, and hence whose distance is known, it is possible to deduce the total mass of the system $(\mu_1 + \mu_2)$ from the equation

$$\mu_1 + \mu_2 = \frac{d^3}{P^2 \, \pi^3}$$

where μ_1 and μ_2 are the masses of the component stars expressed in terms of the Sun's mass, d is the angular separation in seconds of arc and π is the parallax. For binary systems of known parallax the total mass appears to be, on average, about three times the mass of the Sun.

The masses of the individual components cannot be deduced from observations of the binary alone, which provide

Table 5.   Binaries of known mass-ratio

Star	Period (years)	Mass-ratio (μ_1/μ_2)	Masses of components (Sun = 1) μ_1	μ_2
α Aur (*Capella*)	0·285	1·3	4·2	3·3
δ Equ	5·7	1·0	1·0	1·0
α CMi (*Procyon*)	40·2	3·0	1·2	0·4
μ Her	43·2	1·2	0·5	0·4
α CMa (*Sirius*)	50·0	2·5	2·5	1·0
η Cas	346	1·7	0·7	0·4

only the relative orbit; they can however be obtained from meridian-circle observations of one component or positional observations of both components relative to nearby 'background' stars. In these cases the actual orbits around the common centre of gravity can be determined, from which the **mass-ratio** can be deduced. Some typical binaries of known mass-ratio are listed in Table 5.

Visual binaries. These are the binary systems observable as close double stars by visual methods; except in the case of fairly short-period binaries it is, of course, difficult to confirm whether a close double is a binary system or an **optical double**; observations many years apart are required. The Aitken Catalogue gives details for over 17,000 double stars within 120° of the north pole; about 1 in 18 stars down to the ninth magnitude are double.

Among the visual binaries of shortest known period are the stars known as BD 8° 4352 (period 1·7 years), Dawson 31 (4·6 years) and δ Equ (5·7 years). At the other end of the scale periods of hundreds of years are known, but orbits for these systems cannot be reliably determined.

Spectroscopic binaries. These are binary systems whose separation is too small to permit visual observation; the orbital motion of their components can be detected, however, by the Doppler shift of the absorption lines in their spectra. The necessary spectrograms are usually obtained with an **objective prism**.

The Doppler effect results in the effective wavelength of the light reaching us being shortened in the case of an approaching source, and lengthened in the case of a receding source. Measurements of the Doppler shift enable the radial (or line-of-sight) velocity to be determined. In the case of a binary component the radial velocity is a variable quantity, and is plotted against a time scale. The shape, period and amplitude of these velocity curves are then studied and the details of the relative orbit deduced.

Figure 10 is the velocity curve for a hypothetical star having a circular orbit—i.e. an eccentricity $e = 0$; in this case the result would be a simple harmonic curve.

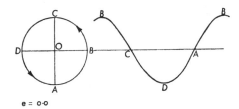

$e = 0·0$

Fig. 10

In the usual case of an elliptical orbit, the shape of the velocity curve is dependent upon the angle between the node and periastron, ω. Figure 11 shows the velocity curves for an elliptical orbit of eccentricity $e = 0·5$, for values of ω of 0°, 45° and 90°.

The periods of spectroscopic binaries

range from 8 hours (in the case of the star W UMa) to several years.

Of the elements required to define a binary orbit, only P, e, w, T and $(a \sin i)$ can be determined from the velocity curve of a spectroscopic binary.

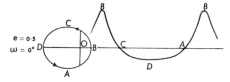

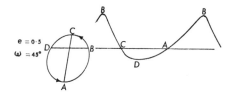

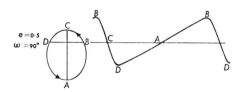

Fig. 11

The first spectroscopic binary to be discovered was *Mizar* (ξ UMa); E. C. Pickering obtained a spectrogram at the Harvard College Observatory which showed that its absorption lines appeared double at regular intervals from which he deduced a period of $20\frac{1}{2}$ days.

Approximately 1 in 5 of the brighter stars have been shown to be spectroscopic binaries, and recent observations suggest that this ratio may be as high as 1 in 2.

Eclipsing binaries. These are binary systems whose light appears to fluctuate, due to the Earth's being in or near the plane of the relative orbit, so that mutual eclipses of the component stars occur at regular intervals.

Figure 12 (a) shows a typical light curve; from a study of this curve the nature of the system can be deduced. The light does

not remain constant for a time during the minima, which proves that the eclipses are partial, not total; the plane of the orbit is therefore not quite in the line of sight. As one minimum is much deeper than the other, one of the component stars must be fainter than the other. As the minima occur at regular intervals the orbit must either be a circle or an ellipse with its major axis in the line of sight. It can also be shown that the brighter component is also the smaller of the two. The appearance this binary would present, in a telescope large enough to separate its components, is shown in Fig. 12 (b) beneath the appropriate parts of the light curve (a); the corresponding orbital positions are shown diagrammatically in (c). In actual fact such systems are observed only by means of their light variation; the frequent and accurate determination of their magnitudes necessary to produce good light-curves has been greatly facilitated by the adaptation of the photoelectric photometer for astronomical use.

It will be appreciated that the mathematical analysis of an accurate light-curve enables the nature of quite complex

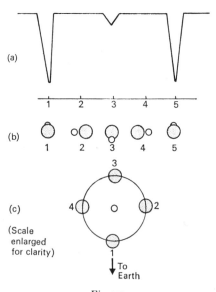

Fig. 12

38

systems to be deduced solely from the fluctuations in their light; in many of the known cases of close binary systems the components are known to be drawn out into ellipsoidal shapes by the tidal forces of their mutual gravitational attraction (β Lyr is an example of this type), and some systems may even have a 'dumb-bell' form and be still in the process of separating into two distinct bodies.

Practically all eclipsing binaries are also spectroscopic binaries; this is very fortunate, since we can obtain the function ($a \sin i$) from the spectroscopic observations as described above, and from the photometric light-curve we can obtain i, and also the actual separation in kilometres (despite the fact that we may not know the diameters of the components or their distance from Earth). Thus combined spectroscopic and photometric observation leads to a more complete analysis of the system.

Spectral classification. The spectral type of the brighter component is recorded where possible, but where the companion cannot be typed the system as a whole is classified.

The incidence of both visual and spectroscopic binary systems in the various spectral classes is shown in Fig. 13, and the distribution of all stars brighter than magnitude +8·25 is also plotted for comparison. The most notable features are the comparatively low incidence of both types of binary in type K, the most common spectral class, and the high incidence of visual binaries in classes A and F and of spectroscopic binaries in B and A.

The majority of eclipsing binaries are of early type, the great majority being of types O, B and A. Most of these, together with the spectroscopic binaries of which the majority are early-type, are concentrated in the Milky Way; this uneven distribution is to be expected, since most of the early-type stars are concentrated towards the centre of the Galaxy.

Where the components of a binary system are comparable in magnitude they are usually of similar spectral type; where

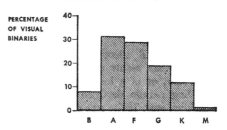

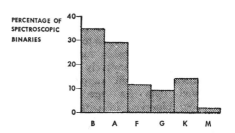

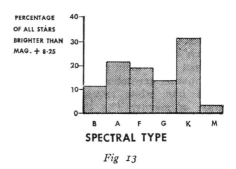

SPECTRAL TYPE

Fig 13

one component is much fainter than the other it is usually of a later type. It is usual to find that both components are main-sequence stars. Where the bright star is a giant its companion is usually either a dwarf of the same spectral type or a giant of earlier type; e.g. F-type giants with A-type companions are quite common.

(See also **Double stars; Double stars—observation of; Spectral classification of stars; Stellar populations.**)

BINARY SYSTEMS, ORIGIN OF There are three main theories of the origin of binary systems, which may be termed the 'fission', 'chance encounter' and 'adjacent origin' theories.

The 'fission' theory suggests that a binary is the result of the fission of a single star, or of a local condensation in a cooling nebula destined to become an individual star. If the star or nebular concentration has its constituent matter less highly concentrated at its centre than is usual, its evolution may be abnormal and it will become elongated and eventually assume a 'dumb-bell' form, before separating into two separate components. Although only tenable for close binary systems of comparatively short period, this theory is well supported by the observed data for spectroscopic and eclipsing binaries; in particular, certain of the latter (e.g. β Lyr) have light curves suggesting that their components are indeed greatly elongated, and in some cases may even be dumb-bell shaped.

The second theory suggests that the motions of two separate and hitherto unconnected stars bring them at some point to such a close approach that they are deflected from their previous paths by their mutual gravitational attraction, and drawn into orbits around a common centre of gravity. The chances of this occurring naturally depend upon the probability of two stars passing sufficiently close to one another, and it has been demonstrated statistically that it is unlikely that many of the known binary systems can have been formed in this way.

The third theory postulates that the components of a binary system were evolved from separate but adjacent condensations of nebular matter, each condensing into a separate star, but that they have remained mutually interdependent throughout their evolution owing to the proximity of the original centres of condensation. This seems a very plausible suggestion for the origin of the visual binaries having wide separations and long periods.

(See also **Binary system**.)

BINOCULARS An optical instrument consisting of two low-power astronomical telescopes mounted together on a framework which is adjustable to suit the eye-separation of the observer. In addition to the usual objectives and eyepieces of the astronomical telescope, each of the optical trains incorporates a system of prisms to reverse and invert the image, so that it appears erect and so that the instrument

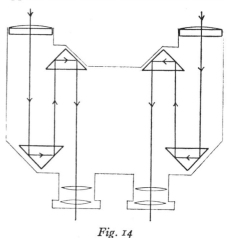

Fig. 14

can be used for normal, non-astronomical purposes. A simplified form of binocular optical system is shown in Fig. 14.

The specification of binoculars is given in the form 'magnifying power × aperture of objective in mm', hence a 7 × 50 binocular has objectives of 50 mm aperture and eyepieces giving a linear magnification of × 7.

BIRT Lunar surface feature, co-ordinates $\xi - 137$, $\eta - 380$. A prominent double crater on the Mare Nubium, just to the east of the Straight Wall. The crater has a diameter of 11 miles, and its walls rise 6,000 ft. above the interior. The western wall is broken by a more recent crater ring, Birt A, some 3 miles in diameter.

BLACK-BODY RADIATION A black body is a concept used by physicists and astrophysicists in calculations about radiation; it is a body which completely absorbs all radiation reaching its surface and reflects none—therefore appearing quite black. The term black-body radiation is thus used to denote a 'perfect' radiation.

BLINK MICROSCOPE An instrument designed to alternate rapidly, in a monocular or binocular eyepiece, images of two photographic plates. If two plates of the same field, exposed at different times, are examined in such an instrument, any object whose position has changed in the interval between the two exposures will appear to oscillate between the two positions and can thus be detected immediately.

This technique is of considerable assistance in the discovery of comets, minor planets, etc.

BLISS, Rev. Nathaniel (1700–1764) The fourth Astronomer Royal, to which office he succeeded on the death of Bradley in 1762; he continued the established programme of observations, but unfortunately died in 1764 after only two years in office.

Bliss had succeeded Halley as Savilian Professor of Geometry at Oxford, and occupied this chair for 20 years.

BLOOMING A process of coating the surfaces of the glass components of optical systems with a suitable material, in order to prevent unwanted reflections. The coating must, of course, be sufficiently transparent for the reduction in the amount of light transmitted to be a minimum. The material normally used is magnesium fluoride, deposited by electro-evaporation *in vacuo*.

BLUE BAND Name sometimes given to the dark border which appears, surrounding the polar caps of Mars, as they melt during the Martian spring and early summer. (See **Mars—observed features and notable phenomena**.)

BODE, J. E. (1747–1846) A Berlin astronomer, remembered for the development of Bode's Law—although priority in this discovery has been claimed for others. It was also Bode who proposed the name **Uranus** for the planet discovered by Sir William Herschel.

BODE'S LAW The formulation of this interesting numerical relationship is traditionally attributed to J. E. Bode of Berlin, who was certainly active in drawing attention to it, at least, but there is some evidence for believing that a Professor from Wittenberg—J. B. Titius—should share the credit for first publishing the Law. It has also been suggested that Christian Wolfe of Halle had discussed it more than twenty years earlier.

There is no theoretical foundation for this empirical law, which is in fact a numerical series which was found to agree closely with the observed mean distances from the Sun of the principal bodies in the Solar System.

To obtain the series, take the progression 0, 3, 6, 12, 24, 48, 96, 192; add 4 to each of these numbers, and divide each by 10; the resulting series then represents the solar distance of each planet, out to Uranus, in astronomical units. The distances calculated in this way are compared with the actual values in the following table:

Table 6.   Mean distance from Sun

Planet	Calculated according to Bode's Law	Actually observed (A.U.)
Mercury .	0·4	0·39
Venus . .	0·7	0·72
Earth . .	1·0	1·0
Mars . .	1·6	1·52
Minor Planets	2·8	2·65 (average)
Jupiter . .	5·2	5·20
Saturn . .	10·0	9·54
Uranus .	19·6	19·2
Neptune .	38·8	30·1
Pluto . .	77·2	39·5

It will be noted that although out as far as Uranus there is close agreement—that is to say the Law accurately represents the true state of affairs, and even the minor planets fall into place—the series if extended does not agree with the actual distances of Neptune and Pluto.

When Adams and Le Verrier were commencing their calculations which ultimately led to the discovery of Neptune, they both used the mean distance predicted by Bode's Law as a starting point. When finally discovered, however, Neptune proved to be well inside the predicted distance. A similar circumstance surrounded the discovery of Pluto, but here the error was very much greater. In fact, Pluto is much closer to the mean distance predicted for Neptune; this is interesting when considered in the light of Lyttleton's theory that Pluto may be a former satellite of Neptune.

Bode's Law may be written in the form $a + bc^n$, where $a = 0.4$, $b = 0.3$, $c = 2$ and n is a variable, $-\infty$ for Mercury, o for Venus, 1 for Earth, 2 for Mars, etc. Other equations of this form have been devised which give a closer approximation to the actual distances, but they too are purely empirical, and have no theoretical basis.

It is possible, however, that there is a sound physical reason for the fact that the planets' mean distances agree so closely with this numerical series; considerable evidence has been found to suggest that there is a morphological relationship between the members of the solar system —e.g. the resonance-grouping of minor planets and particles in Saturn's rings, commensurable mean motions for many of the planetary satellites, etc. (See also **Solar system; Commensurable motions; Pluto—discovery of; Pluto— origin of.**)

BOHNENBERGER EYEPIECE See Eyepiece, Bohnenberger.

BOILING Term used by solar and planetary observers to denote the appear- ance of constant 'rippling', and lack of a sharp, still edge, which characterizes the telescopic appearance of the limbs of the Sun or planets at times when the Earth's atmosphere is rather turbulent.

BOND, George P. (1825–1865) The son of W. C. Bond, and his successor as Director of the Harvard College Observatory. He shared in his father's pioneering work, and was his principal observer; on 1848 September 16 he discovered the eighth satellite of Saturn (**Hyperion**) with the Observatory's 15-in. Merz refractor.

BOND, William C. (1789–1859) An American watchmaker and amateur astronomer, who was appointed the first Director, in 1839, of the Harvard College Observatory. With his son G. P. Bond, he was a pioneer in the use of the Daguerrotype process for astronomical photography. They were also among the first systematic observers of Saturn, and made many important discoveries, notably (with W. Dawes) that of the Crêpe Ring; they were also diligent observers of the surface detail of Mars, and of comets.

BONNER DURCHMUSTERUNG This famous star catalogue, usually known by its abbreviation 'BD', was compiled by F. W. A. Argelander between 1859 and 1862, and extended by E. Schönfeld in 1886. The positions and apparent magnitudes of some 458,000 stars, with declinations from $+90°$ to $-23°$, are given. They are not of high accuracy by present-day standards, but the catalogue is still of considerable value to observers as a ready means of identification, thanks to the great number of stars included.

The stars are numbered in declination zones; a star is thus designated in the catalogue in the form 'BD$+7°$ 1275'.

BOÖTES (The Herdsman. *Genitive* Boötis, *I.A.U. abbreviation* Boo.) A large northern constellation rather short of naked-eye stars, and containing only six brighter than fourth magnitude; nevertheless it stretches from a declination of $+55°$ to within $8°$ of the equator, and covers some 900 square degrees of the sky. It reaches midnight culmination in late April.

BOREOSYRTIS Martian surface feature, approximate position Ω 280°, $\Phi+55°$. An oval dark area almost due north of the Syrtis Major. Two principal dark streaks radiate southwards from it, Casius and Nilosyrtis, forming the northern boundaries of the Neith Regio and Meroe Insula respectively.

BOSPORUS GEMMATUS Martian surface feature, approximate position Ω 60°, $\Phi-45°$. Broad, diffuse streak stretching from the Mare Erythræum to the Mare Australe, forming the north-western border of Argyre. The alternative designation Nereidum Fretum is now usually adopted.

BOSS CATALOGUE The *General Catalogue of 33342 Stars*, compiled by Benjamin Boss and published by the Carnegie Institution of Washington in 1936. This contains the position, proper motion, magnitude and spectral type of all stars down to 7th magnitude, and some others. The abbreviated form of star designations used is GC 13501. (See **Star catalogues.**)

BOWL CRATER A type of lunar surface feature; it appears to have no flat floor, but to have an interior cross-section of a smooth curve. Many of the lunar craters with diameters up to about 10 miles are of this type. (See **Moon—surface features of.**)

BOYDEN OBSERVATORY Situated at Bloemfontein, South Africa, the Boyden Observatory is one of the major observing stations in the Southern Hemisphere. It is administered by an international Council which comprises the Directors of the observatories of Armagh and Dunsink in Ireland, Uccle in Belgium, Hamburg in Germany and Harvard in the U.S.A. Its principal telescopes are a 60-in. reflector,

a sophisticated 16-in. Cassegrain reflector and the well-known 'ADH' instrument— a 32-in. Schmidt–Cassegrain jointly owned by the Armagh, Dunsink and Harvard Observatories, with which magnificent photographs of important southern starfields have been obtained.

BRADLEY, Rev. James (1693–1762) The third Astronomer Royal, from 1742– 1762. Bradley, who held the Savilian Chair of Astronomy at Oxford, was recommended for the position of Astronomer Royal by Halley, who offered to resign in Bradley's favour in 1739 owing to his own failing health. Halley was pressed to stay in office, however, and Bradley therefore succeeded him on his death three years later.

Bradley had achieved fame by his discovery, in 1728, of the **aberration of light.** As Astronomer Royal he pursued the positional observations developed by his predecessors, and obtained a grant from the Board of Admiralty to instal more modern equipment in the Royal Observatory. In 1748 he discovered the Earth's **nutation,** and he also analysed the effects upon observations of atmospheric refraction, air temperature and barometric pressure.

BRAHE, Tycho (1546–1601) Born in Denmark three years after the death of Copernicus, Tycho Brahe was destined to play as large a part in the development of observational astronomy as Copernicus had in theoretical astronomy. Although intended for a legal career, Tycho (as he is now frequently referred to) had developed a passionate interest in astronomy since observing a partial solar eclipse at the age of 14, and by the time he was 26 he had constructed a number of instruments and developed techniques for positional observations.

At this time, in 1572, he observed the great nova in Cassiopeia, and incorporated his fine series of observations of its position and development in a book, *De Stella Nova*.

Following a recommendation by the Landgrave of Hesse, Tycho was established by King Frederick II on the island of Hven, a few miles north of Copenhagen; here he set up his famous observatiories **Uraniborg** and **Stjerneborg**, magnificently equipped and manned at state expense, and commenced the lifetime of accurate observational work which opened up a new era in astronomy.

It is not possible here to catalogue Tycho's many achievements; probably none were of such value, however, as the unprecedentedly accurate series of observations sustained over many years, of the positions and motions of the planets. Not only did these commence the work which continues today in the great national observatories, but they also provide the data from which Kepler derived his **Laws of Planetary Motion.**

BRIDGE, SOLAR Term used to denote the brilliant narrow streaks of photosphere which are sometimes observed to cross large sunspots, dividing the umbra into two or more separate components.

BRIGHT RIM STRUCTURES Many of the diffuse emission nebulae display a bright edge to some of their condensations, usually on the side facing the exciting star; these are known as bright rim structures, and are considered very important evidence in studies of the structure and formation of the emission nebulae.

BRIGHT STAR CATALOGUE The *Catalogue of Bright Stars* published by F. Schlesinger and L. F. Jenkins (Yale, 1940), *q.v.*

BRITISH ASTRONOMICAL ASSOCIATION The 'B.A.A.' is a body founded in 1890 which has made a most notable contribution to astronomy. Its principal functions are the direction and co-ordination—by experts both professional and amateur—of the work of amateur observers so as to ensure that they continue their great tradition of making a useful

contribution to science, and the education of all with an interest in the heavens. It holds regular meetings, publishes an important *Journal, Handbook* and *Memoirs*, and has a valuable library for the use of its members. Details of membership can be obtained from the Assistant Secretary, British Astronomical Association, 303 Bath Road, Hounslow West, Middlesex.

BROWN, Ernest William (1866–1938) The tables of the Moon's position, published in *The Astronomical Ephemeris*, are based upon the Theory of the Motion of the Moon developed over a period of thirty years by E. W. Brown. Only since 1960 have they been independently calculated from the theory—for many years until the date they had been taken direct from Brown's own *Tables of the Motion of the Moon*, published in 1919. A native of Hull, Brown spent many years in the United States, mainly at Yale University. He was awarded the Gold Medal of the Royal Astronomical Society in 1907.

BULLIALDUS Lunar surface feature, co-ordinates $\xi - 354$, $\eta - 350$. A beautifully formed crater, 39 miles in diameter, prominently situated in the eastern point of the Mare Nubium. The terraced walls rise 8,000 ft. above the convex floor, which bears a multiple central mountain.

BUREAU DES LONGITUDES The astronomical computing centre for France, in Paris; responsible for the production of the French equivalent of *The Astronomical Ephemeris*, the *Connaissance des Temps*.

BURNHAM CATALOGUE The *General Catalogue of Double Stars within 121° of the North Pole*, compiled by S. W. Burnham and published by the Carnegie Institution of Washington in 1906. Contains data for 13,665 double stars. The abbreviation used is BGC, but double stars are often referred by non-catalogue designations. (See **Double stars; see** also **Aitken Catalogue.**)

C

C.T. Normal abbreviation for the **Connaissance des Temps,** *q.v.*

CAELUM (The Chisel; formerly Caela Sculptoris, the Sculptor's Chisels. *Genitive* Caeli, *I.A.U. abbreviation* Cae.) A tiny constellation in the southern sky, situated between Columba and the root of the narrow southern 'ribbon' of **Eridanus.** The brightest stars are two of the fourth magnitude, α and γ Cae.

CALCIUM Chemical element, atomic weight 40·08. It is a soft white metal which tarnishes rapidly on exposure to air. It occurs abundantly in the Earth, in various forms of its carbonate ($CaCO_3$), e.g. marble, chalk, limestone, and the sulphate ($CaSO_4$), e.g. gypsum. It is essential to vertebrate life, being the major constituent of bones and teeth.

It occurs in all stars, and has been particularly helpful in observations of the Sun; considerable knowledge of solar activity has been obtained from monochromatic observation of the Sun's surface in the violet Fraunhofer 'K' line due to calcium, at a wavelength of 3934 Å.

CALCIUM K-LINE The Fraunhofer 'K' line in the solar spectrum; it is in the deep violet, at a wavelength of 3934 Å, and is due to calcium. It is widely used for monochromatic studies of the solar surface, using the **spectroheliograph.**

CALCIUM REVERSAL LINE The broad *H* and *K* absorption lines of calcium are very prominent in the spectra of stars in spectral classes *G, K* and *M*. Narrow calcium emission lines appear as bright lines in the middle of the absorption bands; these are termed *reversal lines*. In the case of some stars the reversal lines are double.

It has been found from a study of the spectra of stars of known absolute magnitude that there is a logarithmic relationship between the absolute magnitude and the width of the calcium reversal lines. This has proved to be of the utmost importance as it provides an additional means of determining the absolute magnitudes of other stars, from which their distances can be obtained. (See **Stars—distance of.**)

CALCIUM STARS Name sometimes used to denote stars of spectral class *F*, in whose spectra the absorption bands of calcium are very prominent. (See **Stars—spectral classification of.**)

CALCULUS OF OBSERVATIONS The statistical analysis of a number of observations to determine the best value of the quantity being observed.

CALENDAR A system of time-reckoning devised to meet the requirements of everyday existence. The principal units of time used in the calendar are the year, month and day, based upon astronomical periods, and the week, a purely arbitrary interval.

Early calendars were based upon lunar phenomena, with annual adjustments to conform to the Sun's apparent motion around the heavens. One of the most important of the early calendars was that of the Egyptians, comprising 12 months of 30 days each, plus 5 additional days at the end of each year. As this is a quarter of a day less than the mean solar year, and was not adjusted, the ancient Egyptian New Year was earlier by this amount each year relative to the seasons, retrogressing a full year in a period of about 1,460 years—this was termed the *Sothic cycle*.

In 238 B.C. Ptolemy Euergetes attempted to introduce a sixth additional day every fourth year to counteract this defect, but his suggestion was not accepted. The Roman Emperor Augustus succeeded in gaining acceptance for the addition of an extra day every fourth year with effect from 23 B.C., thus stabilizing the season at which New Year occurred.

The calendar of the Babylonians consisted of 12 lunar months, fixed by observation of the first appearance of the crescent moon after New Moon; its relation to the seasons was roughly preserved by the addition of an extra month from time to time.

A most important reform was the *Julian calendar*, established by Julius Cæsar in 46 B.C. with the aid of an Alexandrian astronomer named Sosigenes. It was based on the lunar calendar used in Rome at the time, which had become badly out of phase with the seasons; Cæsar therefore extended the year 46 B.C. to 445 days to restore parity with the seasons, and then introduced a calendar year of 365·25 days thereafter, the fraction being allowed for by the inclusion of an extra day in every fourth year (*leap year day*). This calendar remained in use until the introduction of the *Gregorian calendar* in 1582.

The Gregorian calendar was devised by Pope Gregory XIII, and is a refinement of the Julian calendar. The adopted year in the Julian calendar, 365·25 days, is about 11 min 14 sec longer than the Tropical Year; this error accumulates to about 18 hours per century, by which amount the calendar dates and the seasons were getting out of phase. To correct for this error Gregory omitted 10 days from his calendar, designating the day after 1582 October 4 as 1582 October 15; to prevent its recurrence he reduced the average length of the calendar year by the omission of the leap year day in century years not divisible by 400—thus 1600 was a leap year, as will be 2000, but 1700, 1800 and 1900 were not. This resulted in a mean Gregorian year of 365·2425 days.

The Gregorian calendar was adopted by most nations only over a period of nearly three and a half centuries. In Belgium, France, Italy, Luxembourg, Poland, Portugal and Spain it was adopted in 1582; in Austria, Czechoslovakia (Bohemia and Moravia), much of Germany, parts of Switzerland, Hungary and parts of the Netherlands in 1583–7; in Denmark, the remainder of Germany, the Netherlands and Switzerland, between 1610 and 1701.

In America and in Great Britain and its Dominions the Gregorian calendar was adopted in 1752, the day 1752 September 3 being followed by 1752 September 14, to make up the accumulated error of 11 days; Sweden followed suit in 1753. In Alaska the change was made in 1867 on its transfer from Russia to America; Egypt followed in 1875 and Albania in 1912. Bulgaria, China, Estonia, Jugoslavia, Latvia, Lithuania, Roumania and the U.S.S.R. adopted the Gregorian calendar during the period 1912–19, Greece did so in 1924 and, finally, Turkey in 1927.

CALLISTO Satellite IV of Jupiter, *q.v.*

CAMBRIDGE CATALOGUES OF RADIO SOURCES Surveys of the heavens made with the radio telescopes of the Mullard Radio Astronomy Observatory of the University of Cambridge, especially the great interferometer, have been published since 1950. They have been widely adopted in turn as the most convenient catalogues of radio sources, which are usually identified by their number in the current Cambridge catalogue. This unfortunately leads to the designation of each source changing with each successive catalogue. The designations have a prefix 1C, 2C, 3C or 4C as an indication of the catalogue used. The published catalogues are as follows:

1C catalogue—M. Ryle, F. G. Smith and B. Elsmore: A preliminary survey of the radio stars in the northern hemisphere, *Mon. Not. R. Astron. Soc.* **110**, 508–523 (1950);

2C catalogue—J. R. Shakeshaft, M. Ryle, J. E. Baldwin, B. Elsmore and J. H. Thomson: A survey of radio sources between Declinations −38° and +83°, *Mem. R. Astron. Soc.* **67,** 106–154 (1955);

3C catalogue—D. O. Edge, J. R. Shakeshaft, W. B. McAdam, J. E. Baldwin and S. Archer: A survey of radio sources at a frequency of 159 Mc/s, *Mem. R. Astron. Soc.* **68,** 37–60 (1959);

Revised 3C catalogue—A. S. Bennett: The revised 3C catalogue of radio sources, *Mem. R. Astron. Soc.* **68,** 163–172 (1962);

4C catalogue—J. D. H. Pilkington and P. F. Scott: A survey of radio sources between Declinations 20° and 40°, *Mem. R. Astron. Soc.* **69,** 183–224 (1965).

(See also **I.A.U. catalogue of radio sources.**)

CAMELOPARDALIS (The Giraffe. *Genitive* Camelopardalis, *I.A.U. abbreviation* Cam. Sometimes given as Camelopardus, *Genitive* Camelopardi.) A large, straggling, northern circumpolar constellation containing no stars brighter than the fourth magnitude. It reaches midnight culmination in December.

CAMERA The photographic camera is essentially a light-tight box, with a means of holding a light-sensitive film or plate at one end and an image-forming lens at the other, the film (or plate) and lens being separated by the focal distance of the lens. There is usually an iris diaphragm to permit control of the aperture of the lens used during a given exposure, and a shutter to permit control of the duration of the exposure.

Astronomical cameras are essentially variations of the same principle; they may be attached to the tube of an existing astronomical telescope, or may be provided with their own equatorial mounting. They are equipped to use plates rather than film, a stable base being necessary especially if the photograph is to be used for astrometric purposes.

Astronomical telescopes are often used optionally or solely as cameras; in this case the telescope objective carries out the function of the camera lens, and the 'camera' is little more than a plateholder at one of the foci of the telescope. Very large reflectors are normally designed only for photographic use. It is usual for refractors to be specifically designed for either visual or photographic use, the requirements being different, but a number of refractors have been made convertible, either by the substitution of a different objective, or by the reversal of an element or the whole objective, etc.

CAMPBELL, W. W. (**1862–1938**) Distinguished American astronomer, Director of the Lick Observatory 1901–1930. William Wallace Campbell was a pioneer in the study of stellar radial velocities, and developed the great programme at Lick which has proved the foundation upon which all work in this field has been built.

CANALI The name given to the narrow dusky streaks observed on Mars by both Secchi and Schiaparelli, in continuation of the convention of naming the dark features as if they were stretches of water. Unfortunately their intentions were misconstrued by many who took it to mean that they were convinced of the artificial nature of these features, as was Lowell. Had they chosen a different name it is probable that the question of the possible artificial nature of the so-called 'canals' would never have become the major controversy that it did.

(See **Mars—observed features and notable phenomena.**)

CANALS Name used by many, erroneously, for the *canali* of Mars; use of the English translation of the term does nothing to quell memories of the unfortunate canals controversy, and there can be no justification for using the English term when the Latin is retained for all the other dark features of the planet.

CANCER (The Crab. *Genitive* Cancri, *I.A.U. abbreviation* Cnc.) Northern zodiacal constellation situated between

Gemini and Leo; reaches midnight culmination in late-January. It contains a fair number of fainter stars, but none brighter than the fourth magnitude.

ζ Cnc is a fine binary with a period of 60 years; the components have magnitudes of 5·0 and 5·7, and last reached their maximum separation (1″·1) in 1960. There is a third component of magnitude 5·5 at a distance of 5″·4. R Cnc is a long-period variable with a period of 362 days and a magnitude range of 6·0–11·3.

Cancer contains one of the most magnificent open clusters in the heavens—*Praesepe* (the 'Beehive'), M 44 in the Messier Catalogue, number 2632 in the N.G.C.

This very scattered cluster is a splendid sight in any wide-field instrument with a very low power; it contains stars of many colours. It can be seen as a misty patch with the unaided eye. It is situated midway between, and slightly to the west of, γ and δ Cnc.

The constellation also contains another open cluster worth examining with a low power—M 67 (N.G.C. 2682) a little to the west of α Cnc.

(See also **Praesepe**.)

CANCER, TROPIC OF The small circle on the celestial sphere of latitude $+23\frac{1}{2}°$, marking the northernmost declination attained by the Sun, at the summer solstice when the Sun is in the constellation Cancer. Also used to denote the parallel of terrestrial latitude $23\frac{1}{2}°$ N, from which the Sun is seen overhead at the summer solstice.

CANDOR Martian surface feature, approximate position $\Omega\ 75°$, $\Phi + 3°$. Bright band south-west of Juventæ Fons, running from Ophir, between Lunæ Lacus and Tithonius Lacus into the Tractus Albus.

CANES VENATICI (The Hunting Dogs. *Genitive* Canum Venaticorum, *I.A.U. abbreviation* CVn.) A constellation containing mostly faint stars, just below The Plough; it is said to represent the hunting

dogs of **Boötes**, the bear-driver. It reaches midnight culmination in late March.

There is one third-magnitude star (α CVn) and only two of the fourth magnitude. α CVn is the very well-known optical double *Cor Caroli* ('The Heart of Charles'; said to have been so called by Halley because it was observed to be particularly bright when Charles II returned to London). The brighter component is a blue-white star of magnitude 2·9; the fainter is an orange star of magnitude 5·4 at an angular separation of some 20″.

R CVn is a long-period variable with a period of 333 days and magnitude ranging between 6·1 and 12·5.

The constellation is rich in nebulæ and clusters; prominent among its five spiral galaxies are M 51 (N.G.C. 5194) close to η UMa, and M 63 (N.G.C. 5055), situated about two-thirds of the distance between η UMa and α CVn.

M 51 is a spiral of magnificent form seen in plan from the Earth, with a satellite nebula at the end of one of its spiral arms; M 63 is a beautiful compact spiral, enhanced by an eighth-magnitude star which appears to adjoin one side of it; it is seen from an inclined viewpoint.

M 3 (N.G.C. 5272), just inside the southern border of the constellation and rather more than half the distance from α CVn to *Arcturus*, is a superb globular cluster.

CANIS MAJOR (The Greater Dog. *Genitive* Canis Majoris, *I.A.U. abbreviation* CMa.) A constellation containing a number of bright stars, in the southern sky but visible from north temperate latitudes in the winter, reaching midnight culmination at the beginning of January.

With **Canis Minor** it is said to represent the dogs of **Orion**, the mighty hunter, who dominates the winter sky just a little to the north-west. The principle star, *Sirius* (α CMa), is sometimes referred to as 'The Dog Star'; it is the brightest star in the heavens, having an apparent magnitude of − 1·4. It is a binary system with a white-dwarf companion.

There is an **Algol**-type variable, R CMa, whose magnitude fluctuates between 5·9 and 6·7 in a period of 1·14 days.

There is a splendid open cluster, M 41 (N.G.C. 2287), some 4° south of *Sirius*; this cluster can just be seen with the unaided eye and is a beautiful sight with an instrument having a low-power eyepiece.

(See also **Sirius**.)

CANIS MINOR (The Lesser Dog. *Genitive* Canis Minoris, *I.A.U. abbreviation* CMi.) A small northern constellation, a little east of Orion, which reaches midnight culmination in early January. The principle star is *Procyon* (α CMi), like *Sirius*, a binary with a White-Dwarf companion.

CANNON, Annie J. (1863–1941) One of the most notable lady astronomers of all time, Miss Cannon was a leading member of the staff of the Harvard College Observatory for 45 years, from 1896 until her death.

She joined the staff under E. C. Pickering at the time the great Henry Draper memorial programme was getting under way, and was entrusted with the development of the system of spectral classification to be used in the Draper Catalogue; Miss Cannon must certainly be regarded as the architect of the Harvard–Draper sequence. The Draper Catalogue contains spectral classifications for 225,300 stars, all classified by Miss Cannon in person; during the last two decades of her life Miss Cannon classified a further 130,000 of the fainter stars in the selected areas of the extension to the Catalogue.

Miss Cannon was internationally honoured for her pioneering work; she was the first woman to receive an honorary doctorate of the University of Oxford, and was also awarded honorary degrees by the Universities of Gröningen and Delaware (her native state) and a number of other American universities. Miss Cannon was an Honorary Member of the Royal Astronomical Society, and in 1931

the National Academy of Sciences in Washington awarded her, most appropriately, the Henry Draper Gold Medal.

CANOPUS The second brightest star in the heavens—α Car. It is a creamy supergiant of magnitude −0·7, spectral class F0.

CAPE OBSERVATORY The Royal Observatory at the Cape of Good Hope; directed by 'H.M. Astronomer at the Cape', it has always had close links with the Royal Greenwich Observatory, and is operated as a sister establishment under the control (formerly) of the British Admiralty and now of the Science Research Council. Many noteworthy programmes have been carried out at the Cape under such great holders of the office of H.M. Astronomer as Gill, Spencer Jones and Jackson.

CAPE PHOTOGRAPHIC DURCHMUSTERUNG In 1882 David Gill, H.M. Astronomer at the Cape, successfully photographed a bright comet using an ordinary hand camera strapped to one of the observatory telescopes. He was so impressed by the excellence of the photographs of the background stars, as well as the comet, that he immediately saw the great possibilities that photography offered to positional astronomy. He immediately set up a programme to extend to the southern skies the survey of the positions and magnitudes of the stars made by Argelander and published as the *Bonner Durchmusterung*.

The Cape Photographic Durchmusterung contains data for about 455,000 stars between Declinations −19° and −90°, and was completed in 1890. The stars are numbered in declination zones and designated in the form 'CPD −47° 9461'.

CAPELLA α Aur, the seventh brightest star in the firmament, and the fifth brightest visible from the latitude of Great Britain. It is a bright yellow star which dominates the pentagon formed by the five principal stars of Auriga, overhead in the December sky.

Capella is in fact a spectroscopic binary with a period of 104 days, the components being giants of spectral classes *G8* and *G0*; the combined visual apparent magnitude is 0·1.

CAPELLA Lunar surface feature, co-ordinates $\xi + 567$, $\eta - 133$. Ring-plain some 30 miles in diameter, north-west of Theophilus. The broad terraced walls are rather low and broken up, and there is a small craterlet on the south-west wall. The eastern rampart overlays that of Isidorus. There is a prominent central hill with a summit crater.

CAPRICORN, TROPIC OF The small circle on the celestial sphere of latitude $-23\frac{1}{2}°$, marking the southernmost declination attained by the Sun, at the winter solstice when the Sun is in the constellation Capricornus. Also used to denote the parallel of terrestrial latitude $23\frac{1}{2}°$ S, from which the Sun is seen overhead at the winter solstice.

CAPRICORNUS (The Sea-Goat. *Genitive* Capriconi, *I.A.U. abbreviation* Cap.) A southern zodiacal constellation between Sagittarius and Aquarius; contains two third-magnitude stars (β and δ Cap) and several of the fourth magnitude.

CARBON Chemical element, atomic weight 12·01. Occurs in several allotropic forms, notably as the crystalline substances diamond and graphite. It is essential to life as we know it, all living organisms containing carbon compounds; carbohydrates are also an essential part of the food of all animals.

Carbon is present in all stars, and in combination with hydrogen as the gas methane (CH_4) it is a prominent constituent of the atmospheres of the major planets.

CARBON–NITROGEN CYCLE One of the processes by which hydrogen atoms

in the stars combine to form helium atoms, with a consequent release of radiant energy.

The reaction may be simply expressed as follows:

$$C^{12} + \text{proton} \rightarrow N^{13}$$
$$N^{13} - \text{electron} \rightarrow C^{13}$$
$$C^{13} + \text{proton} \rightarrow N^{14}$$
$$N^{14} + \text{proton} \rightarrow O^{15}$$
$$O^{15} - \text{electron} \rightarrow N^{15}$$
$$N^{15} + \text{proton} \rightarrow C^{12} + He^4,$$

where C^{12} is the normal carbon atom, C^{13} is a carbon isotope, N^{13} is the normal nitrogen atom and N^{14} and N^{15} are isotopes, O^{15} is an oxygen isotope and He^4 a helium atom. The protons are hydrogen nuclei. It will be noticed that the carbon atom is restored to its original state during the cycle, and is in fact only a catalyst. Four hydrogen nuclei are lost in the process, which produces one helium atom and two electrons are emitted.

The carbon–nitrogen cycle is believed to be the predominating source of stellar energy at temperatures above about 15,000,000 °K.

(See also **Stars—energy of.**)

CARBON SEQUENCE The Wolf–Rayet stars in whose spectra enhanced emission bands due to carbon are predominant, constituting the spectral sub-class *WC*. (See **Stars—spectral classification of.**)

CARBON STARS Term sometimes used to denote stars whose spectra contain prominent absorption bands due to molecular carbon and carbon compounds, especially those of spectral class *N*. (See **Stars—spectral classification of.**)

CARDINAL POINTS The North, East, South and West Points. The North and South Points are the points of intersection of the meridian and the horizon. The East and West Points are the points of intersection of the equator and the horizon.

(See also **Celestial sphere.**)

CARINA (The Keel, *Genitive* Carinae, *I.A.U. abbreviation* Car.) One of three constellations (the others being **Puppis**

and **Vela**) which comprise the constellation formerly known as **Argo Navis**; one set of Bayer Letters is shared between these three constellations. The constellation contains the second brightest star in the heavens—*Canopus* (a Car)—which has a magnitude of $-0·9$; there are also a number of stars of the second and third magnitude, as well as numerous fainter ones.

There are two notable long-period variables, R Car (magnitude $4·5$–$10·0$, period 309 days) and S Car (magnitude $5·8$–$9·0$, period 149 days). There is also a Cepheid-type variable (l Car) varying between $3·6$ and $5·0$ in $35\frac{1}{2}$ days.

In the trapezium formed by β, ν, ι and ϵ Car, about $2\frac{1}{2}°$ south of i Car, is a large, densely packed, globular cluster, N.G.C. 2808.

CARPATHIAN MOUNTAINS A range of lunar mountains north of Copernicus and running almost due eastwards from Eratosthenes, forming the southern boundary of the Mare Imbrium. The range extends for a distance of some 225 miles, from a point some 90 miles east of the rampart of Eratosthenes (approximately $\xi - 260$, $\eta + 270$) to end about 180 miles north-east of Copernicus (approximately $\xi - 520$, $\eta + 260$). There are two peaks of approximately 7,000 ft and several between 3,000 and 5,000 ft.

CARRINGTON, R. C. (1826–1875) English amateur astronomer, who had his own observatory at Redhill, Surrey. Between 1853 and 1861 he made an enormous number of observations of sunspots; these were published as *Observations of the Spots on the Sun* by The Royal Society in 1863. From a study of his observations Carrington discovered the latitude drift of sunspots during the 11-year cycle; unfortunately his astronomical work was terminated abruptly by the need to take over the family brewing business, and his important discovery is commonly attributed to Spörer, who analysed the drift in some detail.

CARTE DU CIEL In 1882 David Gill, at the Cape of Good Hope, photographed a bright comet; as well as a good image of the comet, the plate also showed the background stars remarkably well. This led Gill to the idea that charts of the stars could be made much more accurately and economically by photographic methods than by visual observation and hand mapping, as hitherto. He immediately commenced a photographic survey of the southern skies.

Shortly afterwards a 13-in. photographic refractor, developed by the brothers Paul and Prosper Henry, was erected at the Paris Observatory and found to be most successful.

Gill and Admiral Mouchez, Director of the Paris Observatory, called an international conference to plan the rôle that astrographic work would play in the future. The conference was held in Paris in 1887, and out of it the *Carte du Ciel* project was born. The programme was in two parts: it envisaged a number of observatories collaborating, using similar instruments, in the production of a photographic chart of the entire sky, showing stars down to the fourteenth magnitude, and a catalogue of star places and magnitudes obtained from further plates, containing stars down to the eleventh magnitude.

Eighteen observatories agreed to co-operate, and the design of the brothers Henry was chosen as the basic astrographic telescope with which each would equip itself. The heavens were divided into zones and allocated to the various observatories.

Unfortunately the project was conceived on such a grand scale that some of the smaller observatories involved found the task beyond them. Even now, some zones of the *Astrographic Catalogue* remain unpublished, although the plates have all been obtained.

Many of the plates for the *Astrographic Chart* have never been taken, and of those that have quite a number have yet to be published. It is unlikely now that this part of the programme will ever be completed, as the value of the *Chart* has largely been surpassed by photographs obtained with modern telescopes—notably the Palomar Sky Atlas photographed with the 48 × 72-in. Schmidt camera on Mount Palomar. The plates obtained in the *Carte-du-Ciel* programme are still of immense value, however; if the same fields are re-photographed after many years, using the same instruments, the proper motions of the stars contained in them can be determined with great precision.

The control of the *Carte-du-Ciel* programme is vested in Commission 23 of the International Astronomical Union.

CARTESIAN CO-ORDINATES A system of rectangular co-ordinates attributed to Descartes.

In Fig. 15 O is termed the origin and OX the x-axis; OY is perpendicular to OX and is termed the y-axis.

The Cartesian co-ordinates of the point P are determined by dropping the perpendiculars PA and PB from P to the x- and y-axes respectively. The distance OB is termed the *ordinate* of P, and may be denoted by δy, and the distance OA is termed the *abscissa* of P and denoted by δx; δx and δy are the Cartesian co-ordinates of the point P.

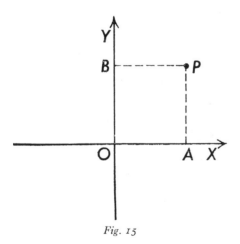

Fig. 15

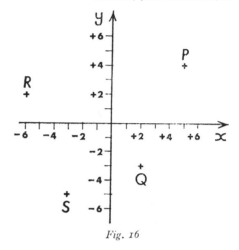

Fig. 16

Abscissae are regarded as positive quantities to the right and negative to the left of the y-axis; ordinates are regarded as positive above the x-axis and negative below it. Cartesian co-ordinates are usually quoted in the form (δx, δy); thus, in Fig. 16, the co-ordinates of the points P, Q, R and S are as follows:

P: (+5, +4)
Q: (+2, −3)
R: (−6, +2)
S: (−3, −5).

(See also **Co-ordinate system.**)

CASIUS Martian surface feature, approximate position Ω 260°, Φ +40°. A prominent, broad canal in the north temperate zone, forming the north-eastern border of the Neith Regio. Is the northern extension of Thoth.

CASSEGRAIN FOCUS The principal focus of a Cassegrain-type reflector, situated just behind the (pierced) primary mirror.

(See **Telescope, Cassegrain.**)

CASSINI, Jean-Dominique (1625–1712) One of the foremost observers of the seventeenth century, Gian-Domenico Cassini was born in Italy and became Professor of Astronomy in the University of Bologna at the age of 25. He soon established an excellent reputation as a theoretical and practical astronomer, and made numerous discoveries during his nineteen years' tenure of this office; *inter alia* he discovered the axial rotations of Mars and Jupiter, and several of their major surface features. In 1669 Cassini was appointed to direct the new Paris Observatory by King Louis XIV, and became a French citizen in 1673, when he adopted the French form of his forenames.

Whilst at Paris Cassini continued to be a prolific observer, and made many further discoveries, especially in connection with the planet Saturn.

In 1671 he discovered a second satellite of Saturn (Iapetus), and the third (Rhea) a year later. He also announced in 1672 his discovery of the periodic fluctuation in the apparent magnitude of Iapetus. In 1675 he discovered the gap between rings A and B of Saturn, now known as 'Cassini's Division', and in 1684 he discovered two further satellites of the planet, Dione and Tethys, thus joining Galileo as the discoverer of four natural satellites—a feat later equalled by Sir William Herschel and S. B. Nicholson. Cassini also realized that the ring system was not solid but composed of myriads of tiny satellites, which hypothesis was proved to be the case, theoretically by Clerk Maxwell in 1857 and spectroscopically by Keeler in 1895.

Cassini's son (Jacques), grandson (César François) and great-grandson (also Jean-Dominique) all became successful astronomers, the first two of them succeeding the elder Cassini in the direction of the Paris Observatory.

CASSINI Lunar surface feature, co-ordinates $\xi+062$, $\eta+647$. A prominent ring formation in the second quadrant, 36 miles in diameter, north-west of Archimedes. The walls are broad and rugged, and double in parts. There are two well defined craters on the floor, in one of which—Cassini A—there is a shallow

depression about $2\frac{1}{2}$ miles in diameter with a minute central pit. Owing to its unusual appearance the depression was dubbed by its discoverers, Wilkins and Moore, the 'Washbowl'.

CASSINI DIVISION The principal division in the ring system of Saturn, separating Rings A and B; it was discovered by J. D. Cassini in 1675. (See **Saturn—rings of**.)

CASSIOPEIA (Mythological character. *Genitive* Cassiopeiae, *I.A.U. abbreviation* Cas.) Northern circumpolar constellation, whose five brightest stars are in the well-known form of a 'W'; reaches midnight culmination in October.

λ Cas is a very close double of equally bright stars (magnitudes 5·6, 5·9; separation 0″6); it is a binary system. η Cas is a long-period binary, with a period exceeding five centuries.

α Cas is an irregular variable with a magnitude range of 2·2–3·1; R Cas is a long-period variable with a period of 432 days and a magnitude range from 5·3–12·0. There are also an *Algol*-type variable, RZ Cas (period 1·19 days, magnitude range 6·4–7·8) and a Cepheid, SU Cas (period 1·95 days, magnitude range 5·9–6·3). Some 2° north-west of κ Cas is the site of Tycho Brahe's great nova of 1572.

Surrounding ϕ Cas (but probably more distant) is a compact cluster of faint stars (N.G.C. 457). Mid-way between γ and κ Cas there is a fine, irregular-shaped cluster (N.G.C. 225). The beautiful cluster M 103 (N.G.C. 581) lies about 1° north-east of δ Cas, and another well worth examination with a low power is N.G.C. 663, which lies slightly east of a point mid-way between δ and ϵ Cas.

CASSIOPEIA A One of the strongest discrete radio sources, numbered 23N5A in the I.A.U. catalogue; its position is R.A. 23 hr 21 min, Dec. 58° 32′ N. It is identified with some patches of peculiar, filamentary nebulosity situated within the

Galaxy, which may be the remnants of a former supernova.

(See also **Radio astronomy**.)

CASTOR The star α Gem, a most interesting multiple star. The combined magnitude of the system is 1·6, and it is quite close to the solar system—rather less than 41 light years. It is a triple system, of which each member is itself a spectroscopic binary.

The principal components are in binary motion with a period of about 350 years; they are a star of class $A1$, magnitude 2·0, and one of class $A5$, magnitude 2·8. The maximum separation is about 6″·5; at the present time it is about 2″. Both components are binaries, with periods of 2·93 days and 9·22 days respectively.

The third member of the system is a binary comprising two red-dwarf stars with a period of 19 hours; they are almost 1¼ minutes of arc from the centre of gravity of the system, and must have a period well in excess of a million years.

CATACLYSMIC VARIABLES Term used to denote those variable stars whose light variation takes the form of a very sudden increase in magnitude, followed by a much slower fading; these stars are also known as *explosive variables*. The principal members of the group are the novae and supernovae, the SS Cygni stars (dwarf novae) and the UV Ceti stars (flare stars).

(See also **Variable stars**.)

CATADIOPTRIC ELEMENT An optical element which utilizes both refraction and reflection to form an image.

CATALOGUE OF BRIGHT STARS A catalogue of 9,110 naked-eye stars, i.e. stars brighter than magnitude 6·5. The stars are the same as those included in the *Revised Harvard Photometry*. The positions, magnitude, spectral types, proper motions, parallax and radial velocities are given and an index to the Bayer and Flamsteed numbers and proper names of the stars is also

included. The catalogue was compiled by F. Schlesinger and L. F. Jenkins and published by the Yale University Observatory (2nd edition, 1940).

CATALOGUE OF ZODIACAL STARS The *Catalogue of 3,539 Zodiacal Stars for the Equinox 1950·0*, compiled by J. Robertson and published in Washington in 1940. This is of particular value in predicting lunar and planetary occultations.

CATHARINA Lunar surface feature, co-ordinates $\xi + 378$, $\eta - 310$. A very rugged walled plain, 55 miles in diameter, the southernmost member of the great connected trio with Theophilus and Cyrillus. The walls are broad and very broken up; a great valley divides the western rampart, which then breaks northward and runs into the wall of Cyrillus. There is a large, low ring in the northern part of the floor.

CAUCASUS MOUNTAINS Lunar mountain range, west of Aristillus, forming the north-east boundary of the Mare Serenitatis. The lunar Alps run northwards and the Hæmus Mountains southwest. There are many peaks between 5,000 and 12,000 ft, and one of nearly 20,000 ft.

CEBRENIA Martian surface feature, approximate position Ω 210°, $\Phi + 50°$. Lightish area north of Elysium.

CECROPIA Martian surface feature, approximate position Ω 320°, $\Phi + 60°$. That part of the dusky north temperate band which adjoins the northern border of Dioscuria.

CELESTIAL MECHANICS The study of the motions of celestial bodies; it is concerned with the analysis of observations of their movements and the formulation of theories of their motion upon which predictions of their future motions can be based.

CELESTIAL SPHERE The fundamental concept in dynamical astronomy. It is a simplification, but the errors it introduces are insignificant and the benefits it offers in facilitating consideration of the position and motions of the heavenly bodies are invaluable.

To an observer on the surface of the Earth the heavenly bodies appear to be at a uniform distance, i.e. on the inside surface of a great hemisphere, although they are in fact at greatly varying distances. Over a period of some hours the bodies will appear to the observer to be moving across the heavens from east to west, due to the Earth's rotation; some will appear to *set* in the west, and others appear to *rise* in the east. Approximately twelve hours after an object sets in the west it will be seen to rise again in the east. Thus the observer has the impression of being at the centre of a giant sphere rotating once per sidereal day. For the purposes of dynamical astronomy this imaginary sphere is supposed to exist, and to have infinite radius; this is termed the *celestial sphere*. It is in fact concentric with the Earth, of course, but the errors introduced by imagining the observer to be at its centre are negligible. Distances between objects 'on' the celestial sphere are always given in angular measure, thus being independent of their distances from the Earth.

The principal features of the celestial sphere are shown in Fig. 17. The observer is situated at O, the centre of the sphere. N, E, S and W are the north, east, south and west points. The observer's zenith is at Z, his nadir at Z'. The observer's meridian plane is therefore defined by the great circle $ZNZ'S$, and his horizon is the great circle having as its poles the zenith and nadir, i.e. $NESW$. Great circles perpendicular to the horizon are termed vertical circles; the vertical circle perpendicular to the meridian ($ZEZ'W$) is termed the *Prime Vertical*.

In Fig. 17 X represents the position of a star (or any other object); then $ZXYZ'$ is the vertical of the star. The position of the star may be recorded by measurements of its *altitude* XY measured as $\angle XOY$, and its *azimuth* SY. Azimuth is usually measured westwards from the south point, i.e. in this case $360° - \angle SOY$; sometimes however it is measured from 0–180° east or west of the south point, i.e. in this case $\angle SOY$ east. The small circle through the star and parallel to the horizon plane, DXF, is termed the *almucantar* of the star. $\angle ZOX$ is the *Zenith Distance* of the star.

In Fig. 18 P and P' are the poles of the celestial sphere and PP' its axis of rotation. The great circle $GEHW$ having P and P' as its poles is the *celestial equator*; it marks the intersection of the Earth's equatorial plane and the celestial sphere. Great circles passing through the poles P and P', and hence perpendicular to the equator, are termed *hour circles*. The meridian $NPZS$ is the hour circle through the zenith—it is perpendicular to the horizon $NESW$. X denotes the position of a star; $PXYP'$ is the hour circle through the star. The angle at the pole between the hour circle through the star and the meridian is termed the *hour angle*; it is measured on the equator as the arc HY. It is usual for the hour angle to be measured westwards from the meridian, i.e., the angle $HWGEY$, or $360° - \angle HOY$. The hour angle may be in angular measure or in time; as the

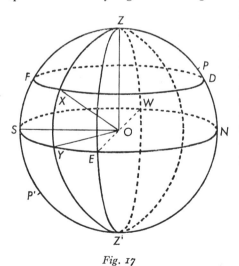

Fig. 17

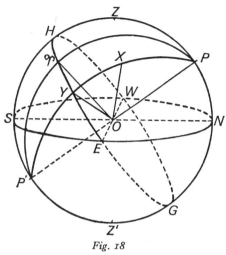

Fig. 18

celestial sphere undergoes one complete revolution in one sidereal day, 360°∼24 hours. Therefore 1° of arc is the equivalent of 4 minutes in time, and 1 hour in time is equivalent to 15° of arc.

In Fig. 18 ♈ is the First Point of Aries, or *vernal equinox*—i.e. the point on the celestial sphere at which the Sun crosses the equator at its ascending node. The hour circle through ♈, *P♈P′*, is termed the *equinoctial colure*. This is used as the zero of Right Ascension, which is defined as the angle at the pole between the hour circle through the star and the equinoctial colure. It is measured in the plane of the celestial equator eastwards from ♈, i.e. as ∠♈*OY*.

The *Declination* of the star is its angular distance from the Equator, i.e. ∠*XOY*. The *North Polar Distance* of the star is the complement of the Declination, i.e. ∠*POX*.

(See also **Co-ordinate systems; Spherical triangle.**)

CENTAURUS (The Centaur. *Genitive* Centauri, *I.A.U. abbreviation* Cen.) A southern constellation, partly circumpolar, containing a number of bright stars.

α Cen is the third brightest star in the heavens (magnitude +0·1) and the second nearest of the 'fixed stars', being 4·3 light

years distant from the Earth. It is a multiple star, the two main binary components being of magnitudes 0·3 and 1·7 and separated by 4″.1, with a period of 80 years. A very faint component of the system is in fact the closest star to the Earth (apart from the Sun), and is known therefore as *Proxima Centauri*; it is 4·2 light years distant.

γ Cen is another fine binary, the magnitude of both components being 3·1, the separation half a second of arc and the period 80 years. There is also a long-period variable, T Cen, having a magnitude range of 5·2–10·0 and a period of 90 days.

One third of the distance from ζ Cen to γ Cen lies ω Cen (N.G.C. 5139), one of the most magnificent of globular clusters; it contains many thousands of stars and has the appearance of a fourth-magnitude star to the unaided eye.

Close to the southernmost tip of the constellation, about 1½° north of λ Cen, lies N.G.C. 3766; to the naked eye this appears as one of an arc of faint stars centred on λ Cen, but with a small telescope or pair of binoculars it is revealed as a superb cluster of some 200 stars.

CENTAURUS A A strong, discrete radio source in the southern hemisphere, number 13S4A in the I.A.U. catalogue, position R.A. 13 hr 22 min, Dec. 42° 46′ S. It is associated with the peculiar galaxy N.G.C. 5128. [Plate 24(b).]
(See also **Radio astronomy.**)

CENTIMETRE Metric unit of length or distance, equivalent to 0·01 metres or 10 millimetres. (See **Metric system.**)

CENTRAL CONDENSATION The bright portion of the head of a comet, which is surrounded by the fainter coma. The central condensation is sometimes seen to contain one or more bright, star-like nuclei, not necessarily situated centrally. (See **Comets—structure of.**)

CENTRAL ECLIPSE The path swept out

on the surface of the Earth by the umbra of the Moon during a total solar eclipse; only from stations within this narrow path can the total phase of the eclipse be observed.

CENTRAL MERIDIAN The meridian of a planet passing through the centre of the apparent disk at a given moment; i.e. an imaginary line bisecting the apparent disk, joining the poles of rotation and perpendicular to the equator of the planet.

CENTRAL-MERIDIAN TRANSIT The transit of a surface feature of a planet across the central meridian, due to the axial rotation of the planet. The timing of central-meridian transits is an important means of determining the planetographic longitudes of planetary surface markings.

CENTRAL PEAK Mountain situated at or near the centre of the floor of a lunar ring-structure. Many central peaks are highly complex structures with multiple summits, others are simple, smooth-sided cones.

CENTRE OF GRAVITY The point from which the gravitational attraction of a body appears to act. (See **Centre of mass**.)

CENTRE OF MASS The dynamical term for that point at which the total mass of a body or system appears to be concentrated. In astronomy it is frequently used in certain specific cases, e.g. the centre of mass of a binary system, of the Sun–Earth system, etc.

It is of course the point from which the gravitational attraction of the body or system appears to act, hence the alternative form often used—'centre of gravity'.

CENTRIFUGAL FORCE A hypothetical concept, introduced as a means of explaining the mechanism which constrains a body revolving about a given point from 'falling' towards that point.

If we consider, for example, a planet in orbit around the Sun, we would expect them to move towards another, due to the gravitational attraction between them; owing to the great mass of the Sun relative to that of the planet we would expect the Sun to remain still and the planet to 'fall' towards it. The orbital velocity of the planet, however, has a component which counteracts this tendency, and if the orbital velocity is high enough offsets it altogether. This stable situation exists, of course, throughout the solar system.

The moment of the planetary body radially towards the Sun is termed the *centripetal force*, and the counterbalancing moment due to the orbital motion is termed the *centrifugal force*. This is a convenient device, and the dynamics of the system can be analysed in Newtonian terms by considering them as forces, although strictly speaking they are not forces, a force being defined as the interaction between two bodies.

CENTRIPETAL FORCE The moment of an orbiting body, such as a planet, radially towards the centre of revolution—i.e. the Sun; it is a hypothetical concept used for convenience. The centripetal force is opposed, and in planetary systems counterbalanced, by the **centrifugal force**, *q.v.*

CEPHEID VARIABLES A type of pulsating variable star whose light curve is usually characterized by a rapid rise to maximum and a slower fall, often rather erratic, to minimum; the name derives from the first of the type to be discovered, δ Cephei, the variability of which was first noted in 1784 by John Goodricke, the 18-year-old deaf mute who first explained the nature of an eclipsing binary (*Algol*). A few 'Cepheids', such as ζ Gem, have near-symmetrical light curves, but in no case is the time of rise longer than the time of fall, and in most cases the time of rise is significantly shorter.

The magnitude range of Cepheid variables is generally small, of the order of one magnitude; that for δ Cep is 3·6–4·3, and its period is 5 days 9 hours. The light curve of δ Cep is shown in Fig. 19. The

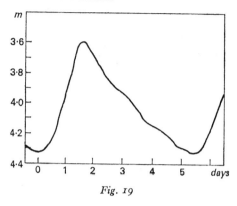

Fig. 19

importance, enabling us to determine the absolute magnitude (M) of a Cepheid from its period and apparent magnitude (m), and hence its distance (r), from the well-known formula, deriving from the inverse square law,

$$M = m + 5 - 5 \log r.$$

Thus the distance of any galactic object containing a Cepheid variable can be obtained. Cepheids have been discovered in the Magellanic Clouds and several of the relatively near galaxies, including the great spiral galaxy in Andromeda, and their distances have been determined using this method.

There is a relation between the periods of light variation of Cepheids and their spectral types, which range from about $F5$ for those with periods of about 3–4 days to $G0$ for periods of about 8 days and to about $G5$ for those with longer periods. The position of the Cepheids in the Hertzsprung–Russell diagram is shown in Fig. 55 on p. 174.

The spectra of Cepheids vary with the fluctuation in luminosity, lines due to ionized metals being much enhanced at maximum (indicating a higher surface temperature). The radial velocities also vary with luminosity, having maximum recessional velocity at the time of minimum luminosity and maximum velocity of approach at maximum luminosity, indicating their actual pulsation in over-all size.

periods of Cepheid-type variables are very regular and range from some 5 hours to about 45 days; the majority fall into two groups, however, having periods of less than one day and several days respectively. It was soon recognized that there were important differences between the two groups, those of longer period (now termed 'classical Cepheids') being found only in the galactic plane whereas the shorter-period Cepheids show little evidence of galactic concentration. The shorter-period variables abound in globular clusters, and are now frequently referred to as *cluster-type variables*; they are also known as *RR Lyrae stars*, after a typical example.

The discovery of the **period–luminosity law** for Cepheid variables by Miss Leavitt in 1912 has proved to be of immense

Table 7. Some typical Cepheid variables

Star	Period (days)	Magnitude range	Spectral type
SU Cas	1·95	6·0–6·4	*F2–F9*
TU Cas	2·14	7·9–9·0	*F5–G2*
Polaris	3·97	2·1–2·2	*F7*
δ Cep	5·37	3·7–4·4	*F4–G6*
β Dor	9·84	4·2–5·7	*F2–F9*
ζ Gem	10·15	3·7–4·1	*F5–G2*
RY Sco	20·31	8·4–9·5	*F8–K0*
U Car	38·75	6·3–7·5	*F8–K5*
SV Vul	45·13	8·4–9·4	*G2–K5*

The variation in the diameter of the star due to the pulsation is of the order of 10 per cent. The Cepheids are supergiant stars with diameters of some 10–150 times that of the Sun. Data for some typical Cepheids are given in Table 7.

About 40 Cepheid-type variables are known with periods of 1–50 days which are some 2 magnitudes fainter than classical Cepheids of corresponding period. They are known as *W Virginis stars*, after a typical example, and sometimes as *Type II Cepheids*. Some of them display a spectral peculiarity in that metallic lines are doubled during the rise in luminosity; this is believed to arise from two distinct 'surges' of radiation from the pulsating star. (See also **Variable stars**.)

CEPHEUS (Mythological character. *Genitive* Cephei, *I.A.U. abbreviation* Cep.) Northern circumpolar constellation reaching midnight culmination late August-early September. It contains one star of the second magnitude (α Cep) and four of the third magnitude.

The most important star in this constellation is δ Cep, the original **Cepheid variable**. It is an interesting double star comprising a yellow variable component whose magnitude varies between 3·6 and 4·3 in a period of 5·37 days, with the sharp rise and slower decline typical of the Cepheid variables, and a blue companion of magnitude 7·5 at a separation of 41″.

The constellation contains a number of other interesting doubles, and two long-period variables: T Cep (magnitude range 5·5–9·5, period 391 days) and V Cep (magnitude range 6·2–7·1, period 360 days). (See also **Cepheid variables**.)

CERAUNIUS Martian surface feature, approximate position Ω 95°, Φ + 20°. Dusky streak running south-westwards from Tempe, forming the northern boundary of the Tractus Albus.

CERBERUS Martian surface feature, approximate position Ω 205°, Φ + 15°. A major canal in the northern temperate regions, radiating south-westwards from

Trivium Charontis to join Pambotis Lacus. Forms the south-eastern border of Elysium.

CERES Minor planet number 1, discovered on 1801 January 1 by Piazzi at Palermo and hence named after the patron goddess of Sicily. Ceres has a diameter of approximately 485 miles, and an apparent magnitude of about +8.
(See also **Minor planets**.)

CETUS (The Sea Monster. *Genitive* Ceti, *I.A.U. abbreviation* Cet.) A vast equatorial constellation, rather short of bright stars; it has one of the second magnitude (β Cet) and six of the third. Reaches midnight culmination during October.

The most interesting star is ο Cet (*Mira*), one of the most spectacular variables in the sky.

T Cet is an irregular variable whose magnitude varies between 5·1 and 7·0.
(See also **Mira Ceti**.)

CHALCE Martian surface feature, approximate position Ω 20°, Φ – 50°. Faint canal forming the eastern border of Argyre I.

CHALLIS, J. C. (1803–1862) Professor of Astronomy at Cambridge at the time of the discovery of Neptune (1846). Had he possessed up-to-date star charts comparable to those used by Galle, Challis would in fact have been the first to identify the planet, it later proving that he had observed it on several occasions prior to Galle's discovery. He might still have been first had he been less tardy in comparing and plotting his observations. (See **Neptune—discovery of**.)

CHAMAELEON (The Chamaeleon. *Genitive* Chamaelontis, *I.A.U. abbreviation* Cha.) A small southern circumpolar constellation containing five fourth-magnitude stars and a few fainter ones.

CHAOS HYBLÆUS Martian surface feature, approximate position Ω 225°, Φ + 35°. Prominent curved canal, forming the north-western border of Elysium.

CHEMICAL ELEMENTS These are the substances which are both chemically unique and are each composed of a single type of atom; all other substances are combinations of these elements. There are 92 naturally occurring elements; they are usually classified by **atomic number** or **atomic weight**, the lightest being hydro-gen and the heaviest uranium. Elements having atomic numbers greater than 92 (that of uranium) also exist, and are known as 'transuranic elements'; they do not occur in nature, but can be produced by nuclear processes. Ten transuranic elements have been obtained in this way.

Many of the naturally occurring elements

Table 8.   The chemical elements

Atomic Number	Element	Symbol	Atomic Weight (physical)	Description	Boiling Point (° C)	Melting Point (° C)	Specific Gravity
1	Hydrogen	H	1·008	Colourless, inflammable gas	−252·8	−259	
2	Helium	He	4·003	Inert gas	−268·9	−272	
3	Lithium	Li	6·939	Silvery-white alkali metal	1336	179	0·535
4	Beryllium	Be	9·013	Hard white metal		1350	1·85
5	Boron	B	10·812	Brown powdery or black crystalline substance	2500	2300	2·4
6	Carbon	C	12·012	Occurs in three forms, including diamond and graphite			1·5–3·5
7	Nitrogen	N	14·007	Invisible inert gas	−195·8	−210·5	0·97
8	Oxygen	O	16·000	Invisible gas	−183·0	−218·8	1·43
9	Fluorine	F	18·999	Yellow liquid halogen	−187	−223	1·14
10	Neon	Ne	20·184	Inert gas	−246·3	−248·6	
11	Sodium	Na	22·991	Alkaline metal	883	97·5	0·97
12	Magnesium	Mg	24·313	White metal	1107	650	1·74
13	Aluminium	Al	26·982	White metal	2270	658·7	2·69
14	Silicon	Si	28·09	Orange crystalline solid	2355	1417	2·34
15	Phosphorus	P	30·975	White crystalline solid	280·5	44	1·82
16	Sulphur	S	32·066	Yellow crystalline solid	444·6	112·8	2·00
17	Chlorine	Cl	35·454	Heavy, greenish-yellow halogen gas	−33·6	−103	1·57
18	Argon	A	39·949	Inert gas	−185·8	−189·3	
19	Potassium	K	39·103	Soft silvery-white, alkali metal	762·2	63·6	0·86
20	Calcium	Ca	40·08	Soft white metal	1439	845	1·54
21	Scandium	Sc	44·958	Rare-earth element			
22	Titanium	Ti	47·90	Iron-like metal		2000	4·5
23	Vanadium	V	50·944	Hard white metal		1715	5·87
24	Chromium	Cr	52·00	Grey metal		1550	
25	Manganese	Mn	54·940	Grey metal	2032	1220	7·3
26	Iron	Fe	55·849	Soft, silver-white metal	3235	1530	7·86
27	Cobalt	Co	58·936	Silvery-white metal	3185	1490	8·8
28	Nickel	Ni	58·71	Hard white metal	3075	1452	8·85
29	Copper	Cu	63·55	Reddish metal	2336	1084	
30	Zinc	Zn	65·37	White crystalline metal	907	419·6	7·12
31	Gallium	Ga	69·72	Silver-white metal		29·8	5·9
32	Germanium	Ge	72·60	Brittle white metal		958·5	5·35
33	Arsenic	As	74·924	Grey, black or yellow solid		818	4·6–5·7
34	Selenium	Se	78·96	Silver-grey crystalline solid		217	4·81
35	Bromine	Br	79·91	Dark red liquid halogen	58·8	−7·3	3·14
36	Krypton	Kr	83·80	Inert gas	−152·9	−169	
37	Rubidium	Rb	85·48	Alkali metal	696	39·1	1·52
38	Strontium	Sr	87·63	Alkali metal	1366	752	2·6
39	Yttrium	Y	88·91	Rare-earth element			
40	Zirconium	Z	91·22	Rare metal		1900	6·4
41	Niobium	Nb	92·91	Rare grey metal		1950	8·4
42	Molybdenum	Mo	95·95	Hard white metal		2620	10·2
43	Technetium	Tc	99	Very rare element			
44	Ruthenium	Ru	101·07	Hard, brittle metal		2450	12·2

Table 8. The chemical elements (continued)

Atomic Number	Element	Symbol	Atomic Weight (physical)	Description	Boiling Point (° C)	Melting Point (° C)	Specific Gravity
45	Rhodium	Rh	102·91	Hard, silver-white metal		2000	12·5
46	Palladium	Pd	106·4	Silver-white metal		1555	11·4
47	Silver	Ag	107·874	White metal	1927	961	
48	Cadmium	Cd	112·41	White metal	767	321	8·64
49	Indium	In	114·82	Soft silver-white metal		155	7·31
50	Tin	Sn	118·70	White metal	2362	231·9	7·28
51	Antimony	Sb	121·76	Dark grey metal	1470	630	6·69
52	Tellurium	Te	127·61	Brittle, silver-white solid		452	6·24
53	Iodine	I	126·909	Solid grey halogen	184	113·7	4·93
54	Xenon	Xe	131·30	Inert gas	−107·1	−140	
55	Caesium	Cs	132·910	Alkali metal	670	28·5	1·87
56	Barium	Ba	137·35	Very reactive white metal	1537	710	3·7
57	Lanthanum	La	138·92	Rare-earth element			
58	Cerium	Ce	140·13	Rare-earth element			
59	Praseodymium	Pr	140·913	Rare-earth element			
60	Neodymium	Nd	144·25	Rare-earth element			
61	Promethium	Pm	147	Rare-earth element			
62	Samarium	Sm	150·36	Rare-earth element			
63	Europium	Eu	151·96	Rare-earth element			
64	Gadolinium	Gd	157·25	Rare-earth element			
65	Terbium	Tb	158·930	Rare-earth element			
66	Dysprosium	Dy	162·50	Rare-earth element			
67	Holmium	Ho	164·937	Rare-earth element			
68	Erbium	Er	167·27	Rare-earth element			
69	Thulium	Tm	168·941	Rare-earth element			
70	Ytterbium	Yb	173·04	Rare-earth element			
71	Lutecium	Lu	174·98	Rare-earth element			
72	Hafnium	Hf	178·50	Rare metal		1700	13·3
73	Tantalum	Ta	180·955	Grey-white metal		2850	16·6
74	Tungsten	W	183·86	Hard grey metal		3370	19·3
75	Rhenium	Re	186·3	Hard, heavy, grey metal		3167	20·53
76	Osmium	Os	190·2	Hard, white, crystalline metal		2700	22·48
77	Iridium	Ir	192·2	Very hard, rare metal		2440	22·42
78	Platinum	Pt	195·10	Hard, silver-white metal		1773·5	21·45
79	Gold	Au	196·977	Softish, bright yellow metal		1063	19·4
80	Mercury	Ag	200·60	White metal, liquid at normal temperatures	356·9	−38·83	13·60
81	Thallium	Tl	204·38	Soft white metal		303·5	11·85
82	Lead	Pb	207·20	Blue-grey metal	1692	327·5	11·34
83	Bismuth	Bi	208·988	Pink-white metal	1470	271	9·80
84	Polonium	Po	210	Radioactive substance			
85	Astatine	At	211	Halogen			
86	Radon	Rn	222	Inert gas	−67	−71	
87	Francium	Fr	223	Radioactive alkali metal			
88	Radium	Ra	226·05	Rare, radioactive metal			
89	Actinium	Ac	227	Radioactive, rare-earth-like substance			
90	Thorium	Th	232·047	Dark grey, radioactive rare-earth-like metal		1845	11·2
91	Protactinium	Pa	231	Radioactive rare-earth-like substance			
92	Uranium	U	238·04	Hard, white, radioactive metal		1850	18·68
93	Neptunium	Np	237	Transuranic element			
94	Plutonium	Pu	239	Transuranic element			
95	Americium	Am	241	Transuranic element			
96	Curium	Cm	242	Transuranic element			
97	Berkelium	Bk	243	Transuranic element			
98	Californium	Cf	244	Transuranic element			
99	Einsteinium	Es		Transuranic element			
100	Fermium	Fm		Transuranic element			
101	Mendelevium	Md		Transuranic element			
102	Nobelium	No		Transuranic element			

are not found in the free state, but only in combination with others.

The elements are listed in Table 8 in order of atomic number; the chemical symbol most usually adopted for each is given, its (physical) atomic weight and a very brief description. The specific gravity (density) is given where a good determination exists, and also the melting and boiling temperatures where appropriate.

The elements of atomic numbers 57–71 are known as the 'lanthanide' or 'rare-earth' elements. These elements form a series whose physical and chemical properties are remarkably similar; they occur naturally in the form of their basic oxides (the 'rare earths') which are, as the description suggests, very rare. The earlier elements scandium (21) and yttrium (39) have similar properties and are sometimes regarded as rare-earth elements. There is a further series of rare-earth type elements, comprising actinium (89) and all subsequent elements, including the transuranic elements. Many of this series, known as the 'actinide elements', are radioactive.

CHERSONESUS Martian surface feature, approximate position $\Omega\ 270°$, $\Phi-60°$. Dusky region at the northern edge of the Mare Australe, where Euripus runs northward to separate Ausonia and Hellas.

CHRISTIE, Sir William (1845–1922) The eighth Astronomer Royal (1881–1910).

William Henry Mahoney Christie became Astronomer Royal on the retirement of Airy, whose tenure of the office for more than half-a-century had left an indelible mark on the Royal Observatory, New instruments had been introduced, carried out their most important programmes, and were (in some cases) heading for obsolescence during this long period. It would have been easy for Christie to sit back and allow the observatory to tick over quietly and efficiently for a decade or so on the wheels so well oiled by Airy, and it is a tribute to his own ability and character that he did not.

Right from the start of his new career Christie asserted his own personality and ideas, and started preparing the Royal Observatory for a further period of expansion and for a broadening of its work so as to keep pace with the rapid development of astronomical techniques. This achievement was also the more creditable in view of the fact that Christie was not a 'new broom' in the fullest sense, having been Chief Assistant to Airy since 1870.

When Airy retired in 1881, the post of H.M. Astronomer Royal was first offered, rightly and inevitably, to John Couch Adams. Adams—then aged 62—declined, however, and Christie was deservedly appointed instead.

It fell to Christie to supervise the development of photographic observation at Greenwich—notably the installation of the astrographic telescope and the commencement of the photography of the Greenwich zone (the polar 'cap' north of latitude $+60°$) of the *Carte du Ciel*.

During Christie's term of office the three largest instruments still in use at the Royal Observatory were installed. In 1886 the Admiralty agreed to provide a new large equatorial refractor; the new instrument, with an aperture of 28 inches and a tube 28 feet in length, was erected in 1894 on the mounting of the old $12\frac{3}{4}$-in. Merz equatorial. Three years later saw the opening of a new building with ample accommodation for offices, darkrooms, library and the observatory workshop, surmounted by a dome containing two new and important instruments—the gift of a leading surgeon, Sir Henry Thompson. These comprised a 26-in. photographic refractor, to complement the 28-in. visual instrument, and a 30-in. Cassegrain reflector which was mounted on the same mounting in place of the usual counterweight. The $12\frac{3}{4}$-in. Merz refractor was coupled to the 26-in. instrument as a guider. [Plate 28(a, b, c).]

The Thompson instruments were used in many important programmes, the 26-in. mainly for astrometric purposes and the 30-in. for photographic studies of comets, minor planets and satellites. The eighth satellite of Jupiter was discovered by Melotte in 1908 with the 30-in. reflector. The principal work of the 28-in. refractor was the visual observation of double stars with the aid of a bifilar micrometer. All three instruments are now in use, separately mounted each in its own dome, at the Royal Observatory's new home at Herstmonceux.

During Christie's period of office there were further developments in meridian astronomy and the time-service, mainly arising out of foundations laid by Airy: in 1884 the meridian of the Airy Transit Circle at Greenwich was adopted by international agreement as the Prime Meridian and zero of longitude, and the zone-time system based upon Greenwich Mean Time was also introduced. Christie also replaced Airy's altazimuth by a new instrument based on the same principle but with many modifications and improvements.

Christie's tenure of his high office has proved in retrospect to be of immeasurable importance in fitting the Royal Observatory for the leading position it holds today in most branches of contemporary astronomical research, notably in astrometry and astrophysics.

Christie was knighted and created a Knight Commander of the Order of the Bath (K.C.B.) for his services to English astronomy. He was a Fellow of the Royal Society, was President of the Royal Astronomical Society (1888–1890) and its Secretary (1880–1882). Perhaps Christie's most enduring achievement was the foundation, in 1877, of the magazine *The Observatory*, edited and published by the voluntary efforts of professional astronomers, usually on the staffs of the Royal Greenwich Observatory and the Cambridge Observatories; now in its 89th volume *The Observatory* is still 'going strong'.

CHROMOSPHERE, SOLAR One of the outermost layers of the Sun, situated immediately above the photosphere. It is a gaseous shell some 5,000 miles deep, and is normally invisible from Earth, its luminescence being lost against the far brighter photosphere. At a total eclipse, however, as the Sun is passing into the total phase, the chromosphere is seen for a few moments, the last visible remnant of the Sun's disk before totality. It appears as a bright crescent of a beautiful rose-pink, hence its name which means 'colour-sphere'; it is visible again for an instant at the end of totality.

The spectrum of the chromosphere can be photographed at these two moments (the second and third contacts of a total eclipse); it is composed of bright emission lines and is known as the **flash spectrum**, *q.v.* Some of the brightest emission lines are visible in the normal solar spectrum. Spectroheliograms obtained in the strongest emission lines (e.g. the **hydrogen-alpha line**) represent activity at the chromospheric level. The predominantly rosy hue of the chromosphere as seen during a total eclipse is due, of course, to the intense hydrogen radiation in the hydrogen-alpha line.

(See also **Sun—physical constitution of.**)

CHRONOGRAPH An instrument for recording the precise time at which events occur; in astronomy it records the times of the various stages of a phenomenon or observation, and also regular pulses from the standard observatory clock.

The original form consisted of a paper-covered rotating drum, driven at a constant speed by a falling-weight through a governor; a pen was caused to travel across the drum by a rotating screw, thus producing a spiral trace on the paper. Provision was made for seconds pulses from the clock to deflect the pen momentarily by means of a solenoid, thus producing a measurable mark on the trace. The observer was also provided with a hand tapper to make similar marks to record the times of his observation. Where appropriate, as in the case of a transit-circle which is fitted with an impersonal micrometer, the observation-taps could be made automatically.

In more recent times chronographs permitting greater accuracy of time recording have been developed; one particularly versatile type utilized a paper tape driven by an electric motor past two fine solenoid-controlled pens, very close together, one recording the clock-pulses and the other the observation.

In some applications the chronograph has been entirely superseded by automatic data-processing methods: transit-circle observations, for instance, are now reduced instantaneously by computer and the observed places punched on cards ready for subsequent analysis.

CHRONOMETER A very accurately constructed clock of the conventional main-spring-balance wheel-escapement type; strictly, one whose movement is designed so that the escapement operates exactly as the balance wheel passes the mid-point of its oscillation. Their main use is for accurate timekeeping at sea, essential for precise longitude determination; they are of considerable value as 'field' time-keepers in astronomy also, as they have a small and constant rate.

CHRYSE Martian surface feature, approximate position Ω 30°, $\Phi + 10°$. Light ochre area in the equatorial regions, bounded in the north-east by the Margaritifer Sinus and to the west by Jamuna.

CHRYSOKERAS Martian surface feature, approximate position Ω 110°, $\Phi - 50°$. Large dusky area in the south temperate region, between Thaumasia and the Mare Australe.

CINEMATOGRAPHY The moving picture camera has found several applications in astronomy. It is a particularly valuable means of recording rapidly changing phenomena—e.g. the aurora, which can be recorded either by direct cinematography or with the aid of an **all-sky camera.**

The principles of slow-motion cine-

photography and time-lapse cine-photography have been used to record phenomena which change less rapidly, especially solar prominences, the cine-recording of which has been brought to a high level of proficiency at the McMath–Hulbert Observatory and the High Altitude Observatory at Climax, Colorado. The rotation of the planet Jupiter has also been successfully filmed at the Lick Observatory.

CIRCINUS (The Compasses. *Genitive* Circini; *I.A.U. abbreviation* Cir.) A small southern circumpolar constellation; has only one third-magnitude star, two of the fourth and a few fainter ones. It lies on the galactic equator and is crossed by one branch of the Milky Way which is divided at this point.

CIRCLE A special case of the ellipse (the basic closed form of conic section), having an eccentricity of zero. It is the locus of a point whose distance (the radius) from a fixed point (the focus) is constant.

CIRCLE A word used in three senses in astronomy: (i) the fundamental instrument of position (see **Circle, mural**); (ii) the great and small circles, etc., used in spherical astronomy (see **Celestial sphere**); (iii) divided circles, with divisions representing degrees of arc and subdivisions thereof, used for measuring the setting of astronomical instruments (e.g. the Declination circle of a transit circle; the setting circles of an equatorially mounted telescope, etc.)

CIRCLE, MURAL Also known as the *meridian circle*, this instrument was designed by Römer in 1704. It was a logical development of the old mural quadrants and sextants. It comprised a large divided circle, firmly mounted on a wall or stone pier, with a refracting telescope pivoted at its centre. The instrument was mounted with the plane of rotation of the telescope in the plane of the meridian. The telescope would be set on an object in transit, and its zenith distance read off on the circle by means of a pointer attached to the telescope. A well known example was constructed by Troughton in 1812 for the Royal Observatory, Greenwich, where it was used until the **Airy Transit Circle** commenced operations in 1851.

With the **transit instrument** the mural circle was, of course, one of the fore-runners of the transit circle.

CIRCULATING CURRENT An abnormal current in the South Tropical Zone of Jupiter, indicated by the behaviour of series of dark spots on numerous occasions between 1919 and 1934. (See **Jupiter—observed features and notable phenomena.**)

CIRCUMPOLAR CATALOGUE The best-known catalogue of circumpolar stars is the **Groombridge catalogue,** *q.v.* Many of the more recent general catalogues include many of the circumpolar stars.

CIRCUMPOLAR STARS Stars whose north polar distance (south polar distance for observers in the southern hemisphere) does not exceed the observer's latitude; as the altitude of the pole is equal to the latitude of the observer, these stars never set and transit the observer's meridian every twelve hours, at upper and lower culmination alternately.

CIRCUMSTANCES The details of a forthcoming eclipse or other phenomenon, calculated for a particular observing station.

CIVIL TWILIGHT The periods during which the depression of the Sun's centre below the theoretical horizon is between 0° and 6°. (See **Twilight.**)

CLARITAS Martian surface feature, approximate position Ω 110°, $\Phi - 30°$. A canal in Thaumasia, not usually very very prominent, running westwards from the Solis Lacus to join the Sirenum Sinus.

CLARK, Alvan (1808–1887) Famous American optician, whose firm was responsible for the manufacture of many of the world's finest telescope objectives, including the 40-in. at the Yerkes Observatory, the 36-in. at Lick, the 30-in. at Pulkowa, the 26-in. at the U.S. Naval Observatory, Washington, and the 24-in. at the Lowell Observatory.

CLASSICAL CEPHEIDS Term used to denote the normal Cepheid variables—Population I stars with periods of 1–50 days and light variations of approximately one magnitude—to distinguish them from the **cluster variables,** *q.v.*
(See also **Variable stars.**)

CLAVIUS Lunar surface feature, co-ordinates $\xi - 140$, $\eta - 850$. One of the largest ring formations on the Moon, surpassed only by Bailly; it is almost 150 miles in diameter, and is one of the most prominent objects in the very mountainous area surrounding the lunar south pole.

The floor is depressed far below the level of the surrounding terrain; the walls are a broad and rugged rampart towering 12,000 ft above the interior, with peaks rising to 17,000 ft.

The dominant feature is a great chain of craters ranged in an arc crossing the entire floor. The south-western wall is broken by the superb crater Rutherfurd, 25 miles in diameter, with a well-defined wall and prominent central peak; from Rutherfurd the great arc of five craters, almost regularly diminishing in size, stretches north-east : east : south-east : south, to rejoin the southern rampart at the point where it is broken by Clavius K, a crater of some 10 miles diameter.

The north-western wall is broken by another 25-mile diameter crater, Porter—almost a twin of Rutherfurd; it contains a triple-peaked mountain mass.

The floor of Clavius also contains many crater pits, especially in the southern area contained by the great chain of craters.

CLEFT Term formerly used for the trench-like features occuring in various parts of the lunar surface. The term rille is now preferred, especially for the large, broad, examples such as those associated with the ring structures Ariadæus and Hyginus.

CLEOMEDES Lunar surface feature, co-ordinates $\xi + 730$, $\eta + 460$. A vast ring plain, 80 miles in diameter, close to the southern end of the Mare Crisium. The walls are very rugged, and rise to more than 8,000 ft. The floor is broken up with numerous clefts and craterlets. Cleomedes forms part of the vast meridional chain of ring formations stretching from Endymion in the north to Furnerius in the south.

CLOCK An instrument used to measure intervals of time. The measurement of time intervals is one of the fundamental processes of astronomical observation. Several of the basic time intervals are, in fact, based upon observable astronomical phenomena, e.g. the day (axial rotation of the Earth), the year (orbital revolution of the Earth), etc. The development of clocks capable of measuring small intervals to a high accuracy, and having low and constant rates, is therefore a major adjunct to progress in observational astronomy.

(See also **Clock, observatory.**)

CLOCK DRIVE The mechanism to drive an equatorially mounted telescope around the polar axis to counteract the diurnal rotation of the Earth. In most cases it is a clockwork mechanism (hence the name) driven by a falling-weight and provided with a centrifugal governor; in the case of large, modern instruments the drive is usually electrical.

CLOCK ERROR The amount by which the time registered by an observatory clock differs from the correct time; clock slow on right time is regarded as a positive quantity, clock fast on right time as negative.

CLOCK, OBSERVATORY Clocks of the maximum possible accuracy and reliability are required in an observatory for a number of purposes.

A sidereal clock is required to facilitate the accurate setting of equatorial telescopes and the prediction of stars approaching the meridian for transit-circle observers. Many of the observations made involve accurate timing of events against a sidereal clock, normally by means of a chronograph.

It is also usual to provide a time-service for national or local purposes, for which a clock keeping mean solar time is required.

In most observatories these functions are met by free-pendulum clocks, e.g. a **Shortt clock**; in the national observatories, however, it is more usual to use a battery of **quartz clocks** and perhaps even an **atomic clock.**

CLOCK RATE The amount by which the **clock error** changes in 24 hours; clock losing is regarded as a positive rate, clock gaining as a negative rate.

CLOCK STARS Bright stars whose position and proper motion in Right Ascension are known with great accuracy, and whose apparent place can therefore be assumed; meridian-circle observations of their times of transit can then be used to determine the error of the observatory clock.

CLUSTER CEPHEIDS Name sometimes given to the **RR Lyrae stars,** *q.v.*

CLUSTER, GALACTIC General term used to embrace the open clusters, which are concentrated in the galactic plane. (See **Star clusters.**)

CLUSTER, GLOBULAR A star cluster of approximately spheroidal form, the concentration decreasing with distance from the central nucleus. They are approximately spherically distributed about the galactic centre, unlike the open clusters which are concentrated in the galactic plane. (See **Star clusters.**)

CLUSTER, MOVING From its nature it is obvious that the component stars of a globular cluster must share a common motion in space, but this is a requirement for any association of stars to be strictly termed a cluster, and must therefore be applied to the open clusters. The term 'open cluster' is, however, sometimes applied to groups of stars which are apparently fortuitously close together in space, but which will break up in time as the component stars pursue their entirely different courses in space. The true clusters whose component stars share a common motion are therefore often termed *moving clusters* to distinguish them from these impermanent bodies. (See **Star clusters.**)

CLUSTER, OPEN A star cluster containing some 100–2000 stars in a more or less random distribution. Strictly, the member stars should share a common motion in space if the cluster is to be classified as such.

The open clusters are concentrated in the galactic plane, and are therefore frequently termed *galactic clusters*. (See **Star clusters.**)

CLUSTER-TYPE VARIABLES A class of short-period pulsating variables, first discovered in globular clusters by E. C. Pickering in 1889. They have similar characteristics to the Cepheid variables, save for their very short periods—all less than a day. Stars of the same type were later discovered within the Galaxy, including RR Lyr, the brightest of the class, which are therefore more usually referred to as the 'RR Lyrae stars'.

COALSACK The most prominent of all the dark absorption nebulæ, visible to the unaided eye as a very dark patch, approximately $5° × 6°$, in the Southern Milky Way. It is immediately adjacent to the Southern Cross, one of its sides lying practically on the line $α–β$ Cru.

When viewed through a telescope of moderate aperture it can be seen that light from the background stars is not totally absorbed, although there are only about a quarter the number of faint stars visible that are present in the surrounding fields.

(See also **Nebula, dark.**)

CŒLOSTAT A device for receiving a beam of light from the Sun as it traverses the sky and reflecting it in a given direction; unlike the **heliostat** and **siderostat** its whole field remains stationary. It consists of a plane mirror in an equatorial mounting, clock-driven at half the rate of rotation of the Earth, i.e. 1 rotation in 48 hr; the reflecting surface must pass through the axis of rotation. A horizontal telescope trained on this mirror will always see the same field, but in order to allow the observation of objects at any declination it is necessary to have a second equatorially mounted mirror to gather light rays from a selected declination and feed them into the main cœlostat mirror.

The cœlostat is normally used with a **spectroheliograph**, so that this cumbersome instrument can be kept stationary and precisely mounted; cœlostats are also an integral part of a tower telescope. (See **Telescope, tower.**)

COLATITUDE The complement of the latitude ($φ$) of a body, i.e. $(90 − φ)°$.

COLLIMATION In optics, the process of rendering a beam of light parallel-sided. The term is also used to indicate the constraining of a light-beam within a prescribed, straight path.

COLLIMATION ERROR OF A TRANSIT INSTRUMENT The angle by which the optical axis (in the plane of the meridian) and the mechanical (east–west) axis of a transit instrument depart from being perpendicular. (See **Transit circle —errors of.**)

COLOUR The sensation created in the human brain by the reception of light of a particular wavelength—or group of wavelengths—by the eye. Comparisons of colour therefore provide an approximate means of determining the wavelengths of the light observed.

COLOUR FILTER A plate, usually of dyed glass, gelatin, perspex or similar material, which will only transmit light of a specific waveband and absorbs all other wavelengths. It is thus possible to make comparative measures of the proportion of light of various wavelengths contained in the total light received from a celestial body, by means of intensity estimates carried out with a calibrated set of colour filters. A similar technique can be used to determine the colours of planetary surface features, etc.

COLOUR INDEX The difference between the photographic and photovisual magnitudes of a star is known as its colour index (usually denoted by C); i.e.

$$C = m_{pg} - m_{pv}$$

It is usual for m_{pg} to be measured at a wavelength of 4250Å and m_{pv} at 5280Å. The relation between colour index and spectral type is practically uniform (see

Table 9), and hence the comparatively simple determination of the colour index of a star is sufficient to give a fairly accurate indication of its spectral type.

The colour index is affected by **space-reddening**; if adjustment is made for this the effect is to shift the zero of colour index from spectral type $A0$ to $A4$.

(See also **Stars—spectral classification of; Stellar magnitude—determination of**.)

COLOUR TEMPERATURE The apparent 'colour' of a radiant body is a function of the distribution of its intensity of radiation in wavelength. The colour temperature is defined as the temperature of a blackbody radiator having the same spectral intensity as that of the body observed.

The practical application of this principle to the determination of stellar temperatures comprises the comparison of the radiation intensity of a large number of stars in certain selected wavelengths; the scale of colour temperatures so obtained is calibrated by terrestrial laboratory experiment. It is necessary to make allowance for a number of complicating

Table 9. *Colour index and equivalent temperature of the various spectral classes*

Spectral class	Colour index (mags)		Equivalent temperature (° K)	
	(Main sequence)	(Giants)	(Main sequence)	(Giants)
O5	−0·6		79,000	
B0	−0·33		25,200	
B5	−0·18		15,500	
A0	0·00		10,700	
A5	+0·20		8,500	
F0	+0·33		7,500	
F5	+0·47		6,500	
dG0	+0·57		6,000	
gG0		+0·67		5,200
dG5	+0·65		5,400	
gG5		+0·92		4,600
dK0	+0·78		4,900	
gK0		+1·12		4,200
dK5	+0·98		3,900	
gK5		+1·57		3,600
dM0	+1·45		3,500	
gM0		+1·73		3,400

factors—notably absorption by the Earth's atmosphere.

COLUMBA (The Dove; formerly Columba Noachii, Noah's Dove. *Genitive* Columbae, *I.A.U. abbreviation* Col.) A southern constellation containing two third-magnitude stars (α and β Col) and five of the fourth magnitude.

COMA A fault encountered in optical systems when incident light strikes the objective obliquely; the rays of a point-source, such as a star, are not brought to a point focus, but are pear-shaped, with the sharpest and brightest part of the image towards the optical axis and the 'tail' pointing radially away from it. This error increases with distance from the optical axis; thus star images in the centre of a plate will be sharp, but those towards the edges will be subject to coma.

COMA BERENICES (Berenice's Hair. *Genitive* Comae Berenicis, *I.A.U. abbreviation* Com.) A beautiful constellation of faint stars and nebulous objects situated between Leo and Boötes. It reaches midnight culmination at the end of March. There are no bright stars, the brightest being three of the fourth magnitude (α, β and γ Com).

There are many notable nebulæ in this region, including N.G.C. 4565, some 3° south-east of γ Com (this is the largest known example of a spiral galaxy presented edgewise to the Earth, having an angular diameter of 15′), and M 64 (N.G.C. 4826), a bright spiral with dark obscuration at the centre, situated about 5° north-west of α Com.

The north galactic pole is located in this constellation, between β and γ Com.

COMA OF A COMET The faint hazy light which surrounds the central condensation of a comet. (See **Comet—structure of.**)

COMET A body moving under the gravitational influence of the Sun, usually consisting of a multiple solid nucleus surrounded by a coma of gas and dust.

Comets travel in orbits which are in most cases elongated ellipses or possibly parabolae or hyperbolae. They are very faint except for a short time around perihelion passage, and are only observable at such times; their orbits are therefore difficult to determine with accuracy. They usually present a very diffuse image through the telescope, and many form a luminous tail during perihelion passage, due to the expulsion of material from the coma by solar radiation pressure.

The name derives from *stellæ cometæ* ('hairy stars')—the term coined by ancient observers to describe their characteristic diffused appearance.

(See below, also **Biela's Comet; Encke's Comet; Halley's Comet,** etc.)

COMET CROMMELIN The comet formerly known as Comet Pons–Coggia–Winnecke–Forbes. It was shown by Crommelin in 1936, after a long and complex analysis of their motions, that Comets 1818 I (discovered by Pons), 1873 VII (discovered independently by Coggia and Winnecke) and 1928 III (discovered by Forbes) were all reappearances of the same short-period comet, having a period of 28 years.

The comet was thenceforward known as 'Pons–Coggia–Winnecke–Forbes' in accordance with usual practice, but some astronomers began referring to it as 'Crommelin's comet' and the situation was finally ratified at the General Assembly of the International Astronomical Union held in Zurich in 1948, when the name 'Comet Crommelin' was officially adopted —a fitting memorial to a great computer of cometary orbits.

COMET FAMILIES The aphelia of many of the short-period comets are found to lie close to the orbits of the major planets, if referred to the plane of the Ecliptic (i.e. if the inclination of the orbit to the plane of the Ecliptic is ignored). This results in the existence of groups or families of comets with very similar orbits. There is a large group, of fifty or so comets, associated with Jupiter, and much smaller groups apparently associated with Saturn, Uranus and Neptune. If the orbital inclination (which is very high in many cases) is taken into account, however, it is found that the members of these smaller groups are likely to make closer approaches to Jupiter than to the planet with which they appear to be associated, and little importance is now attached to these three families.

The orbits of the Jupiter family are remarkably similar, however, with 24 comets having their aphelion at the solar distance of Jupiter's orbit, and a further 26 within 1 A.U. of it. It is probable that Jupiter has captured these bodies at some time in the past, its gravitational attraction having pulled them out of their former orbits and into new ones dominated by the planet.

COMETS—CATALOGUES OF There are few catalogues of the elements of cometary orbits that need concern us, as thanks to action taken by the International Astronomical Union a definitive catalogue containing elements for all well-determined orbits was published in 1961.

The standard reference for many years was Galle's 'Cometenbahnen'—the *Verzeichniss der Elemente der bischer berechneten Cometenbahnen*, published in Leipzig in 1894. The principal successors to Galle's catalogue were the extensions compiled by Crommelin and published as *Memoirs* of the British Astronomical Association in 1925 and 1932. None of the later catalogues were free from errors and defects, however, and a new catalogue was planned some years ago. This was to be compiled by the Computing Section of the B.A.A., under the Directorship of Dr. J. G. Porter, and was to be compiled from original sources—thus avoiding the inclusion of errors transferred from other catalogues—and the elements of all comets were to be reduced to a common equinox (1950·0). This ambitious project was completed and published as the *Catalogue of Cometary Orbits 1960,* again in the form of a B.A.A. *Memoir.* This had been decided at the 1955 General Assembly of the I.A.U., who made a grant towards the cost of publication. The catalogue contains 829 sets of elements; these include data for 317 apparitions of 54 periodic comets observed at more than one return, there being thus a total of 566 comets. Of these 94 (17%) have truly elliptical orbits, 65 (11%) have hyperbolic orbits and 407 (72%) have apparently parabolic or near-parabolic orbits.

COMETS—DISRUPTION OF In addition to the gradual dissipation of a comet's component material, which is accelerated around perihelion by the effects of solar radiation pressure, comets have been known to disintegrate when their structure has been reduced to a comparatively unstable state. This disruption is sometimes hastened by a very close approach to a major planet. The classic examples of this are comets P/Biela and P/Brooks (2). The former was discovered by Biela in 1826 and has a period of 6·7 years. Shortly after the first observation of the 1846 return the nucleus divided into two parts which gradually separated, each forming its own tail. The twin comets returned in 1852, much farther apart—about 1½ million miles—but have not been observed since. There is, however, a great meteor swarm travelling in the same orbit as the former comets, suggesting that they have completely disrupted into fragments. This meteor swarm has given rise to some splendid showers when the Earth has crossed its path in late November. The shower is often described as the Bielids, although it is more correctly designated the Andromedids, the radiant being close to γ And. [Plate 15(c, d).]

Comet Brooks was observed multiple in 1889; the two principal parts were slowly separating at such a rate that the disruption could be traced back to the close approach of the comet to Jupiter in 1886, when it passed within the orbit of

Jupiter's innermost satellite. This close approach also radically altered the orbit of the comet; its period, previously 29·2 years, was reduced to 7·1 years.

Among other examples of comets disintegrating are Comet 1897 III Perrine and 1913 VI P/Westphal, both of which faded and disappeared before reaching perihelion.

Probably the most catastrophic disruption known was that of Comet 1926 III Ensor, which attained naked-eye brightness before reaching a perihelion distance of some 30 million miles, but was invisible thereafter. B. M. Peek, later to become one of the leading planetary observers of the day, succeeded in obtaining a photograph which showed the comet's remains as a faint stain spreading over an area of the plate equivalent to about a million square miles. This was confirmed by a photograph taken at the Bergedorf Observatory.

COMETS — NOMENCLATURE OF

Comets are usually given proper names in honour of their discoverers, but this rule has been broken on occasion in order to honour an astronomer who has carried out important work on the problems of a particular comet. Thus 'Halley's Comet', in recognition of Halley's feat in identifying it as the first example of a periodic comet and successfully predicting its return, and 'Encke's Comet', in honour of the man who recognized the comet discovered by Pons in 1818 as the second known periodic comet and predicted its return in 1822.

Cases of multiple discovery led to some confusion, and it is now usual to include the names of no more than three independent discoverers; thus the comet which had for many years been known as Comet Pons–Coggia–Winnecke–Forbes was renamed **Comet Crommelin** (q.v.), again recognizing the feat of the computer who proved that three separate comets were in fact returns of the same periodic comet.

When its discovery is first announced a comet is given a provisional designation consisting of the year of discovery and a serial letter indicating the order of its discovery during the year, thus: 1966a, 1966b, etc. Later, when the orbit and date of perihelion passage have been reliably determined, the final designation is allocated by the International Astronomical Union. This is in the form of the year of perihelion passage followed by a roman numeral indicating the order of perihelion passage within the year; thus: 1966 I, 1966 II, etc. Some comets will never receive final designations, insufficient data being obtained to permit the calculation of a reliable orbit.

It is not uncommon for comets to reach perihelion in a different year from that of their discovery; thus the second discovery in 1940, Comet Whipple, was provisionally designated 1940b, but as it was the third comet to reach perihelion in 1941 its final designation was 1941 III P/Whipple, the 'P' signifying that it was a periodic comet. Where the same observer has discovered more than one comet, periodic comets discovered by him are allocated a serial number in parentheses following his name. Thus: 1944 III P/du Toit (1); 1945 II P/du Toit (2); 1945 III du Toit; 1945 VII du Toit.

COMETS—OBSERVATION OF

Comet observations are of two kinds—the search for a new comet or the return of a known periodic comet, and the study of the structure of known comets.

Comet-seeking is an arduous pursuit requiring great patience, and rarely brings any returns; in the rare cases where a comet is discovered, however, the satisfaction must be immense. An instrument giving a fairly wide field is required, either a small refractor (say a 3-in.) with a low-power eyepiece (preferably not exceeding × 25) or a pair of powerful binoculars. It is best to concentrate on a selected area of the sky and to search it by systematic 'sweeps' in narrow zones. A comet will normally present a fuzzy appearance; if such an object is seen careful checks must be made to verify its probable nature. The first step should be to change the eyepiece for one giving a higher power, as close multiple stars or small clusters can have a cometary appearance under a low power. Changing the eyepiece also enables one to rule out the possibility that the fuzzy object is a 'ghost' reflection formed within the eyepiece. A detailed chart of the background stars is required, of course; for the amateur observer **Norton's Star Atlas** (*q.v.*) is an invaluable aid, but for telescopic comet seeking a chart giving fainter stars is preferable, though difficult to obtain. **Webb's Atlas of the Stars** (*q.v.*) is ideal for the purpose. In order to avoid confusion with the fainter nebulae and star clusters it is necessary to consult the 'N.G.C.' However, one of the surest indications is to record the position of the suspected object relative to the background stars as accurately as possible, preferably by a very careful drawing, and to repeat this at intervals of 1–2 hours. If the object is in fact a comet its motion will be revealed.

Comets may appear in any part of the sky, but the chances of discovering one are greater in areas within about 90° of the Sun, i.e. in the west or north-west after sunset, or the east or north-east before dawn.

Observations of the physical structure of a comet may be made visually or photographically. If the former, a drawing should be made showing the exact form of the head and tail and any 'beard' or 'spikes': care must be taken to reproduce the relative size of each feature accurately and, as far as possible, the relative intensity of each part of the structure. It is important to mark in any stars in the field as accurately as possible, this may be a help in determining the exact position, orientation and size of the comet. The diameter of the coma and length of the tail (if any) are important, and estimates of the total apparent magnitude of the whole comet, and that of its nucleus separately, should be made. If a simple (e.g. cross-bar) micrometer is available the position

relative to nearby stars can be measured.

Photographic observations of comets, using a good camera lens (e.g. an $f/5\cdot6$ aeroplane camera lens), can be most valuable. The camera must be equatorially mounted and carefully guided (it should preferably be clock-driven). Exposures ranging from a few minutes to an hour will be required for good results, depending upon the instrument used and the magnitude of the comet.

COMETS—ORBITS OF It is exceedingly difficult to determine the orbital elements of a comet with precision, since the comet is only observable over a very small part of its orbit and is usually a diffuse object whose position is difficult to measure with certainty. The elements of more than 500 comets are known with reasonable accuracy. Approximately 72 per cent of these have apparently parabolic orbits—that is to say they appear to have orbital eccentricities of approximately 1·0. A further 11 per cent seem to have hyperbolic orbits and only about 17 per cent appear to have elliptical orbits. However, it would be unwise to place too much reliance on these figures, which taken at their face value suggest that more than 80 per cent of all comets come from outside the solar system; were this the case we should expect a greater proportion of the comets to arrive from the solar **apex**, with a corresponding sparsity in the direction of the solar **antapex**, but no such distribution exists. It is probable that most of the hyperbolic and parabolic comets are in fact in elliptical orbits of very long period, the confusion arising from the similarity of the three types of orbit over the short arc in which the comets are observable (see Fig. 20) and the difficulty of determining the orbital elements with sufficient accuracy.

A further complication is the considerable alteration to which cometary orbits are subject, due to planetary perturbations.

Comet orbits are found with inclinations to the Ecliptic of all values between 0° and 90°; a few—including Halley's Comet—

have inclinations greater than 90°, i.e. have 'retrograde' motion.

The comets of known elliptical orbits are the so-called 'periodic' comets; rather more than 50 of these have been observed on at least one return; the periodic comet

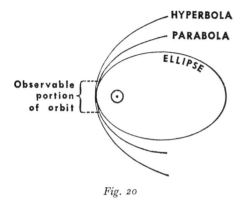

Fig. 20

of longest-known period (156 years) is Comet P/ C. Herschel–Rigollet which was first discovered in 1783 by Caroline Herschel as comet 1788 II and detected at its return as 1939 VI by Rigollet.

The comet of shortest period known is Encke's Comet, which has a period of 3·3 years and has been observed at almost 50 apparitions.

(See also **Comet families.**)

COMETS—ORIGIN OF The place and mechanism of formation of the comets is still a matter of speculation. There is very little evidence other than the orbit, which is both difficult to determine accurately, owing to the comet being observable only for a short time near perihelion, and very much affected by the perturbations of the major planets. Statistical studies of cometary orbits show that the major influence in determining a comet's orbit is Jupiter.

Among early theories were those of Laplace, who suggested that comets were formed in a cloud of interstellar material captured by the Sun, and Lagrange, who suggested that comets were formed by the disruption of a planet or were ejected by

volcano-like eruptions on the major planets.

A modern development of Laplace's capture hypothesis is the theory of R. A. Lyttleton, who suggested that the comets were formed by a process of accretion as the Sun passed through a cloud of interstellar dust and gas. The theory accounts satisfactorily for many of the orbital peculiarities shown by some comets; it does however assume that the comets are of more recent origin than the planets, whereas some theoretical astronomers regard them as 'original' members of the solar system.

A recent development of Lagrange's theory that comets are debris from a planet which disintegrated is due to J. H. Oort of Leiden. Oort suggested that a planet formerly existed in an orbit between those of Mars and Jupiter; the planet is presumed to have been disrupted, either by some outside agency or due to internal stresses. Many of the fragments would have escaped the solar system altogether; some would be retained in near-circular orbits (the asteroids) and others would be drawn into highly elliptical heliocentric orbits (the comets) by the perturbing influences of the major planets and some of the nearer, massive stars. Oort suggests that about 3–5 per cent of the fragments which 'escaped' from the solar system formed a cloud situated about 150,000 A.U. from the Sun. Due to their mutual perturbative influences and those of massive stars the fragments in the cloud will be in a state of random motion; at any one moment some of them will be moving in the direction of the Sun. When they approach the solar system their path will be affected by the gravitational attraction of the major planets. As a result some will be captured as short-period comets, others will be turned into hyperbolic orbits and will be lost to the solar system. The continuing perturbations due to the stars will ensure that a small proportion of the fragments in the cloud continues to be directed towards the Sun to form new comets in the future.

COMETS—SPECTRA OF If a spectrogram of a comet is obtained with a slitless spectrograph it normally comprises a faint continuum, with several separate images of the comet superimposed upon it. If the spectrogram is obtained with a slit spectrograph each of these superimposed images is broken up into a number of emission lines which can be positively identified [Plate 16(d)].

The continuum is the solar spectrum, and shows the usual Fraunhofer absorption lines; the separate images are due to molecular emissions from the comet itself. The number of emission lines usually increases as the comet approaches the Sun.

The first comet spectrogram was obtained by Donati in 1864; the presence of the absorption lines, which confirms that the continuum is attributable to reflected sunlight, was detected by Huggins in 1868.

The spectrum of a comet's tail frequently differs from that of the head. There is an interesting resemblance between the chemical composition of comets' tails and of meteorites: many of the gases whose presence can be inferred from the spectra of comets' tails are obtained when meteorites are heated *in vacuo*. This implies that cometary nuclei are formed of quasi-meteoric material, the coma being formed in part by the occluded gases being driven off by the heat of the Sun as the comet approaches perihelion.

The head. The molecules identified in the spectra of comet heads are mainly combinations including carbon, hydrogen, nitrogen and oxygen, especially C_2, CH, CH^+, CH_2, CN, NH_2, OH and OH^+. Most of these molecules are unstable, but they are able to exist in comets owing to the very low density and consequently low collision frequency. It has been propounded that the unstable molecules giving rise to the observed emissions are only present when the comet is close to the Sun, being formed by the breakdown of more stable parent molecules by solar ultra-violet radiation; likely 'parent' molecules are C_2, CO_2, CH_4, C_2N_2, NH_3 and H_2O. Some comets making close approaches to the Sun have also shown metallic lines such as those of iron, magnesium, nickel and—especially—sodium.

The tail. The spectra of comet tails contain similar emission lines to those found in the spectra of the heads, due to both neutral and ionized forms of the same molecules. The presence of highly ionized molecules in the tail is quite possible, the density being even less than that of the head.

COMETS—STRUCTURE OF The 'head' of a comet comprises a bright *central condensation* surrounded by a fainter *coma* whose brightness fades with distance from the centre. There is frequently a stellar *nucleus*, separable from the central condensation only with telescopes of large aperture and a high-power eyepiece. This is the comet proper; the 'tail' which often appears around perihelion passage is quite impermanent, being due only to the effect of the Sun at close range; its component material is lost to the comet for ever.

The density of comets is extremely low; although in terms of volume they are generally larger than any body in the solar system except the Sun itself, their density is only of the order of one ten-thousand-millionth of the density of the Earth. A typical comet might have a total mass of 800,000,000,000 tons. This mass is concentrated almost entirely in the nucleus.

The nucleus. The nucleus of a comet comprises a conglomeration of pieces of matter of various sizes; that these must include some blocks of quite large size—perhaps several miles in diameter—is indicated by the survival by numerous comets of passage very close to the Sun without dissolution by the intense radiation. (Comet 1843 I passed within one tenth of a solar radius of the surface of the Sun.) Observations of the magnitude of cometary nuclei at varying distances from the Sun show that there can be no blocks significantly larger than this, a fact also confirmed by the fact that comets in transit across the Sun's disk are totally invisible throughout the transit.

The central condensation. This is often taken to be the nucleus, especially by observers using small telescopes, with which the stellar nucleus cannot be detected. It is really the bright, inner portion of the coma.

The coma. This is a bright, nebulous cloud of considerable size—often more than 100,000 miles in diameter. It has a bright centre—the central condensation—and fades rapidly outwards; this indicates that the conglomerate nucleus of a comet is surrounded by a mass of particles whose dimensions and density of distribution decrease rapidly from the centre. Much of this matter is left by the comet, scattered along its orbit; where the orbit crosses that of the Earth some of the particles collide with the Earth and are burnt up in its atmosphere as **meteors**. It is apparent from the high reflectivity of the coma that it also contains a substantial quantity of very fine dust particles. The burning up of this dust during perihelion passage may account for the frequently observed phenomenon of a comet reappearing from perihelion much fainter than predicted.

The coma is quite transparent, and often appears to be in the form of concentric shells or envelopes surrounding the nucleus.

The tail. The tail of a comet comprises small particles expelled from the head by the radiation-pressure of the Sun's light; this pressure naturally increases as the comet approaches the Sun, hence the observed lengthening of the tail. As the comet recedes from the Sun after perihelion the radiation-pressure falls and the tail shortens and eventually disappears. This mechanism provides the explanation of the observed fact that the tail of a comet is always directed approximately

away from the Sun, and is not 'trailed' behind the comet in its orbit.

Comet tails were classified by the Russian astronomer Bredichin into three main types, which he termed I, II and III (see Fig. 21). The different shapes arise from variations in the effect of radiation-pressure upon particles of different densities. Many comets have more than one tail, when the component tails are often

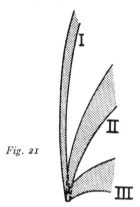

Fig. 21

directed not quite radially away from the Sun and may be of different types. The curvature of the tails is due to the motion of the comet in its orbit, and as this can be determined it is possible to calculate the velocity of ejection of the tail material from the apparent curvature of the tail.

The structure of the tail is sometimes very complex with rapid and involved changes, and separate 'jets' and 'streamers' may also be formed. Sometimes in particularly active comets we see eruptions of cloud-like condensations of matter which travel rapidly along the tail. In 1910 June such an eruption travelled the length of the tail of Halley's comet in only four days, and was visible for some time quite separated from the comet. It is likely that these sudden eruptions are due to abnormal solar activity such as a solar flare, with its consequent increase of radiation-pressure in the ultra-violet. Comet Morehouse (1908 III) was outstanding for its complex and changing structure. [Plates 15(e); 16(a–c).]

Beards and spikes. Comets sometimes display a fan-shaped sunward extension of the coma, known as a *beard*, or a long, thin, sunward marking, usually termed a *spike*. These may be either truly sunward projections, perhaps matter torn from the coma by the gravitational pull of the Sun, or simply multiple tails which appear to be directed towards the Sun due to effects of perspective. Comet 1957 III Arend-Roland was notable for a long, apparently sunward, spike. [Plate 15(f).]

COMMENSURABLE MOTIONS The mean motions of a number of bodies in the solar system are found to be commensurate to a remarkable degree, quite beyond the probability of accidental commensurabilities. The mean motion of an orbiting body is directly related to its distance from the primary (Kepler's third law of planetary motion), and hence a commensurability in mean distances is indicative of commensurable mean motions.

The earliest noted commensurability was probably Bode's Law, attributed both to J. E. Bode and J. B. Titius; this drew attention to the fact that the mean distances of the planets from Mercury to Uranus were commensurate with a simple numerical series.

In 1913 Miss M. A. Blagg published a more complicated formula which demonstrated the commensurability of the mean distances of the planets of the solar system and also of the satellites of the systems of Jupiter, Saturn and Uranus. In 1953 A. E. Roy showed that the six bodies discovered since Miss Blagg's paper was published (Pluto and the satellites Jupiter IX, X, XI, XII and Uranus V) all fitted the formula very closely.

It was noted by Laplace that the mean motions (n) of three of the principal satellites of Jupiter, Io (I), Europa (II) and Ganymede (III), were related by the formula

$$n_I - 3n_{II} + 2n_{III} = 0.$$

Hermann Struve's detailed investigation of the satellites of Saturn showed that the mean motions of Mimas (I), Enceladus (II),

Tethys (III) and Dione (IV) are similarly commensurable, being related by the formula

$$5n_I - 10n_{II} + n_{III} + 4n_{IV} = 0.$$

In 1954 it was pointed out by A. E. Roy and M. W. Ovenden that a similar relation holds for the four principal satellites of Uranus, Ariel (I), Umbriel (II), Titania (III) and Oberon (IV), as follows:

$$n_I - n_{II} - 2n_{III} + n_{IV} = 0.$$

Roy and Ovenden carried out a detailed study of commensurabilities among the satellites of the solar system, and found that there is a clear tendency for stable orbits to form at commensurable mean distances.

A number of similar studies of bodies in the solar system provide further evidence of commensurability between the present motions of bodies which may be indicative of a relationship that has existed since their mutual formation. Particularly important are Kirkwood's studies of the gaps in the rings of Saturn and in the asteroid belt, which he found were commensurate with the distances of some of the satellites and of Jupiter, respectively; these gaps are attributed to a resonance effect.

(See also **Bode's Law; Minor planets; Saturn—rings of.**)

COMMON, A. A. (1841–1903) One of the leading English astronomers of the nineteenth century, and a pioneer of astronomical photography. In 1883 he obtained with his 36-in. reflector by Calver, the first really successful photograph of the Orion nebula. This photograph represented an enormous stride forward in the development of the techniques of astronomical photography; it caused great excitement in astronomical circles. In 1884 Common was awarded the Gold Medal of the Royal Astronomical Society for his achievement.

Common was a firm believer in the use of large apertures; working first with a $5\frac{1}{2}$-in. refractor, he then commissioned from Calver an 18-in. and later the 36-in. reflector.

Common's astronomical work was

carried out entirely as an amateur, he was an engineer by profession; perhaps this led to his long interest in the manufacture of telescope mirrors. His largest mirrors were two of 60 inches aperture. One of these Common mounted as a Newtonian, but following a fall from the high observing platform he ceased to use this form, and after an unsuccessful attempt to convert it to an inclined form of Cassegrain he abandoned the mirror. He returned to one he had cast with the central aperture necessary to use it as a Cassegrain; he had abandoned the attempt to figure it, however, owing to the distorting effects of the internal stresses varying under the heat of polishing. He now tackled the problem again, by polishing for only a minute and then allowing the mirror to cool completely before polishing for a further minute.

Common died before he was able to make real use of this instrument, but it was used for many years at the Harvard College Observatory in Cambridge, Massachusetts; in 1933, refigured and remounted by Fecker, it was transferred to the Harvard southern station at Bloemfontein, where it has been used to obtain an invaluable series of photographs of southern nebulae and clusters.

Several other large mirrors by Common are in use at observatories throughout the world. Notable among these was the 36-in. Calver–Common reflector which Common had sold to Edward Crossley of Halifax, who presented it to the Lick Observatory in 1895; this was the first large reflector in the United States, and was used by Keeler in the discovery of innumerable galaxies, nebulæ, etc. Common also figured the mirror of the 30-in. Thompson reflector at the Royal Observatory, Greenwich.

Common was President of the Royal Astronomical Society 1895–1897 and its Treasurer 1884–1895. He was elected a Fellow of the Royal Society in 1885, and received the honorary degree of Doctor of Letters from the University of St. Andrews in 1891.

COMMONWEALTH ASTRONOMER The Director of the Commonwealth Observatory at Mount Stromlo, Australia.

COMMONWEALTH OBSERVATORY See **Mount Stromlo Observatory**.

COMMUTATION, ANGLE OF The difference between the geocentric longitudes of the Sun and a planet, measured in the plane of the Ecliptic.

COMPARISON STARS Stars of known magnitude, selected as a standard for comparison when determining the magnitude of a nearby variable star, asteroid, etc.

COMPOUND LENS A lens comprising two or more elements, which may either be cemented together or separated by an air-space.

COMRIE, L. J. (1893–1950) The pioneer of modern methods in the computation of astronomical ephemerides and mathematical tables in general.

Leslie John Comrie was born in New Zealand and obtained the degrees of B.A. and M.A. at the University of Auckland. Following service in France in the First World War, during which he suffered the loss of a leg, Comrie became a research student at St. John's College, Cambridge; he obtained his doctorate in 1923, and then spent two years in the United States as a visiting professor.

In 1925 he joined the staff of H.M. Nautical Almanac Office, and became its Deputy Superintendent in the following year; in 1930 he was appointed Superintendent. During his service at the N.A.O. Comrie completely reorganized the methods and procedures in use there, substituting calculating machines, both manual and punched-card operated, for tables of logarithms. He soon became the acknowledged master of utilizing mechanical aids in the production of printer's copy for tabular matter of all kinds, as one operation integral with its calculation.

He also set the highest possible standards of accuracy and rigour in computation, and played a considerable part in the training of a large band of computers, both professional and amateur. Whilst at Cambridge he had founded the Computing Section of the British Astronomical Association, and produced the first two editions of the Association's *Handbook*.

In 1936 Comrie resigned from the N.A.O. and founded a unique organization to provide, on a commercial basis, computing services based upon the best scientific methods.

Although first and foremost a computer and compiler of mathematical tables, Comrie was deeply interested in astronomy, wherein lies the reason for his success in developing new techniques of astronomical computation. His death at a comparatively early age left a most important gap in the ranks of astronomers which has never been filled.

Comrie was elected a Fellow of the Royal Society in 1949 and from 1932–1938 was Chairman of Commission 4 (Ephemerides) of the International Astronomical Union.

CONCENTRIC RING - STRUCTURES

Type of lunar surface feature in which two ring-structures of different diameters are exactly concentric. The inside ring is always found to have a lower wall than the outer. A perfect example of the type is Hesiodus A. (See **Moon—surface features of**.)

CONIC SECTIONS

The curves formed by the intersection of a plane and a cone. Fig. 22(*a*) shows a cone in cross-section; a number of planes of intersection are indicated, and the resulting curves are shown in Fig. 22(*b*).

If the plane intersects only the sloping sides of the cone, as at *EE'*, the resulting curve is an *ellipse*. If the intersection plane is parallel to the base, however, as at *CC'*, the result is a *circle*. If the plane intersects with a sloping side and the base of the cone, as at *HH'*, the result will be a *hyperbola*,

unless the plane is parallel to the sloping side of the cone as at *PP'*, when a *parabola* is produced. It will be noted that both the parabola and the hyperbola are open curves, and that any hyperbola has a reversed but otherwise identical companion curve caused by the plane intersecting with the second cone formed by the sides of the first cone produced beyond its apex.

The ellipse is the basic closed form of conic section; it may be defined as a conic section for which the ratio between the distances of any point on it from a focus and from a fixed line is constant. The fixed line is termed the *directrix* and the constant the *eccentricity* (see Fig. 35, p. 116).

The circle may be regarded as the special case of the ellipse where the eccentricity is zero; in this case the two foci of the ellipse are coincident.

The hyperbola is an open conic section, for which the ratio between the distances of any point on it from the focus and from the directrix is constant; this constant, the *eccentricity*, is greater than 1. The parabola may be regarded as a special case of the hyperbola where the eccentricity is exactly 1.

CONICAL CRATER

A lunar ring-structure whose internal cross-section is conical. (See **Moon—surface features of**.)

CONJUNCTION

This term, used to describe certain fundamental configurations of bodies in the solar system, is used in several ways, depending upon the object concerned.

Two planets are said to be in conjunction when they share the same heliocentric longitude.

A planet is said to be in conjunction with the Sun when they both share the same geocentric longitude. Thus, a superior planet is said to be in conjunction when it lies beyond, and in the same direction, as the Sun. (The opposite position, when the Earth lies between the Sun and a superior planet, is termed *opposition*.)

An inferior planet is in conjunction at two points in its orbit; that when it is

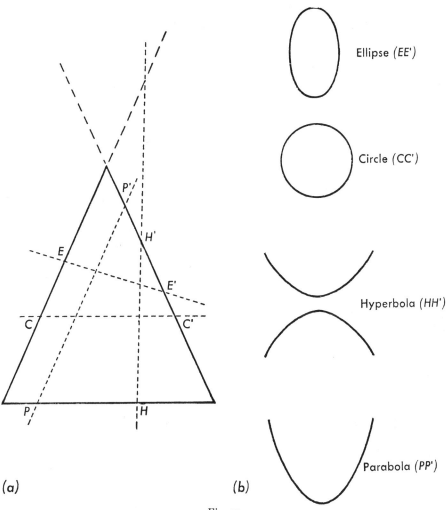

Ellipse (EE')

Circle (CC')

Hyperbola (HH')

Parabola (PP')

(a)

(b)

Fig. 22

between the Sun and the Earth is termed *inferior conjunction*, that when it lies beyond the Sun is termed *superior conjunction*.

The Moon is also said to be in conjunction when it shares the same geocentric longitude, i.e. at New Moon.

(See also **Moon, motion of; Planetary motion.**)

CONNAISSANCE DES TEMPS The French equivalent of *The Astronomical Ephemeris*, produced in Paris by the Bureau des Longitudes. Usually abbreviated to C.T.

CONSANGUINEOUS RING-STRUCTURES Type of lunar surface feature consisting of two or more similar ring-structures in close proximity. The similarity extends to the detailed structure of the ramparts, etc., as well as to the over-all shape. Many such pairs are known. Cases where the members of a pair are also equal in size are termed *twin ring-structures*. (See **Moon—surface features of.**)

CONSTANT OF ABERRATION The apparent displacement of a star, θ, due to the aberration of light may be determined from the expression

$$\theta = \frac{v}{c} \sin a$$

where v is the orbital velocity of the Earth, c is the velocity of light and a the angle between the apparent direction of the star and the direction of the Earth's motion. The constant $\frac{v}{c}$ is termed the constant of aberration; it has a value of $20''.47$.

CONSTANTS, ASTRONOMICAL As most of the so-called constants used in astronomy can only be derived from observations, their values are redetermined from time to time as observing techniques improve and more observations become available for analysis. However, many of the constants have to be assumed in the routine calculations of astronomy, such as the computation of planetary ephemerides, etc. In order to facilitate these computations, and to permit the intercomparison of observed results obtained over many years, it was decided in the late nineteenth century that standard values of the astronomical constants should be adopted, and that these should be used in future computations notwithstanding any improved values that might be obtained subsequently.

After half a century it is not surprising that a number of the adopted standard values differ significantly from the best recent determinations, and it has become desirable for a new set of standard values to be adopted for future use. To ensure that the new values should form both a consistent system and the most practicable system, the I.A.U. convened a symposium on 'The Fundamental Constants of Astronomy' at the Paris Observatory in 1963. As a result of this symposium a Working

Group was set up to prepare a new system of fundamental constants on the basis agreed at the symposium, and the new system was adopted by the General Assembly of the I.A.U. held in Hamburg in 1964. The new constants will be introduced, as far as is practicable, into the ephemerides for 1968. The new adopted values are not tabulated here, as they are principally of interest to the mathematical astronomer; they are tabulated in *Q. Jl R. astr. Soc.* **6,** 70 (1965).

(See also **Notation.**)

CONSTELLATION A number of stars, apparently adjacent in the sky, which have been traditionally regarded as a single group and more recently defined as such as an aid to identification.

There is no evidence to indicate the earliest identifications of the constellations with well-known terrestrial persons and objects; the oldest star catalogue known is that in Ptolemy's *Almagest*, compiled in the second century A.D. Forty-eight constellations are listed in the *Almagest*, all of them being still in use today; they include most of the well-known figures, such as Ursa Major, Leo, etc. Constellations have been added at intervals until now, in the list adopted by the International Astronomical Union, there are 88.

The first atlas to show, in addition to the traditional figures, specific boundaries to the constellations was that of Bode; inevitably the outlines varied in the atlases which followed, and it became increasingly difficult to allocate stars in the border region between two constellations to one constellation consistently, thus making accurate identification well-nigh impossible. Following the adoption by the I.A.U. in 1922 of a definitive list of abbreviations for the constellation names, it was proposed by the Belgian National Committee for Astronomy that a definitive atlas of the constellation boundaries should be prepared. This proposal was adopted by the I.A.U. at its general assembly of 1925, and E. Delporte of the Royal Observatory of Belgium, at Uccle, was allocated the task. Delporte's catalogue of the boundary lines for the entire heavens, with charts showing them, was published by the I.A.U. in 1930.

CONSTELLATION NAMES AND ABBREVIATIONS

The First General Assembly of the International Astronomical Union, held in Rome in 1922, accepted the recommendation of its Commission on Notations that it should adopt a definitive list of standard abbreviations for the names of the constellation names. The Assembly adopted a list of 3-letter abbreviations which had been proposed by E. Hertzsprung and H. N. Russell. At the General Assembly held at Cambridge, Massachusetts, in 1932, the Union adopted an additional list of 4-letter abbreviations.

The list of 3-letter abbreviations is that most commonly used, and has therefore been adopted throughout this book where the constellation names require abbreviation. The full list is appended for reference:

Andromeda	And
Antlia	Ant
Apus	Aps
Aquarius	Aqr
Aquila	Aql
Ara	Ara
Aries	Ari
Auriga	Aur
Boötes	Boo
Caelum	Cae
Camelopardalis	Cam
Cancer	Cnc
Canes Venatici	CVn
Canis Major	CMa
Canis Minor	CMi
Capricornus	Cap
Carina	Car
Cassiopeia	Cas
Centaurus	Cen
Cepheus	Cep
Cetus	Cet
Chamaeleon	Cha
Circinus	Cir
Columba	Col
Coma Berenices	Com
Corona Austrina	CrA
Corona Borealis	CrB

Corvus	CrV
Crater	Crt
Crux	Cru
Cygnus	Cyg
Delphinus	Del
Dorado	Dor
Draco	Dra
Equuleus	Equ
Eridanus	Eri
Fornax	For
Gemini	Gem
Grus	Gru
Hercules	Her
Horologium	Hor
Hydra	Hya
Hydrus	Hyi
Indus	Ind
Lacerta	Lac
Leo	Leo
Leo Minor	LMi
Lepus	Lep
Libra	Lib
Lupus	Lup
Lynx	Lyn
Lyra	Lyr
Mensa	Men
Microscopium	Mic
Monoceros	Mon
Musca	Mus
Norma	Nor
Octans	Oct
Ophiuchus	Oph
Orion	Ori
Pavo	Pav
Pegasus	Peg
Perseus	Per
Phoenix	Phe
Pictor	Pic
Pisces	Psc
Piscis Austrinus	PsA
Puppis	Pup
Pyxis	Pyx
Reticulum	Ret
Sagitta	Sge
Sagittarius	Sgr
Scorpius	Sco
Sculptor	Scl
Scutum	Sct
Serpens	Ser
Sextans	Sex
Taurus	Tau
Telescopium	Tel
Triangulum	Tri
Triangulum Australe	TrA
Tucana	Tuc
Ursa Major	UMa

Ursa Minor	UMi
Vela	Vel
Virgo	Vir
Volans	Vol
Vulpecula	Vul

CONTACT Term used to describe the various stages of eclipses, transits, etc. Thus, in the case of a transit of Ganymede across the disk of Jupiter, the instant when the preceding limb of the satellite encroaches on the limb of the planet is termed 'first contact'; that at which the following limb passes onto the disk, 'second contact'; that at which the preceding limb leaves the disk, 'third contact'; and that at which the following limb leaves the disk of the planet, 'fourth' or 'last contact'.

CONTIGUOUS CRATERS A type of lunar surface feature, in which ring-structures are in contact. The walls are usually low, broken or absent at the point of contact. (See **Moon—surface features of.**)

CONTINUOUS SPECTRUM The spectrum of the Sun and the other stars consists of a continuous band of colour, called the 'continuous spectrum' or 'continuum', on which absorption or emission lines may be superimposed at specific wavelengths. (See **Spectra.**)

CONTINUUM The **continuous spectrum,** q.v.

CONVECTIVE ZONE The radiation from the very hot core of the Sun is so intense that the temperature gradient at the level of the photosphere is too steep to permit a state of equilibrium to be reached; tiny convection currents are set up, which appear as white spots against a darker background—termed granulation—these being the tops of hot currents seen against cooler surroundings. The **photosphere** may, in fact, be regarded as the upper layer, or 'skin', of the convective zone.

(See also **Sun—physical constitution of.**)

COOKSON, Bryan (1874–1909) A young English astronomer who achieved great success during his tragically short life. Perhaps his best-remembered achievement was the design of the floating zenith telescope with which, at Cambridge, he redetermined the constant of aberration, and which following his death was used at the Royal Observatory, Greenwich, for the measurement of latitude variation for about 40 years.

Cookson left Cambridge for two years in 1901–1903 to work with Gill at the Cape; there he used the famous heliometer to obtain a new series of observations of the Galilean satellites of Jupiter. Using these observations and astrographic plates exposed simultaneously Cookson produced an important new discussion of the orbital motions of the satellites.

Cookson's early death robbed the astronomical world of a remarkable talent and a most promising scholar of both practical and theoretical astronomy.

COOKSON FLOATING ZENITH TUBE A zenith telescope designed by Bryan Cookson of the Cambridge Observatory in 1900 for the purpose of determining the variation of latitude. It consisted of a vertical telescope tube supported in an iron stand having an annular base which floated in an annular trough of mercury. This arrangement permitted the instrument to be rotated about a vertical axis, and also obviated the level errors to which the conventional transit instrument was prone. [Plate 29(d).]

The telescope was a photographic refractor with a $6\frac{1}{2}$-in., $f/10$, O.G. by Cooke. The observations comprised the photographing of pairs of stars approximately equidistant from the zenith, each star being allowed to trail across the plate during its meridian passage, the instrument being rotated through 180° between the component stars of a pair. The variation in the latitude of the zenith can be inferred from variations in the separations between trails of pairs of stars obtained over a long period.

This unusual instrument proved most successful; it was used by Cookson in Cambridge, and following his untimely death it was loaned to the Royal Observatory at Greenwich. A series of observations was commenced there in 1911 and continued for some 40 years before the instrument was finally taken out of service. It was, of course, the forerunner of the **photographic zenith tube.**

(See also **Latitude variation.**)

CO-ORDINATE SYSTEMS A system of co-ordinates is used to provide a means of defining the position of an object; no one system is suitable for use in all circumstances, and a number of systems have been devised to meet specific requirements.

Probably the most familiar system of co-ordinates is the **Cartesian co-ordinates** (*q.v.*) used in the plotting of conventional graphs. These are simple *rectangular co-ordinates*, the position of the point on the graph being defined by measures of its distance from two axes which are at right angles to each other. This system can be extended into three-dimensional use, a third axis being used perpendicular to the other two.

Most astronomical requirements are for systems in which the position of a point on a spherical surface can be defined; this may be the position of a point on the hypothetical *celestial sphere*, or the position of a feature on the near-spherical surface of the Moon or a planet, etc. Other requirements are for recording positions within large systems—e.g. the solar system, the Galaxy, etc.

Positions on celestial sphere

Three systems of spherical co-ordinates are used to define positions on the celestial sphere:

. *Horizontal system.* This system is based upon the plane of the observer's horizon. Positions are measured in *azimuth* (angle between the vertical plane through the object and the plane of the meridian) and *altitude* (angular elevation of object above horizon). Measurements are sometimes made in *zenith distance* instead of altitude (Z.D. = 90° − alt.).

Equatorial system. This system is based upon the plane of the celestial equator. Positions are measured in *hour angle* and *polar distance* or, more frequently, in *Right Ascension* and *Declination.*

The hour angle is the angle between the declination circle through the object and the meridian; the polar distance is the angular distance between the object and the pole. Right Ascension is the angle between the declination circle through the object and the First Point of Aries; Declination is the complement of the polar distance (Dec. = 90° − N.P.D.).

Ecliptic system. This system is based upon the plane of the Ecliptic. Positions are measured in *celestial longitude* and *latitude.* Celestial longitude is the angle between the secondary to the Ecliptic containing the body and the First Point of Aries; celestial latitude is the angular distance of the body from the Ecliptic measured along a secondary.

Positions on surface of a near-spherical body

There are two principal co-ordinate systems for determining the position of a point on the surface of a body such as the Sun, Moon or a planet.

Planetocentric co-ordinates. These are idealized co-ordinates based upon the equatorial plane of the body concerned; they are the co-ordinates used in dynamical calculations, etc. *Planetocentric longitude* is measured in the conventional manner, from a prime meridian adopted for the body by international agreement. *Planetocentric latitude* is measured above or below the planet's equator in the usual way.

Planetocentric co-ordinates are described as *heliocentric* in the case of the Sun, *geocentric* for the Earth, *selenocentric* (Moon), *areocentric* (Mars), *zenocentric* (Jupiter), *saturnicentric* (Saturn), etc.

Planetographic co-ordinates. Most of the planets are not true spheres, but are oblate. It is usual therefore for the positions of their surface markings to be recorded in planetographic co-ordinates, which are referred to the mean surface of the planet. *Planetographic longitude* and *latitude* are determined from observations. They can however be converted to planetocentric co-ordinates if required, provided that the figure of the planet is known.

In practice, as the planets are symmetrical about their axes of rotation, differences between planetocentric and planetographic longitudes are negligible; differences between planetocentric and planetographic latitudes are, however, quite significant in some cases, notably Jupiter and Saturn.

Positions in large systems

For investigations of the satellite system of a planet, the positions of the satellites are usually given in planetocentric co-ordinates, the parallels of planetocentric longitude and latitude being considered to extend beyond the surface of the planet. Similarly for considerations of the solar system as a whole the positions of the constituent planets are used in the form of heliocentric longitude and latitude.

For studies of galactic structure, etc., *galactocentric co-ordinates* are used; usually known as *galactic longitude* and *latitude*, these were first devised by Sir William Herschel. The system was revised at the instigation of the International Astronomical Union; the new system was introduced in 1960 (see **Galactic co-ordinates**). The system is referred to the galactic plane; the zero of galactic longitude (new system) is the direction of the galactic centre as seen from the Earth.

COPAÏS PALUS Martian surface feature, approximate position Ω 280°, $\Phi + 55°$. Dark condensation between Utopia and Dioscuria, due north of Neith Regio. Separated from Nilosyrtis by Umbra.

COPERNICAN SYSTEM General term used to indicate a model for the solar system in which the Sun is at the centre and the planets are in circular orbits around it and in one plane. The actual system proposed by Copernicus postulated a more complex planetary motion, in terms of epicycles and eccentric circles.

COPERNICUS, Nicholas (1473–1543) Born at Torun in central Poland, Niklas Koppernijk later became known by the Latinized version of his name, as was the custom in those days among men of learning, who used Latin as the universal academic language.

The son of a merchant from Cracow, Copernicus studied for holy orders and for much of his life supported himself by occupying various ecclesiastical posts whilst furthering his studies in astronomy and mathematics.

Copernicus studied at the University of Cracow and later in Italy. In 1512 he settled in Frauenburg, where he remained for the remainder of his life.

Copernicus is remembered as the originator of the heliocentric theory of the universe. He was content to expound and discuss his revolutionary theories among the small circle of his acquaintances, however, and had to be pressed by others into publishing any account of them.

The only complete account was a work in six volumes which was first published within hours of Copernicus' death; this work had no title, but later became known as *De Revolutionibus Orbium Cœlestium*. In it Copernicus postulates the heliocentric concept of the Earth and the other planets being in orbital motion around the Sun, and he also explained the apparent diurnal motion of the heavenly bodies by an axial rotation of the Earth itself, which had previously been believed to be static. Needless to say, these novel theories met with some opposition from officials of the church, although Copernicus had done much to lessen their opposition by dedicating his work to the Pope and by treating the heliocentric theory as a convenient means of analysing the planetary motions rather than emphasizing the concept of a moving Earth. (See **Copernican system.**)

COPERNICUS

COPERNICUS Lunar surface feature, co-ordinates $\xi - 337$, $\eta + 167$. Certainly one of the most magnificent and interesting ring formations on the Moon's surface, standing alone in the Oceanus Procellarum. The walls are extremely broad and complex, consisting of a number of concentric mountain ridges and valleys, with an almost continuous crest-ridge about 12,000 ft above the interior. The form is not circular, but an irregular polygon of twelve main sections.

There are many ridges radial to Copernicus reaching far across the surrounding terrain, which is notable for the great number of craterlets and small pits it contains, especially south and west of Copernicus.

To the north lie the Carpathian mountains, and the land to the east is also very rugged, containing many mountain masses and small craters.

There are three great mountain masses in the interior, of which the centre one is central to the formation; these mountains present seven distinct peaks, of which the highest is 2,500 ft in height.

Copernicus is the centre of a great ray system, of the 'splash' type associated with its neighbours Kepler and Aristarchus; the rays are rather less bright, though longer, than those of these other two features, but Copernicus itself stands out as a brilliant spot under Full Moon illumination. The floor is remarkably free from pits and other detail.

COPRATES Martian surface feature, approximate position Ω 70°, $\Phi - 15°$. Prominent canal running westwards from Auroræ Sinus to the Tithonius Lacus, sometimes known as Agathodæmon.

COR CAROLI The star αCVn, magnitude 2·9; it is the only star in the constellation brighter than the fourth magnitude. Its name, which means 'The Heart of Charles', derives from the belief of Royalists of the time that it shone with exceptional brilliance on the night preceding the return of Charles II to London after the Restoration; it is not a variable so there is no scientific foundation for this pleasant legend. It is in fact an optical double, with a companion (12 CVn) of magnitude 5·4 at a separation of 20″ and position angle of 280°.

CORDOBA DURCHMUSTERUNG A southern extension of the **Bonner Durchmusterung,** compiled from observations made at the Cordoba Observatory, Argentina, by J. M. Thome and published in the *Resultados del Observatorio Nacional Argentino* from 1892 onwards. Covers stars down to about the tenth magnitude, south of Dec. $-22°$, about 614,000 stars in all. The stars are referred to in the form 'CD $-34°$ 6041'; CoD is an alternative abbreviation.

CORONA AUSTRINA (The Southern Crown. *Genitive* Coronae Austrinae, *I.A.U. abbreviation* CrA. An erroneous form sometimes used is Corona Australis, *Genitive* Coronae Australis.) A small constellation in the southern sky, whose principle stars (θ, η^2, ζ, δ, β, α and γ CrA) are arranged in a beautiful arc that really does suggest a jewelled circlet. The arrangement is very similar to the stars of the Northern Crown, **Corona Borealis**.

CORONA BOREALIS (The Northern Crown. *Genitive* Coronae Borealis, *I.A.U. abbreviation* CrB). A tiny but beautiful northern constellation, situated between **Boötes** and **Hercules** and reaching midnight culmination in mid-May. The principal feature is the arrangement of seven of the brightest stars, θ, β, α, γ, δ, ϵ and ι CrB, in a perfect arc; it is easy to understand why the ancients visualized it as a diadem or crown.

There are several interesting stars: η and σ CrB are both binaries; the latter of very long period. ζ CrB is a beautiful double, with components of magnitude 4·0 and 4·9, separated by 6″·3.

S CrB is a long-period variable, varying between the sixth and twelfth magnitudes over a period of almost a year (361 days).

R and T CrB are both irregular variables, the former having a magnitude variation of 5·8–12·5, and the latter 2·0–9·5. Both stars have interesting histories; R CrB remains at its brightest for several years, sometimes as many as nine, and then fades rapidly to its minimum, where it remains with minor fluctuations for a period which may be weeks or years, then rises again to its maximum. T CrB is sometimes referred to as the 'Blaze Star'; in 1866 May it flared up suddenly from magnitude 9·5 to 2·0; nine days later it had fallen to below sixth magnitude, and after some weeks was down to 9·0; after a temporary revival to the seventh magnitude it fell again to 9·5, where it has remained.

CORONA, SOLAR A vast, faintly radiant envelope surrounding the Sun. The brightest part extends, on average, 2–3 solar radii beyond the limb; the inner corona was formerly visible only during the total phase of a solar eclipse, but can now be observed at other times from high-altitude observatories with the aid of the **coronagraph** invented by Lyot.

The shape of the inner corona varies markedly with the sunspot cycle; at sunspot maximum it is almost uniform, as in Plate 2(a), whilst at sunspot minimum it shows the well-known 'magnetic field' form, brightest in the equatorial regions and faintest in the polar regions, where the 'polar plumes' are also seen (Plate 2(b)).

(See also **Sun—physical constitution of.**)

CORONAE Coloured rings of light around the Moon (or Sun), caused by diffraction of the light as it passes through light clouds or haze consisting of water droplets. They usually appear coloured, approximating to a spectrum with the violet edge towards the Moon (or Sun). There is usually a central aureole with a radius of up to 5°, and two or more outer rings with radii between 5° and 10°.

(See also **Halo; Parhelion; Parselenae.**)

CORONAGRAPH Instrument devised in 1930 by B. Lyot to permit the study of the solar corona and limb prominences. Hitherto this had only been possible during the brief duration of a total solar eclipse.

The principle of the instrument is shown schematically in Fig. 23. The telescope objective L_1 is a single-element planoconvex lens, so as to avoid the diffusion and internal reflections formed by a compound lens; a stop S_1 is placed before the objective to eliminate off-axis rays. A focused image of the Sun is produced on a blackened occulting disk D; the diameter of this disk is identical to that of the focused image of the photosphere, thus permitting the light from the corona only to pass on. The disk is also inclined so that any light reflected is passed out of the telescope tube. A field lens L_2 forms an image of the corona on the diaphragm stop S_2; the stop eliminates any diffracted light. A circular stop S_3 is placed centrally in the beam to cut out 'ghost' images of the Sun formed by reflection from the surfaces of lens L_2. A narrow-band filter F then selects the wavelength in which the Sun is to be examined, the filtered beam passing into an eyepiece or, as shown in Fig. 23, focused by a camera lens C onto a photographic plate P. The filter and camera are

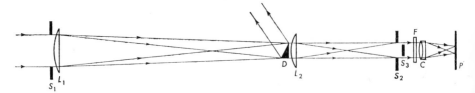

Fig. 23

often replaced by a spectrograph. All internal surfaces of the instrument must be painted matt black to prevent stray reflections, and the lenses must be manufactured from glass of the highest quality, free from bubbles or other imperfections, and free from surface scratches. Even after these precautions the operation of the instrument is jeopardized by stray light, atmospheric diffusion, etc.; it is therefore usually used only at a high-altitude observatory where the rarified atmosphere is steadier and more transparent.

CORVUS (The Crow. *Genitive* Corvi, *I.A.U. abbreviation* Crv.) A very small constellation in the southern hemisphere, just south of the Ecliptic on the southern boundary of **Virgo**. It contains one second- and three third-magnitude stars in the form of a rhombus, and a number of fainter ones.

COSMIC ABUNDANCE The amount of a substance believed to be present in the universe as a whole, relative to the other constituents.
(See also **Russell mixture**.)

COSMIC RAYS Highly energized particles which impinge on the upper atmosphere of the Earth. Some are emitted by the Sun, but most of them originate outside the solar system. For many years cosmic rays were thought to be γ-rays—ultra-short wavelength radiation—before their particulate nature was established. The direction of arrival of the particles is governed by the Earth's magnetic field. The particles do not reach the surface of the Earth, as they collide with the atoms constituting the upper atmosphere. These collisions release colossal quantities of energy—the process is identical to that of the 'splitting' of an atom—and some fragments of the disrupted atomic nuclei float through the atmosphere to reach the Earth's surface. Some of these 'secondary particles', known as *mesons*, have been studied in great detail and have provided much information about the mode of arrival of the primary cosmic 'radiation'.

The nature of the particles constituting this so-called radiation is very difficult to study; it seems to consist principally of nuclei of atoms of heavy elements— notably oxygen. It is believed that most or all elements may be present to some extent. It has been suggested however that cosmic rays may consist, *ab initio*, solely of heavy elements, any lighter elements present by the time they reach the Earth having been formed by nuclear fission.

The origin of cosmic rays is still a matter for speculation; it has been suggested that they may arise out of a process of electromagnetic acceleration of low-energy particles in interstellar space—a process similar to that which takes place in a cyclotron. The low-energy particles are assumed to be emitted by the stars, as indeed some of the low-energy cosmic rays received on Earth are known to originate from the Sun.

COSMOCHEMISTRY The study of the chemical nature of celestial bodies. The only practical application is the analysis of the composition of meteorites, but there is a great deal of analysis of celestial bodies by deductive reasoning from physical observations, supported by comparative experiments in the laboratory (e.g. spectral analysis of the composition of a star).

COSMOGONY The study of the origin of the heavenly bodies; usually used in the sense of the origin of the solar system, the origin of stellar systems and the universe as a whole being inseparable from theories of **cosmology**, *q.v.*

COSMOGONY—THEORIES OF The mechanism by which the heavenly bodies in general, and the planets in particular, were formed has been a major topic of speculation since the late sixteenth century. Prior to that the concept of a divine creation was generally accepted and the mechanism was unquestioned. The application of deductive reasoning to astronomical observations, led by Copernicus and Galileo, stimulated a great deal of theorizing about the actual processes involved.

The fact that all the planets orbited the Sun in approximately the same plane and in the same direction of revolution was clearly important in considerations of their origin. Other observed factors were possibly pointers to the mechanism of formation, e.g. the fact that the planets' distances from the Sun are in a simple numerical progression, and the progressive increase in their diameters with distance from the Sun as far as Jupiter, thereafter a progressive decrease (with minor departures).

The great German philosopher Immanuel Kant suggested in about 1755 that the solar system had formed from a huge rotating nebula which condensed into several smaller parts, each rotating, which in turn condensed into the planets revolving about the nucleus of the nebula which itself condensed into the Sun.

In 1796 P. S. Laplace formulated a similar theory. Laplace also supposed the solar system to have been formed from a primordial nebula. He suggested that the nebula was hot and slowly rotating; as it cooled its constituent gas would contract and hence, by the conservation of angular momentum, the rate of rotation would increase. As a result of this Laplace believed that concentric rings of nebular matter would be ejected by centrifugal force, each of which would condense into a planet. It is now known that the mechanism proposed by Laplace is not valid, but his theory represented a major step forward and, known as the *nebular hypothesis*, was one of the two fundamental theories used as a basis for speculation for many years.

The second basic hypothesis did not appear until a century after that of Laplace; it was formulated by T. C. Chamberlin and F. R. Moulton between 1895 and 1900. Chamberlin and Moulton suggested that the planets were formed by the accretion of small cold particles

(*planetesimals*) in the Sun's gravitational field; they suggested the planetesimals were portions of material drawn from the Sun by the close approach of another star.

The 'passing star' theory and the nebular hypothesis are the ideas from which most of the more recent theories have been developed.

In 1917 the English astronomers J. H. Jeans and H. Jeffreys produced a development of the passing-star theory, suggesting that the effect of the passing star had been to draw off a long, cigar-shaped filament of solar material which then condensed into the planets—the largest planets being formed from its central, thickest, part. In 1930, however, it was pointed out by H. N. Russell of Princeton that such a mechanism would not have imparted sufficient angular momentum to establish the planets in their orbits. An interesting suggestion to overcome this problem was made in 1936 by R. A. Lyttleton, who suggested that the Sun was formerly a binary system, its companion being captured by the passing star; in these circumstances it would be possible for the filament of solar material to be drawn out with sufficient angular momentum. A further variant of this theory was devised by F. Hoyle in 1944, who suggested that one of the components of a binary system exploded, rather asymmetrically, as a form of nova, being propelled away by the explosion leaving its companion star (the Sun) and a filament of stellar material from which the planets later condensed. The concept of the 'passing Star' was finally dropped in 1939 when L. Spitzer showed that material drawn from a star by any of these mechanisms would not condense to form planets, but would expand explosively to form a very diffuse gaseous nebula.

A development of the nebular hypothesis was produced by Birkeland, a Norwegian, in 1914; Birkeland suggested that charged particles ejected from the Sun would fall into concentric orbits at distances from the Sun governed by their charge–mass ratios under the influence of the Sun's magnetic field, the planets then forming from these rings of charged particles. This theory was further developed by Berlage, a Dutchman, in 1930. In 1942 H. Alfvén, the eminent Swedish astrophysicist, suggested that such rings of electrically charged particles were formed as the Sun passed through a nebula. In 1945 the German physicist C. F. von Weizsäcker developed a theory based upon Kant's original concept of a simple rotating nebula—Weizsäcker showed that most of the gaseous matter in the nebula would be dissipated, but the dust particles would slowly accrete to form the planets. He explained the separation of the dust into the various *protoplanets* by an ingenious hypothesis of eddy-formation in the rotating disk of nebular dust.

More recent theoretical work has largely been concentrated on the abundance and distribution of the various chemical elements; this approach was originally tried by Russell and has been highly developed in recent years by H. C. Urey. An important theory was published by G. P. Kuiper in 1951; Kuiper envisaged a huge nebulous disk breaking up by gravitational contraction into a number of huge protoplanets which, in turn, contracted to form the planets with their satellite systems.

(See also **Cosmology.**)

COSMOLOGICAL PRINCIPLE The assumption made in theories of cosmology that the average constitution of the universe is homogeneous. It follows from this that the universe would present the same appearance at any one moment to any observer at any part of it.

(See also **Cosmological principle, perfect; Cosmology—theories of.**)

COSMOLOGICAL PRINCIPLE, PERFECT An extension of the **cosmological principle**, proposed by Bondi and Gold in 1948, that the universe is, on average, homogeneous throughout time. On this assumption the universe would present the same appearance to any observer situated

anywhere within it *at any time;* the steady-state theory of cosmology is founded upon this principle.

(See also **Cosmology—theories of.**)

COSMOLOGY The study of the structure and origin of the universe as a whole.

COSMOLOGY — OBSERVATIONAL TESTS OF Due to the fact that radiation from a celestial object takes a finite time to traverse the distance between the object and the Earth, we observe the body not as it is but as it was when the radiation left it. As the radiation travels at a constant velocity it is clear that the light-time is directly related to the distance. Thus, as we observe objects farther and farther from the Earth we are in fact examining the universe as it was longer and longer ago.

This important fact opens up the prospect of testing the rival evolutionary and steady-state theories of cosmology. If the steady-state theory is correct, the average distribution of galaxies in the universe will be constant however far back in time we sample it, but if the evolutionary theory holds, the further we go back in time the closer we will approach the primordial explosion and hence the more densely distributed the galaxies will appear to be. If we can determine the spatial distribution of galaxies at intervals out to a sufficiently large distance (i.e. over a sufficiently long time-span) it should be possible to decide whether it has remained constant (in which case the steady-state theory is correct) or whether it is becoming less dense (which would confirm the evolutionary theory). If the time-span over which the observations are made is too short for the difference to be detectable (i.e. if the galactic distribution cannot be measured over a sufficiently large distance) the distribution will appear constant in any case; it is thus a question of extending the range of our instruments to a point where the apparent validity of the steady-state theory could be disproved, if in fact it is not correct, by incontrovertible evidence that the density of distribution of the galaxies increases with distance. This result has not been obtained to date. It appears that no optical instrument yet in operation can record galaxies to a sufficiently great distance; some of the most powerful radio telescopes are able to detect radio-galaxies at much greater distances, and it is believed that it should be possible to demonstrate the accuracy of one theory or the other by this means in the foreseeable future. An early attempt to do so with the radio telescope of the Government Observatory, Sydney, could be interpreted as slightly favouring the evolutionary theory, but much more evidence with even more powerful instruments will be required before statistically valid conclusions can be drawn.

(See also **Cosmology—theories of.**)

COSMOLOGY—THEORIES OF

Studies of the present structure of the universe as a whole, its origin and past structure and development; these constitute the subject of cosmology—the study of which is one of the major occupations of the theoretical astronomer.

The cosmologist formulates a theory of the structure of the universe and the processes taking place in it; he then develops a model of the universe at the present time on the basis of his theory. This model may then be compared with observed data in order to test its accuracy.

Contemporary theories of cosmology fall into two groups, the *relativistic* theories and the *steady-state* theories.

Relativistic cosmology is based upon Einstein's General Theory of Relativity— the theory which best accounts for the many observed effects of gravitation. General Relativity is assumed to apply to the universe as a whole; in addition a further assumption is made, that the large-scale structure of the universe at any one time is homogeneous. This is the so-called *cosmological principle;* it implies that the universe would look the same, at a given moment, to any observer situated anywhere within it. The principle relates,

of course, to a broad view of the universe, small local irregularities being ignored.

Relativistic theories of cosmology are evolutionary theories; that is to say, they assume that the universe is constantly undergoing change and development. Most cosmologists believe that the evolutionary theories imply an instant of creation at some epoch long past.

The most satisfactory evolutionary model of the universe was set up by the Belgian Abbé Lemaître. Lemaître postulated that the total amount of matter now diffused throughout space was once confined within a very small volume at very high density and a high temperature. At some instant very long ago, possibly about 40,000,000,000 years ago, this highly condensed body was disrupted by a nuclear explosion and commenced to expand very rapidly; the rate of expansion was decreased by the contracting force of its own gravitation. As the system expanded a point would be reached at which the opposing forces of expansion and gravitational contraction were almost equal. At this stage the expansion would have slowed almost to a standstill; after a long period of near standstill the force of expansion once again became dominant and the universe would continue to expand, at an ever accelerating rate. The universe is now believed to be in this second expanding phase. During the first phase of expansion the hot nebular material is believed to have slowly cooled; during the long period of near standstill the cool gas is supposed to have condensed into large masses which eventually sub-divided to become clusters of galaxies. This phase is now passed, and no new galaxies are being formed. The distances between all of those already existing are constantly increasing— this agrees of course with the concept of the *expanding universe* based upon the observed recession of the galaxies.

Some cosmologists have suggested that the 'primeval explosion' of Lemaître's theory was not the instant of creation of a universe of finite age, but merely the beginning of a new cycle—perhaps a reversal of a previous contracting phase. This concept of alternating cycles of expansion and contraction implies that the age of the universe is infinite; this corollary is shared by the steady-state theory.

The steady-state theory is based upon an extension of the cosmological principle proposed by H. Bondi and T. Gold in 1948; this suggested that the universe is homogeneous in space *and time*—i.e. that the universe would look the same to any observer situated anywhere within it *at any time* (local irregularities again being ignored). This is termed the *perfect cosmological principle.*

The many aspects of the theory were developed by Bondi and Gold with Hoyle, Lyttleton and others. It depends upon the concept of the *continuous creation* of matter. Although the average age and distribution of galaxies is the same at any time, each individual galaxy is ageing and all galaxies are receding from each other (the concept of the expanding universe which is confirmed by observation); the homogeneity in time required by the perfect cosmological principle is maintained by the formation and growth of new galaxies in the spaces between the older ones as they recede from each other. This is a quite tenable suggestion, for as the individual stars in a galaxy age they are radiating energy (and hence mass) into space; the total amount of energy/mass in the universe must remain constant, and thus the energy dissipated by the stars in the ageing galaxies is the raw material from which new stars (and hence galaxies) are formed.

The steady-state theory provides an elegant and satisfactory explanation of the observed universe, and is considered by many scientists to be more cogent than the relativistic theories, which by comparison seem rather contrived to fit the observed facts whereas the concept of continuous creation throughout infinite time is a much simpler mechanism from which the observed facts naturally follow.

(See also **Cosmogony; Cosmology—observational tests of.**)

COSMOS Term sometimes used to indicate the universe in its entirety.

COSMOS Name of a long series of artificial earth satellites launched by the Soviet Union for scientific investigation of the upper atmosphere and meteorological studies. A continuation from the *Sputnik* programme (*Cosmos 1* and *Cosmos 2*, launched on 1962 March 16 and April 6, are sometimes referred to as *Sputnik 11* and *Sputnik 12*). By the end of 1966, 137 Cosmos satellites had been launched.

COUDÉ FOCUS A focus to which light rays can be brought along the polar axis of a telescope, as in the coudé telescope; most modern large instruments are designed to be used at several foci, including the coudé; thus they may be termed coudé–Newtonian–Cassegrain, for example.

(See **Telescope, coudé.**)

COWELL, P. H. (1870–1949) Distinguished mathematical astronomer. Senior Wrangler at Cambridge in 1892, he became Chief Assistant at the Royal Observatory, Greenwich, in 1896. In 1910 became Superintendent of the Nautical Almanac Office, retiring in 1930.

Whilst at Greenwich he made notable contributions to the theory of the motion of the Moon, and collaborated with A. C. D. Crommelin in the investigation of the motion of Halley's Comet and the highly successful prediction for its 1910 return. For this work both he and Crommelin were awarded the degree of Doctor of Science (*honoris causa*) by the University of Oxford. He was a Fellow of the Royal Society, and in 1911 was awarded the Gold Medal of the Royal Astronomical Society.

CRAB NEBULA The object numbered M1 in Messier's Catalogue; it is situated in the constellation Taurus at R.A. 05 hr 31·5 min, Dec. +21° 59' (Epoch 1950·0), and is also designated N.G.C. 1952. It is the remains of a **supernova**, one of only three that are known in the Galaxy.

The Crab Nebula is a large elliptical nebula with a very complex filamentary structure which is particularly prominent in photographs taken in red light. It has a diameter at present of about 3 light years (approximately 18 million million miles) and is situated some 3,500 light years from the Earth. It has been found from a study of photographs made over several decades that the radius of the Nebula is increasing at the rate of about 750 miles per second. This expansion is centred on a faint star in the centre of the nebula, the remains of the original star, now a white dwarf. It can be calculated from the rate of expansion of the nebula that the supernova explosion must have occurred about 900 years ago, and in fact a brilliant 'new star' was observed on 1054 July 4 in the exact position now occupied by the Crab nebula and recorded for posterity by astronomers in both China and Japan. The long history of this interesting object has therefore been remarkably well chronicled. [Plate 23(e).]

The Crab Nebula is also the fourth most intense radio source, known generally to radio astronomers as 'Taurus A' and numbered O5N2A in the *I.A.U. Catalogue of Radio Sources*.

(See also **Radio astronomy; Supernova.**)

CRATER (The Cup. *Genitive* Crateris, *I.A.U. abbreviation* Crt.) A small southern constellation at the south-west corner of **Virgo**, adjoining **Corvus**. The brightest stars are four of the fourth magnitude.

CRATER ARC A curved chain of lunar ring-structures. They occur in three forms: *contiguous arcs*, in which the craters are in contact; *open arcs*, in which they are separated; and *decremental arcs*, in which the craters progressively decrease in diameter from one end of the chain to the other. (See **Moon—surface features of.**)

CRATER CHAIN A line of lunar ring-structures, occurring in three forms: *contiguous chains*, in which the craters are in contact; *open chains*, in which they are

separated; and *decremental chains*, in which the craters progressively decrease in diameter from one end of the chain to the other.

The term crater chain is normally reserved for linear chains, curved chains being termed *crater arcs*. (See **Moon—surface features of.**)

CRATER, LUNAR The general term used to indicate the circular formations of all sizes that are such a prominent feature of the lunar landscape; the term is most frequently used by selenographers to refer to ring-formations of about 10–40 miles diameter, *ring structure* being preferred as a general term. (See **Moon—surface features of.**)

CRATER PIT A small lunar ring-structure having no raised walls. (See **Moon—surface features of.**)

CRESCENT PHASE The Moon and the inferior planets are said to be in a crescent phase when their phase is less than 0·5, i.e. when the apparent shape is less than a semi-circle.

CRIMEAN ASTROPHYSICAL OBSERVATORY The leading centre for astrophysical research in the Soviet Union, and one of the world's major astrophysical observatories. Situated at Simeis in southern Crimea, between Sevastopol and Yalta. The observatory is splendidly equipped for its work, which is mainly in solar physics and stellar photometry and spectroscopy. Some physical observation of the Moon and planets is also carried out. The principal instruments are a new 102-in. reflector and a 50-in. Zeiss reflector. There are numerous smaller instruments and a 20-in. Maksutov telescope. [Plates 31(c), 29(c).]

CRITERION Used by scientists to denote a standard against which the accuracy or value of experimental methods or results can be measured.

CROMMELIN, A. C. D. (1865–1939) Born in Northern Ireland, Crommelin was educated at Marlborough and Trinity College, Cambridge. After a few years as an assistant master at Lancing College he obtained in 1891 a newly created position at the Royal Observatory, Greenwich, as Assistant in charge of Airy's altazimuth. A few years later this famous instrument was replaced by a new, more elaborate version. This work remained in Crommelin's charge throughout his professional career; he was destined however to make his name in a quite different field. Having become an enthusiastic computer of comet and minor-planet orbits, he soon became an acknowledged expert in the technique; few new comets or asteroids were discovered but Crommelin was first with an ephemeris! This interest led him to consider the expected return of Halley's comet in 1910. In 1906 he published a paper indicating the need for a careful analysis of the comet's past motions in order to provide accurate data for the coming apparition. He then approached P. H. Cowell, Chief Assistant at the Royal Observatory, and together they carried out this tremendous task. So accurate were their results that their prediction of the time of perihelion passage proved to be within three days of the actual moment —in a period of 76 years! Both were awarded the degree of Doctor of Science (*honoris causa*) by the University of Oxford for this achievement.

Crommelin took part in numerous eclipse expeditions, and was a member of the team which observed the total eclipse of 1919 May 29 from Brazil and obtained confirmation of the Einstein displacement.

Crommelin was President of the Royal Astronomical Society 1929–1931, and served as its Secretary 1917–1923. He was President of the British Astronomical Association 1904–1906 and its Secretary 1900–1904. He served as the Director of its Comet Section for the remarkable time of 43 years (1897–1939). In 1937 the Association awarded him the Walter Goodacre Medal and Gift.

Crommelin's major contributions to the study of cometary orbits are commemorated in a particularly apposite way; after a lengthy investigation Crommelin

was able to show in 1936 that the comets discovered by Pons in 1818, by Coggia and Winnecke in 1873, and by Forbes in 1928 were all returns of the same periodic comet; the comet then became known as Comet Pons–Coggia–Winnecke–Forbes, but at the General Assembly of the International Astronomical Union held in Zurich in 1948 it was agreed that the comet should henceforth be known as 'Comet Crommelin'.

CROWN GLASS A form of optical glass having a rather low refractive index compared with that of **flint glass**, with which it is often used in conjunction in the manufacture of achromatic compound lenses.

CRUX (The Cross; often referred to as 'The Southern Cross'. *Genitive* Crucis, *I.A.U. abbreviation* Cru.) A small but very prominent constellation in the southern circumpolar region; it is in fact the smallest constellation, in terms of area, in the sky. The five brightest stars (α, β, γ, δ and ϵ Cru) form the well-known pattern, and are surrounded by a number of fainter stars, of which one—κ Cru—is at the heart of a magnificent cluster (N.G.C. 4755). The cluster is within 1° of β Cru, and consists of more than 100 stars of every hue; κ Cru itself is a fine red object, so that the whole cluster looks like a splendid collection of jewels.

α Cru is a fine double star, with components of magnitude 1·4 and 1·9 separated by 4″.7—easily separated with good binoculars.

CULMINATION The transit of a star or other celestial body across the observer's meridian.

CULMINATION, LOWER The transit of a (northern) circumpolar star from west to east, between the pole and the northern horizon. (For southern circumpolar stars, between the pole and the southern horizon.) At the instant of lower culmination a star's hour angle is exactly 12 hr.

CULMINATION, UPPER The transit of

a circumpolar star from east to west, between the pole and the zenith. At the instant of upper culmination a star's hour angle is exactly 0 hr.

CURTATE DISTANCE The projection onto the plane of the Ecliptic of the distance from the Earth or the Sun of a planet or comet.

CURVATURE OF FIELD A condition of some optical systems, in which the rays from the objective form a focused image not in a plane, but in a curved field, normally part of a spherical surface.

CUSP Term used to indicate one of the extremities of the crescent phase of the Moon or an inferior planet.

CUSP CAP Term used for the bright areas often observed at the cusps of Venus when in a crescent phase; this is the correct term for Venus, preferred to 'polar cap' as the inclination of the axis of rotation of the planet is not known and there is no justification for assuming that the poles of rotation will necessarily lie at the cusps.

CYCLOPIA Martian surface feature, approximate position $\Omega\ 230°$, $\Phi - 5°$. A dusky northward extension of the western end of the Mare Cimmerium, connecting it to Pambotis Lacus. Forms the western boundary of Æolis.

CYDONIA Martian surface feature, approximate position $\Omega\ 0°$, $\Phi + 40°$. Prominent light area in the north temperate zone, adjoining the eastern border of the Mare Acidalium. It is bounded to the east by Arnon and the Ismenius Lacus and to the south by Deuteronilus.

CYGNUS (The Swan. *Genitive* Cygni, *I.A.U. abbreviation* Cyg.) A large northern constellation, very prominent owing to the cruciform configuration of the five brightest stars (α, β, γ, δ and ϵ Cyg), often termed 'the Northern Cross'. The constellation is symmetrically placed on the Galactic Equator, almost all of it lying within the Milky Way. It reaches midnight culmination during July.

There are numerous interesting **stars**

in this constellation—not least 61 Cyg, the first to have its parallax measured (by Bessel in 1838).

Albireo (β Cyg) is one of the most beautiful doubles in the sky, being a yellow primary of magnitude 3·0 with a blue-green companion of magnitude 5·3; the separation is 34″.6.

δ Cyg is a long-period binary (magnitudes 3·0 and 7·9, separation 1″.9, period 321 years; τ Cyg is a close binary with a period of 49 years (magnitudes 3·8 and 8·0, separation 0″.9).

χ Cyg is an interesting long-period variable of the same type as **Mira Ceti**; the magnitude varies between 4·2 and 13·7 in a period of 409 days. W Cyg is another long-period variable with a period of 132 days (magnitude range 5·0–6·7).

Notable short-period variables are SU Cyg (magnitude 6·2–7·0, period 3·8 days) and X Cyg (magnitude 5·9–7·0, period 16·4 days).

There is a large open cluster, M 39 (N.G.C. 7092), some 3° north of ρ Cyg.

CYGNUS A One of the strongest discrete radio sources, numbered 19N4A in the I.A.U. catalogue; its position is R.A. 19 hr 58 min, Dec. 40° 36′ N. It is an extra-galactic source, being identified with a pair of spiral galaxies in collision. [Plate 24(a).]

(See also **Radio astronomy**.)

CYRILLUS Lunar surface feature, co-ordinates $\xi + 398$, $\eta - 230$. Prominent and rather rugged walled plain, 55 miles in diameter; forms a magnificent trio of connected formations with Catharina to the south, to whose western rampart it is connected by a great mountain massif, and with the apparently younger and perfectly formed Theophilus which breaks into its northern wall. The outline of Cyrillus is almost diamond-shaped, and the walls are broad, rugged and terraced. There is a fine central mountain with two major peaks.

CYTHEREA Old Sicilian name for Venus, hence the adjective 'Cytherean' which most planetary astronomers prefer to the clumsy 'Venusian'.

D

DAGUERROTYPE Product of the earliest practicable photographic process, invented in 1837 by J. M. Daguerre. The process utilized a silver plate coated with a light-sensitive layer of silver iodide; after exposure the plate was developed by heating in mercury and then fixed with sodium thiosulphate in the usual way. The image produced was very faint, but was later improved by the use of silver bromide as the light-sensitive coating, by gold-toning, etc. The process was super-seded by the 'wet' collodion process after little more than a decade.

DANJON PRISMATIC ASTROLABE The impersonal prismatic astrolabe developed by A. Danjon of the Paris Observatory. (See **Prismatic astrolabe**.)

DARWIN Lunar surface feature, co-ordinates $\xi - 888$, $\eta - 368$; named after the great English naturalist. A vast mountain-walled plain, some 65 miles in diameter, on the eastern limb of the Moon. The walls are low but clear, and there is a large, prominent dome in the northern part of the floor.

DATE, ASTRONOMICAL It is a convention among astronomers that dates are always expressed in a certain form with the largest units first, e.g. year, month, day; this facilitates the date and the time of an event to be expressed as one concept, which they are. Thus dates are written in the form 1966 January 1, and the time of a particular observation is expressed in the form 1966 January 1, 0635 G.M.T. Decimal subdivisions of the day are sometimes used, especially '. . . ·o' to represent midnight, e.g. 1966 January 1·0.

DAWES, Rev. William R. (1799–1868) A British non-conformist minister who was one of the leading planetary observers of his day. He was in particular a pioneer in the study of the surface features of Saturn. He was awarded the Gold Medal of the Royal Astronomical Society in 1855.

DAY A unit of time measurement, devised in ancient times and based upon the period of axial rotation of the Earth with its consequent alternation of daytime and night-time circumstances. It is equal to 24 hours in the system of time measurement being used.

The *sidereal day* is the interval between successive meridian transits of the First Point of Aries.

The *apparent solar day* is the interval between successive meridian transits of the Sun. It is the time given by a sundial and is variable (see **Equation of time**); for this reason it is not used but is replaced by the *mean solar day*. This is the interval between successive meridian transits of the 'Mean Sun'—a hypothetical concept in which an imaginary Sun moves around the celestial equator at a uniform rate, completing one revolution in exactly the same time as the true Sun. (See also **Time, determination of; Time systems**.)

DE LA RUE, Warren (1815–1889) A leading English amateur astronomer. One of the pioneers of astronomical photography, he obtained photographs of the Moon in 1852 which showed the principal surface features and were the first really successful lunar photographs ever taken. de la Rue was using a 13-in. equatorial reflector which he had made himself, and the photographs were made on the then newly devised collodion wet-plates.

de la Rue was also concerned with solar photography; he designed the first photoheliograph, which was financed by the Royal Society and erected at Kew Observatory in the 1850's; it was moved several times during its many years of active use, and was finally installed in the Royal Observatory at Greenwich in 1873.

de la Rue was awarded the Gold Medal of the Royal Astronomical Society in 1862, for his pioneering work in astronomical photography; he was President of the Royal Astronomical Society from 1864–1866 and its Secretary from 1855–1863.

DE REVOLUTIONIBUS The six-volume work in which Copernicus presented his heliocentric theory of the motion of the heavenly bodies. Completed and published at the time of Copernicus' death in 1543, the work was untitled but later became known as *De Revolutionibus Orbium Cœlestium*.

DE SITTER, Willem (1872–1935) Born at Sneek, Holland, de Sitter was both an outstanding practical astronomer and a leading cosmologist; he was appointed Professor of Astronomy at Leiden in 1908 and was Director of the Leiden Observatory from 1919 to his death in 1935. de Sitter played a leading part in the development of theoretical models for the universe based upon Einstein's theory of relativity, and in relating them to observed data.

During two years' post-graduate work with Sir David Gill at the Cape Observatory, de Sitter analysed observations of the motions of the four principal satellites of Jupiter; this work, carried out with great distinction, stimulated an interest in celestial mechanics which was to remain with de Sitter and to colour his work for life.

DECLINATION One of the two co-ordinates commonly used to define the position of a celestial object (the other being **Right Ascension**). It is the angular distance of the object north or south of the celestial equator, and is reckoned positive for bodies north of the equator and negative for bodies south of the equator.

(See also **Celestial sphere; Co-ordinate systems**.)

DEGREE (OF ARC) A unit of angular measure, being one three-hundred-and-sixtieth part of a full circle, or 2π radians.

DEGREE (OF TEMPERATURE) A unit of temperature measurement, defined as a certain fraction of the heat change between the ice-point and the steam-point. This fraction depends upon the scale used; that normally used for scientific purposes is the Centigrade scale, sometimes known as the Celsius scale. In this scale the fraction is 1/100, and the temperatures at the ice-point and steam-point are defined as 0°C and 100°C respectively. The Fahrenheit scale was formerly more widely used for domestic purposes; in this scale the fraction is 1/180, and the ice-point and steam-point temperatures are 32°F and 212°F.

DEIMOS Satellite II of Mars, *q.v.*

DELPHINUS (The Dolphin. *Genitive* Delphini, *I.A.U. abbreviation* Del.) A small northern constellation containing no stars brighter than the third magnitude, situated between Pegasus and Aquila; reaches midnight culmination at the end of June.

DELTA AQUARIDS A meteor shower occurring at the end of July from a radiant near δ Aqr, and believed to be associated with the Arietids (a daytime shower observed by radar methods).

DELTOTON SINUS Martian surface feature, approximate position Ω 105°, $\Phi-4°$. Dusky streak running southwestward from the Syrtis Major to the eastern end of the Sinus Sabbæus.

DEMETER Proposed name of satellite X of Jupiter, *q.v.*

DENEB The star α Cyg at the head of the 'Northern Cross', marking the tail of the Swan in the ancient constellation figure; a white star of type *A2* with an apparent magnitude of 1·3.

DENEBOLA The northern star β Leo, the hind end of the Lion in the ancient constellation figure; a type *A2* (white) star of apparent magnitude 2·2.

DENNING, W. F. (1848–1931) A leading English amateur; an outstanding observer who contributed greatly to the systematic observation of the planets and of comets, and perhaps the greatest meteor observer of his day. In 1916 he discovered a meteor shower associated with Comet Pons–Winnecke, and in 1920 he discovered Nova Cygni.

Denning was awarded the Gold Medal of the Royal Astronomical Society in 1898. He was Director of the Comet Section of the British Astronomical Association from 1891–1893, and of its Meteor Section from 1899–1900.

DENSITY FUNCTION A term used to denote the total number of stars in a given volume of space; the density function varies, of course, with the position of the chosen volume in relation to the structure of the galaxy in which it is situated.

DEPRESSIONES   HELLESPONTICÆ Martian surface feature, approximate position Ω 0°, Φ − 62°. A dusky streak stretching between the 60th and 65th parallels of latitude, bordering in winter the south polar cap.

DESCENDING NODE The node at which the body concerned crosses the ecliptic from north to south.

DEUCALIONIS REGIO Martian surface feature, approximate position Ω 340°, Φ − 15°. A light area lying between the Pandoræ Fretum and the Sinus Sabæus.

DEUTERONILUS Martian surface feature, approximate position Ω 0°, Φ + 32°. A rather diffuse canal, connecting the Ismenius Lacus and the Niliacus Lacus, and forming the southern border of Cydonia.

DIACRIA Martian surface feature, approximate position Ω 180°, Φ + 50°. Light area north of Trivium Charontis.

DIAGONAL Device employed to direct the light-path in a telescope through an angle, usually 90°, to facilitate access to an awkwardly placed eyepiece or to reduce the intensity of the solar image so as to permit direct observation of it. The diagonal is usually integral with the eyepiece, or constitutes an extension tube to which standard eyepieces can be fitted. It consists of an optical flat, or the hypotenuse face of a right-angled prism, set (usually) at 45° to the light-path. In the *star diagonal* the flat or prism-face is silvered, but in the *solar diagonal* it is unsilvered so that a high proportion of the light and heat passes through and an image of much reduced intensity results.

DIAMETER, ANGULAR The apparent diameter of a body, expressed in angular measure. It may be defined as the angle subtended at the observer by a diameter of the body being observed.

DICHOTOMY The point in the cycle of phases of an inferior planet, or the Moon, when the phase is 0·5; i.e. when the disk appears half-illuminated and the terminator is a straight line. The Moon is in dichotomy at both First and Last Quarter.

DIFFRACTION An optical phenomenon resulting in the 'spreading' of optical images, due to interference with the waveform of light rays situated at the outside of a light-beam or **pencil** by the limiting obstacle (edge of pin-hole, lens cell, etc.).

The effect upon a star image, formed in an accurately focused telescope, is to give the image a 'diffraction pattern' consisting of a central disk of light surrounded by a series of concentric light-rings of diminishing intensity, alternating with dark interspaces. In the case of a reflector, the diffraction pattern will also be affected by a secondary mirror and by its supports; e.g. a four-legged 'spider' mounting will add a bright cross of four rays to the normal pattern.

The effect of progressively defocusing the telescope is to reduce the intensity of the central disk and to increase that of the rings, until the former disappear entirely.

DIFFRACTION GRATING A plane surface upon which a series of narrow, equidistant, parallel lines have been engraved. Gratings are usually of the reflecting type, ruled upon speculum or similar metal, but can also be of the transmission type, ruled upon glass. Ideally the line separation should be comparable with the wavelength of light, of the order of 50,000 lines to the inch; in practice, gratings usually have between 15,000 and 40,000 lines to the inch.

The diffraction of incident light rays by the rulings produces a series of images in certain directions, where the waveforms of adjacent rays are in phase; in the intervening areas, no images will be formed

owing to interference between the rays.

Figure 24 shows, in diagrammatic form, the formation of images from part of a reflection-type grating. Rays reflected without diffraction can be brought to a focus to produce a zero-order image I_0 which is not dispersed, the adjacent wave-forms being exactly in phase. The next image can be produced where the adjacent rays are in phase, but with a displacement of one wavelength; this produces a first-order image I_1, which is dispersed into a short spectrum. The next image is produced where the rays are in phase with a displacement of two wavelengths, forming the second-order image I_2, which owing to the greater dispersion is approximately twice as extended as I_1. And so on.

The diffraction grating is often used as the spectrum-forming element in spectroscopic apparatus, especially in instruments such as the **spectroheliograph** which requires a very long light-path, as the use of a reflecting-type grating enables the overall length of the instrument to be halved.

Diffraction gratings are very costly to manufacture, and for work where the highest standard of performance is not required 'replica gratings' are often used; these are copies of a proper grating manufactured by a photographic process.

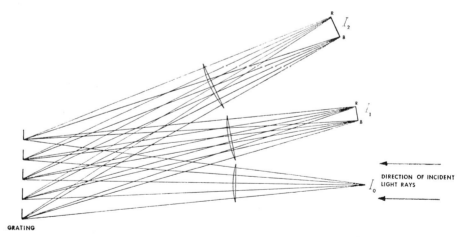

GRATING

DIRECTION OF INCIDENT LIGHT RAYS

Fig. 24

DIFFRACTION RINGS The concentric rings of light surrounding the **Airy disk** in the in-focus image of a point source produced by a telescope objective, due to **diffraction**. They are much less intense than the Airy disk, and each successive ring outwards is fainter than the previous one. They are separated from each other and from the Airy disk by dark interspaces.

DIONE Satellite IV of Saturn, *q.v.*

length of the light, and the component colours are therefore separated; this phenomenon is known as dispersion. It was demonstrated and explained by Sir Isaac Newton in 1666, in a classic experiment; Newton passed a beam of sunlight, from an aperture in a window blind, through a triangular prism and picked up the resulting image on a white screen. He found that the image consisted of a band of colour—the *spectrum*. The spectrum is usually said

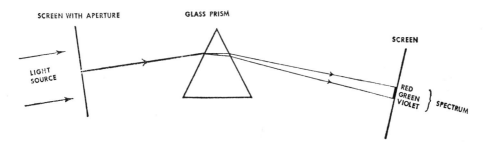

Fig. 25

DIONYSIUS Lunar surface feature, co-ordinates $\xi +297$, $\eta +048$. A quite prominent crater, 12 miles in diameter, on the eastern border of the Mare Tranquillitatis; its prominence is greatly enhanced by a miniature ray-system, in the form of a brilliant halo surrounding the crater wall.

DIOPTRIC ELEMENT Any optical component (e.g. a lens) which forms its image by **refraction**.

DIOSCURIA Martian surface feature, approximate position Ω 320°, $\Phi +50°$. A light area in the north temperate region of Mars.

DIPPER Abbreviation of 'Big Dipper', the term used in the United States for that part of Ursa Major known elsewhere as 'The Plough'.

DISPERSION If a beam comprising light of several wavelengths (e.g. 'white' light) is refracted by a lens or prism, the amount of refraction varies according to the wave-

to consist of light in seven distinct colours —red, orange, yellow, green, blue, indigo and violet—but these merge into one another, of course, and there are no distinct boundaries.

Newton found that the light of shortest wavelength underwent the greatest degree of refraction—i.e. violet light was refracted most, and red light the least (see Fig. 25). This is the basic principle of the **spectroscope**.

Dispersion is also achieved, in many of the more refined spectroscopic appliances, by the use of a diffraction grating instead of a prism. (See also **Refraction; Spectroscope.**)

DISPERSION, ATMOSPHERIC Scattering of sunlight in the Earth's atmosphere, mainly by air molecules and in part by suspended dust particles. It was shown by Lord Rayleigh that shorter wavelength light is most affected—hence the predominantly blue appearance of the daylight sky.

DISTANCE OF THE SUN The mean distance of the Earth from the Sun; a most valuable quantity which needs to be determined to a high degree of accuracy. The quantity actually determined from observation is the **solar parallax**, from which the mean distance can be computed.

Observations of the distances and motions of the other bodies in the solar system are essentially comparative, and in order to determine their true scale the distance of the Sun must be known. It may therefore be regarded as one of the yardsticks of astronomy.

The actual mean distance of the Sun, computed from the latest determinations of the solar parallax, is 93,009,000 miles.

DISTORTION A defect of optical systems in which the magnification of an objective varies with distance from the optical axis; this can result in the images of straight lines being curved, etc., depending on how they are orientated with respect to the optical axis.

DIURNAL ABERRATION The apparent displacement of a star due to the observer's changing position, caused by the rotation of the Earth. Its effect upon a positional observation is a function of the term $0''3 \cos \phi$, and is maximal when the star is at culmination, being then $0''3 \cos \phi \sec \delta$ where ϕ is the observer's latitude and δ the declination of the star.

DIURNAL MOTION The apparent westward motion of the heavens, due to the axial rotation of the Earth.

DOME A type of lunar surface feature; lunar domes are usually shallow and have diameters of up to about 50 miles. Many of them have small summit craters. They are similar in form to terrestrial shield volcanoes. About a hundred have been discovered. (See **Moon—surface features of**.)

DOPPELMAYER Lunar surface feature, co-ordinates $\xi - 580$, $\eta - 478$. A walled plain, 40 miles in diameter, at the southern end of the Mare Humorum; its northern wall appears to have been largely eroded away so that the Mare runs into the plain. There remains, however, a prominent central mountain with two peaks, which rises 2,500 ft. above the floor.

DOPPLER EFFECT If a radiating body is in motion with respect to the observer, the apparent wavelength of the radiation is shortened if the motion is towards the observer, lengthened if the motion is away from the observer; this is usually known as the Doppler effect.

The most commonly encountered example of this phenomenon is the change in pitch of the sound of a locomotive or other fast-moving vehicle as it passes the observer, the pitch being higher during the approach. The phenomenon occurs in all forms of electromagnetic radiation as well as sound, however, and has considerable importance in astrophysical observation. The wavelength of the light received from a celestial body is lengthened if it is receding from the observer (i.e. the light appears to be reddened); this results in a shift in the observed positions of the lines in its spectrum (the so-called **red shift**, q.v.). Measures of this shift can be used to calculate the velocity of recession of the object.

The effect on the colour of the light from a moving source was first pointed out in 1843 by Christian Doppler, an Austrian mathematician; in 1848 A. H. L. Fizeau correctly interpreted this as an apparent alteration in the wavelength of the light arising from the motion of the body relative to the observer. The phenomenon is sometimes referred to as the Doppler–Fizeau effect.

The mechanism of the phenomenon is shown in Fig. 26. A body is assumed to be radiating at a constant wavelength (λ); if the body is stationary the wavefronts after a given interval of time will be concentric spheres as shown in section in Fig. 26 (*a*). If the body is in motion along the path A—B—C . . . (see Fig. 26 (*b*)),

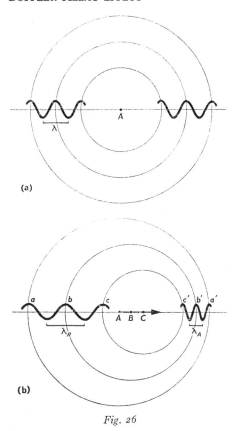

(a)

(b)

Fig. 26

circumpolar constellation containing no bright stars of importance. Notable only in that it contains the larger Magellanic Cloud (Nubecula Major), in which can be seen the bright, complex 'Great Looped Nebula' (NGC 2070) surrounding the star 30 Dor.

DÖRFEL MOUNTAINS A mountain range along the south-east limb of the Moon, containing some magnificent peaks of more than 25,000 ft. and numerous peaks around 20,000 ft.

DORPAT CATALOGUE The double-star catalogue compiled from his own observations by F. G. W. Struve, published in Dorpat in 1827 as the *Catalogus Novus Stellarum Duplicium et Multiplicium;* stars in this catalogue are designated by the prefix *Σ*. (See also **Struve, F. G. W.**)

DORPAT OBSERVATORY Nineteenth observatory in Estonia, famous for the 9·6-in. refractor by Fraunhofer erected there in 1824, and for the work done with it by F. G. W. Struve (notably the compilation of the 'Dorpat catalogue'—the first of Struve's great double-star catalogues).

The Dorpat refractor was the first telescope to be successfully mounted as an equatorial, and was for some years the world's largest telescope. It was later removed to the Pulkowa Observatory on the appointment of Struve as the first Director.

DOUBLE CLUSTER See **Perseus—double cluster in.**

DOUBLE STARS Stars seen to be double fall into two distinct classes, those pairs which are actually close together in space and which constitute a local gravitational system (termed a *binary system*), and those which appear double purely from an optical effect, being two stars at quite different distances from the Earth but lying on adjacent lines of sight (an *optical double*). The distinction between these two

the spherical wavefronts will be compressed in the direction in which the body is moving ($a'\ b'\ c'$), and hence the apparent wavelength for an observer in the direction of approach, λ_R, will be shortened—that is to say the light will appear bluer. In the opposite direction, however, the wavefronts will appear further apart ($a\ b\ c$) and the wavelength for an observer in the direction of recession, λ_R, is thus lengthened—i.e. the light is reddened.

DOPPLER–FIZEAU EFFECT Alternative name for the **Doppler effect,** *q.v.*

DOPPLER SHIFT (See **Doppler effect; Red shift.**)

DORADO (The Swordfish. *Genitive* Doradus, *I.A.U. abbreviation* Dor.) A southern types is shown in Fig. 27, from which it will be seen that there is no means of deciding to which category a double star belongs on the evidence of a single visual observation. In Fig. 27 the size of the component stars as drawn represent their actual magnitudes at (a) and their observed apparent magnitudes at (b), from which it will be seen that the observed relative brightness gives a valid picture of the binary system, whereas the appearance of the optical double is spurious.

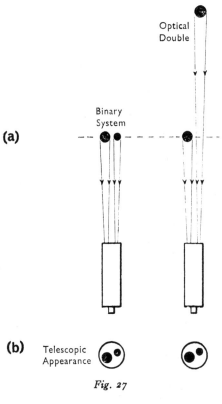

Fig. 27

The true binary system can be recognized by means of a series of observations over a long period, as its components are in orbital motion around a common centre of gravity.

Some double stars have been known from the earliest times—e.g. *Alcor*, the naked-eye companion of *Mizar* (ξ UMa)

in the handle of the Plough, the separation being more than 11 minutes of arc. The earliest recorded observation of a close double also relates to *Mizar*, which was observed to be itself a double by Father Riccioli, a Jesuit astronomer-priest, in 1650; Riccioli found that *Mizar* had two components at a separation of about 15 seconds of arc.

The first systematic search for close doubles was made by Sir William Herschel in the years following 1779. About $5\frac{1}{2}\%$ of all stars brighter than the ninth magnitude are now known to be double. The incidence of spectroscopic doubles is much greater, however—between 20 and 50%. (See also **Binary system.**)

DOUBLE STARS—OBSERVATION OF

The observation of double stars is a most rewarding pastime even with quite modest equipment; the juxtaposition of two stars of contrasting colours is often most beautiful. Where wide doubles are concerned, this is almost the only form of astronomical observing that can be somewhat enhanced, rather than diminished, by moderate or poor atmospheric conditions; some of the bright, wide pairs are a magnificent sight through slight haze. Two beautiful examples that can be observed with very small telescopes are α Her (components orange, green; magnitudes 3·0, 6·1; separation 4″.4) and γ And (gold, blue; 3·0, 5·0; 9″.7). For the person observing for more than his own delectation, however, there is useful work to be done in the case of those doubles which are true binary systems, although to make significant contributions to our knowledge of the orbits requires a very powerful telescope and outstanding visual acuity, so that few amateurs are able to carry out this work.

The observation of a double star consists of determining the place of the fainter component relative to the brighter; this is done by measuring the angular separation between the components (ρ) in seconds of arc, and the position angle of the fainter component relative to the brighter. The position angle (*P.A.*) is measured anticlockwise from the North Point and is expressed in degrees of arc (see Fig. 28).

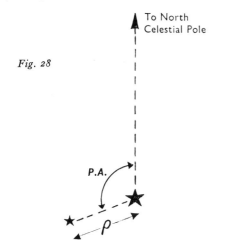

Fig. 28

Double-star observations are usually carried out with the aid of a large refracting telescope, using either a **filar micrometer** or a **parallel-slit interferometer.**

DOUBLET A lens composed of two components, usually but not necessarily cemented together; they are normally manufactured from different types of glass having refractive indexes carefully chosen so as to minimize **chromatic aberration.**

DRACO (The Dragon. *Genitive* Draconis, *I.A.U. abbreviation* Dra.) Northern circumpolar constellation covering a wide area of the sky between Ursa Major and Cepheus, and straggling around Ursa Minor. Contains the planetary nebula NGC 6543 (originally designated H IV 37 in Sir William Herschel's catalogue). This object has a bright oval disk and a central ninth magnitude star; the appearance is much like that of a star out-of-focus.

Owing to its length and straggling nature, parts of this constellation are reaching culmination at midnight from mid-March to mid-June.

DRAPER, Henry (1837–1882) One of the earliest workers in astronomical photography, Draper was Professor of Natural Science at New York University. He was a prolific telescope-maker in his spare time, and many of his early experimental photographs were made at his private observatory using 15½-in. and 28-in. reflectors of his own construction.

Draper is principally remembered for his work in stellar spectroscopy; in May 1872 he obtained the first successful stellar spectrogram—of **Vega**—using a quartz prism attached to his 28-in. reflector. Three months later he obtained another spectrogram of this star, the first plate to show **absorption lines.**

Draper had paved the way for a programme of mass spectral-typing of stars before his early death, and his widow endowed a department of stellar spectroscopy at the Harvard College Observatory to ensure that the work continued. (See also **Draper Catalogue; Spectral classification.**)

DRAPER CATALOGUE The standard catalogue of stars classified by spectral type. The original Draper Catalogue was published in 1890 and 1897, and gave data for more than 10,000 stars.

The name is now used to denote the modern catalogue which has replaced the original, produced by A. J. Cannon and E. C. Pickering as *The Henry Draper Catalogue of Stellar Spectra* in 1918–1924 and *The Henry Draper Extension* a year or two later. The former gives the spectral classifications of 225,300 stars, including all stars down to magnitude 8·25 in the northern hemisphere and to 8·75 in the southern hemisphere; the latter gives the spectral classifications of a further 133,700 stars in various parts of the heavens, down to the twelfth magnitude. The Harvard–Draper sequence of spectral classification was first used in the original Draper Catalogue of 1890, for which it had been drawn up by E. C. Pickering with Mrs. Fleming and Miss Cannon.

Henry Draper was the pioneer of

astronomical spectrography, and had established the observing techniques and programme for the work which was to bear his name when published, seven years after his early death, under the supervision of E. C. Pickering. This was made possible by the action of Henry Draper's widow, who presented her late husband's 11-in. photographic refractor to the Harvard College Observatory in 1896, together with a large sum of money which was used to finance the colossal research programme which led ultimately to the publication of the two modern catalogues as *The Henry Draper Memorial*.

DRIFT I One of the streams of stars discovered by Kapteyn in 1904 from a study of the proper motions of the brighter stars. Some 60 per cent of the stars whose proper motions are known are members of Drift I, which has an apparent vertex in Lepus. (See **Star streaming**.)

DRIFT II A stream of stars discovered by Kapteyn from proper-motion studies in 1904. The stream comprises about 40 per cent of the brighter stars and has an apparent vertex in Pavo. (See **Star streaming**.)

DUNHAM, Theodore, Jr. Contemporary American astronomer, one of the leading figures in the field of astronomical spectroscopy. Developed, with W. S. Adams, the high-resolution spectrograph at the coudé focus of the Mount Wilson 100-in. reflector.

Dunham has undertaken most of the discussion of spectroscopic observations of the atmospheres of the planets, and has himself made many of the most important identifications. Notably, Dunham's Mount Wilson spectrograms confirmed the dominance of methane and ammonia in the outer atmospheres of Jupiter and Saturn.

DUNSINK OBSERVATORY The principal observatory of the Irish Republic. Situated some five miles north-west of the centre of Dublin, it was founded in 1785 by a bequest of Francis Andrews, Provost

of Trinity College, Dublin. Its first Director was Rev. Henry Ussher, first Andrews Professor of Astronomy in Trinity College. Ussher was succeeded in 1791 by Rev. John Brinkley. Brinkley was appointed Royal Astronomer for Ireland by Royal Letters Patent, although his post and the Observatory remained entirely the responsibility of Trinity College. The next seven Directors of the Observatory bore the Royal title; they included Sir William Rowan Hamilton and Sir Edmund Whittaker—each probably the leading mathematical astronomer of his day—and the equally illustrious Sir Robert Ball.

Following the establishment of the Republic in 1919 the title of Royal Astronomer lapsed on the resignation of H. C. Plummer in 1921; the Observatory then became largely inactive, and on the death of the Acting Director in 1936 it was closed.

In 1947 the buildings and instruments were purchased from Trinity College by the Dublin Institute for Advanced Studies, and re-opened as part of its School of Cosmic Physics. Dr H. A. Brück was appointed Director of the Observatory and Senior Professor in the Institute. Brück equipped the Observatory as a centre for research in solar physics. On his resignation ten years later, to become Astronomer Royal for Scotland, Brück was succeeded by **M. A. Ellison** (*q.v.*); this appointment, and that of P. A. Wayman, the present Director, ensured that the Observatory remained one of the leading research establishments in solar studies.

The Observatory shares the Boyden Observatory, South Africa, as its Southern-Hemisphere station, where photographic and photometric studies of the star-fields of the Milky Way and Magellanic Clouds, and of the cluster variables, are carried out.

(See also **Royal Astronomer for Ireland**.)

DWARFS Stars whose spectral–luminosity classification places them low down in the **Hertzsprung–Russell diagram**; they are mostly the white dwarfs and red dwarf stars at the lower end of the main sequence. The term is no longer used to describe all main-sequence stars. (See **Stars, dwarf.**)

DWARF NOVAE A class of irregular variable stars characterized by light-curves similar in form to those of novae, in which the star's luminosity increases rapidly to a maximum several magnitudes higher than previously, and then falls more slowly to the normal minimum. There are two main groups of stars of this type, as follows.

The U Geminorum stars. These have a range of about four magnitudes and periods at a constant minimum brightness which vary from a few days to a few months. For example, the type star, U Gem, discovered by Hind in 1855, remains at +13·5 for periods varying between 40 and 130 days, and rises to +9·5 or more in the course of a day or two. At alternate maxima the star takes about 18 and 10 days to revert to its normal minimum. The group is sometimes known as the 'SS Cygni stars', after SS Cyg, another very well observed member which has three distinct types of maximum.

The Z Camelopardalis stars. The light-curves of the stars in this class are very similar but are subject to unpredictable pauses, of varying duration, at intermediate magnitudes during the fall from maximum to normal minimum. The range of variation is also less, about three magnitudes. Another well-known example is RX And.

(See also **Novae; Variable stars.**)

DYSON, Sir Frank W., K.B.E. (1868–1939) Chief Assistant at the Royal Observatory, Greenwich, from 1894–1905, Astronomer Royal for Scotland from 1905–1910, and the ninth Astronomer Royal, from 1910 until his retirement in 1933. During his term of office numerous important programmes of observation were carried out at the Royal Observatory, notably the completion of the astrographic plates for the Greenwich zone of the **Carte du Ciel**, and programmes to determine the photographic magnitudes, colour-temperatures, proper motions and parallaxes of the stars contained therein.

Dyson also continued the long Greenwich series of latitude-variation observations with the Cookson floating zenith telescope, and organized two expeditions to obtain plates of the total solar eclipse of 1918 November 11 which confirmed the existence of the **Einstein displacement**.

E

E.M.P. Abbreviation for the **Ephemerides of the Minor Planets,** *q.v.*

EARTH The third planet of the Solar System, in order of increasing distance from the Sun, whose orbit lies between those of Venus and Mars. It is the innermost planet having a known natural satellite (the Moon).

EARTH—DIMENSIONS AND PHYSICAL DATA The equatorial diameter of the Earth is 7,927 miles; polar flattening is only very slight, the polar diameter being about 7,900 miles. The Earth has a mean density 5·52 times that of water—a higher figure than any other body in the solar system, which is attributed to the presence of a high proportion of iron in the Earth's core.

The velocity of escape for gases is 7·0 miles per second, hence the Earth's retention of a substantial atmosphere. The albedo has been calculated to be about 0·36.

EARTH—ORBITAL DATA The semimajor axis of the Earth's orbit is (by definition) 1 Astronomical Unit; this corresponds to a mean distance from the Sun of 92·96 million miles. The orbital eccentricity being 0·0167, this distance varies between about 91½ and 94½ million miles. The mean orbital velocity is 18·5 miles per second, resulting in a mean sidereal period of 365·256 days.

EARTH—SATELLITE OF The Earth has only one known natural satellite—the **Moon,** *q.v.*

EARTH'S WAY Name sometimes given to the angle between the direction of the Earth's motion and the apparent direction of a star displaced by the effect of the **aberration of light,** *q.v.*

EARTHSHINE The phenomenon sometimes seen during the first few days of a lunation and popularly termed 'the Old Moon in the New Moon's arms'. The still-narrow crescent of the New Moon is brilliantly illuminated, and the remaining portion can also be seen, though much more faintly. This is due to its being illuminated by sunlight which is reflected by the Earth, which at this time would be nearly at 'Full' phase as seen from the Moon.

EAST POINT The point on the celestial sphere, due east of the observer, at which the equator intersects the horizon.

ECCENTRIC ANOMALY A term used in celestial mechanics, relating to the orbit of a planet. It is, like the **true anomaly,** a quantity which is constantly varying as the planet travels around its orbit.

It refers to the motion of a point around a circle circumscribed upon the major axis of the elliptical orbit of the planet, the point being that where the circumscribed circle is cut by the perpendicular produced, dropped from the planet to the major axis of the orbit. The eccentric anomaly is the angular distance, measured at the Sun, between this point and perihelion. It is usually designated E, and is defined by

$$\cos E = (a - r/ae).$$

(See also **Planetary motion.**)

ECCENTRIC RING-STRUCTURE Term used to denote a lunar crater or ring-structure which is situated eccentrically inside a larger one, so that it touches the wall of the outer ring at one point only. (See **Moon—surface features of.**)

ECCENTRICITY, ORBITAL One of the elements of a planetary orbit, usually designated e. It is really an indication of the shape of the orbit, being a measure of the amount by which the ellipse differs from a circle.

In Fig. 35 (page 116) S represents the Sun, at one focus of the orbit, and $CA = a$, the semi-major axis; the eccentricity is then defined by

$$e = \frac{CS}{CA}$$

ECLIPSE The phenomenon of a body being partially or totally obscured by the shadow of another body falling upon it or immersing it.

(See **Eclipse, lunar; Eclipse, solar; Eclipses of planetary satellites.**)

ECLIPSE, LUNAR Lunar eclipses occur when the Earth lies between the Sun and the Moon, and wholly or partially prevents the Sun's light from falling upon the Moon's surface. The Moon's orbital plane is inclined to the plane of the Ecliptic (the plane of the Earth's orbit around the Sun) by 5°·2, and consequently an eclipse can only occur when the Moon is both at opposition—i.e. at 'Full Moon'—and also at or near one of its nodes. If the Moon is more than 12°·1 from a node at the time

of opposition an eclipse cannot take place; if the Moon is less than 9°·5 from the node then an eclipse must take place. These limits are known as the **lunar ecliptic limits**; if the Moon's distance from a node is between these limits at conjunction an eclipse may or may not occur, depending upon whether the diameter of the shadow-cone of the Earth is sufficiently large at the distance of the Moon at the instant of conjunction.

Figure 29 shows in diagrammatic form the limits of the shadow-cone of the Earth, the **umbra** (VCD). The figure also shows the limits of a much larger region in which the Sun's light can only partially penetrate—the **penumbra** ($FCDG$). If the Moon, at the moment of conjunction, lies entirely within the umbra as at R, then the eclipse will be 'total'. If the Moon is only partly within the umbra at conjunction, as at S, the eclipse is described as 'partial' and only part of the Moon's surface is seen to be obscured by the Earth's shadow. If the Moon is within the penumbra at conjunction (T), the eclipse is termed a 'penumbral' eclipse. In the case of a total eclipse the Moon will be seen to pass through all these phases in turn, i.e. penumbral, partial, total, partial, penumbral.

When the Moon first enters the penumbra (at P) no obvious effect will be noticed; as it approaches Q it will slowly fade, although the diminution in its brightness is often very difficult to detect

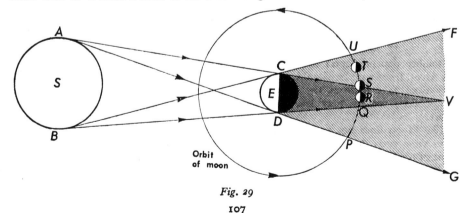

Fig. 29

Table 10. *Lunar eclipses 1970–1985*

Date		Time of mid-eclipse (U.T.) hr min		Visible in United Kingdom	U.S.A.
1970	Feb. 21	08	31	No	Yes
1970	Aug. 17	03	25	Partly	Yes
1971	Feb. 10	07	42	Partly	Yes
1971	Aug. 6	19	44	Partly	Yes
1972	Jan. 30	10	53	No	Yes
1972	July 26	07	18	No	Yes
1973	Dec. 10	01	48	Yes	Yes
1974	June 4	22	14	Yes	No
1974	Nov. 29	15	16	No	No
1975	May 25	05	46	No	Yes
1975	Nov. 18	22	24	Yes	Partly
1976	May 13	19	50	Partly	No
1977	Apr. 4	04	21	Partly	Yes
1978	Mar. 24	16	25	No	No
1978	Sept. 16	19	03	Partly	No
1979	Mar. 13	21	10	Yes	No
1979	Sept. 6	10	54	No	Partly
1981	July 17	04	48	Partly	Yes
1982	Jan. 9	19	56	Yes	No
1982	July 6	07	30	No	Yes
1982	Dec. 30	11	26	No	Yes
1983	June 25	08	25	No	Yes
1985	May 4	19	57	Partly	No
1985	Oct. 28	17	43	Partly	No

with the naked eye; when the 'preceding limb' of the Moon passes the point Q the Moon is partially eclipsed to a progressively increasing extent, until the 'following limb' passes Q and 'totality' begins. When the preceding limb reaches S totality ends and the Moon undergoes the reversed sequence of partial and penumbral eclipse as it passes S and passes from S to U, respectively. The duration of totality depends upon the distance of the Moon from a node; should it be at or very close to a node at the moment of conjunction, totality may last for three hours.

The Moon does not usually disappear from view even during totality, as sufficient of the Sun's light is refracted by the Earth's atmosphere to illuminate its surface. As the short wavelength light is absorbed by the Earth's atmosphere, only the longer wavelength (red and orange) light reaches the Moon's surface, thus giving it the characteristic coppery colour.

Lunar eclipses are simultaneously visible from any part of the hemisphere of the Earth for which the Moon is above the horizon at the time. From areas close to the perimeter of this hemisphere, however, the Moon may be seen to rise or set during the eclipse, so that only part of the eclipse can be observed.

The movements of the Sun, Moon and the Moon's nodes are such that no more than three lunar eclipses can occur in any calendar year; even this number is rarely experienced, as can be seen from the accompanying table of forthcoming lunar eclipses.

The Sun, Moon and nodes return to almost exactly the same relative positions at intervals of 223 lunations, or 18 years and

11 days, and therefore eclipses of the Sun and Moon recur in the same order and with similar circumstances after this period. This cycle is known as the **Saros**, and was known to the Chaldeans more than 2,500 years ago. It was successfully used by Thales to predict an eclipse which occurred in 585 B.C.

Eclipses of the Moon have long been regarded as of little scientific value, although long ago they were used as evidence that the Earth could not be flat; recently, however, the rapid changes in the surface temperature of the Moon during the beginning and ending of totality have been carefully measured with a view to deducing the nature of the material of which the lunar surface is composed.

(See also **Ecliptic limits (lunar); Phases of the Moon.**)

ECLIPSE, SOLAR A solar eclipse takes place when the Moon lies between the Sun and the Earth, and wholly or partially prevents the Sun's light from falling upon part of the Earth's surface.

The Moon's orbital plane is inclined to the Ecliptic (the plane of the Earth's own orbit) by 5°·2, and consequently an eclipse can only occur when the Moon is both at conjunction—i.e. at New Moon—and also at or near one of its nodes. The other criteria which determine whether or not an eclipse will take place, the **solar ecliptic limits**, are as follows. If the

Sun's angular distance from one of the Moon's nodes at the moment of conjunction is less than 15°·4, a solar eclipse must occur; if it is more than 18°·5 an eclipse cannot occur. If the distance lies between these limits an eclipse may possibly take place, depending upon the relative positions of the Sun, Moon and node at the time.

Figure 30 shows the limits of the shadow-cone of the Moon (the umbra) and of the areas from which the Sun's light is partially cut off (the penumbra).

Figure 31 demonstrates how the circumstances of the eclipse are governed by the distance of the Moon from the Earth at conjunction, and hence by the diameter of the shadow-cone where it reaches the Earth's surface. At A the cone is shown as having a very small diameter, and the eclipse will have a short duration and be seen total only from a very narrow track; in the case shown at B the cone has a large diameter, and the eclipse will have a longer duration and be seen as total from a wider track. If the vertex of the shadow-cone fails to reach the Earth's surface at all, as at C, there will be an **annular eclipse**, the perimeter of the Sun's disk appearing as a brilliant circle of light surrounding the dark disk of the Moon.

During a total eclipse the relative motions of the Sun and Moon cause the shadow-cone of the Moon to sweep across the surface of the Earth, forming a long, narrow track from all points on which

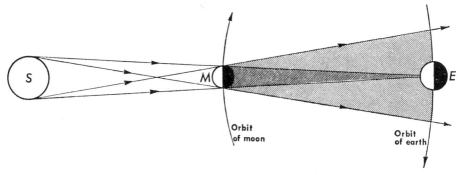

Fig. 30

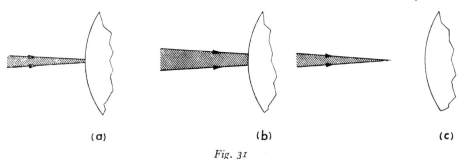

(a) (b) (c)

Fig. 31

the total phase will be visible in succession. As each total eclipse is visible only from such a small area of the Earth's surface, they are a very rare phenomena in any given part of the world. There have been only seven visible from the British Isles in the last six hundred years, the last being on 1927 June 29. The next one is due on 1999 August 11, when totality will be visible only from Land's End.

Total eclipses are visible as partial eclipses from a much larger area of the Earth's surface, the fraction of the Sun's disk obscured being progressively less for observers situated further and further from the path of totality.

The relative motions of the Sun and Moon are such that up to five eclipses of the Sun can take place in a year. The total number of eclipses of the Sun and the Moon in any year cannot be more than seven (five solar and two lunar, or four solar and three lunar) nor less than two; if only two occur, both will be solar.

As the Sun, Moon and the Moon's nodes return to almost identical relative positions after 223 lunations, or 18 years and $11\frac{1}{3}$ days, eclipses will recur in very similar circumstances after this period—the **Saros**, which has been used to predict eclipses for many centuries. The use of the Saros permits predictions of considerable accuracy, but these predict only the occurrence of an eclipse which will not be visible from the same part of the Earth's surface as its predecessor. A series of five or six eclipses visible from the same part

of the sky on their recurrence can be predicted by use of the **Metonic cycle**, a period of 19 tropical years.

Predictions of solar eclipses in the astronomical almanacs are usually accompanied by a map showing the path of totality and the area from which the partial phase can be observed. Total eclipses observed from stations on the track will, of course, be both preceded and followed by a partial phase.

A total eclipse of the Sun is a spectacular and beautiful sight; from the moment when the dark disk of the Moon first appears, obscuring a tiny lune of the Sun's disk (First Contact), through the partial phase, with more and more of the Sun obscured, to the moment when the last ray of sunlight is extinguished (Second Contact), the light slowly fades, the air grows chill, the birds cease their singing and there is a sense of mounting tension as the observers wait, glancing worriedly at any approaching clouds and (if they are on high ground) watching for the Moon's shadow as it steadily approaches across the landscape. A few seconds before Second Contact the beautiful phenomenon known as **Baily's beads** is seen, when the Sun is visible only through the valleys between mountains on the Moon's limb, in the form of a shining necklace. After a few seconds even these fade away, and totality has begun. All is silent and still—save for the furious activity among the hundreds of astronomers, amateur and professional alike, who will have set up their equipment at suitable points. [Plates 1(b); 2(c).]

Unlike the comparatively unimportant lunar eclipse, a total solar eclipse provides an opportunity for a number of diverse and most valuable observations to be made. During totality, the Sun's corona is visible and its often complex shape and structure can be studied and photographed; this was the only opportunity of doing so, until the development by the late Bernard Lyot of his coronagraph in the 1930's. Solar eclipses still provide the opportunities for obtaining the best photographs of the corona. [Plate 2(a, b).]

The many absorption lines in the solar spectrum are formed in the so-called **reversing layer**; immediately above this is the **chromosphere**, which has an emission spectrum. The chromosphere can be seen as a reddish crescent for a few moments immediately before and after totality. Its emission spectrum can be photographed at these times without the absorption spectrum of the eclipsed reversing layer. This is known as the **flash spectrum**. [Plate 1(e).]

Any prominences at the limb of the Sun are also visible during totality; as they are principally composed of hydrogen, however, they are readily observable in hydrogen light at all times, by means of the **spectroheliograph**, etc.

Total eclipses are the only occasions when we can readily study that part of the heavens against which the Sun is seen; at all other times this is prevented by the Sun's glare. For many years observers utilized the opportunity so provided in searching for an intra-Mercurial planet (see **Vulcan**). A more profitable observation seeks to confirm Einstein's **theory of relativity**. Einstein predicted that one effect of relativity theory would be that rays of starlight passing close to the Sun would be deflected towards it, and the star would consequently appear to be displaced away from the Sun. To test this effect, the star field surrounding the eclipsed Sun is photographed during totality, and the resulting plate is compared with plates of the same field exposed

months earlier or later; the positions of the star images on the plates can be precisely measured and the displacement determined.

Partial solar eclipses are also of use to the astronomer, especially for the study of solar ultra-violet radiation and observations of solar radio noise.

Ancient records of eclipses have been used to determine the relative positions of the Sun and Moon at the time, and (consequently) secular changes in the orbital revolution periods of the Earth and the Moon, etc.

'Central' total eclipses have been photographed on cine film from a carefully chosen station outside the track of totality where the eclipse can be observed as a partial one. Measurements of the position of the visible part of the Sun on the films can be used to determine corrections to the tabulated position of the Moon. (See also **Motion of the Moon; Einstein displacement; Saros; Metonic cycle.**)

ECLIPSES OF PLANETARY SATELLITES At times when the Earth is in or nearly in the equatorial plane of Jupiter or Saturn, it is possible to see satellites eclipsed by the parent planet. Such phenomena are frequently observed in the case of Jupiter, owing to its very small orbital inclination; in the case of Saturn, it is possible to observe these phenomena only during comparatively short periods many years apart.

When the Earth lies actually in the orbital plane of the satellites, series of mutual phenomena occur in which one satellite may be seen to be eclipsed by another; in the case of the four great satellites of Jupiter these phenomena are possible for a few weeks every five years or so.

(See **Satellite phenomena.**)

ECLIPSING BINARY A short-period **binary system**, whose nature is discovered from observations of its fluctuating light due to mutual eclipses of the component stars.

ECLIPSING VARIABLE An **eclipsing binary**, *q.v.*

ECLIPTIC The projection on the celestial sphere of the path of the Sun as it appears to travel against the background stars due to the revolution of the Earth; it is a great circle inclined to the celestial equator by approximately $23\frac{1}{2}°$.

(See also **Celestial sphere**.)

ECLIPTIC LIMITS Owing to the inclination between the ecliptic and the plane of the Moon's orbit, there are obviously limiting distances of the Moon from its nodes, beyond which eclipses are impossible.

Lunar ecliptic limits. A lunar eclipse can take place when the Moon is Full and also at or near one of its nodes; if the Moon is less than $9°·5$ from the node at the time of opposition it is bound to pass through the shadow-cone of the Earth and an eclipse will take place. If the Moon is more than $12°·1$ from the node at the moment of conjunction it cannot pass through the shadow-cone and no eclipse is possible. If the Moon's distance from the node at opposition lies between $9°·5$ (the 'inferior ecliptic limit') and $12°·1$ (the 'superior ecliptic limit') an eclipse may occur, depending upon the precise relative positions of the Sun, Earth and Moon at the time.

Solar ecliptic limits. A solar eclipse occurs when the Moon is at conjunction (i.e. at New Moon), and also at or near one of its nodes. If the Sun is less than $15°·4$ from the node at the moment of conjunction it will be at least partially obscured by the Moon as observed from Earth, and an eclipse will take place. If the Sun is more than $18°·5$ from the node it cannot be obscured by the Moon and an eclipse cannot occur. If the Sun lies between $15°·4$ (the 'inferior ecliptic limit') and $18°·5$ (the 'superior ecliptic limit') at conjunction a solar eclipse may occur, depending upon the exact relative posi-

tions of the Sun, Earth and Moon at the time.

(See also **Eclipse, lunar**; **Eclipse, solar**.)

EDDINGTON, Sir Arthur (1882–1944) Arthur Stanley Eddington was one of the leading astrophysicists of his generation, and one of the greatest English men of science. After a brilliant career at Trinity College, Cambridge, where he was Senior Wrangler and Smith's Prizeman, he became Chief Assistant at the Royal Observatory, Greenwich, in 1906. In 1913 Eddington became Plumian Professor of Astronomy in the University of Cambridge, which post he held until his death. From 1914 he was also Director of the Cambridge University Observatory.

Eddington was an acknowledged master in many diverse fields of astronomy and physics, but he was particularly noteworthy for his studies of stellar dynamics and the internal constitution of stars. Perhaps his greatest triumphs were in the development of relativity theory and theories of galactic structure. Eddington also did much to bring about the two expeditions which observed the solar eclipse of 1919 May 20, and led the Cambridge expedition himself; the plates obtained by these expeditions were used to prove the existence of the **Einstein displacement**. In 1924 Eddington discovered the **mass–luminosity relationship**. He was a prolific author, producing not only highly mathematical treatises, but also a number of masterly explanations of the complexities of cosmology and astrophysics for the non-mathematical reader, notably *The Expanding Universe* and *Space, Time and Gravitation*.

Eddington was the recipient of many honours; he was knighted in 1930 and received the Order of Merit in 1938. He was elected a Fellow of the Royal Society in 1914, and in 1928 was awarded its Royal Medal. He was President of the International Astronomical Union from 1938 until his death, and achieved the rare distinction of being the President of both the Royal Astronomical Society (1921–1923) and the Physical Society (1930–1932). He was awarded the Gold Medal of the Royal Astronomical Society in 1924, and was a member of its Council for many years; he also served the Society as Secretary (1912–1916) and Foreign Secretary (1933–1944).

EDEN Martian surface feature, approximate position Ω 350°, $\Phi + 27°$. A small, light area in the centre of the triangle formed by the Sinus Meridiani, Ismenius Lacus and Niliacus Lacus.

EDOM Martian surface feature, approximate position Ω 340°, $\Phi + 10°$. A lightish area north of the Sinus Sabæus and bounded by the southern portions of the canali Euphrates and Hiddekel.

EDOM PROMONTORIUM Martian surface feature, approximate position Ω 345°, $\Phi - 5°$. A very bright oval area at the southern end of Edom and adjoining the northern edge of the Sinus Sabæus. Bounded by the Sinus Meridiani to the west and Portus Sigeus to the east.

EFFECTIVE TEMPERATURE A theoretical concept, the effective temperature of a star is defined as the temperature of a black-body radiator having the same dimensions and radiative output as the star in question.

The effective temperature of the star can be derived from its total luminosity if the radius of the star is known.

EGRESS Term used to denote the concluding stage of a transit or shadow-transit of a planetary satellite.

(See **Satellite phenomena**.)

EINSTEIN, Albert (1879–1955) Possibly the greatest theoretical scientist in history, and certainly the most advanced mathematician of his time. Einstein was born at Ulm, Germany, and demonstrated a natural flair for mathematics from a very early age; he later studied in Switzerland and qualified as a teacher of mathematics and physics. His energies were largely devoted to research, however, and he was soon involved in a completely original approach to the broad framework of cosmological theory.

In 1905 Einstein published his Special Theory of Relativity, whilst employed in the Swiss Patent Office; this was followed in 1916 by the General Theory of Relativity. With this work, Einstein completely revolutionized cosmological thinking; he became widely regarded as the greatest scientist since Newton.

In 1913 Einstein became a Professor at the University of Berlin, but fled to the United States in 1933 as a result of the Nazi purge; he became a Professor at the Institute for Advanced Studies, Princeton, New Jersey. Although the last years of his life were spent in semi-retirement, Einstein still spent much time on his research, especially the development of his Unified Field Theory.

Einstein received many honours from many countries, among them a Nobel Prize and the Copley Medal of the Royal Society, and one of the many honorary degrees he was awarded was that of Doctor of Science of the University of Oxford.

EINSTEIN DISPLACEMENT In his General Theory of Relativity, published in 1916, Einstein predicted that rays of light from a distant star should be deflected by a close approach to the Sun *en route* to the Earth, the displacement, *D*, being calculated from the formula

$$D = \frac{4\,\mathbf{G}\,M}{\mathbf{C}^2\,r}$$

where $\mathbf{G}$ is the gravitational constant, M the mass of the Sun, $\mathbf{C}$ the velocity of light and r the distance of closest approach of the light-ray from the Sun's centre (Fig. 32). The maximum value of D (when r = the Sun's radius, that is for a light-ray which just grazes the surface of the Sun) is 1·75 seconds of arc, but this

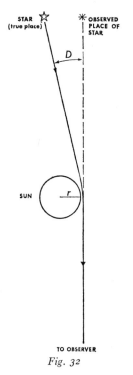

Fig. 32

theoretical limit cannot be observed in practice, as will be seen.

The observations necessary to verify Einstein's prediction are very difficult, and must be carried out to the highest standards of precision. The method is to photograph the star field surrounding the Sun during a total solar eclipse, and to compare the positions of the stars photographed with those on other plates ob-

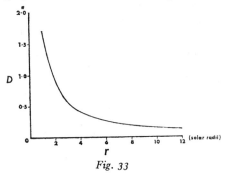

Fig. 33

tained some months earlier or later, when the Sun is no longer in that part of the sky. If the prediction is correct, each star should be displaced by an amount dependent upon its distance from the Sun, in accordance with the formula cited above. In practice, no stars can be satisfactorily photographed closer than about 2 solar radii from the centre of the Sun, and therefore the maximum observable displacement is less than one second of arc.

The values of the displacement (D) predicted by the theory are plotted against various values of r in Fig. 33.

Expeditions were sent out to photograph the eclipse field at the total eclipse of 1919 May 29 by the Royal Observatory, Greenwich, and the Cambridge University Observatory; the former expedition operated from Brazil and the latter from the island of Principe. This eclipse was a particularly favourable one for the purpose of testing the theory, as the Sun was at the time situated against a background of the Taurus cluster, and there would therefore be numerous stars in the eclipse field whose apparent position could be measured. Both expeditions were successful, and the final results demonstrated the validity of Einstein's prediction quite clearly, despite the extremely small displacements involved.

EL NATH The star β Tau, magnitude 1·6; situated at the tip of one of the Bull's horns in the ancient constellation figure of Taurus.

ELECTRIS Martian surface feature, approximate position Ω 190°, $\Phi-45°$. A lightish area in the south temperate zone of the planet, separated from the Mare Sirenum by the brighter Atlantis.

ELECTROMAGNETIC SPECTRUM The entire range of frequencies of electromagnetic radiation. A diagrammatic representation of the spectrum is shown in Fig. 34, in which all wavelengths have been expressed in centimetres for sim-

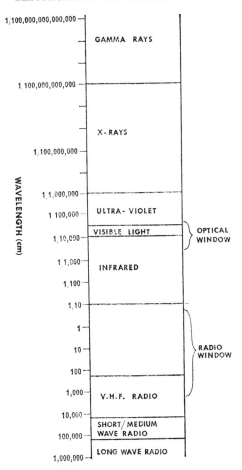

Fig. 34

a proportion of the radiation being able to penetrate, thus forming a 'window' through which observational use of the radiation can be made. These two bands are known as the optical window and the radio window.

ELECTRON One of the particles of an atom, which bears a negative electrical charge and is in orbit around the atomic nucleus.
(See **Atom**.)

ELECTRON DENSITY A figure indicating the number of electrons present in a given volume of a substance; usually applied to gaseous media such as a planetary atmosphere, the outer layers of a star, etc.

ELECTRON SHELL A term used to describe an area where certain of the electrons in an atom are free to move; it has the form of the surface of a sphere centred on the nucleus (see **Atom**).

ELEMENT (CHEMICAL) A substance that is chemically unique and composed of atoms of only one type. (See **Chemical elements**.)

ELEMENT (ORBITAL) One of the quantities necessary to define an orbit or the position of the orbiting body at a given time. (See **Orbit; Planetary motion**.)

ELEMENTARY RING-STRUCTURE A type of lunar surface feature in which a simple wall of even cross-section encloses a floor of the same level as the surrounding area. Also known as a 'simple ring'. (See **Moon—surface features of**.)

ELGER, Thomas Gwyn (1838–1897) A notable English amateur astronomer, and first Director of the Lunar Section of the British Astronomical Association (1891–1896). In 1895 he published a book describing the surface detail of the Moon, included with which was an excellent map of the surface features. This map has been thoroughly revised and augmented, and is once again available, at modest cost. It

plicity. Typical wavelengths, measured in **Ångström units**, are: violet light, 4,000 Å, blue, 4,200 Å; green, 5,000 Å; yellow, 5,600 Å; red, 6,800 Å. These, of course, constitute the 'visible spectrum', or 'light' as we usually conceive it.

To the astronomer, electromagnetic radiation is his principal connection with the objects he observes; his use of it is severely limited by the fact that much of the radiation falling upon the Earth is absorbed in the atmosphere. There are two bands of the electromagnetic spectrum, however, where this is not the case, is still of immense value and is undoubtedly the best small-scale outline map obtainable.

ELLIPSE An ellipse is the basic closed form of conic section, having an eccentricity less than 1. The circle is a special case of the ellipse, having zero eccentricity. All the planets of the solar system are in elliptical orbits around the Sun, as are planetary satellites around their primaries, etc., subject only to the effects of **perturbations**.

An ellipse may be defined as a conic section where the ratio of the distances of any point on it from a focus and from a given fixed line is constant. The fixed line is known as the *directrix* and the constant is the *eccentricity* (e). This is shown in Fig. 35 in which

$$\frac{SA}{AO} = \frac{SL}{LK} = \frac{SP}{PQ} = e.$$

A further property of the ellipse is that the distance $(SP+PF)$ is constant for any position of P, hence the well-known means of constructing an ellipse with the aid of two pins and a loop of cotton.

The standard form of the equation for an ellipse is

$$S \equiv \frac{x^2}{a^2} + \frac{y^2}{2} - 1 = 0.$$

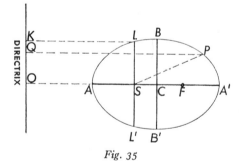

Fig. 35

Also in Fig. 35, AA' is the *major axis* and BB' the *minor axis* (AC being known as the *semi-major axis* (a) and BC as the *semi-minor axis* (b)). A and A' are the *apsides*, C is termed the *centre* and LL' the *latus rectum*. If the ellipse shown were

the orbit of a planet P, the Sun being at S, then SP would be the *radius vector* of the planet; it will be seen that the length of the radius vector varies according to the position of P in its orbit at the time.

The area of an ellipse may be calculated from the expression πab.

(See also **Orbit; Planetary motion**.)

ELLIPTICAL GALAXY One of the major forms of galaxy, and believed to be the 'latest' type, i.e. that most advanced in its evolution. (See **Galactic evolution; Galactic structure**.)

ELLIPTICAL RING-STRUCTURE Term used to denote a lunar crater or ring-structure whose peripheral wall is elliptical in form. Small elliptical craters are often found in the bright ray-systems, and they also tend to occur in chains, indicating fault-lines in the lunar crust. (See **Moon—surface features of**.)

ELLISON, Mervyn Archdall (1909–1963) Born in Southern Ireland, Ellison inherited an interest in astronomy from his father, who later became Director of the Armagh Observatory. After a brilliant career at Trinity College, Dublin, he failed to find a suitable vacancy in astronomy and, instead, became senior science master of Sherborne School. Ellison rapidly became one of the best known solar observers of his day, and one of the world's leading amateur astronomers; during the 1930s he constructed his own spectrohelioscope, as had Newbegin and Sellers, and commenced a long series of observations of solar flares and prominences that was interrupted only by the Second World War.

Having extended his spectrohelioscope to include a spectrograph, Ellison obtained in 1946 a very fine spectrogram of a hydrogen flare associated with a giant sunspot, just at the moment of maximum intensity.

In 1947 Ellison turned professional, joining the staff of the Royal Observatory,

Edinburgh; his observational work was regarded as of such importance, however, that his spectroheliograph was re-erected at Edinburgh and his programme continued. In 1954 Ellison published *The Sun and its Influence*, still the standard introductory text on solar–terrestrial relationships.

Ellison was the Solar Reporter for the International Geophysical Year (1958–1960), and edited the two vast volumes detailing solar activity throughout the period. Late in 1958 Ellison was appointed Senior Professor of the School of Cosmic Physics at the Dublin Institute for Advanced Studies, and Director of the Dunsink Observatory. At the time of his death he was heavily involved in the preparations for the International Quiet Sun Year.

Ellison was elected a Fellow of the Royal Society of Edinburgh in 1948, and served on the Council of the Royal Astronomical Society (1940–1950).

ELONGATION Term used in celestial mechanics, denoting the angle planet–Earth–Sun. For a superior planet it can have values between 0° and 180°; for an inferior planet it is always less than 90° and is subject to a specific maximum value known as the 'Greatest Elongation East (or West)'; this is the form in which it is usually encountered. An inferior planet has its greatest apparent distance from the Sun at times of Greatest Elongation.

(See also **Mercury—visibility from Earth; Planetary motion; Venus—visibility from Earth.**)

ELYSIUM Martian surface feature, approximate position $\Omega\,210°$, $\Phi+25°$. A prominent oval area, adjoining the western edge of the Trivium Charontis. Bounded on all other sides by prominent canali—Cerberus, Eunostos, Chaos Hyblæus and Styx.

EMERSION Term sometimes used for the **reappearance** phase of an eclipse or occultation.

EMISSION LINES The bright lines of the **emission spectrum**.

EMISSION SPECTRUM The 'brightline' spectrum emitted by substances in an incandescent state under low pressure. (See **Spectra**.)

ENCELADUS Satellite II of Saturn, *q.v.*

ENCKE, Johann Franz (1791–1865) A notable German mathematical astronomer. Encke obtained a value for the solar parallax, based upon all the observations of the transits of Venus of 1761 and 1769, of 8″57, which was for many years the best available result.

Encke, a pupil of Gauss, is perhaps best known through the comet now named after him, but which was discovered by Pons in 1818. Encke demonstrated that this comet was periodic, being identical with comets observed in 1786, 1795 and 1805. This was only the second periodic comet to be discovered, and has the shortest known orbital period (3·3 years).

ENCKE'S COMET In 1818 Pons, working at Marseilles, discovered a new comet and Encke, who was a pupil of Gauss, computed its orbit by a method recently devised by his master. The results of his labours showed the comet to have a period of 3·3 years, which remains to this day the shortest-known comet period. Encke also demonstrated that the new comet was in fact identical with three observed earlier: those discovered by Méchain in Paris in 1786, by Caroline Herschel in 1795 and by Pons himself in 1805. Encke also predicted the next return of this comet, in 1822; this was only the second occasion on which the return of a comet had been successfully predicted (the first being **Halley's Comet**, *q.v.*).

Encke's Comet has been regularly observed since 1818, including an unbroken sequence of observations of each return from 1818 to 1941, and has presented a number of features of particular interest in addition to its very short period. Observations made over more than a century showed that the period of Encke's Comet had been slowly decreasing, in other words the comet had been accelerating in its orbit; in 100 years the period had reduced by 2½ days. This discovery indicated that the orbit must be slowly shrinking, and it was calculated that a few thousand years ago the orbit must have extended out to that of Jupiter. It has been suggested that this comet was hitherto a long-period comet that made a close approach to Jupiter and was deflected by the gravitational attraction of the planet into a new, smaller and slowly shrinking orbit.

Encke's comet is typical of the older type of comet, having a very small nucleus and a tenuous head which is shown by spectroscopic analysis to contain mainly gaseous constituents. The tail of Encke's Comet frequently appears fan-shaped, and the coma is often seen to shrink substantially around the time of perihelion.

There is a fair amount of evidence to support the belief that the β Taurid meteor shower is associated with this comet.

ENCKE'S DIVISION A dusky streak in the ring-system of Saturn, first observed by Encke on 1837 May 28. It is situated about four-tenths of the distance from the outer to the inner edge of ring A. Observations made under excellent seeing conditions at the Pic-du-Midi Observatory by Lyot suggest that the Division is not a true gap in the ring, like Cassini's Division, but a portion containing fewer orbiting ring particles. This is due to the Division occupying a resonance position where the period of a ring particle would be three-fifths that of Mimas. The Division has been observed double by Tombaugh on three separate occasions of excellent seeing; this is no doubt due to the proximity of a second resonance position, of period two-fifths that of Enceladus. (See **Saturn—rings of.**)

ENDYMION Lunar surface feature, co-ordinates $\xi + 492$, $\eta + 803$. A great crater-

ring, 78 miles in diameter, situated near the Moon's north-western limb between the Mare Humboldtianum and the Mare Frigoris. It is particularly prominent, owing to its very dark floor. Its outline is well defined, the walls rising to more than 15,000 ft. in the west and north. Overlaps a larger and older ring-plain.

ENHANCEMENT, SPECTRAL If a substance is raised to a very high temperature, its atoms reach a state of excitation and may become ionized. Certain of the emission lines in its spectrum are intensified, or 'enhanced', and additional bright lines may appear. The degree of enhancement, and the number of lines affected, increase as the substance becomes progressively more ionized. (See **Spectra**.)

EOS Martian surface feature, approximate position Ω 37°, $\Phi - 15$°. Light oval area in south tropical area between Margaritifer Sinus and Auroræ Sinus.

EPACT A concept used in calendar-making for the fixing of religious festivals such as Easter, etc. It is, for any given year, the age of the Moon, in days, at January 1·0.

EPHEMERIDES OF THE MINOR PLANETS An important publication giving ephemerides for observers of minor planets; it was produced from 1898–1946 by the Astronomisches Rechen-Institut, Berlin, and from 1947–1951 by the Minor Planet Center, Cincinnati, U.S.A. It was also produced from 1947–1951 by the Institute of Theoretical Astronomy of the Academy of Sciences of the U.S.S.R., Leningrad, who have continued to produce it since 1952. It is often abbreviated to E.M.P.

EPHEMERIS (plural: Ephemerides) A table of the calculated position, at regular intervals, of a celestial body. Sometimes used in the wider sense to denote a compendium of such tables—such as the **Astronomical Ephemeris**, *q.v.*

EPHEMERIS TIME In recent years observational techniques for the determination of time have greatly increased in accuracy, but simultaneously physicists and technologists have demanded ever more precisely determined time intervals; meridian-transit observations of stars of known place is no longer a sufficiently accurate basis, as the length of the day deduced from such observations is not constant, due to very small variations in the rate of rotation of the Earth on its axis.

As the astronomer needs to prepare accurate ephemerides well in advance, he needs an invariable basis of time measurement. It was therefore decided to introduce a new time system, based upon gravitational theory and the laws of planetary motion, in which the fundamental unit would be not the period of the Earth's axial rotation (the day), with its unfortunate variations, but its period of orbital revolution (the year).

Accordingly, it was resolved by the International Astronomical Union to adopt the length of the Tropical Year as at 1900 January 1 as the basis of a new system, known as 'Ephemeris Time' and in use from the beginning of 1960. The Ephemeris Second was defined as the fraction $1/31,556,925\cdot9747$ of the Tropical Year for 1900 January 1 at 12 noon, and Ephemeris Time is calculated (in effect) by counting the appropriate number of Ephemeris Seconds from that moment. This moment was itself defined in the words 'Ephemeris Time is reckoned from the instant, near the beginning of the calendar year A.D. 1900, when the geometric mean longitude of the Sun was $279° \ 41' \ 48''\!\cdot\!04$, at which instant the measure of Ephemeris Time was 1900 January 0 d 12 hr precisely.'

Observatory clocks are still, of course, set to keep Universal Time (U.T.) and Sidereal Time (S.T.), and observations are related to whichever of these systems is convenient; when analysing the ob-servations it is a simple matter to convert the observed times to Ephemeris Time.
(See also **Time, determination of; Time systems.**)

EPOCH A point in time selected as a fixed reference; thus star maps, etc., are currently being produced showing star positions as at the Epoch 1950·0. Similarly the Epoch is selected as the starting point in the calculation of ephemerides, and series of observations made over a period of time are normally reduced to a common Epoch so as to facilitate ready comparison.

EQUATION OF THE CENTRE An inequality in the Moon's motion, due to the eccentricity of the Moon's orbit. (See **Moon—motion of.**)

EQUATION OF TIME The correction which must be applied to 'apparent solar time' (time based upon the observed position of the Sun, as given by a sundial) in order to obtain **mean time**. It is necessary to use mean time for everyday purposes, as apparent time is not constant. The variation arises from two distinct causes; these are the effect of the eccentricity of the Earth's orbit, and that due to the obliquity of the ecliptic.

The effect of the eccentricity of the Earth's orbit on a given date is calculated from the difference in Hour Angle between the true Sun and the dynamical Mean Sun. As the Sun's apparent angular velocity is greatest at perihelion and least at aphelion, it can be shown that the true Sun will appear to be ahead of the mean Sun from perihelion to aphelion (i.e. January to June) and behind it from aphelion to perihelion (July to December). The difference will be greatest at the beginning of April and October respectively (Fig. 36 (a)).

The effect of the obliquity of the ecliptic is calculated from the difference in Hour Angle between the dynamical mean Sun and the astronomical mean Sun. The former is the concept of a Sun coinciding with the true Sun at perigee and moving

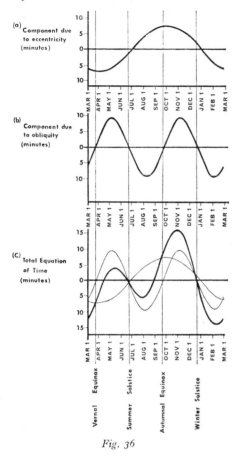

Fig. 36

minutes on November 3, and its maximum negative value is about 14½ minutes on February 12.

EQUATOR, CELESTIAL The great circle in which the plane of the Earth's equator meets the celestial sphere. It has the north and south celestial poles as its poles.
(See also **Celestial sphere**.)

EQUATORIAL HORIZONTAL PARAL-LAX The angle subtended at the body concerned (usually the Sun or Moon) by the equatorial radius of the Earth. (See **Parallax, stellar**.)

EQUATORIAL MOUNTING A telescope mounting having freedom of movement in two planes, around two axes at right angles. One of these, the *polar axis*, is set parallel to the Earth's axis of rotation; the telescope can thus be rotated about the other (*declination*) axis, and clamped at the desired declination. The instrument is then rotated, by means of an electrical or mechanical drive, around the polar axis, at the rate of one revolution per sidereal day and in the counter direction to the Earth's rotation. This enables a celestial object to be maintained accurately at the centre of the field for long periods, thus making possible long-exposure photography, etc. (See **Mountings, telescope**.)

EQUINOCTIAL COLURE The declination circle which passes through the north and south celestial poles and also the **equinoctial points**.
(See also **Celestial sphere**.)

EQUINOCTIAL POINTS The positions of the Sun at the vernal and autumnal equinoxes. At these times the Sun's declination is zero, and the equinoctial points are the points of intersection of the ecliptic and the celestial equator.
(See also **Celestial sphere**.)

EQUINOX Term given to both of the **equinoctial points**, and also to the days on which the Sun occupies these points.

around the *Ecliptic* at a uniform rate; the latter is conceived as moving around the celestial *equator*, in such a way that its longitude is always the same as that of the dynamical mean Sun. This correction is zero at the solstices and equinoxes (Fig. 36 (b)).

The two component effects are added so as to obtain the total correction, known as the equation of time (Fig. 36 (c)). If applied to time measurements made with a sundial they will produce a fairly accurate result.

The total correction required is nil four times during the year, on or about April 15, June 15, August 31 and December 24. Its maximum positive value is about 16½

On these two days the Sun rises and sets exactly in the east and west points, and day and night are of exactly equal length.

(See also **Celestial sphere; Autumnal equinox; Vernal equinox.**)

EQUULEUS (The Little Horse. *Genitive* Equulei, *I.A.U. abbreviation* Equ.) A tiny constellation just north of the celestial equator, between Pegasus and Delphinus, and north of Aquarius. Contains three stars of the fourth magnitude and one of the fifth. The star 1 Equ (sometimes designated ϵ Equ) is an interesting multiple; it is a triple star, consisting of a close binary (magnitude 5·7, 7·0, separation 0″2) and a third companion (magnitude 7·1) at a separation of about 11″. Reaches midnight culmination in mid-August.

ERATOSTHENES Lunar surface feature, co-ordinates $\xi - 190$, $\eta + 250$. A splendidly formed crater, in a very prominent situation in the Oceanus Procellarum, where at times of low illumination it vies for prominence even with nearby Copernicus. It stands out partly owing to its location at the end of the great Appenines range, and partly owing to the sharply defined, terraced walls, rising to 16,000 ft. above the floor (about 8,000 ft. above the surrounding terrain). Like many such features, however, under high illumination at Full Moon Eratosthenes becomes very difficult to locate, being hidden in the ray system of Copernicus. The diameter is 38 miles, and there is a complex central mountain.

ERIDANIA Martian surface feature, approximate position Ω 220°, $\Phi - 45°$. A lightish area in the south temperate zone of Mars, between the southern end of the Mare Tyrrhenum and the Mare Chronium.

ERIDANUS (The River Eridanus. *Genitive* Eridani, *I.A.U. abbreviation* Eri.) A southern constellation, one of the largest and farthest-reaching in the heavens; it covers a large area south of the equator, between Orion and Cetus, and has a long, narrow 'river' of stars extending to within 32° of the South Pole. The southernmost star, *Achernar*, is also the brightest.

EROS Minor planet number 433, discovered in 1898 by Witt in Berlin; at the time its mean distance from the Sun was the smallest known for any asteroid—136 million miles.

Eros became the subject of great interest among astronomers as soon as its orbit was determined, for it was found that its perigee distance could be as little as 14 million miles. This was unique at the time, although some asteroids discovered more recently pass much closer to the Earth.

Its occasional close approaches provided ideal opportunities for the redetermination of the **solar parallax**. A number of observatories collaborated to obtain the necessary positional observations of Eros at the close approach of 1901, when it approached to within 30 million miles; the even closer approach of 1931 (16 million miles) was the subject of an even more extensive programme, in which scores of observatories all over the world took part. The value obtained for the solar parallax was the most accurate yet determined, and has been almost universally adopted ever since.

Eros is also noteworthy for the rather erratic variations in its magnitude; these were attributed to its having an unusual, 'splinter'-like, shape; this was confirmed in 1937 by Finsen and van den Bos of Johannesburg, who were able to detect and measure its shape. Their measurements suggest that the planet is some 14 miles long and 4 miles wide.

ESCAPE VELOCITY The minimum velocity at which a particle must be projected if it is to escape from the gravitational field of the primary body and travel onward into space. Usually encountered in the form of the *velocity of escape for gases*, it is calculated from the formula $V = \sqrt{(2g\,R)}$ where R is the radius of the body and g is the gravitational force at its surface.

The escape velocity for a space vehicle or other projectile at a height r above the centre of the body can also be calculated from the formula $V_r = \sqrt{\left(\dfrac{2g\,R^2}{r}\right)}$.

The approximate escape velocities for the principal members of the Solar System are:

	mile/sec		mile/sec
Sun	384	Jupiter	37·4
Moon	1·5	Saturn	22·5
Mercury	2·6	Uranus	14·0
Venus	6·4	Neptune	15·4
Earth	7·0	Pluto	3
Mars	3·1		

ETA AQUARIDS A meteor shower occurring from a radiant near η Aqr, and lasting for a week or more in early May. This is the first of two showers associated with Halley's Comet, the others being the **Orionids.**

EUCLIDES Lunar surface feature, co-ordinates η–488, ξ–129. A small bright crater, 7 miles in diameter, situated in the Mare Nubium about 250 miles south-south-east of Copernicus. Its walls rise to about 2,000 ft. Under a high illumination it is seen to be surrounded by a fine nimbus, triangular in outline, perhaps the best example of the halo type of ray system.

EUDOXUS Lunar surface feature, co-ordinates ξ+202, η+699. A well-defined crater, 40 miles in diameter, which makes a fine pair with the larger Aristoteles situated a little to the north. Has well-defined walls, rising to 11,000 ft. in the west, and a very rugged interior.

EULER, Leonard (1707–1783) A leading Swiss mathematician and scientist. Very active in the development of optical systems, he also made important contributions to the study of dynamical astronomy. He was the first to undertake the development of gravitational theory beyond the point reached by Newton, and made numerous contributions of value to the science.

EUNOSTOS Martian surface feature, approximate position Ω 225°, Φ+15°. A dusky canal forming the south-western border of Elysium.

EUPHRATES Martian surface feature, approximate position Ω 335°, Φ+20°. A long canal, running south from the Ismenius Lacus and joining the Sinus Sabæus at the Portus Sigeus.

EURIPUS I Martian surface feature, approximate position Ω 275°, Φ−57°. Dusky canal forming south-eastern border of Hellas.

EURIPUS II Martian surface feature, approximate position Ω 265°, Φ−30°. Northern extension of Euripus I forming the north-western border of Ausonia.

EUROPA Satellite II of Jupiter, *q.v.*

EVECTION The variation in the value of the **equation of the centre** (*q.v.*), due to the variation in the eccentricity of the Moon's orbit caused by the perturbative effects of the Sun upon the Moon's motion. (See **Moon—motion of.**)

EVERSHED, John (1864–1956) Born in England, John Evershed became a solar observer of international repute. He began his long astronomical career as an amateur, whilst employed as an analytical chemist. After participating successfully in a number of eclipse expeditions, however, Evershed was appointed Assistant Director of the Kodaikanal Observatory in India in 1905, and in 1911 became its Director.

Much of Evershed's early work was carried out with instruments of his own design and manufacture, and he was responsible for extensively re-equipping the Kodaikanal. Much of his effort was devoted to the photoheliographic study of prominences in hydrogen light, but he is perhaps best known for his demonstration of the radial motion of the constituent gases of sunspots, now known as the **Evershed effect.** For this important step forward in our knowledge of solar physics Evershed was elected a Fellow of the

Royal Society in 1915 and was awarded the Gold Medal of the Royal Astronomical Society in 1918.

Evershed retired from the Kodaikanal Observatory in 1923, and was made a Companion of the Order of the Indian Empire (C.I.E.) for his distinguished work there. His observing career was far from finished, however; he established a private observatory at Ewhurst, Surrey, and made many important contributions to solar observation before he finally closed the observatory in 1950 (he was then aged 86) and presented some of his equipment to the Solar Department of the Royal Greenwich Observatory at Herstmonceux.

Evershed was a founder member of the British Astronomical Association, and was Director of its Solar Spectroscopy Section 1893–1899 and of its Spectroscopy Section 1893–1900 and 1924–1926.

EVERSHED EFFECT It was demonstrated by the late John Evershed, working at the Kodaikanal Observatory, that the motion of the gases in the penumbral region of sunspots is radially outwards from the central umbra. Evershed's technique was to set the slit of his spectrograph across a spot area and along a radius of the Sun's disk; the motion of the gases was revealed by displacements of the spectral lines. For spots near the centre of the disk these were negligible, but for spots nearer to the limb the line displacements indicated a radial motion towards the observer on the nearer side of the spot and away from him on the farther side. In later work Evershed found that this motion in the reversing layer, due no doubt to vapourized metals, is present in the reverse direction when the gases in the higher levels of the chromosphere are observed.

EVOLUTION, GALACTIC See **Galactic evolution.**

EVOLUTION, STELLAR See **Stellar evolution.**

EXCITATION The state wherein an atom has been subjected to an influx of energy, and as a result one or more of its electrons have been transferred to a higher shell. An important consideration in astrophysics, as the high temperature and pressure obtaining in the stars result in a high incidence of 'excited' atoms.

EXIT PUPIL Sometimes known as the *Ramsden disk*, this is the part of the emergent pencil of light rays having the smallest cross-section area, and through which the rays from all parts of the field pass. It is the point at which the eye should be placed in order to see the largest field possible and enjoy the brightest image. Most telescope eyepieces are fitted with a cap which has an aperture of appropriate size slightly in front of the exit pupil, so that the observer is led automatically to the best position.

EXOSPHERE The outside layer of the Earth's atmosphere, beyond the ionosphere. (See **Atmosphere, Earth's.**)

EXPANDING UNIVERSE The concept of a universe that is constantly expanding arises from the fact that almost all observed extragalactic objects are found to be receding from us at velocities proportional to their distance. The few cases found to have a measurable approach velocity are readily explained as an optical effect due to the rotation of the Galaxy.

If the observed velocities of recession are corrected for the effects of galactic rotation, they are found to conform to a model of the universe in which all distances will be increased in a given ratio in a given time, such that the present distances between the individual galaxies will be doubled in a period of the order of a thousand million years.

(See also **Cosmology; Galactic evolution.**)

EXPLOSIVE VARIABLES Term sometimes used for the **cataclysmic variables,** *q.v.*

EXTINCTION, ATMOSPHERIC An effect of the Earth's atmosphere, which reduces, by absorption and dispersion, the light reaching us from all celestial objects; the effect varies, depending upon the

Table 11. Effect of atmospheric extinction

Altitude of object	Approximate length of light-path through atmosphere (miles)	Approximate amount of dimming (magnitudes)
90°	10	0·3
60°	13	0·4
30°	21	0·6
20°	40	0·9
10°	60	1·6

direction of the object and the distance its light-rays consequently have to travel within the atmosphere.

The approximate effects for objects observed at various altitudes are shown in Table 11.

EXTRAGALACTIC NEBULAE This was the name originally given to the many nebulous objects known and believed to be outside our own Galaxy, before their true nature was known. In the light of modern knowledge they are better referred to as galaxies, as the term nebulae can lead to confusion with the gaseous nebulae observed within the Galaxy.

EXTRAPOLATION A process, similar to interpolation except insofar as it is used to determine values for a tabulated function outside the range of values given; it assumes an extension of the trend(s) shown by the differences within the range of figures tabulated.

The accuracy of the method obviously diminishes rapidly at increasing intervals from the tabulated range, and it is therefore of very limited use.

EXTRINSIC VARIABLE Term sometimes used to denote a variable star whose observed light variation is due to some external cause (e.g. an eclipsing binary), as opposed to a true, or intrinsic, variable.

EYEPIECE The component of a telescope used to magnify the image produced by the objective; it may be a single lens but is usually a multiple-lens system. Eyepieces are normally interchangeable, eyepieces of different powers and types being used with the same telescope, depending upon the nature of the observation to be made, the limitations imposed by the state of the atmosphere, etc.

The term 'ocular' is sometimes used to denote an eyepiece. (See **Telescope**, etc.)

EYEPIECE, ACHROMATIC RAMSDEN A modern development of the traditional Ramsden form, devised as an improvement on the **Kellner eyepiece** by A. Steinheil of Munich. In this eyepiece both the field-lens and eye-lens are achromatic doublets, each consisting of a biconvex element in crown glass cemented

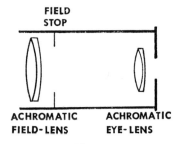

FIELD STOP

ACHROMATIC FIELD-LENS **ACHROMATIC EYE-LENS**

Fig. 37

to a flint-glass meniscus (Fig. 37). This eyepiece has all the good qualities of the Kellner, together with a wider field and far less tendency to produce ghost images.

EYEPIECE, AIRY A development of the **Huyghenian eyepiece**, consisting of a strong, convergent, meniscus field lens and a crossed biconvex eye lens; its spherical aberration is rather less than that of the Huyghenian.

EYEPIECE, APLANATIC A modified form of **Kellner eyepiece**, having a larger and flatter field and greater freedom from scattered light.

EYEPIECE, BAKER ORTHOCROMAT See **Eyepiece, Gifford.**

EYEPIECE, BOHNENBERGER A special form of **Ramsden eyepiece**, used in the determination of the **level error** of a transit instrument. It contains a thin glass plate, mounted between the field- and eye-lenses at an angle of 45° to the optical axis (Fig. 38); the function of this

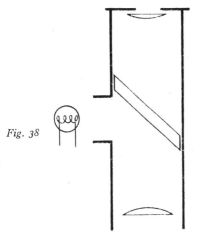

Fig. 38

plate is to reflect a beam of light introduced through the side of the eyepiece down the (vertical) telescope tube, thus illuminating the field and revealing the fixed and moving wires. (See **Transit circle, errors of.**)

EYEPIECE, COOKE A five-element improved form of **orthoscopic eyepiece**, comprising a cemented triplet as field-lens and a doublet eye-lens. Its aberrations are very small, enabling it to be used at focal ratios down to $f/4$, where it gives a flat field of more than 60°.

EYEPIECE, GAUSS A modification of the **Kellner eyepiece**, embodying an illuminated reference scale in the focal plane; it is used for the autocollimation of a telescope.

EYEPIECE, GIFFORD Sometimes known as the Baker Orthocromat, this is a development from the **orthoscopic eyepiece**; it gives fairly large flat fields with little scattered light.

EYEPIECE, HUYGHENIAN One of the earliest compound eyepieces, introduced by Huyghens about 1664, and still very widely used today. The Huyghenian eyepiece is of the type known as 'negative' eyepieces—these are compound eyepieces whose focal plane lies between their component lenses; they cannot therefore be used as magnifying glasses or be used with a reference wire or graticule.

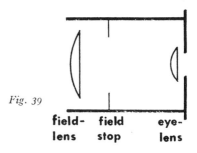

Fig. 39

field-   **field**   **eye-**
lens   **stop**   **lens**

The Huyghenian eyepiece consists of two plano-convex lenses, both mounted with the convex surface towards the telescope objective, the field-lens having a focal length two to three times that of the eye-lens; the distance between the two component lenses is half the sum of their focal lengths, at which position their individual chromatic aberrations cancel out so that the compound eyepiece is practically achromatic (Fig. 39). Huyghens was also the first person to introduce a stop to define the field.

The Huyghenian eyepiece has disadvantages if off-axis rays are used—spherical aberration, coma, image distortion and astigmatism are all encountered; it is therefore unsuitable for use at focal ratios smaller than $f/12$. It will give usable fields of up to 20°.

EYEPIECE, KELLNER A compound eye-piece developed from the **Ramsden** by Carl Kellner of Wetzlar in 1849. In this form the single eye-lens is replaced by an achromatic doublet—a biconvex crown-glass element cemented to a plano-concave one in flint-glass (Fig. 40). In the strict form a crossed bi-convex field-lens should be used, but the plano-convex field-lens of the Ramsden is usually retained.

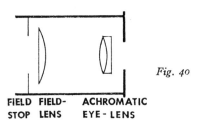

Fig. 40

FIELD FIELD- ACHROMATIC
STOP LENS EYE-LENS

The Kellner is an excellent eyepiece, especially for low-power observation; it has a wide, flat field of about 40° and small aberrations. It is, however, rather prone to produce ghost images, and has therefore tended to be superseded by the **Achromatic Ramsden.**

EYEPIECE, KEPLER Ths most common form of single-lens eyepiece, consisting of a plano-convex lens mounted with the convex side towards the object-glass.

Single-lens eyepieces have many disadvantages, despite their high transmission and consequently bright images; they are subject to severe chromatic aberration, they tend to produce distorted images and have only a small usable field (10–15°).

EYEPIECE, MITTENZWEY A development of the **Huyghenian eyepiece,** comprising a convergent meniscus field-lens and a plano-convex eye-lens. Spherical aberration is less than that of a Huyghenian, and this eyepiece yields excellent definition over fields of 50° or more.

EYEPIECE, MONOCENTRIC One of the most successful eyepieces ever produced;

it consists of a cemented triplet, the centre component being a bi-convex lens in crown glass and the outer components being flint glass meniscus lenses (Fig. 41). All the surfaces are spherical and have a common radius of curvature, and the glasses used are carefully selected so as to ensure minimum chromatic aberration.

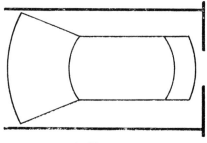

Fig. 41

Monocentric eyepieces offer, in addition to near-perfect achromatism, practically no spherical aberration, superb definition over a field of some 25°, very little scattered light, and better transmission even than that of an **orthoscopic eyepiece.**

EYEPIECE, ORTHOSCOPIC One of the most refined and fully corrected eye-pieces, occurring in a number of variants. The original design was by Mittenzwey. The field-lens is usually an achromatic cemented triplet (as in Fig. 42) or a pair

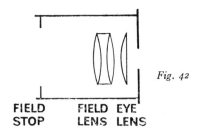

Fig. 42

FIELD FIELD EYE
STOP LENS LENS

of separated bi-convex elements, and the eye-lens is a plano-convex. Orthoscopics give excellent definition over wide fields, even at low focal ratios (e.g. 25° at $f/6$), with minimized aberrations and freedom from ghosts and scattering.

EYEPIECE, POLARIZING An adaption of a normal eyepiece which enables it to be used to measure the polarization of the light received from a celestial object. It may also be used as a dimming device which does not affect the colours of the image.

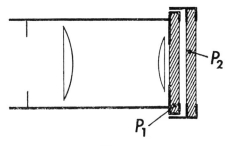

Fig. 43

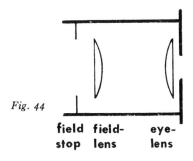

Fig. 44

field field- eye-
stop lens lens

It consists of two pieces of polaroid filter, one (P_1) fixed over the eye-end of an eyepiece of normal design (that shown in Fig. 43 being a **Ramsden**), and the other (P_2) fixed in a cap which is free to rotate over the eye-end. It is thus possible to vary the angle between the planes of polarization of the two Polaroid filters by rotating this cap.

EYEPIECE, RAMSDEN The second important form of classical compound eyepiece, developed rather more than a century after the **Huyghenian**, and also in use to this day. The design was submitted by Ramsden to the Royal Society and published by them in 1782. It consists of two plano-convex lenses, often identical and always of the same focal length, mounted with their convex surfaces facing each other and separated by a distance equal to about one-third of the sum of their focal lengths (Fig. 44).

The Ramsden is known as a 'positive' eyepiece, the focal plane being outside its length, thus enabling the eyepiece to be used with a graticule or reference wires. It also has a flatter and wider field (up to 35°) than the Huyghenian, and less spherical aberration. It is therefore suitable for use at lower focal ratios than the

Huyghenian. Later modifications of the Ramsden eyepiece (notably the **Kellner**) offer much better performance, although a great many Ramsdens are still in use.

EYEPIECE, TERRESTRIAL The erecting eyepiece used in a terrestrial telescope. It normally comprises four elements, as shown in Fig. 45; two of them form the

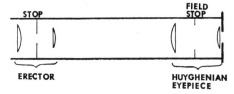

STOP FIELD STOP

ERECTOR HUYGHENIAN EYEPIECE

Fig. 45

erector, and two a normal **Huyghenian eyepiece**. A typical terrestrial eyepiece, such as that illustrated, has a field of about 35°.

EYEPIECE, TOLLES Developed from a principle devised by Coddington, the Tolles eyepiece is in fact a solid form of **Huyghenian eyepiece**. The layout is shown in Fig. 46; it is formed from a rod of glass with appropriately spherical ends,

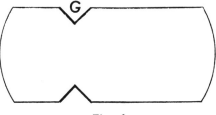

G

Fig. 46

and the field stop is formed by a blackened or frosted groove cut around the lens one-third of the distance from the field-end to the eye-end (*G*).

The dimensions of a Tolles eyepiece can be so arranged as to ensure that its transmission is higher than that of the corresponding Huyghenian, and its spherical aberration much lower. It is very free from internal scattering, giving a very dark field, and has a very wide field of good definition. Its disadvantages are the impossibility of using reference webs (since they would need to be situated inside the glass), and the fact that the exit pupil is at the eye-end surface, rendering it rather inconvenient in use.

EYEPIECE MAGNIFICATION For the purposes of identification eyepieces are usually designated by an indication of their magnifications—thus: × 150, × 210, etc. This is in fact meaningless, as the magnification produced by an eyepiece depends not only upon the focal length of the eyepiece itself but also upon that of the objective of the telescope with which it is used. It is therefore better to identify eyepieces by their focal length (e.g. $\frac{3}{16}$-in., $\frac{1}{4}$-in., etc.) when accuracy is desired, although the magnification produced with the telescope concerned is a simple and convenient description in cases where a set of eyepieces is used permanently with one telescope.

The magnification is given by the formula

$$M = \frac{F_o}{F_e},$$

where F_o is the focal length of the objective and F_e is that of the eyepiece. Thus the magnification obtained by using a $\frac{3}{4}$-in. eyepiece with a reflector embodying an 8-in. mirror of 64-in. focal length would be $\frac{64}{\frac{1}{4}} = \times 256$.

Where the focal lengths are not known, the magnification may be determined from measurements of the diameter of the **exit pupil**, or by visual estimate.

F

F STARS Stars of spectral class F; they are yellowish-white stars having surface temperatures in the range 6,000–7,500°K. *Procyon* is a notable example.

FK3 CATALOGUE The usual abbreviation for the *Dritter Fundamentalkatalog des Berliner Astronomischen Jahrbuchs*, published by the Astronomisches Rechen-Institut, Berlin, in 1937, and adopted by the International Astronomical Union as the standard catalogue of fundamental reference stars in 1938.

FK4 CATALOGUE A revision of the **FK3 Catalogue**, now in preparation for adoption as the standard catalogue of fundamental reference stars.

FABRICIUS Lunar surface feature, co-ordinates $\xi + 490$, $\eta - 680$. A prominent crater some 55 miles in diameter, near the south-western limb of the Moon. It has well-formed terraced walls and a complex central mountain, and is situated in the western end of the older and larger feature Janssen.

FACULAE Regions of great intensity seen in photographs of the surface of the Sun taken in ordinary light; owing to the brightness of the Sun's image they are only visible when close to the limb, aided by the limb-darkening effect; observation of a given area of faculae is therefore sporadic, being governed by the Sun's 28-day period of axial rotation. They also tend to drift considerably, especially in longitude.

Faculae are often seen in areas containing sunspots, but last much longer than sunspots (sometimes for months), and are therefore frequently seen where no sunspots exist. They are not normally seen outside the belt in which sunspots occur, i.e. 35°N–35°S. Faculae are believed to be areas of incandescent gas raised above the surrounding photospheric surface.

(See also **Solar activity; Sun—physical constitution of**.)

FALCATED OBJECT When the Moon or an inferior planet presents less than half of the illuminated hemisphere to the observer (i.e. when it is in a crescent phase) it is said to be 'falcated'.

FAULT A discontinuity in the crust surface of a planetary body, caused by movements of the crustal rocks at some time during their history. In astronomy the term usually implies lunar faulting. The terminology used is that applied to terrestrial faults by the geologist. Lunar faults are often referred to as *selenofaults*. (See **Moon—surface features of**.)

FIELD-FLATTENER A device used to permit flat photographic plates to be used in certain types of telescope whose optical design produces a curved (i.e. spherical) focal plane. It usually consists of a thin plano-convex lens of the appropriate curvature, located just in front of the photographic plate and with its flat side towards the plate. The device was first used by C. Piazzi-Smyth in 1874. It was an important feature of many of the early designs of **Schmidt camera**.

FIELD OF VIEW The area of the heavens visible in a telescope at a given time; it depends, of course, upon the eyepiece being used. In general, the higher the magnification the smaller the field of view.

The apparent field of a telescope, using a given eyepiece, is expressed in terms of its angular diameter.

FIGURING, OPTICAL The final fine-grinding or polishing process by which glass components of optical instruments are given the desired surface form (which is frequently aspherical).

(See also **Optics; Telescope**, etc.)

FILAMENTS Long dark streaks seen in high-dispersion spectroheliograms; they are associated with prominences and are dark, due to the light from the photosphere being absorbed by the relatively cool prominences.

(See also **Flocculi; Solar activity; Sun—physical constitution of.**)

FILAR MICROMETER See **Micrometer, Filar.**

FINDER A small low-power telescope attached to a larger one, and so adjusted that its field of view is accurately centred on the field of view of the main instrument; it can thus be used to facilitate the training of the main instrument onto a particular object. Finder telescopes are usually equipped with cross-wires.

The finder telescope is also used by an observer manipulating the controls of the main instrument (normally a clock-driven equatorial) during the long exposures necessary in most types of astronomical photography, in order to ensure that it remains accurately trained; for this reason it is sometimes termed a 'guider'.

FIREBALL Name given to an outstandingly bright **meteor.** Fireballs may have a magnitude equal to that of Venus or Jupiter at their brightest, and may leave a luminous trail lasting for several minutes.

FIRMICUS Lunar surface feature, co-ordinates $\xi + 887$, $\eta - 127$. A small crater, 35 miles in diameter, in the western limb region of the Moon. Its extremely dark floor makes it very prominent, having the appearance of a satellite to the Mare Undarum.

FIRST LUNAR MERIDIAN The zero of selenographic longitude; it is designated as being $\mathbb{C} + 180°$, where $\mathbb{C}$ is the mean longitude of the Moon. (See **Lunar surface features—co-ordinates of.**)

FIRST POINT OF ARIES The vernal equinox, one of the points of intersection of the Ecliptic and the celestial equator. The name originates from the time of Hipparchus, when the vernal equinox was actually situated in the constellation Aries; owing to the effect of the **precession of the equinoxes** it is located in Pisces at the present time. The First Point of Aries is denoted by the symbol Υ.

(See also **Sun—apparent motion of.**)

FIRST POINT OF LIBRA The autumnal equinox, one of the points of intersection of the Ecliptic and the celestial equator. Due to the **precession of the equinoxes** it is now situated not in Libra but in Virgo. The First Point of Libra is denoted by the symbol $\simeq$.

(See also **Sun—apparent motion of.**)

FIRST QUARTER The phase of the Moon at the eastern quadrature; exactly half of the illuminated surface is visible from the Earth, in the characteristic 'half-moon' shape.

(See **Phases of the Moon.**)

FITZGERALD, G. F. (1851–1901) Distinguished physicist who postulated that a body moving in space at a high velocity (i.e. a velocity that is significant when compared with the velocity of light), is contracted in the direction of its motion. (See **Lorentz–Fitzgerald contraction.**)

FIXED STARS Term used since ancient times to denote the background stars as opposed to the Sun, Moon and planets and other members of the solar system; all of the latter show a readily detectable (and in many cases rapid) motion relative to the background stars.

It is in fact rather a misnomer as all stars have a proper motion, but this apparent movement is so small that it is detectable only by means of very precise observation over a long period of time.

FLAMSTEED, Rev. John (1646–1719)
The man who was to become the first Astronomer Royal left school at fifteen and was largely self-taught; such was his astronomical knowledge acquired in this manner, however, that he was able to enter Cambridge University in his late twenties and obtain his M.A.

In 1675 he was appointed one of a committee created to examine a proposal by the Frenchman Le Sieur de St. Pierre, of a method of determining longitudes at sea by positional observations of the Moon against the background stars. The committee reported favourably on the proposed method, but pointed out that there were no star catalogues or tables of the Moon's motions of sufficient accuracy; as a result of the committee's report, Charles II founded the Royal Observatory, Greenwich, and appointed Flamsteed 'Our Astronomical Observator' at a salary of £100 per annum, 'forthwith to apply himself with the most exact care and diligence to rectifying the tables of the motions of the heavens, and the places of the fixed stars, so as to find out the so-much desired longitude of places for perfecting the art of navigation'.

Out of his far-from-princely income Flamsteed was expected to provide his own instruments and any skilled assistance he required. For some years, his main instrument was a 7-ft. sextant by Thomas Tompion, given by Sir Jonas Moore; becoming less impecunious on the death of his father in 1688, Flamsteed appointed Abraham Sharp as his assistant and commissioned him to construct a new 140° mural arc of nearly 7 ft. radius. With his sextant and later with the mural arc, Flamsteed obtained more than 30,000 observations of about 2,800 stars; these observations were of far greater accuracy than any previous work, and Flamsteed may be regarded as having set the pattern of high-precision observation which made possible the great advances in our knowledge of dynamical astronomy made during the eighteenth and nineteenth centuries.

Owing to a dispute regarding the publication rights of his observations they were not published for many years, and when they were produced, under the title *Historia Cœlestis Britannica* in 1712 it was without Flamsteed's approval and in a very inaccurate form; Flamsteed was not unnaturally furious and, managing to obtain three-quarters of the copies printed, he publicly burnt them. He commenced the preparation of an accurate, revised edition himself, but this was not completed by the time of his death in 1719.

The task was completed by his loyal assistants Sharp and Crosthwait and published, in three volumes, in 1725, followed by the associated Atlas in 1729. The first great contribution to fundamental astronomy from the Royal Observatory, Greenwich—the *'Historia Coelestis'*—also stands as a lasting memorial to the patience and diligence of its creator, who had served as the first Astronomer Royal for nearly 44 years.

(See also **Royal Observatory, Greenwich.**)

FLAMSTEED Lunar surface feature, co-ordinates $\xi - 696$, $\eta - 078$. A bright crater, 9 miles in diameter, on the southern wall of a ruined ring (60 miles in diameter) on the floor of the Oceanus Procellarum. This larger ring is a twin of Letronne, and makes a meridional chain with Letronne and Gassendi.

FLAMSTEED NUMBERS Star identifications consisting of the numbers allocated to the stars in each constellation by Flamsteed and published in the *Historia Coelestis Britannica* in 1725.

(See also **Star catalogues; Star nomenclature.**)

FLARE STARS A type of intrinsic variable, usually red dwarfs of spectral type M. The variability occurs as a sudden flare-up, often of several magnitudes, of very short duration (usually a very few minutes). These outbreaks are quite unpredictable.

Spectroscopic study of flare stars shows

that during an outburst extremely high surface temperatures are attained. The spectra of many flare stars show emission lines due to hydrogen and ionized calcium between outbreaks. The flare stars are often referred to as *UV Ceti stars* after the best-known of the type.

FLARES, SOLAR Short-lived solar phenomena, sometimes referred to as 'chromospheric eruptions'; they have been seen in integrated light, but are more frequently observed in hydrogen light with the aid of the spectrohelioscope. A patch of great brilliancy forms very suddenly, rapidly gaining in intensity, until a maximum is reached and the flare dies down with equal rapidity. If the flare occurs near the solar limb a 'surge', or short-lived prominence consisting of a jet of matter shooting from the limb and then falling back, is often seen. Flares are usually associated with large, newly-formed sunspots.

(See also **Solar activity; Solar–terrestrial relationships; Sun—physical constitution of; Sunspots.**)

FLASH SPECTRUM The spectrum of the solar chromosphere, which 'flashes out' for an instant at the commencement and conclusion of the total phase of a solar eclipse, when the photosphere and reversing layer are occulted by the Moon and the higher chromosphere remains, briefly, in view. [Plate 1(e).]

(See **Chromosphere, solar; Sun—physical constitution of.**)

FLAT, OPTICAL An optically plane surface, usually of silvered or aluminized glass, used to redirect light-beams in telescopes and other optical instruments. The plane surface is produced by a carefully controlled polishing process; for most astronomical purposes it is essential that deviations from a true plane must not exceed one tenth of a wavelength of light.

(See also **Telescope, Newtonian,** etc.)

FLINT GLASS A form of **optical glass** (*q.v.*) having a refractive index which is rather high compared with that of crown glass with which it is often used in conjunction.

FLOCCULI The small, bright patches which, with darker interstices, form the granulated surface of the solar photosphere, as revealed in photographs and spectroheliograms. They are believed to be the tops of columns of gas carried by convection up to an altitude at which the temperature is low enough for it to re-condense. The substance most involved in this process is calcium, the flocculi being excellently seen in spectroheliograms made in the light of the Fraunhofer K line. The distribution of flocculi is constantly changing; they are normally very concentrated in areas surrounding sunspots.

(See also **Solar activity; Sun—physical constitution of.**)

FOCAL LENGTH The distance between a lens or curved mirror and its **focus.**

FOCAL RATIO The ratio of the aperture of a telescope to its focal length; i.e. the focal ratio (f) is obtained from $f = F/D$, where F is the focal length of the objective and D its effective aperture. Refractors are usually constructed with focal ratios of $f/15$ or higher, whereas conventional reflectors are now seldom designed to operate at higher ratios than $f/8$.

(See also **Telescope.**)

FOCUS The point at which a lens or curved mirror will cause previously parallel light-rays to converge. In the case of a convergent element the focus is 'real', but in the case of a divergent element the focus is the point at which the diverging rays would meet if produced back, and is said to be 'virtual'.

FOGGING A factor which reduces the maximum permissible exposure that can be used with a photographic telescope; it varies with the conditions obtaining at the time of observation. It is caused by extraneous light darkening the plate to such an extent that the images of faint stars cannot be distinguished from the background 'fog'. The most usual causes are the reflection of light from the Sun (when not far below the horizon) by dust, smoke or vapour in the atmosphere; the presence of the Moon; the existence of nearby artificial lights, etc.

FOLLOWING LIMB The 'trailing' limb of a planet or other body having an appreciable disk, as it moves across the field of view due to the diurnal motion. The term is used in the description of observational results.

(See also **Preceding limb**.)

FOMALHAUT The star α PsA, magnitude 1·16. It is visible low down in the southern sky in late summer and autumn, but is visible only in first-class conditions from northern England and Scotland, owing to its low southern declination. It is, in fact, the most southerly first-magnitude star visible from the British Isles.

FORBIDDEN LINES Emission lines in the spectra of gaseous nebulae which could not be identified by comparison with laboratory spectra; they were therefore attributed to an unknown element, to which the name 'nebulium' was assigned. Two very prominent lines attributed to nebulium were at wavelengths of 4959 Å and 5007 Å—both in the green part of the spectrum, hence the rather greenish tint displayed by the gaseous nebulae. It is now known that there is no such element as nebulium, and that these lines, which therefore became known as 'forbidden lines', are caused by doubly ionized atoms of oxygen.

FORKED BAY Martian surface feature, approximate position Ω 0°, Φ − 5°. Name used by Dawes and other early English observers for the feature now usually

known by the designation **Sinus Meridiani**, *q.v.*

FORNAX (The Furnace. *Genitive* Fornacis, *I.A.U. Abbreviation* For.) A small southern constellation, south of Eridanus and Cetus. The brightest stars are three of the fourth magnitude.

FOUCAULT PENDULUM An apparatus to demonstrate the rotation of the Earth, consisting of a heavy metal ball suspended by a very long wire with very little friction at the point of support. Once the pendulum is set swinging, it will continue to swing in a constant plane in space, there being no force acting upon it to change this. If the Earth were not rotating, the pendulum would, therefore, continue to swing over the same line on the Earth's surface; if the initial line of swing is marked, however, the pendulum's line of swing is seen to depart from this by an ever-increasing angle. The period of axial rotation of the Earth (24 hr.) can be deduced from observation of this changing angle.

The experiment was originally devised by the French physicist L. Foucault (1819–1868), who in 1851 hung an iron ball from the dome of the Panthéon on a 200-ft. wire.

FRACASTORIUS Lunar surface feature, co-ordinates ξ + 505, η − 363. One of the best examples of a partially ruined ring formation. Formerly a huge ring plain some 60 miles in diameter, it seems to have been engulfed by an overflow of the Mare Nectaris. Its floor now appears to be an extension of that of the Mare, at whose southern end it is situated. Only a few hills and ridges mark the line of the former northern rampart. There is still a vestigial central mountain, and the present floor of the feature presents a wealth of fine detail.

FRANKLIN-ADAMS, John (1843–1912) English amateur astronomer of considerable private means, and an expert in astronomical photography. He conceived a plan to chart the heavens photographically, and during a sojourn in South Africa for the benefit of his health, in 1903–1904, his 10-in. refractor was erected in the grounds of the Royal Observatory at the Cape. A series of plates was obtained covering the whole of the southern sky, prior to Franklin-Adams' return to his new observatory at Godalming, Surrey; a further series of plates was then obtained, covering the northern skies.

Franklin-Adams also commenced the vast task of measuring the plates, but ill health forced him in 1910 to dispose of his instruments and hand the plates over to the Astronomer Royal; the measurement of the plates and the photoprinting of the Franklin-Adams Charts from them was completed by the staff of the Royal Observatory.

A second set of plates of the southern sky, again from the Cape, was commenced in 1910 by Franklin-Adams' assistant and subsequently completed by R. T. A. Innes.

FRANKLIN-ADAMS CHARTS A series of photographic star charts covering the entire heavens, printed from the plates obtained by John Franklin-Adams and his assistants at the Cape of Good Hope and at Godalming, Surrey, between 1903 and 1912.

FRAUNHOFER, Josef von (1787–1826) Born at Staubing, Bavaria, Fraunhofer was destined to become one of Germany's greatest opticians and astronomers and, indeed, a world pioneer in the development of physical optics.

Orphaned in boyhood, Fraunhofer was apprenticed to a miserly Munich mirror-maker, Weichselberger, who taught him little; two years later, however, Weichselberger's house collapsed, killing his wife and burying Fraunhofer.

Fraunhofer had the double good fortune to be protected by a strong cross-beam, and to be rescued before the eyes of the Elector Maximilian of Bavaria, for the Elector gave him money which enabled

him to gain a measure of independence and, eventually, to buy himself out of his unsatisfactory apprenticeship. Fraunhofer rapidly increased his knowledge of optics and in 1806 obtained a post in the Optical and Physical Institute in Munich where he was responsible for many notable developments in optical instrument design. Of particular value were his researches into the design of achromatic object glasses for large refractors, and of the original divided-object-glass **heliometer**; he made a number of superb objectives, notably that of the 9½-in. refractor erected at Dorpat in Estonia, and the heliometer (which was almost completed when Fraunhofer died) was used by Bessel to measure the parallax of 61 Cygni—an angle of only one-third of a second of arc.

Fraunhofer is principally remembered for his study of the solar spectrum. The seven most prominent absorption lines had been observed by Wollaston in 1802, but he believed them to be merely the edges of the principal bands of the spectrum. In 1814 Fraunhofer used a flint-glass objective prism, in conjunction with a small theodolite telescope, to observe a narrow shaft of sunlight admitted through a slit in a window shutter. He later used a 4½-in. refractor fitted with a high-dispersion objective prism. With these instruments he observed not only the lines discovered by Wollaston but a total of 574; he plotted the position in the spectrum of 324 of these.

Fraunhofer's pioneering work in this field was commemorated by the adoption of the name **Fraunhofer lines** for the solar absorption lines. Fraunhofer identified the most prominent bands with letters of the alphabet; thus the well known **Hydrogen-alpha line** was originally known as the 'Fraunhofer C Line'.

(See also **Sun—spectrum of.**)

FRAUNHOFER LINES The absorption lines in the solar spectrum, originally studied and plotted by **Josef von Fraunhofer.** Fraunhofer observed 574 lines, and plotted the position of the 324 most

Table 12. Fraunhofer lines

Fraunhofer designation	Location in spectrum	Wavelength (Ångstroms)		Identification
A	Infra-red	7100	⎱	Telluric bands, due to oxygen in the Earth's
B	Red	6875	⎰	atmosphere.
C	Red	6563		The H_α hydrogen line.
a	Orange	6278		Oxygen.
D	Yellow	5896 (D_1)		The double line due to sodium.
		5890 (D_2)		
E	Green	5270		Iron.
		5178	b_1	Iron.
b	Green	5173	b_2	Double line of magnesium.
		5169	b_3	
		5167	b_4	Iron and magnesium lines superimposed.
c	Blue-green	4958		Iron.
F	Blue-green	4861		The H_β hydrogen line.
d	Blue	4668		Iron.
e	Indigo	4384		Iron.
f	Indigo	4340		The H_γ hydrogen line.
G	Indigo	4308		Iron and calcium lines superimposed.
g	Indigo	4227		Calcium.
h	Violet	4102		The H_δ hydrogen line.
i	Violet	4048		Iron.
H	Violet	3968		Calcium.
K	Violet	3934		Calcium.

prominent. The most obvious he designated with the letters of the alphabet, in two series; the nine most prominent bands he designated *A* to *K* (reading from red to violet), and the next most obvious *a* to *i*. These lines, with their wavelengths and identifications, are listed in Table 12.

(See also **Sun—spectrum of.**)

FULL MOON The phase of the Moon when it is at opposition; the entire illuminated hemisphere is presented to the Earth, and the outline of the apparent disk of the Moon therefore appears circular.

(See **Phase of the Moon.**)

FUNDAMENTAL CATALOGUE A catalogue of the places of the fundamental stars adopted by the International Astronomical Union, used as a basis of reference for all positional observations.

(See also **FK3 catalogue; Meridian astronomy; Star catalogues.**)

FUNDAMENTAL STARS Stars whose positions and proper motions have been very accurately determined, and whose place can therefore be assumed as a basis to which positional observations of other bodies can be referred. For this purpose it is essential that ephemerides are prepared and published, tabulating the predicted positions of these stars at frequent intervals throughout the year concerned, and in order to keep the ephemerides as accurate as possible the fundamental stars are constantly re-observed as part of the meridian programmes of observatories throughout the world.

In 1935 the International Astronomical Union adopted the 1535 stars contained in the *Dritter Fundamentalkatalog des Berliner Astronomischen Jahrbuchs* (universally known by its abbreviation 'FK3') as the fundamental reference stars to be used thenceforward; annual ephemerides of these stars are published under the title *Apparent Places of Fundamental Stars*. A revision of this catalogue, to be known as the FK4, is in process of preparation and will eventually be adopted by the International Astronomical Union as the standard **fundamental catalogue.**

(See also **Meridian astronomy; Star catalogues.**)

FURCA Martian surface feature, approximate position $\Omega\ 0°$, $\Phi - 5°$. Alternative version of Sinus Furcosis, the latinized form of 'Forked Bay'; the designation **Sinus Meridiani** is now preferred.

FURNERIUS Lunar surface feature, co-ordinates $\xi + 704$, $\eta - 587$. A walled plain, 80 miles in diameter, close to the south-western limb of the Moon; it is the most southerly major member of the great meridional chain of crater formations stretching to Endymion in the north. Its position renders it a difficult object to observe in detail, but over the years of patient observation much small detail has been recorded in its interior. The walls are terraced and rise to 11,000 ft.; they are rather broken in parts.

G

G STARS Stars of spectral class *G*; they are yellow stars with surface temperatures in the range 4,200–5,500 °K in the case of giants, 5,000–6,000 °K in the case of dwarfs. The Sun and *Capella* are the best-known examples.

GFH Usual abbreviation of the **Geschichte des Fixstern-Himmels**, *q.v.*

GACRUX The star γ Cru, magnitude 1·74. The northernmost star of the Southern Cross.

GALACTIC CENTRE The centre of the Galaxy may be defined as the point at which the axis of rotation of the Galaxy intersects the galactic plane. The region surrounding the galactic centre is densely populated with stars, the redder Population II stars predominating. The discrete radio source **Sagittarius A** (17S2A) appears to be situated at the galactic centre.

GALACTIC CENTRE—DIRECTION OF The direction of the galactic centre was adopted in 1960 as the zero of galactic longitude in the revised system of galacto-centric co-ordinates. Its direction coincides with that of the radio source **Sagittarius A,** and is defined as being the intersection of the galactic plane and the great semi-circle originating at the galactic pole (as newly defined in 1960) at a position angle of 123° with respect to the equatorial pole for 1950·0.

The apparent position of the galactic centre on the celestial sphere is R.A. 17 hr 42 min 37 sec, Dec. −28° 57′ (Epoch 1950·0).

(See also **Galactic co-ordinates.**)

GALACTIC CONCENTRATION An index of the increasing density of stars towards the galactic plane. (See **Stars— galactic concentration of.**)

GALACTIC CO-ORDINATES The study of the structure of the Galaxy is one of the most important fields in current astro-physical research, and many contemporary programmes for the observation of stars are conceived with the intention of further-ing our knowledge of the Galaxy in which they are situated. For such purposes the conventional geocentric co-ordinate system of celestial latitude and longitude provides a very inconvenient frame of reference, and a system of galactocentric co-ordinates has been in use for many years.

The need for a galactocentric co-ordinate system was first recognized by Sir William Herschel in 1785. The pole of the system adopted by Herschel and those of the various systems propounded by his successors during the following century and a half were all within a couple of degrees of each other. For his extensive observations at the Harvard College Observatory E. C. Pickering used a position for the pole of R.A. 12 hr 40 min, Dec. +28° 00′ (Epoch 1900·0); in 1932 Ohlsson of the Lund Observatory also adopted this position for the pole in compiling his tables for the conversion of galactic into equatorial co-ordinates. For the zero of galactic longitude Ohlsson used the intersection of the galactic plane and the celestial equator at 1900·0. Ohlsson's system became adopted as the standard system of galactocentric co-ordinates.

The development of radio-astronomy, however, and in particular the study of the distribution of interstellar hydrogen arising from observations of the 21-cm hydrogen radiation, led to greatly improved knowledge of galactic structure and showed that the Ohlsson co-ordinate system is not sufficiently accurate for continued use. The General Assembly of the International Astronomical Union held in Dublin in 1955 consequently formed a new Sub-Commission "to investigate the desirability of a revision of the position of the galactic pole and of the zero point of galactic longitude". At the General Assembly of the I.A.U. held in Moscow three years later the Sub-Commission presented its interim report, recommending that a new system be devised and setting out the principles upon which it should be based. The Sub-Commission completed the new system in 1959; its derivation is described in full in a series of 5 papers published, on the authority of the I.A.U., by the Royal Astronomical Society in 1960 (*Mon. Not. R. Astron. Soc.* **121**, pp. 123–173).

The Sub-Commission found that radio observations of the interstellar hydrogen were the most significant factor in determining the orientation of the galactic plane as observed from Earth, and hence the position of the galactic pole. The revised position of the (north) galactic pole is defined as R.A. 12 hr 49 min, Dec. +27° 24′ (Epoch 1950·0). This is within 2° of Ohlsson's pole. The galactic equator is, of course, the locus on the celestial sphere of a point 90° from the galactic poles.

The zero of galactic longitude has, by comparison, undergone a much more drastic change; instead of the intersection of the galactic plane and the celestial equator, the direction of the centre of the Galaxy is adopted as the zero—a change of about 32°. The radio source **Sagittarius A** is believed to lie at the galactic centre; its direction is the adopted zero of galactic longitude, defined as the great semi-circle originating at the new galactic pole, as defined above, at a position angle of 123° with respect to the equatorial pole for 1950·0.

Galactic longitude is measured from 0° to 360° along the galactic equator, 0° being the direction of the galactic centre, increasing in the direction of increasing Right Ascension.

Galactic latitude is measured from +90° at the north galactic pole through 0° at the galactic equator to −90° at the south galactic pole.

Notation. The symbols adopted by the I.A.U. are l and b for galactic longitude and latitude respectively. To distinguish between the old and new systems these are usually used with superscripts, thus l^I, b^I for the old system, l^{II}, b^{II} for the revised system.

GALACTIC EQUATOR The zero of galactic latitude; it may be regarded as the locus on the celestial sphere of a point 90° from both galactic poles. It marks the intersection of the galactic plane with the celestial sphere. Its path across the heavens is marked by the Milky Way.

GALACTIC EVOLUTION The need to determine what evolutionary processes are involved in the formation of the many different types of galaxy present in the universe is one of the major problems of cosmology; it is just as fundamental to our understanding of the nature and history of the universe as the study of the evolution of individual stars. It is the astrophysicist who provides the observational data from which the cosmologist pieces together his theories, and in the past half-century or so the galaxies have figured largely in astrophysical observation.

So many galaxies have been discovered, of so many forms, that purely morphological studies of them have led to some remarkably cogent suggestions. In his early attempt to classify the galaxies Hubble set up a classification sequence which he also believed to be an evolutionary sequence, from the spherical galaxy, through increasingly elliptical forms, through the spiral galaxies of ever more widely opening form, and finally to the irregular galaxy—thus:

$$E \rightarrow Sa \rightarrow Sb \rightarrow Sc \rightarrow I.$$

Hubble envisaged the spherical galaxy 'flattening' into ellipsoidal form as a result of its rotation; later he rearranged his sequence to provide an alternative 'stream' for the barred spirals, separate from the normal spirals:

$$Eo \rightarrow E3 \rightarrow E7 \rightarrow So$$
$$\nearrow \quad Sa \rightarrow Sb \rightarrow Sc \rightarrow I$$
$$\searrow \quad SBa \rightarrow SBb \rightarrow SBc$$

This sequence formed, of course, the basis of Hubble's famous 'tuning-fork' diagram (Fig. 48, p. 144.) Later Shapley and others suggested that the tuning-fork diagram might indeed be an evolutionary sequence, as Hubble believed, but that the direction should be reversed—i.e. the irregular galaxy was the 'youngest' type; it would gradually develop spiral arms and evolve into a wide, open spiral; the spiral arms would gradually close up until they became almost part of the nucleus, which would thus become a very ellipsoidal elliptical galaxy; this would become progressively less elongated, until the spheroidal form (*Eo*) was reached.

Further support for this view of the evolutionary sequence arises from Baade's separation of the stars into two Populations. Population I stars, the bright bluish stars found in the spiral arms, are believed to be very young stars. The cooler, redder, Population II stars found in the galactic nuclei are believed to be older. This supports a picture of hot Population I stars being formed in the spiral arms (which, perhaps, are themselves just forming in a hitherto irregular galaxy) and progressing along the spiral arm towards the nucleus as the galaxy slowly rotates and the stars grow older. The galaxy meanwhile is metamorphosed through the spiral (or barred spiral) sequence, eventually becoming a highly condensed ellipsoidal or spheroidal object. The stars by this time will be old, cool, Population II stars and will have reached the nucleus. It is significant that the stars in the irregular galaxies appear to be almost entirely of Population I, whereas those in the elliptical galaxies are mostly of Population II.

It is probable that we are fortunate in having a close view of an irregular galaxy in the process of becoming a barred spiral —*Nubecula Major*, the larger Magellanic Cloud—which has a structure strongly suggestive of the 'bar' of the *SBc*-type barred spiral.

Other astrophysical results tend to support this interpretation, which is now widely accepted; it must be recognized however that it is only a broad summary of the evolutionary history of a galaxy, and that there are many problems awaiting solution as new techniques of observation and analysis are developed.

(See also **Galactic structure; Galaxies; Galaxies—classification of.**)

GALACTIC LATITUDE The angular distance of a body from the galactic plane. (See **Galactic co-ordinates.**)

GALACTIC LIGHT That part of the faint background illumination of the night sky which originates from the stars but is diffused through interstellar space. (See **Night sky, illumination of.**)

GALACTIC LONGITUDE A measure, in the galactic plane, of the position of a body, referred to the galactic centre. The zero of galactic longitude was formerly the intersection of the galactic plane and the celestial equator, but in the revised system adopted by the International Astronomical Union in 1960 the zero is defined as the apparent direction of the galactic centre. (See **Galactic co-ordinates.**)

GALACTIC PLANE The plane about which the component stars of the Galaxy are symmetrically distributed. It is the fundamental plane of reference for the system of galactic co-ordinates. (See **Galactic co-ordinates; Galactic structure.**)

GALACTIC POLE A point having a galactocentric latitude of $+90°$ or $-90°$; from his star-gauge counts Sir William Herschel deduced the general shape of the

Galaxy, and that the Milky Way represented the abundance of stars in and close to the galactic plane. Using the centre line of the Milky Way band as a galactic equator he was able to estimate the position of the north galactic pole, in Coma Berenices; later workers amended this position very slightly, the point used by E. C. Pickering and adopted by Ohlsson for the Lund tables for the conversion of galactic into equatorial co-ordinates in 1932 becoming the accepted standard for many years. This position, usually referred to as the 'Ohlsson pole', was R.A. 12 hr 40 min, Dec. +28° 00' (Epoch 1900·0). In 1960 a revised system was adopted by the International Astronomical Union, based largely upon radio observations of the distribution of interstellar neutral hydrogen in the galactic plane. The position of the new galactic pole is R.A. 12 hr 49 min, Dec. +27° 24' (Epoch 1950·0). (See **Galactic co-ordinates.**)

GALACTIC RECESSION The spectra of all extragalactic objects show a shift of their lines towards the red; this is interpreted as a result of the Doppler effect, showing that these objects are receding. It was shown by Hubble in 1929, using the red shifts measured by V. M. Slipher and M. Humason, that the galaxies are receding at velocities which are directly proportional to their distance (Fig. 47); thus was born the concept of the 'Ex-

panding Universe'. If the distance of any galaxy is divided by its observed annual recession a period of approximately 7,000 million years results in all cases. This is known as the *Hubble Constant*; it implies that 7,000 million years ago all the clusters of galaxies were densely packed together in one mass.

Plate 19(b) shows the spectra of five galaxies at different distances; their distances and observed rates of recession are given. The arrows beneath each spectrum indicate the red shift of the H and K lines of calcium. The comparison spectra above and below each spectrogram are of helium.

(See also **Red shift.**)

GALACTIC ROTATION The Galaxy is in a state of rotation about its centre, which can be demonstrated by comparisons of the radial velocities of stars within the Galaxy but at different distances from the Sun; the radial velocities show a differential effect depending upon their distance from the Sun and their position in the Galaxy.

(See also **Galaxy, The; Star streaming.**)

GALACTIC STRUCTURE The investigation of the dimensions and shape of the system of stars of which the Sun is one has been one of the main preoccupations of the observational astronomer for about 150 years; in recent years it has been one of the most actively pursued branches of the subject, and has been considerably advanced by the development of radio-astronomical methods of investigation to supplement the classical optical methods.

The study of the structure of the Galaxy may be said to have had its origin in the speculations as to the nature of the Milky Way recorded by ancient observers, such as Anaxagoras (born *ca.* 500 B.C.) who suggested that "the Milky Way is the light of certain stars". This remarkable piece of foresight could not be proved until Galileo, some 2,000 years later, first examined the Milky Way with a telescope and pronounced it "a mass of innumerable stars".

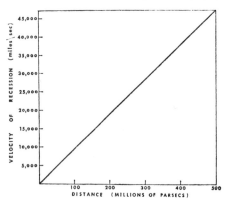

Fig. 47

The first observational programme designed specifically to investigate the structure of the Galaxy was that commenced by Sir William Herschel in 1783. Herschel used his famous '20-foot' telescope—a reflector of $18\frac{3}{4}$ inches aperture and 20 feet focal length—and an eyepiece which gave him a field of view 15 minutes of arc in diameter. Herschel's programme consisted of counting the number of stars visible in the field, moving the telescope to an adjacent part of the sky and repeating the count. Herschel made such sample counts in a number of closely adjacent fields, and averaged the count: the resulting average he termed the star gauge for that part of the sky. By comparing the gauges obtained in about 3,000 areas representative of the whole of the visible sky Herschel was able to study the distribution of the stars. He found that they are most numerous in the regions crossed by the Milky Way and least numerous in those regions farthest from it. Herschel made a number of assumptions which are now known to be invalid in interpreting the star-gauge evidence, but nevertheless arrived at a fairly accurate picture of the galactic system, which he described as a flattened disk, like a grindstone, the Milky Way marking the plane of the disk; the Sun he believed to be situated fairly close to the centre of the disk. William Herschel's star-gauge counts were extended to the southern hemisphere by his son John, during his great survey of the southern heavens made from the Cape of Good Hope between 1834 and 1838.

The next great achievement bearing upon the structure of the Galaxy was the discovery of the spiral form of the galaxy M 51 by the third Earl of Rosse in 1845; many more spiral galaxies were found in the years that followed, and those seen 'edge-wise on' to the Earth showed them to have a cross-section like that of a biconvex lens. Inevitably the Galaxy itself was assumed to be a spiral having this lenticular form.

Herschel's star-gauge principle was developed by J. C. Kapteyn in 1906:

Kapteyn selected 206 sample areas of the sky to be surveyed in great detail with large telescopes at some of the major observatories of the world—the first important programme to obtain extensive observatorial evidence of the distribution of stars within the Galaxy for statistical analysis since those of the Herschels, and one of the foundations upon which later studies have been built.

The next development came in the 1920s; it arose from Harlow Shapley's study of the globular clusters. Of more than a hundred globular clusters known very few are visible in the northern hemisphere; not only are most of them in the southern skies but they also seem to be most frequent in the region around Scorpio and Sagittarius. They are, however, scarce on the galactic equator, no doubt due to the presence of light-absorbing dust-clouds. The globular clusters form, in fact, a spherical system roughly concentric with the Galaxy. Using the cluster variables (**RR Lyrae stars**) as a yardstick Shapley determined the diameter of the globular cluster system as approximately 30 kpc. More important, he found that the system appeared to be centred on a point some 16 kpc from the Sun. This was a major breakthrough—the first concrete evidence that Herschel's assumption that the Sun lay close to the galactic centre, a view also held by Kapteyn, was incorrect. It is now known that Shapley overestimated the distance of many clusters, owing to their being dimmed by interstellar absorption, but nevertheless the importance of his achievement must not be overlooked. The corrected distance of the Sun from the galactic centre is 8·2 kpc, and it is believed to be very approximately 8 pc north of the galactic plane. This realization of the Sun's true position in the Galaxy immediately explained several anomalies in the results of the earlier studies of galactic structure, and a much more accurate picture began to emerge.

William Herschel had recorded numerous dark patches in the Milky Way; these were later studied by E. E. Barnard, who catalogued 182 of them. More than 1,500 were found on the Franklin-Adams charts, in which the entire heavens were photographed on a uniform scale; they were found to occur predominantly in the Milky Way. They are not, as Herschel supposed, 'gaps' in the star fields, but clouds of non-luminous interstellar dust which effectively obscure the star-clouds beyond. Clouds of obscuring dust occur extensively in the Galaxy, but are mainly confined to the galactic plane; they are probably common to all spiral galaxies — they are very prominent in those which present an edge-wise view to the Earth [Plate 18(b)]. The obscuring clouds of interstellar gas and dust are also responsible for the dimming and 'reddening' of many stars in the region of the galactic plane; they are also the reason for the band along the galactic equator, termed by Hubble the *zone of avoidance*, in which no spiral galaxies are found.

The prediction by van de Hulst in 1944, that the cool clouds of neutral hydrogen should be emitting radiation at the radio wave-length of 21 cm, and the constant observation of this radiation since it was first detected in 1951, have led to remarkably precise delineation of the structure of the Galaxy; the spiral arms have now been mapped for the greater part of the system, using the radio observations of neutral hydrogen made at Leiden and Sydney [Plate 20(d)]. The overall diameter of the system is about 25 kpc, and its maximum thickness (at the centre) about 4 kpc.

(See also **Galaxy—rotation of**.)

GALACTOCENTRIC CO-ORDINATES

A system of co-ordinates (termed galactic longitude and latitude) used to denote the position of a body with reference to the galactic plane. The system of galactic co-ordinates used for *ca.* 150 years was revised by a Sub-Commission of the International Astronomical Union in 1960. (See **Galactic co-ordinates**.)

GALAXIES The term 'galaxy', from the Greek synonym for 'Milky Way', was formerly used both to denote the latter feature of the night sky and also to denote the entire universe. As knowledge of the star system of which the Sun is a member grew, it was a logical development that the star system should become known as the Galaxy. This led to the distant star systems discovered later being termed 'extragalactic nebulae, an unfortunate term as they are certainly not true nebulae. Of late the term 'galaxy' has been applied to these objects, however, the capitalized form 'The Galaxy' being used to indicate our own system.

Principal types of galaxy

The spiral form of some galaxies was first discovered in the case of M 51 in Canes Venatici, by Lord Rosse in 1845. The spiral structure of M 31, the great galaxy in Andromeda, was discovered photographically by Isaac Roberts in 1888. Others which displayed no spiral structure but were spherical or ellipsoidal in form were also discovered in the mid-nineteenth century: these were termed *elliptical galaxies* by S. Alexander in 1852. A different class of spiral galaxy, the *barred spirals*, was set up by H. D. Curtis in 1918; Curtis also deduced the nature of those spirals which are presented edge-wise to the Earth. A number of galaxies do not show any regular form and do not fit into any of these classes—the *irregular galaxies*.

Elliptical galaxies. These range from spherical systems to very elongated ellipsoidal ones. They rarely show any detailed structure, showing normally a bright, highly condensed nucleus surrounded by nebulosity decreasing evenly in brightness with distance from the nucleus [Plate 18(a)].

Spiral galaxies. These show a bright central nucleus with two spiral arms emerging from opposite sides of it [Plate 18(b–d)]. Those seen edge-on have a flat, lenticular cross-section and show a dark band of absorption, across their entire diameter, in the equatorial plane

[Plate 18(b)]. The overall appearance varies enormously; it depends principally upon the degree to which the spiral arms are 'opened out'—they may be tightly closed as in Plate 17(d), or very open as in Plate 18(d). The size of the nucleus appears to be directly related to this, being much larger in the case of the closed spirals.

Barred spiral galaxies. These have a bright nucleus located centrally on a bright 'bar' of nebulosity; in this class the spiral arms commence perpendicularly from the ends of this bar. In the most closed form the spiral arms join to form a circle, giving the general appearance of the Greek letter Θ [Plate 19(a)] but very open forms also occur [Plate 19(c)].

Classification

Morphological classification systems, sub-dividing these classes, were set up by Hubble and Lundmark in 1926; Hubble used and developed his system during his great study of the galaxies carried out at the Mount Wilson Observatory, summarized in his classic work *The Realm of the Nebulae* published in 1936. Hubble's system became widely adopted, and is frequently referred to as the 'standard classification'. In recent years much more comprehensive systems of classification have been proposed, but these are of value only to the specialist and are beyond the scope of the present work. They include a new class of *lenticular galaxies*, in form mid-way between the ellipticals and the spirals.

Distribution

The distribution of galaxies throughout the heavens was studied by Hubble: he found that there is a belt of irregular width (approximately 20° wide, on average) along the galactic equator in which very few galaxies are found. (Hubble termed this belt the *zone of avoidance*.) Elsewhere the galaxies are much in evidence with frequencies of up to 1,800 per square degree in some areas of the sky. It has been estimated that the total number of detectable galaxies in the entire sky is of the

order of 75–100 million. The frequency of occurrence of the principal types is: barred spirals, 26·3%; normal spirals, 24·4%; ellipticals, 23·4%; lenticulars, 21·0%; irregulars, 3·4%; peculiar galaxies, 1·5%.

Clusters of galaxies

The average separation between individual galaxies is about 500 parsecs; there are numerous examples of clusters of galaxies, however, in which they are much more densely distributed. Some of the larger clusters, e.g. those in Virgo and Coma Berenices, contain thousands of member galaxies. Our own Galaxy is part of a small cluster of twenty or so members, including the great spiral in Andromeda (M 31) and the Magellanic Clouds, which is known as the *Local Group*. [Plate 19(d).]

General

Some of the nearer galaxies are resolvable into stars: these are found to comprise the same types of star as are found in our own galactic system. The same globular and open clusters, novae and supernovae, etc., are also found.

In some cases the rotation of the galaxy can be established; it is found that the nucleus rotates as a rigid body, but the stars in the spiral arms revolve around the centre of the galaxy with a velocity which decreases progressively with distance from the centre.

Many double and multiple galaxies are known, and some examples of galaxies in collision have been photographed—a notable example of this is associated with the strong radio source known as Cygnus A. [Plate 24(a).]

Hubble believed that his classification sequence (Fig. 48) represented an evolutionary pattern for the galaxies, and the classification of the galaxies, of which he was the pioneer, has continued to be an invaluable basis for the development of theories of galactic evolution.

(See also **Galactic evolution; Galactic structure; Galaxies—classification of**).

GALAXIES—CLASSIFICATION OF

Galaxies were being discovered in con-

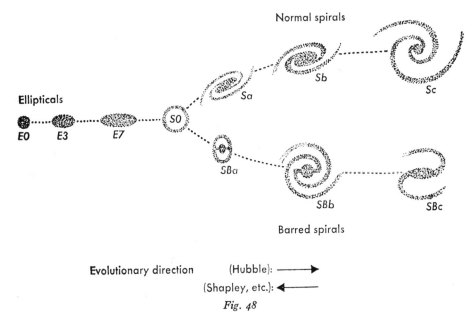

Normal spirals

Barred spirals

Evolutionary direction   (Hubble): ⟶

(Shapley, etc.): ⟵

Fig. 48

siderable numbers during the latter part of the last century and the early years of the present one, following the application of photographic methods; these were found to be in so many differing (yet obviously related) forms that some means of classification was badly needed. The descriptive terms *spiral, elliptical* and *barred spiral galaxy* had been applied to the various types over the years, and these terms were adopted as the basis of a classification system by Hubble in 1926. A similar system was developed simultaneously by Lundmark.

Hubble developed his system and used it to classify the thousands of galaxies studied by him at the Mount Wilson Observatory, and for many years Hubble's classification system has been the adopted standard. It is essentially a morphological system, in which a classification index is assigned to each galaxy, denoting its apparent structure.

Elliptical galaxies. These Hubble denoted by the letter *E*, with a suffixed numeral between o and 7 to indicate the degree of ellipticity: thus *Eo*-type galaxies

were spheroidal and *E7*-type galaxies were highly ellipsoidal.

Spiral galaxies. These were denoted by the letter *S*, suffixed *a*, *b* or *c* to indicate the general shape: thus *Sa* were those galaxies with large nuclei and closed-up spiral arms, *Sb* were those with smaller nuclei and spiral arms more open, and *Sc* were those with the spiral arms very opened out and little, if any, obvious nucleus.

Barred spiral galaxies. These were designated *SB* and again sub-divided with the suffixes *a*, *b* and *c* to indicate the general shape: the closed-up spiral arms of the *SBa*-type galaxies often formed a ring, giving it the appearance of the Greek letter theta Θ.

It was noted by Hubble that these various types fell naturally into a morphological sequence; he prepared his now-famous 'tuning-fork' diagram (Fig. 48) to illustrate this and to give an impression of some of the principal types.

In recent years revised systems of classification have been proposed, notably by G. de Vaucouleurs. The main effect of these is to introduce a category of *lenticular galaxies* (type *SO*, with sub-divisions) to cater for the many galaxies found which are intermediate between the elliptical and spiral forms. The sub-divisions of the de Vaucouleurs system are much more precise and definitive than those of the earlier Hubble system, of which it is a refinement; the allocation of the appropriate category requires expert knowledge and skill, however, and hence details of the system need not concern us here.

(See also **Galactic evolution; Galactic structure; Galaxies.**)

GALAXY, THE The star system in which the Sun (and hence the solar system) is situated. The term as first used implied the whole of the contents of the universe, for the existence of bodies outside this system was not envisaged. When it was realized that many of the nebulous objects catalogued by Herschel, Messier and others were probably outside the system they were termed extragalactic nebulae. When they were resolved many of them were found to be other star systems in their own right; they were therefore termed— understandably if somewhat confusingly— *galaxies*. In order to distinguish a galaxy (i.e. an extragalactic star system) from the star system in which we ourselves are situated ('*the* galaxy'), it is usual to denote the word in the latter sense with a capital initial—the *Galaxy*.

The Galaxy is a spiral star-system, believed to have a form very similar to that of the great spiral galaxy in Andromeda. The determination of its structure from within is extremely difficult, but since it was first attempted by Sir William Herschel in 1783 considerable progress has been made. Most of the spiral arms have now been plotted, principally from radio observations [see Plate 20(d)].

The Galaxy is of the usual lenticular shape, approximately 25 kpc in diameter and about 4 kpc thick at the core. The Sun is situated at the edge of one of the spiral arms, approximately 8 kpc from the galactic centre and slightly 'above' (i.e. north of) the galactic plane. The core consists principally of the cooler Population II stars, the spiral arms contain mostly hot, bluish Population I stars. There is a great deal of interstellar dust and neutral hydrogen in the spiral arms, largely confined to the galactic plane. The clouds of interstellar dust act as absorption nebulae, obliterating or dimming stars lying beyond them as seen from the Earth. The neutral hydrogen can be surveyed by means of its radio emission at a wavelength of 21 cm, a process which has provided by far the most accurate and detailed evidence of the structure of the Galaxy.

Every spiral galaxy in which radial velocities can be determined for stars situated in the outer parts of its spiral arms is found to be rotating, about an axis through its centre and perpendicular to its equatorial plane—rather like a huge cartwheel. The 'flatness' of the galaxy seems to be dependent upon the rate of rotation—the faster the system rotates the thinner it is. We naturally expect our own Galaxy to follow suit, and the proper motions of the stars of the Galaxy have been carefully examined with this in mind. From a study of the proper motions of bright stars it was found that the Sun has a motion relative to nearby stars—the *local solar motion*—with a velocity of about 12 miles per sec. This is not the over-all effect of galactic rotation, however; further, the discovery of *star streaming* by Kapteyn in 1904, showing that stars exhibit two preferred directions of motion which are directly opposed to each other if the effect of the local solar motion is removed, and which are also in the galactic plane, was a further problem.

It was realized that as the globular clusters did not conform to the flattened, lenticular shape of the Galaxy, but were in a roughly spherical distribution, they probably did not share in the rotation of the Galaxy and would therefore provide a fixed reference against which the rotation of the other bodies in the system could be measured. The apparent motions of the stars relative to the globular clusters were derived from their radial velocities. The rate of rotational velocity was found to decrease with distance from the galactic centre, i.e. the outer parts of the galaxy were rotating more slowly than the inner parts. This is predictable for a gravitational system in which the mass is concentrated towards the centre (the solar system is an example of this). The predicted velocities of rotation for stars at various radii from the centre were calculated by Oort; the observed values were found, on average, to agree. Further, it was shown by Lindblad that the departures from the predicted motion displayed by individual stars could explain the star-streaming effect discovered by Kapteyn.

The rotational velocity of stars in the neighbourhood of the Sun, about the galactic centre, is about 135 miles per sec. (See also **Galactic co-ordinates; Galactic structure; Star streaming.**)

GALILEI, Galileo (1564–1642) Famed as the first astronomer to use the telescope, Galileo (as he is universally referred to) was one of the leading theorists of his day, as well as an observer of outstanding ability.

Born in Pisa on 1564 February 15, Galileo was the eldest son of a Florentine noble, Vincenzo de' Bonajuti de' Galilei; his early life was nevertheless one of considerable poverty. He entered the University of Pisa at the age of 17 to study medicine; he soon developed a strong interest in mathematics, however, and eventually his medical studies ceased altogether. Even as an undergraduate Galileo acquired the reputation of an heretic which was to dog him throughout his life, having had the temerity to question the validity of the Aristotelian principles of philosophy and natural science. Nevertheless, Galileo's remarkable ability enabled him to overcome this handicap, and at the age of 25 he was appointed Professor of Mathematics at Pisa.

In 1852 Galileo discovered that the period of oscillation of a pendulum is independent of the length of its swing (it is said that his discovery arose from watching the swing of a chandelier in Pisa Cathedral), and used this principle to develop the first pendulum-clock mechanism.

Galileo continued to oppose the accepted teachings of Aristotle, and eventually the growing hostility of the university authorities forced him to relinquish his Chair. He was soon appointed to the Chair of Mathematics at Padua, however, where he remained from 1592 to 1610. This period of Galileo's life appears to have been uneventful; it is clear that much of his time was devoted to the continuing study of the conflicting cosmological theories of the day. During this period Galileo came to accept the Copernican heliocentric theory of the universe, although he was forced to continue teaching the Aristotelian–Ptolemaic geocentric theory in his university lectures.

In 1610, thanks to the patronage of Cosmo dei Medici, Grand Duke of Tuscany, Galileo was able to return to Pisa as Professor and with the additional title of 'First Philosopher and Mathematician' to the Grand Duke. This change, which brought financial stability to Galileo for the first time, also marked a remarkable change in the pattern of his life. Henceforward he was to be frequently in the public eye (principally as a result of his rebellious attitude and willingness to champion 'reactionary' theories) and was also to become a prolific writer in support of his views. In consequence there is a wealth of evidence about the second half of Galileo's life, but space permits here only a very brief summary of the main aspects.

During 1609 Galileo heard of the success of Dutch opticians in the construction of a telescope; he deduced the optical principles involved for himself, regarding this tour de force as merely the first step in the design and construction of several small telescopes. Two of his instruments are still preserved in Florence. [Plate 25(c).]

Two Englishmen, Thomas Harriot and Simon Marius, are among several reputed to have preceded Galileo in using the telescope to study astronomical bodies; Galileo's observations were however systematic studies and were carefully documented, and he must therefore be credited with being the first to make useful astronomical observations with the instrument.

The range of Galileo's telescopic discoveries is remarkable, notwithstanding the fact that the whole field of telescopic discovery lay before him as the pioneer of this branch of scientific research. Consequently his list of first discoveries is a lengthy one, headed by the discovery of the four principal satellites of Jupiter in 1610 January—ever since these satellites have been distinguished as the 'Galilean' satellites. The disks of the planets, the phases of Venus, the 'craters' on the lunar surface—all of these were first revealed to Galileo. He also noted that Saturn was accompanied by two peculiar appendages whose true nature (the ansae of the rings) he was unable to determine, and made the first telescopic study of sunspots. Galileo did not neglect the stellar universe either, discovering *inter alia* that the *Pleiades* and *Præsepe* clusters contained a great many more stars than were visible with the unaided eye, and that the Milky Way was resolvable with the telescope into myriads of faint stars.

Galileo's discoveries rapidly brought him widespread fame, and although many of his contemporaries must have been led to construct and use telescopes he remained the pre-eminent observer of the period. This was probably due to three attributes: his skill in manufacturing instruments of remarkably high quality; his enquiring mind, coupled with a tremendous intellect, which led him to produce carefully reasoned explanations of the phenomena he discovered; and finally, his irrepressible urge to utilize his discoveries to clarify and support the cosmological theories in which he believed so strongly. An indication of the quality of Galileo's instruments and the proficiency of their user was his discovery of the Moon's librations from studies of the lunar surface features.

Galileo published the details of his telescopic discoveries in 1610 in a monograph entitled *Siderius Nuncius* ('The Sidereal Messenger'). This was followed in 1613 by a review of his studies of sunspots, in *Istoria e Dimostrazioni intorno alle Macchie Solari* ('History and Demonstration about the Solar Spots'), in which he also first indicated publicly his belief in the Copernican theory. About this time Galileo was becoming conscious of the growing opposition to his beliefs, especially on the part of the heirarchy of the Roman Catholic Church. He made a personal visit to Rome to discuss the problem in 1611 and was reasonably well received, but he was secretly denounced to the Inquisition and in 1616 was instructed by Papal Decree to abandon his 'heretic' opinions.

In 1623 Galileo published *Il Saggiatore* ('The Assayer'), in which he dealt with the Copernican theory but in a very circumspect manner; this was followed in 1632 by his famous *Dialogo sopra i due massimi sistemi del Mondo, Tolemaico e Copernico* ('Dialogue on the Two Greatest Systems of the World, the Ptolemaic and the Copernican'). This was in effect a powerful expression of the validity of the Copernican system, but it was again very cleverly camouflaged and publication was allowed. The following year however it was condemned and Galileo was summoned to Rome to appear before the Inquisition on a charge of disobeying the Papal injunction of 1616. He was forced to make a public retraction of his views, and was sentenced to be confined for life. Fortunately he was allowed to spend his last years, under house arrest, at his villa at Arcetri, near Florence (where today there is an important astrophysical observatory). Galileo died at Arcetri on 1642 January 8, having continued his studies there in secret; his final work, a monograph on mechanics and motion, was published in Holland in 1638 using a manuscript which, according to Galileo, had been 'stolen' from him.

Galileo's parallel contributions to the

development of both observational and theoretical astronomy have seldom been equalled; with his predecessor Copernicus, his contemporaries Tycho Brahe and Kepler, and Newton (who was born in the year of Galileo's death), he must rank as one of the most important figures in the history of astronomical science. In the sixteenth and seventeenth centuries these men laid the firm foundations upon which the highly sophisticated sciences of contemporary astronomy and astrophysics have been built.

GALLE, Johann G. (1812–1910) Notable German astronomer, chiefly remembered for his first observation of the planet Neptune on 1846 September 23. Galle was then Assistant Astronomer at the Berlin Observatory, and was helped in the search by Heinrich D'Arrest; they found the planet close to the position predicted by Le Verrier.

Galle was also the first observer to detect the Crêpe Ring of Saturn, in 1838, although the true significance of his observation was not realized until after the rediscovery of the ring in 1850.

In 1872 Galle suggested the observation of minor planets as a means of determining the solar parallax.

In 1894 Galle's catalogue of comet orbits (*Verzeichniss der Elemente der bischer berechneten Cometenbahnen*) was published, and remained for many years the standard work of reference in this field.

GANGES Martian surface feature, approximate position Ω 62°, $\Phi + 10°$. Canal radiating north-westwards from the Auroræ Sinus, linking it to the Lunae Lacus.

GANYMEDE Satellite III of Jupiter, *q.v.*

GASSENDI Lunar surface feature, co-ordinates $\xi - 611$, $\eta - 301$. A magnificent walled plain, 55 miles in diameter, situated in the south-east limb region of the Moon, at the northern end of the Mare Humorum. The wall is very eroded in the south, but is otherwise very prominent.

There is a chain of sub-craters running southwards from Gassendi, and a wealth of fine detail on its floor, including a highly complex system of clefts. The floor itself is 2,000 ft. higher than the surrounding plain. The walls rise to over 9,000 ft. in places.

GAUSS Lunar surface feature, co-ordinates $\xi + 789$, $\eta + 592$. One of the largest walled plains on the Moon. It is 110 miles in diameter and is situated very close to the north-west limb; it is therefore extremely difficult to observe. There is a central mountain ridge bearing both the peak and a small crater.

GEGENSCHEIN A rather brighter, oval patch in the **zodiacal band,** 180° from the Sun (i.e. at the anti-solar point); it may be 20° × 10° or more, but it is rarely observable outside the tropics. Sometimes called the 'counterglow'.
(See **Zodiacal light.**)

GEHON Martian surface feature, approximate position Ω 0°, $\Phi + 15°$. Faint canal running northwards from the western fork of Furca (Sinus Meridiani). Forms western boundary of Moab.

GEMINI (The Twins. *Genitive* Geminorum, *I.A.U. abbreviation* Gem.) A zodiacal constellation reaching midnight culmination in early January, situated between Taurus and Cancer. Although not a large constellation, contains a number of bright stars, there being eleven of the third magnitude or brighter. The principal stars are Castor (α Gem) and Pollux (β Gem).

Castor is a most interesting multiple star, comprising three binary systems. The principle components have a period of 380 years and magnitudes of 2·0 and 2·8; their maximum separation is about 6·5″, but they are about 2″ apart at the present time. They are both spectroscopic binaries, with periods of about 3 days and 9 days. There is also a third star, much fainter, which is also a spectroscopic binary.

The constellation contains a Cepheid variable (ζ Gem) and two fine long-period variables (η Gem and R Gem). There is a fine open cluster of bright stars (M35), between ϵ Gem and ζ Tau.

GEMINI Name given to the vehicles in a United States space-flight development programme, and to the programme itself. The *Gemini* programme was a follow-up to the very successful *Mercury* programme. Each *Gemini* vehicle carried a crew of two. During several of the *Gemini* flights one of the crew left the spacecraft and performed simple tasks in space. The latter part of the programme was aimed at the development of rendezvous and docking techniques, and was conspicuously successful. The close rendezvous of *Gemini 6* with *Gemini 7* (launched earlier) was a notable step forward, as was the first docking carried out by *Gemini 8* with the *Agena 8* target vehicle. *Gemini 10* achieved its scheduled docking with *Agena 10* on 1966 July 19 and was then manoeuvred by its crew to a rendezvous with *Agena 8* (still in its orbit after the docking with *Gemini 8*) only 19 hours later.

The *Gemini* flights are listed in Table 13.

GEMINIDS One of the most important meteor showers, occurring about December 11–13 from a radiant in Gemini; the orbit of the meteor stream proves to be un-usually small, having a semi-major axis of 1·396 A.U. This is little more than half the value for Comet Encke, the shortest-period comet known; there is therefore no possibility of the Geminid shower being associated with any known comet.

GEMINUS Lunar surface feature, co-ordinates $\xi+690$, $\eta+565$. A beautiful crater 55 miles in diameter, in the north-western limb regions. Its terraced ramparts rise to 16,000 ft. in places. There is a small central mountain.

GENERAL CATALOGUE The *General Catalogue of 33342 Stars*, was compiled by Benjamin Boss and published by the Carnegie Institution of Washington in 1936. This publication is usually referred to as the 'G.C.'. The G.C. contains the position, proper motion, magnitude and spectral type of all stars down to 7th magnitude, and some additional ones. The abbreviated form of designation used is GC 13501.

(See also **Star catalogues**.)

Table 13.   Gemini manned space-vehicles

Vehicle	Date of launching	Date of descent	Flight duration (days)	Result	(date)
Gemini 1	1964 Apr. 8	Apr. 12	4·20	Unmanned test flight, no re-entry	
Gemini 2	1965 Jan.			Unmanned re-entry test	
Gemini 3	1965 Mar. 23	Mar. 23	0·20	Manned test flight	
Gemini 4	1965 Jun. 3	Jun. 7	4·07	First U.S. 'space walk'	
Gemini 5	1965 Aug. 21	Aug. 29	7·96	Various systems tested	
Gemini 6	1965 Dec. 15	Dec. 16	1·08	Rendezvous with *Gemini 7*,	Dec. 15.
Gemini 7	1965 Dec. 4	Dec. 18	13·78	Rendezvous with *Gemini 6*,	Dec. 15.
Gemini 8	1966 Mar. 16	Mar. 17	0·44	Docked with *Agena 8*,	Mar. 16.
Gemini 9	1966 Jun. 3	Jun. 6	3·01	Rendezvous with *ATDA*,	Jun. 3.
Gemini 10	1966 Jul. 18	Jul. 21	2·95	Docked with *Agena 10*, / Rendezvous with *Agena 8*,	Jul. 19. / Jul. 19.
Gemini 11	1966 Sep. 12	Sep. 15	2·97	Docked with *Agena 11*,	Sep. 12 *et seq.*
Gemini 12	1966 Nov. 11	Nov. 15	3·93	Docked with *Agena 12*,	Nov. 12 *et seq.*

GENERAL CATALOGUE OF DOUBLE STARS The *General Catalogue of Double Stars within 121° of the North Pole*, compiled by S. W. Burnham and published by the Carnegie Institution of Washington in 1906. Also known as the **Burnham Catalogue,** *q.v.*

GENERAL CATALOGUE OF STELLAR RADIAL VELOCITIES A catalogue of 15,107 stars, compiled by R. E. Wilson and published by the Carnegie Institution of Washington in 1953. It contains all the radial velocities known in 1950.

GENERAL CATALOGUE OF TRIGO-NOMETRICAL STELLAR PARAL-LAXES The most comprehensive catalogue of stellar parallaxes, compiled at Yale University Observatory and published in 1952. It contains the parallaxes of 5,822 stars—all those determined by 1950.

GENERAL CATALOGUE OF VARI-ABLE STARS An important compilation of data relating to 14,700 variables by B. V. Kukarkin *et al.* The 2nd edition—which contains an introduction in English—was published in Moscow in 1958.

GEOCENTRIC CO-ORDINATES Co-ordinates measured with reference to the centre of the Earth. Thus, for astronomical purposes, the geocentric co-ordinates of a body define its position as seen from the centre of the Earth.
(See also **Co-ordinate systems.**)

GEOCENTRIC PARALLAX The angle subtended at an observed body by a line joining the observer and the centre of the Earth. (See **Parallax, stellar.**)

GEODESY The study of the figure and dimensions of the Earth.

GEODETIC CO-ORDINATES Geographical co-ordinates, *q.v.*

GEOGRAPHICAL CO-ORDINATES A system of co-ordinates referred not to the centre of the Earth (geocentric co-ordinates) but to a specific point on the Earth's surface.
(See also **Co-ordinate systems.**)

GEOID The concept of the Earth as a geometrical solid, used in theoretical calculations; the surface of the geoid is approximately equal to mean sea level extended over the entire globe.

GEOPHYSICS The study of the physical state and physical phenomena of the Earth. It includes the studies of seismology, geomagnetism and the physics of the Earth's interior, and is closely related to atmospheric physics, meteorology, geodesy and oceanography.

GEORGE DARWIN LECTURE An annual lecture to the Royal Astronomical Society, endowed by Sir James Jeans in 1926 in memory of G. H. Darwin, President of the Society 1899-1900 and recipient of its Gold Medal in 1892. The Lecturer is usually, but not necessarily, a Gold Medalist of the Society.

GESCHICHTE DES FIXTERN-HIM-MELS An important collection of all meridian observations of the fixed stars made prior to 1900, re-reduced to a common epoch (1875·0); published in Karlsruhe, 1922-23. Usual abbreviation: GFH.

GIACOBINIDS A meteor shower occurring about October 10, associated with Comet P/Giacobini-Zinner.

GIANT A star whose spectral/luminosity classification places it in the giant sequence of the Hertzsprung-Russell diagram. (See **Stars, giant.**)

GIBBOUS PHASE The Moon or a planet is said to be gibbous when its phase is greater than 0·5 but less than 1·0, i.e. when the apparent shape is more than a semi-circle but less than a full circle.

GILL, Sir David (1843-1914) Born in Scotland, Gill gave up a family business in 1872 to direct the private observatory founded by Lord Crawford at Dun Echt. In 1874 he went to Mauritius to observe the transit of Venus, and in 1877 went to Ascension Island and made a series of heliometer observations of Mars, from which he deduced a value for the solar parallax of 8″.78.

In 1879 Gill was appointed H.M. Astronomer at the Cape of Good Hope; when he retired from this post in 1907 he had transformed the small, ill-equipped, poorly housed and under-staffed observatory into one of the great national observatories, with a permanent and important role in the future development of fundamental astronomy.

Gill may also be regarded as the father of modern astrometry; in 1882 he strapped an ordinary hand-camera to an equatorial telescope so as to photograph the great comet then visible. Using exposures of 1–2 hours, he obtained plates that not only recorded the comet but also the background stars, and so good were the stellar images obtained that Gill immediately conceived the idea of making a much needed southern extension to Argelander's *Bonner Durchmusterung* by photographic means. Gill was only able to carry out this enormous task with the voluntary assistance (for more than a decade) of J. C. Kapteyn; the resulting *Cape Photographic Durchmusterung* was the first fruit of a collaboration that was to last many years. Between 1888 and 1889 Gill organized co-operation between observers at the Cape, New Haven, Leipzig and Göttingen, to observe the minor planets Victoria, Iris and Sappho; from these observations Gill deduced a revised value of the solar parallax of 8″.80.

During the seven years of his retirement Gill played a vigorous part in the scientific life of London. He was widely honoured, and was created a Knight Commander of the Order of the Bath (K.C.B.) for his pioneering work at the Cape; he was a Fellow of the Royal Society, and was awarded its Royal Medal in 1903; he received the Gold Medal of the Royal

Astronomical Society twice, in 1882 and 1908, was President of the Society (1909–1911) and its Foreign Secretary (1911–1914).

(See also **Cape Observatory; Cape Photographic Durchmusterung; Kapteyn selected areas; Solar parallax.**)

GIORDANO BRUNO Very bright ring structure on the far side of the Moon, notable as the centre of a great ray system comparable to that of Tycho. Some of the rays can be seen extending onto the Moon's visible hemisphere. Discovered on the photographs obtained by *Lunik III* in 1959 October. (See **Moon—far side of.**)

GLASS Transparent material manufactured by the fusion of a silicaceous mixture of oxides; most glasses in everyday use are formed from silica (SiO_2), soda (Na_2O) and lime (CaO). A typical mixture (weight for weight) would be SiO_2 75%, Na_2O 15%, CaO 10%; the proportions may vary considerably, however, and small quantities of other constituents may be added, depending upon the qualities required of the resulting glass. Potassium is frequently used in place of sodium, in the form of K_2O. In order to achieve a strong glass it is necessary for the fused mixture to be carefully *annealed* (cooled in a controlled manner over a long period of time).

Among the oxides commonly added to achieve certain characteristics are those of lead, boron, barium, phosphorus, titanium and lanthanum.

(See also **Optical glass.**)

GLOBULES Small, dense, absorption nebulae of approximately spherical form which are found at the edges of emission nebulae. It is believed that they may be proto-stars, actually in the process of being formed. (See **Evolution, stellar; Nebulae, dark.**)

GNOMON A rod or straight-edge of a plate, inclined so as to point to the celestial pole; its shadow in sunlight can then be utilized to indicate local apparent solar time. In ancient times gnomons were erected on the ground and pegs inserted to mark the shadow positions for each hour.

The modern meaning of the word is the shadow-forming plate of a **sundial**, q.v.

GOLD, Thomas Contemporary theoretical astronomer; one of the group of cosmologists who developed the concept of the continuous creation of matter and the steady-state universe. Formerly a Chief Assistant at the Royal Greenwich Observatory, now Professor of Astronomy at Cornell University, U.S.A.

GOLDEN NUMBER The number of a year in the Metonic Cycle; its name derives from the practice of the ancient Greeks of recording the dates of Full Moons for the complete cycle on public monuments in letters of gold.

The series now used commences with the year 1 B.C. The Golden Number of a given year may therefore be determined by adding 1 to the year and dividing by 19; the remainder is the Golden Number. If there is no remainder the Golden Number is taken to be 19. Thus, the Golden Number for 1965 is the remainder when 1966 is divided by 19, i.e. 9.

(See also **Calendar; Metonic cycle.**)

GOODACRE, Walter (1856–1938) Distinguished English amateur, who became the second Director of the Lunar Section of the British Astronomical Association in 1897, succeeding T. G. Elger. In 1910 he published a map of the lunar surface, on the scale 77 inches to the Moon's diameter, based mainly upon his own observations; this map was revised and republished, reduced to 60 inches, in his book *The Moon, with a Description of its Surface Features* which appeared in 1931. Goodacre was President of the B.A.A. for the period 1922–1924.

GRANULATION Photographs of the Sun's surface, especially those made in light of a single wavelength with a spectroheliograph, show the photospheric surface to have a mottled, or granulated, appearance. The bright 'grains' are termed **flocculi**, q.v. The granular structure is constantly changing. [Plate 2(e).]

(See also **Sun—physical constitution of.**)

GRATICULE A system of fiducial or reference marks in the focal plane of a telescope; they may be single or double crosswires, a series of parallel, vertical wires as in a transit circle, or a reticule (or grid) covering the entire field. They may be engraved on a plane glass plate, or consist of wires or spider's webs mounted on a frame.

GRATING See **Diffraction grating.**

GRAVITATION, NEWTON'S LAW OF Newton propounded the concept of gravitation as an explanation of the motions of the planets, summarized by Kepler's laws. The law of gravitation states that every particle of matter in the universe attracts every other particle, the force of attraction being proportional to the masses of the particles and inversely proportional to the square of their distance apart. This may be expressed in the form

$$F = G\frac{m_1 m_2}{r^2}$$

where F is the gravitational force of attraction between two bodies, m_1 and m_2 are their masses, r is the distance separating them and G is the **Constant of gravitation.**

GRAVITATIONAL ACCELERATION The acceleration of a body in the gravitational field of a planet, towards the centre of mass of the planet. In the case of the Earth it is 980·665 cm/sec² (about 32 ft. per second per second).

GRAVITATIONAL COLLAPSE A suggested mechanism whereby a star might, as a result of some internal instability, 'collapse' or implode under the compressive force of its own gravitation. Such an event would release enormous quantities of energy. The concept has been discussed by F. Hoyle and A. Fowler; it has been suggested as the mechanism of creation of quasars, and may also be a fundamental process of star formation.

GRAVITATIONAL CONSTANT Newton's Law of Gravitation may be expressed in the form

$$F = G\frac{m_1 m_2}{r^2},$$

where F is the gravitational force of attraction between two bodies, m_1 and m_2 are their masses, and r is the distance separating them; the constant G is the *constant of gravitation*, and is $6 \cdot 658 \times 10^{-8}$ dynes if m_1, m_2 are expressed in grams and r in centimetres.
(See **Gravitation, Newton's law of.**)

GRAVITY, STANDARD VALUE OF The acceleration due to the force of gravity at the Earth's surface; the standard value is taken to be $980 \cdot 665$ cm/sec^2.

GREAT CIRCLE A circle formed on the surface of a sphere by the intersection of a plane passing through the centre of the sphere; the diameter of a great circle is thus equal to the diameter of the sphere on which it is described.
(See also **Celestial sphere.**)

GREAT NEBULA IN ANDROMEDA See **Andromeda, great nebula in.**

GREAT NEBULA IN ORION See **Orion, great nebula in.**

GREAVES, W. M. H. (**1897–1955**) British astronomer of outstanding ability; after a distinguished career at Cambridge he succeeded H. Spencer Jones as a Chief Assistant at the Royal Observatory, Greenwich. He made substantial contributions in the fields of dynamical astronomy and geomagnetism, but his outstanding work was the pioneering of new techniques for astrophysical research, especially in stellar spectrophotometry; notable among these were his programmes of colour-temperature determinations, carried out first with the Thompson 30-in. and later with the Yapp 36-in. reflectors at Greenwich.

In 1938 Greaves was appointed Astronomer Royal for Scotland and Professor of Astronomy in the University of Edinburgh; he held these posts until his untimely death, and directed the Royal Observatory, Edinburgh, with great distinction even through the trying period of the Second World War, when an emergency national time service had to be established and maintained there.

Greaves was elected a Fellow of the Royal Society in 1943; he was President of the Royal Astronomical Society 1947–1949, and its Secretary 1933–1939. He also served as President of Commission 25 (Stellar Photometry) of the International Astronomical Union and as Vice-President of the Royal Society of Edinburgh.

GREEK ALPHABET Widely used in astronomy, notably in the **Bayer Letters** used for the identification of stars; both the capital and lower-case form of the letters are given in the following list:

Alpha	A	α
Beta	B	β
Gamma	Γ	γ
Delta	Δ	δ
Epsilon	E	ε
Zeta	Z	ζ
Eta	H	η
Theta	Θ	θ
Iota	I	ι
Kappa	K	κ
Lambda	Λ	λ
Mu	M	μ
Nu	N	ν
Xi	Ξ	ξ
Omicron	O	o
Pi	Π	π
Rho	P	ρ
Sigma	Σ	ϲ

Tau	T	τ
Upsilon	Υ	υ
Phi	Φ	ϕ
Chi	X	χ
Psi	Ψ	ψ
Omega	Ω	ω

GREEN, Nathaniel E. (1823–99) A leading British amateur astronomer, who made important contributions to our knowledge of the surface features of the planets, especially Saturn and Mars. Green was a Founder Member of the British Astronomical Association and its fourth President (1896–98); he was also the first Director of its Saturn Section (1891–93 and 1895–99).

GREEN BANK RADIO OBSERVATORY See **National Radio Astronomy Observatory.**

GREEN FLASH A phenomenon that may be observed as the Sun is setting at times when the effect of atmospheric refraction is abnormally high; the Sun appears tinged with red at its lower limb and green at its upper, and as the last lune of the disk approaches the horizon it becomes entirely green, and there is a sudden, brief, upwards flash of green light at the moment of setting. A similar effect can occur at sunrise.

GREENWICH The district in south-east London where, in 1675, the Royal Observatory was founded in the Royal Park. Time based upon observations at Greenwich was accepted as standard for Great Britain throughout for many years, and Greenwich Mean Time was legally adopted in 1880. In 1884 an international conference was held in Washington which adopted the meridian of Greenwich as the Prime Meridian of longitude for the whole world, and also adopted the zone-time system based upon Greenwich Mean Time.

(See also **Royal Observatory, Greenwich.**)

GREENWICH CIVIL TIME (G.C.T.) The legal time for Great Britain, adopted

in 1880; it is in fact synonymous with Greenwich Mean Time.

GREENWICH MEAN ASTRONOMICAL TIME (G.M.A.T.) Mean solar time at Greenwich, reckoned from midday in order to avoid a change of date at midnight. Now used by few astronomers, the adopted system being **Universal Time.** Note that $G.M.A.T. = U.T. - 12$ hr.

GREENWICH MEAN TIME (G.M.T.) Mean solar time for the meridian of Greenwich, adopted in 1880 as legal time in Great Britain. Before 1925 it was reckoned from midday, since 1925 from midnight. In order to avoid confusion the International Astronomical Union recommend that the term **Universal Time** (U.T.) be used for G.M.T. reckoned from midnight. In order to avoid a change of date in mid-watch, some astronomers continued to use time reckoned from midday, known as **Greenwich Mean Astronomical Time** (G.M.A.T.). Note that $U.T. = G.M.A.T. + 12$ hr.

(See also **Ephemeris time; Time systems.**)

GREGORIAN CALENDAR A modification of the **Julian Calendar,** introduced by Pope Gregory XIII in 1582, to take account of the accumulated surplus by reducing the number of Leap Years in a period of 400 years by 3. (See **Calendar; Leap year.**)

GRIMALDI Lunar surface feature, co-ordinates $\xi - 926$, $\eta - 093$. A vast, well-formed walled plain close to the eastern limb of the Moon. It is 120 miles in diameter, and has very rugged and broken-up walls; these average about 4,000 ft. in height, but there is one peak of about 9,000 ft. on the south-western rampart. The floor is extremely dark, rendering it quite prominent despite its proximity to the limb.

GROOMBRIDGE CATALOGUE A *Catalogue of Circumpolar Stars,* compiled by

Stephen Groombridge from his own observations with a reversible transit circle made for him by Troughton. It was edited by the Astronomer Royal, Sir George Airy, and published in 1838; it contained the positions of 4,243 stars for the epoch 1810·0. It was revised by F. W. Dyson and W. G. Thackeray and republished in 1905 as the *New Reduction of Groombridge's Circumpolar Catalogue, Epoch 1810·0*.

Some of the stars are still known by their designation in this catalogue, e.g. Groombridge 1830; (this particular star became very well known in view of its very large proper motion, 7″ per annum).

GRUBB, Sir Howard (1844–1931) Head of the famous telescope-maufacturing firm of Dublin, which he inherited from his father in 1868. Many medium and large instruments were made by the firm for major observatories between 1870 and 1925. Among the first Howard Grubb instruments were the twin 15- and 18-in. reflectors made for The Royal Society, who loaned the instrument to Huggins; with it Huggins made many of his epoch-making spectroscopic observations. Grubb manufactured *Carte-du-Ciel* astrographic refractors for the Royal Observatories at Greenwich and the Cape of Good Hope, and for the observatories at Oxford, Melbourne, Perth (W. Australia) and Tacubaya (Mexico).

The 20-in. prime-focus photographic reflector for Dr Isaac Roberts, the Thompson 26-in. refractor for Greenwich, the 27-in. visual refractor for the Vienna Observatory, the 24-in. 'Victoria' refractor at the Cape, the 24-in. refractor for the Radcliffe Observatory (Oxford) and the 26½-in. visual refractor for the Union Observatory at Johannesburg were among the fine products of Grubb's firm.

Grubb retired in 1925, when his business was acquired by the Hon. Sir Charles Parsons, F.R.S., son of the third Earl of Rosse and head of an important company manufacturing marine turbines. The telescope firm was moved to Newcastle upon Tyne, adjoining the turbine factory, as Sir Howard Grubb, Parsons & Company, under which name many more superb instruments have been manufactured for the leading observatories of the world.

GRUS (The Crane. *Genitive* Gruis, *I.A.U. abbreviation* Gru.) Southern constellation, situated south of Piscis Austrinus. Contains two second- and one third-magnitude star.

GUIDER Alternative name for a **finder** telescope, *q.v.*

H

HD Prefix of serial numbers for the stars listed in the **Henry Draper Catalogue,** e.g. HD 36395.

H–R DIAGRAM Common abbreviation for the **Hertzsprung–Russell diagram,** *q.v.*

HADAR The star β Cen, magnitude 0·61; also known as *Agena*.

HADES Martian surface feature, approximate position Ω 188°, $\Phi + 30°$. Canal radiating north-eastwards from the Trivium Charontis.

HADES Proposed name of satellite IX of Jupiter, *q.v.*

HADRIACUM MARE Martian surface feature, approximate position Ω 270°, $\Phi - 40°$. Prominent dark marking forming the northern and eastern boundaries of the bright area Hellas.

HÆMUS MOUNTAINS A range of lunar mountains forming the south-eastern boundary of the Mare Serenitatis. There are many peaks between 4,000 and 8,000 ft. The range is broken in the centre by the bright crater Menelaus.

HALE, George Ellery (1868–1938) Few Americans have contributed more to astronomy and its related sciences than Hale, one of the most inventive practical astronomers and one of the most able and far-sighted scientific administrators of all time. Born in Chicago, he acquired an early interest in astronomy which was carefully nurtured by S. W. Burnham, the great double-star observer. Hale graduated in engineering at the Massachusetts Institute of Technology; whilst there he developed the principle of the spectroheliograph, thus solving a problem which had defeated many distinguished workers.

Through the generous support of his father Hale was enabled to spend the years 1891–1895 in developing his instrument in an observatory built for the purpose and equipped with a 12-in. equatorial refractor. As the photographic plates then available were largely insensitive to red light, Hale soon dispensed with the hydrogen-alpha line and chose instead the *H* and *K* lines of calcium in the violet spectrum. As a result of this he procured superb photographs of calcium prominences and discovered the bright calcium flocculi.

Hale became Assistant Professor of Astrophysics in the University of Chicago and—with the aid of the President of the University, Dr. W. R. Harper, and the great telescope lens-maker Alvan Clark—led the negotiations which led to the endowment of a new observatory for the University by C. T. Yerkes, a Chicago businessman, and the construction of the great Yerkes 40-in. refractor.

Hale chose the site of the Yerkes Observatory—at Williams Bay, Wisconsin, on the shores of Lake Geneva some 80 miles from Chicago—and became its first Director. His own instruments were transferred from Kenwood, and Hale continued his interest in solar observation. When the great 40-in. refractor was completed one of Hale's first activities was to have a special spectroheliograph (known as the 'Rumford spectroheliograph') made to be used with it. With this instrument Hale obtained the first spectroheliograms in the hydrogen-gamma line, and discovered the dark hydrogen filaments. Hale soon realized, however, that attachment to a moving telescope tube would not permit the development of the high-dispersion spectroheliographs he desired, and he therefore designed a fixed horizontal telescope fed by a coelostat; the prototype of this instrument was replaced at Yerkes by an instrument paid for by Miss Helen Snow and therefore named the 'Snow telescope'.

Hale had by now become convinced that a mountain site was necessary to provide sufficiently good observing conditions, and pressed strongly for the establishment of a mountain observatory through the Astronomy Committee of the Carnegie Institution of Washington, of which he became a member and later, Secretary. Mount Wilson (5,886 ft.), near Pasadena, California, was selected and in 1904 the Snow telescope was transferred to a solar laboratory specially built for it on the south-east edge of the mountain. This was followed in 1907 by the construction of the 60-ft. tower telescope and later by one of 150-ft. With this equipment Hale made many contributions to our knowledge of the Sun. He established the vertical motion of the hydrogen clouds above sunspots, and the existence of a magnetic field surrounding the Sun similar in form to that of the Earth; in 1912 he proposed a theory of the nature of sunspots, based upon his discovery in 1908 that they have intense magnetic fields. [Plate 29(a).]

Hale had yet one more contribution to make to the development of solar observation; in 1923, following his retirement from the Directorship of the Mount Wilson Observatory, he devised a means of converting the spectroheliograph into an instrument for visual observation—the spectrohelioscope. It should also be mentioned that Hale was a great believer in the ability of amateur observers, and helped many to build and use their own spectrohelioscopes and other equipment.

Hale's interest in the Sun was only as a first step in the study of the constitution and evolution of the stars, and he was therefore most anxious to obtain a telescope of large aperture for astrophysical research. He therefore continued his ceaseless efforts to raise financial support, with the result that a 60-in. reflector was erected on Mount Wilson in 1908; this was followed by the announcement that J. D. Hooker, a Los Angeles businessman, would provide the mirror for a 100-in. reflector. The Carnegie Institution paid the remaining costs, and the Hooker reflector, destined to be the largest telescope in the world for thirty years, came into operation in 1917. [Plate 30(c, d).]

The last of Hale's great works in the field of observational astronomy came after his retirement; he had long wished to see an even larger instrument made available for astrophysical research, and once again he commenced the enormous task of discussing the design and negotiating the finance for another huge telescope. It was soon agreed that a new instrument, double the aperture of the Hooker reflector, should be built and that owing to deteriorating atmospheric conditions at Mount Wilson a new site should be found. Despite constant ill-health, Hale remained Chairman of the observatory council and dominated the project until his death in 1938; by then construction of the telescope was well advanced. Delayed by the Second World War, it finally came into operation in 1948 January. On 1948 June 3 it was formally dedicated in the presence of Mrs. Hale; in the entrance foyer to the new observatory a bust of Hale was unveiled, with a bronze plaque bearing the words:

The 200-inch telescope is named
in honor of
George Ellery Hale
whose vision and leadership made
it a reality.

[See Plate 31(d).]

(See also **Flocculi; Mount Palomar Observatory; Mount Wilson Observatory; Snow telescope; Spectroheliograph; Spectrohelioscope; Sun— spectrum of; Telescopes, some famous; Tower telescope; Yerkes Observatory.**)

HALL, Asaph (1829–1907) American astronomer, who discovered the satellites of Mars with the 26-in. refractor of the U.S. Naval Observatory, Washington, in 1877 August. (See **Mars—satellites of.**)

HALLEY, Edmond (1656–1742) One of the most notable English scientists of his time, who became the second holder of the office of H.M. Astronomer Royal at the age of almost 64 and occupied it with distinction for twenty-two years.

Halley made notable contributions to astronomy whilst still a student at Oxford; he went up to Queen's College in 1673, and commenced the study of a number of problems relating to the determination of planetary orbits and other aspects of dynamical astronomy. In 1676 Halley travelled to the South Atlantic island of St. Helena, where he set up a $5\frac{1}{2}$-ft. sextant and proceeded to make the first map of the southern sky to supplement the work of Hevelius and Flamsteed in the north. On his return in 1678 he presented the King (Charles II) with a chart of the southern sky, and received his M.A. degree from the University of Oxford by the King's command. Halley's catalogue of the southern stars was presented to the Royal Society, and he was also elected a Fellow of that body, in the same year. Whilst in St. Helena Halley had also discovered that ω Cen was really a globular cluster (N.G.C. 5139) and had observed the transit of Mercury in 1677. His observations of the latter enabled him to derive a value of the **solar parallax**, and led him to propose the observation of the transit of Venus due in 1761 for the same purpose. In 1678 Halley also published improvements to the theory of the motion of the Moon.

Halley travelled a great deal at this stage of his life, visiting Hevelius in Danzig in 1679 and touring in Europe, particularly France and Italy, during 1680 and 1681. Whilst in France in 1680 he visited Cassini at the Paris Observatory and made observations of the Great Comet of that year. In 1682 he returned to England, married and settled in Islington, where he commenced regular observations, notably of the Moon's place.

In 1684 Halley visited Newton at Cambridge and persuaded him to finalize his mathematical proof of the theory of gravitation so that it might be published; in the following year Halley was appointed Clerk to the Royal Society (the post now known as Executive Secretary) and Editor of the *Philosophical Transactions*, which posts he held until 1699 and 1693 respectively. Halley achieved his aim of seeing Newton's great work on gravitation in printed form when the **Principia** was published in 1687—but only by bearing the heavy costs of printing and publication himself.

During the next decade Halley continued to make important contributions to many branches of science, including meteorology, terrestrial magnetism, algebra, geometry, optics and archaeology, as well as fundamental astronomy; he also made a number of voyages between 1698 and 1703 which enabled him to publish, *inter alia*, magnetic charts for the major seas of the world and an accurately surveyed chart of the English channel.

Halley had commenced perhaps his most memorable research in 1695—his study of all the known observations of comets made during the previous two centuries; these he then analysed and deduced the orbital elements of many comets. This enabled him to state that the orbits of most comets were, to a close approximation, parabolic. After much labour Halley was satisfied that the great comets observed in 1531, 1607 and 1682 were in fact the same comet, having an elliptical orbit and a period of 76 years; he predicted that this comet would return in 1758, and asked that those who would be alive to observe it would acknowledge his prediction. The comet did indeed return, being first observed on Christmas Day 1758, and Halley's prediction has become part of the history of science; in his lifetime, however, his cometary work received scant notice. In view of his request for posthumous recognition it would no doubt have pleased him to know that the comet whose return he predicted has, as **Halley's Comet,** made his name a household word the world over. Halley's researches into cometary orbits were published in 1705 as the *Synopsis of Cometary Astronomy.* [Plate 15(e).]

It is remarkable that despite his immense standing as a scientist Halley was not offered a position compatible with his ability until comparatively late in his life; this change finally came in 1704 when he became Savilian Professor of Geometry in the University of Oxford. In this position Halley undertook many important researches and published papers in almost every branch of astronomy; among the more notable were a comparison between contemporary observations of star places and those made by Hipparchus and Ptolemy, from which he derived the first proper motions, and a paper on the concept of a finite universe which was an important forerunner of modern cosmological theory.

Flamsteed died at the end of 1719 and Halley was appointed Astronomer Royal in his place in 1720. It was inconceivable that anyone else could be appointed, despite Halley's age. Flamsteed's instruments had been his own property and were removed after his death, and Halley's first task was therefore to re-equip the Royal Observatory; he obtained a grant of £500 from the Board of Ordnance for this purpose. The principal instruments he installed were a small transit (the first transit instrument *per se*), installed in 1721 and an 8-ft. mural quadrant by Graham, in 1725.

Flamsteed had concentrated principally on the fixed stars, and had not studied the motion of the Moon, which had long interested his successor; Halley therefore determined to pay particular attention to the Moon, and to obtain observations of its place throughout a **Saros.** It is as much a tribute to his health and stamina as to his diligence that Halley not only succeeded in completing this severe pro-gramme, occupying 19 years, but that he made his meridian observations unaided and is reputed never to have missed an occasion when the Moon was visible at transit. The improved lunar tables published seven years after Halley's death as a result of his labours greatly improved the accuracy of navigation possible.

Although forced by failing health to give up observing in 1739, Halley continued in office until his death early in 1742; he was succeeded by Bradley, whom he had himself chosen to be the next Astronomer Royal.

HALLEY LECTURE An annual lecture in astronomy, delivered in the University of Oxford to commemorate Edmond Halley, Savilian Professor of Geometry in the University, 1704–20.

HALLEY'S COMET The best-known of all comets, named after Halley who analysed all the observations of bright comets recorded in the sixteenth and seventeenth centuries, deduced that the comets observed in 1531, 1607 and 1682 were in fact one and the same comet, and predicted that it would be seen again in 1758. The comet duly arrived, being first detected on Christmas Day, 1758, thus confirming both Halley's prediction and his deduction that the comet was in fact a periodic one in a closed orbit. Halley's studies of cometary orbits, hitherto largely ignored, now became very highly regarded, and added a new facet to his already great reputation. The comet has since been known officially as Comet P/Halley and, popularly, as 'Halley's Comet'. The period of Halley's Comet is about 76 years, but this is rather variable depending upon the perturbing effects of Jupiter and the other massive planets.

The orbit of Halley's Comet was studied in very great detail by A. C. D. Crommelin and P. H. Cowell, prior to its 1910 return; they showed that observations of it could be identified at the twenty-eight previous returns, the earliest recorded observation being that of 240 B.C. which was made by ancient Chinese astronomers.

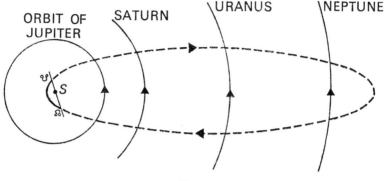

Fig. 49

The orbit of Halley's Comet is shown in Fig. 49. Unlike most other comets, the motion of Halley's Comet is retrograde; the inclination (between the planes of the orbit and the ecliptic) is therefore more than 90°—actually it is about 162°.

If the direction of revolution of the comet is ignored this is tantamount to an orbital inclination of 18°. Only one other periodic comet is known to have retrograde motion. In view of the high inclination, as will be seen in Fig. 49, the distance from ascending node (☊) to descending node (☋) is a negligible fraction of the total orbit, being only a short distance around perihelion, whereas the comet is 'below' the plane of the ecliptic for practically the whole of its journey out beyond the orbit of Neptune and back.

Owing to the **Law of equal areas** much of the comet's time is spent at the distance of Neptune and beyond, as can be seen from the positions shown in Fig. 50 for a number of dates between the last apparition (1910) and the next one, due in 1986.

At its 1910 return Halley's Comet passed between the Earth and the Sun, but no sign of it could be detected whilst in transit; the Earth also passed through the tail of the comet without any obvious effect. Both of these phenomena emphasize the tenuous nature of a comet's constitution.

There is evidence that the Eta Aquarid meteor shower has a connection with Halley's Comet, and also the Orionids; it is extremely difficult to make such identifications with certainty, however.

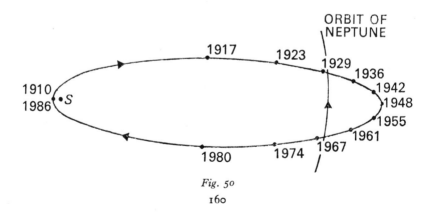

Fig. 50

HALO A ring of light, 22° in radius, surrounding the Sun or Moon, due to the presence of suspended ice crystals in the Earth's atmosphere. A secondary halo, of 46° radius, is sometimes seen. They are regularly seen in the polar regions, but are less common elsewhere.

(See also **Coronae; Parhelion; Parselena.**)

HALO, LUNAR Name frequently given to a type of **lunar ray system,** found especially in association with smaller ring-structures; the bright nimbus surrounding Euclides is a particularly good example.

HAMAL The star α Ari, magnitude 2·2, spectral type $K2$.

HAROLD JEFFREYS LECTURE An annual lecture to the Royal Astronomical Society, endowed out of the proceeds from sales of the volume *The Earth Today* published by the Society in 1961 in commemoration of Sir Harold Jeffreys' 70th birthday. The lectureship is dedicated to Jeffreys, President of the Society 1955–1957 and recipient of its Gold Medal in 1937; the Lecture is devoted to a topic of geophysical interest. The first Lecture was delivered by Jeffreys himself in 1963.

HARVARD–DRAPER SEQUENCE The system of classification of stellar spectra devised by E. C. Pickering, Miss A. J. Cannon and Mrs. W. P. Fleming for the **Draper Catalogue,** published in 1890.

The sequence originally consisted of six classes designated B, A, F, G, K and M; five additional classes were added later, W and O at one end and N, R and S at the other end of the sequence. Arranged in order of descending temperature, the full sequence is:

$$W—O—B—A—F—G—K < \frac{M—S}{R—N}$$

Classes B to K were subdivided decimally, a numeral being used to indicate the subdivision, thus: $A4$, $G5$, etc. The other classes were originally subdivided into fewer parts and identified by letters, thus: Ob, Md, etc.; it is now quite usual for these classes to be decimally subdivided also.

(See also **Stars—spectral classification of; MK-system.**)

HARVARD–MOUNT WILSON SYSTEM OF LUMINOSITY CLASSIFICATION The system defining the luminosity class of a star by an examination of the sharpness or otherwise of the lines in its spectrum, first devised by Miss Maury of the Harvard College Observatory and developed by Adams and Kohlschütter at Mount Wilson. Now largely superseded by the Yerkes (MKK) system. (See **Stars—luminosity of; Stars—spectral classification of.**)

HARVARD PHOTOMETRY The first major photometric catalogue, compiled at Harvard College Observatory by E. C. Pickering and published as *Observations with the Meridian Photometer, 1879–82* in volume 14 of the *Harvard Annals* in 1884. It includes the magnitudes of 4,260 stars, including all brighter than the sixth magnitude north of Dec. − 30°. The usual abbreviation is 'HP'. Pickering later published the *Revised Harvard Photometry*, containing the magnitudes of 9,110 stars mostly brighter than magnitude 6·5 (abbreviation HR or RHP), and a *Supplement to the Revised Harvard Photometry* containing the magnitudes of 36,682 stars fainter than magnitude 6·5.

HARVEST MOON The Full Moon occurring nearest to the autumnal equinox (September 23). At this time the Moon is in that part of its orbit most nearly parallel to the horizon, and rises only a few minutes later each night instead of the usual 50 minutes; there is therefore an unusually long sequence of moonlit evenings. The name derives from the assistance this phenomenon gave to the harvesters of long ago. In the southern hemisphere Harvest Moon is the Full

Moon nearest to the vernal equinox (March 21).

(See also **Hunter's Moon.**)

HEAD, COMET'S The principal part of a comet, often the only part seen when the comet is some distance from the Sun. It comprises the central condensation and surrounding coma. (See **Comets—structure of.**)

HELIACAL RISING AND SETTING Owing to the Sun's apparent motion around the Ecliptic in the course of a year, the stars rise and set about four minutes earlier each (solar) day; the Sun therefore 'overtakes' every star in turn, and there is a period of about a month during which the star is so close to the Sun that it cannot be observed with the unaided eye. The last observable setting of the star prior to this interval is termed its *heliacal setting*, and the first observable rising thereafter the *heliacal rising*. In modern usage the latter term is also sometimes used to denote the simultaneous rising of the Sun and another body.

HELIOCENTRIC CO-ORDINATES A system of co-ordinates referred to the centre of the Sun. Thus, the co-ordinates a body would appear to have to an observer situated at the centre of the Sun.

(See also **Co-ordinate systems.**)

HELIOMETER The principle of this instrument was originally devised by Römer in 1675 and elaborated by Savery in 1743, but the instrument was first made by the great optician John Dolland in 1754. It consists of a refracting telescope whose object glass is cut in two along a diameter; the semi-lenses can be moved relative to one another along this diameter, and the whole divided objective can be rotated about the optical axis of the telescope so that the semi-lenses can be separated in any chosen direction. The amount of separation is measured by means of a micrometer screw.

With the heliometer, the distance apart

of two celestial objects, or the diameter of a large object such as the Sun's disk, can be measured with great precision. The principle is shown in Fig. 51. If a double star is being observed with the semi-lenses in their normal position (o), the images of the component stars appear as at A_0, B_0. If one semi-lens is then moved, it will produce second images of the component stars, A_1 and B_1; its position is then adjusted until B_1 coincides with A_0 (position 1).

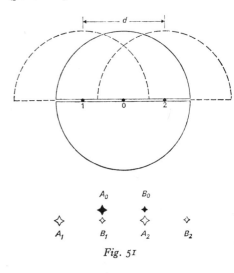

Fig. 51

The micrometer is read, and the semi-lens is then moved to a new position (2), such that A_2 coincides with B_0; a second micrometer reading is taken. If d is the distance the semi-lens is moved between positions (1) and (2), the angular separation of the component stars, s, is given by $s = d/2f$, where f is the focal length of the objective. [Plate 26(c).]

A famous heliometer was made by Fraunhofer for the Königsberg Observatory; Fraunhofer died before it was quite completed, and it was finally erected in 1829. With this instrument Bessel made the first determination of a stellar parallax, that of 61 Cygni, in 1838; he obtained a value of $0''.3483$. Heliometers were also used to make early determinations of the solar parallax. The observations and their reduction were very slow and tedious, however, and this instrument, once so important, has now been superseded by photographic methods.

HELIOSTAT An instrument used to receive a beam of light from the Sun as it traverses the sky and reflect it in a fixed direction; it consists of two mirrors, usually a plane mirror in a clock-driven equatorial mounting and a concave parabolic mirror to produce a focused image in the desired direction.
(See also **Cœlostat; Siderostat.**)

HELIUM A very light inert gas, second only to hydrogen in cosmic abundance. It was first 'discovered' in the Sun by Sir Norman Lockyer in 1868; Lockyer attributed certain lines in the solar spectrum to a new element which was named helium (from the Greek ἥλιοσ, the Sun). Helium was not detected on Earth until 1894, when a gas found occluded in a specimen of the mineral cleveite was identified by Sir William Ramsay as the same substance as that identified by Lockyer in the solar spectrum.

It is believed that the principal source of stellar energy is the disruption of hydrogen nuclei, the remaining protons combining by the carbon–nitrogen reaction or the proton–proton reaction to form helium nuclei. This suggests that the amount of helium in a star is steadily increasing as that of hydrogen decreases.

The atomic number of helium is 2; its atomic weight is 4·002.

HELIUM STARS Name sometimes used for stars of spectral class B, owing to the prominence of the absorption lines of helium in their spectra. (See **Stars— spectral classification of.**)

HELLAS Martian surface feature, approximate position Ω 290°, $\Phi - 40°$. Bright orange area in the south temperate zone of the planet; almost circular in form, and very prominent due to the contrast with

the dark areas by which it is surrounded. These are the Mare Australe to the south, Mare Amphitrites (south-west), Hellespontus (north-west), Mare Hadriacum (north and north-east) and Euripus I (south-east). There are some faint features to be seen occasionally in the interior, notably Alpheus and Peneus.

HELLESPONTUS Martian surface feature, approximate position Ω 325°, $\Phi - 50°$. One of the largest and most prominent of the canali; it forms the north-western boundary of the bright orange area Hellas, but continues south-westwards along a tangent. At its northern end it runs into the Mare Serpentis.

Hellespontus is a most important feature which requires careful and regular observation, as it undergoes extreme changes of a seasonal nature. Towards the end of the Martian winter a dark blob appears at its southern end, adjoining the south polar cap; this dark coloration spreads northwards along the canal as spring advances, meanwhile diminishing somewhat in intensity; by mid-spring it reaches the northern end of the canal where it merges with the Mare Serpentis, forming a much more obvious north-west boundary to Hellas than earlier in the season. This change in intensity is also accompanied by a progressive narrowing of the feature, and in late spring it appears to be extended as a dark rift across the polar cap.

HERA Proposed name of satellite VII of Jupiter, *q.v.*

HERCULES (Mythological character. *Genitive* Herculis, *I.A.U. abbreviation* Her.) A rather straggling constellation in the northern sky, reaching midnight culmination in early June. Contains no first- or second-magnitude stars, but there are seven third- and many fourth- and fifth-magnitude stars. The constellation stretches from Draco in the north to Ophiuchus in the south, and from Lyra in the east to Corona Borealis and Serpens Caput in the west. Despite the large area it spans, however, Hercules is not a particularly prominent constellation.

There are a number of double and variable stars—notably S Her, a long-period variable (period 300 days); α Her and 30 Her are irregular variables. Between η and ζ Her is M13—the 'Great Cluster in Hercules'; this is a splendid globular cluster, resolved into individual stars with quite moderate apertures. Forming a triangle with π and η Her is another splendid globular cluster—M92. Between β and δ Her there is a small planetary nebula.

HERCULES Lunar surface feature, co-ordinates $\xi + 434$, $\eta + 728$. A well-formed crater in the north-western limb region, making a fine pair with Atlas. It is 45 miles in diameter and has terraced walls which rise to 11,000 ft. in places. The floor is depressed, and has a fair amount of fine detail; there is also a deep craterlet (Hercules D) in the south-west part of the floor. The eastern wall adjoins the dark Lacus Mortis.

HERMES; HERMES TRISMEGISTUS In Greek mythology, Hermes was the son of Zeus, king of the gods, and Maia the titaness, daughter of Atlas (now re-membered as one of the stars in the Pleiades). He was the god of the Earth, bringer of abundant crops. Later he became the conductor of the dead to the underworld, and the messenger of the gods. He was represented as a young man, wearing the broad-brimmed hat of a traveller and the messenger's winged sandals, and bearing the 'caduceus', his traditional staff of office, bewinged and entwined with serpents.

The corresponding god in the mythology of ancient Egypt was *Thoth*, the scribe of the gods; he recorded the judgements of the gods and was later named *Hermes Trismegistus*—'The thrice-greatest Hermes' —and was the author of many astronomical and other scholarly treatises, among which the origins of astrology and alchemy were supposed to have been found.

The ancient Romans adopted Hermes, the Greek Earth-god, in the hope of improving their poor agricultural record; they named him Mercury.

Appropriately, in view of his supposed part in the origin of astrology, the fore-runner of astronomy, Hermes is com-memorated in several forms: the planet Mercury, the minor planet Hermes, the *Solitudo Hermae Trismegisti* (a dark area on Mercury) and *Thoth* (a canal on Mars).

HERODOTUS Lunar surface feature, co-ordinates $\xi - 701$, $\eta + 394$. A well-defined crater 23 miles in diameter, the 'twin' of Aristarchus; its dark floor contrasts strongly with its brilliant neighbour. Its walls are very narrow, and their inner edge is almost a perfect circle; they reach a height of about 4,000 ft. The southern part of the floor is crossed by a white streak running east-west. The serpent-like Herodotus Valley runs out of the crater through a discontinuity in the north wall.

HERODOTUS VALLEY The first major valley or cleft to be detected on the Moon, by Schröter in 1787 (hence its alternative name 'Schröter's Valley'). Leaving Hero-dotus ($\xi - 701$, $\eta + 394$) through a break in the north wall, it is little more than an ill-defined depression for the first six or seven miles; it then runs into a feature which appears to be two crater formations whose common wall is broken by the valley. This feature has been aptly termed the 'Cobra's Head'—especially appropriate as the whole Valley has a very serpentine appearance ($\xi - 693$, $\eta + 408$).

The Valley passes out of the Cobra's Head as a deep, parallel-sided cleft some two miles wide, and runs almost due north to ($\xi - 690$, $\eta + 424$), where it bends sharply and runs north-east to ($\xi - 702$, $\eta + 434$); here it narrows to about half its previous width and turns sharply south-eastward. With a sharp double bend it runs to ($\xi - 709$, $\eta + 430$) where it is joined by a fine rille running straight back to the Cobra's Head; the main Valley turns north-east again as an extension of this rille, to $(\xi-710, \eta+432)$. Here the Valley again changes its form, becoming narrower (approximately half a mile) and more sinuous; it runs approximately south-eastward for some distance, and then sweeps almost back on itself in a great curve at about $(\xi-725, \eta+415)$, where it passes through a gap in the mountain chain into the northern extension of the Oceanus Procellarum. It then runs north-ward parallel to the mountains, narrows, and finally disappears at about $(\xi-726, \eta+440)$.

HERSCHEL, Caroline (1750–1848)

Caroline Herschel, the younger sister of Sir William, was the fifth child in a family of six; she was twelve years younger than William. She was born in Hanover in 1750 March, and was educated, like her brother, at the Garrison School there. Following the death of their father in 1767 March (at which time William was just settling in Bath), Caroline's position in the family home in Hanover became little more than that of an unpaid servant. William was very distressed when he learned of this, and resolved to bring her to England; she possessed an excellent soprano voice and William intended that she should have it trained. He went to Hanover in 1772, and having agreed to reimburse the family for the cost of a servant to take her place he returned to Bath, bringing Caroline with him. Not the least important result of this action is the fact that the remaining half-century of William's life was very fully chronicled for posterity, for Caroline kept a most detailed diary. She was devoted to William, and immediately took over the management of his home. Her time was very fully occupied, for in addition to the housekeeping and at least two singing lessons every day, she was also given lessons by William in English and mathematics.

At this period William was developing his interest in the manufacture of tele-scopes, and every available corner of the home was soon commandeered for some aspect of this work; Caroline herself was

pressed into service as secretary and general assistant to her brothers (Alexander, a brother four years younger than William, was also living in the household in Bath at this time and entered enthusiastically into William's new occupation). Caroline continued to fulfil singing engagements for some years, but inevitably her musical career suffered more from the time she was devoting to assisting William, until in the end it ceased altogether. Following William Herschel's discovery of Uranus and their removal to Datchet at the King's behest, Caroline's time became totally devoted to astronomy. She played an invaluable part in Herschel's star-gauge counts, recording the position of the tele-scope, the time and the counts called out by her brother at the eyepiece. She was also trained by William in the art of tele-scopic observation herself, being given a small refractor with which to search for comets. A year later she exchanged this for a 4-in. Newtonian reflector with a low-power, wide-field eyepiece.

In 1786 April the Herschels moved to Slough, William to *Observatory House* and Caroline to a residence converted from the adjoining stable buildings, which later became known as *Observatory Cottage*. Four months after the move Caroline discovered her first comet, in 1786 August. At the end of 1788 she discovered another, and two more in 1790. At the end of 1790 Herschel completed the construction of a larger comet-seeking telescope for Caroline's use, a 9·2-in. Newtonian reflector. With this instrument she discovered four more comets, in 1791, 1793 (this comet was independently discovered by Messier), 1795 (this comet was shown by Encke in 1819 to have been a return of the comet discovered in 1876 by Méchain—it is now known as Encke's Comet) and in 1797. Although she made no more discoveries Caroline remained an active comet observer for many years.

At about this time the great 40-foot reflector was built, largely thanks to two grants of £2,000 by the King; at the same time he awarded Caroline a life pension of

£50 per annum in recognition of her work as William's assistant.

At her brother's suggestion Caroline produced an *Index to Flamsteed's Observations of the Fixed Stars* which was read before The Royal Society in 1798; she also produced a catalogue of 560 additional stars not included in Flamsteed's catalogue.

Following William Herschel's death in 1822 Caroline returned to Hanover, after half a century away. She continued the compilation of a catalogue embodying all the nebulae and clusters observed by William, listing them in zones of Declination; this was completed in 1825. Caroline sent the manuscript to her nephew John, to whom it was an invaluable aid in re-observing the objects discovered by his father. For this invaluable work Caroline was awarded the Gold Medal of the Royal Astronomical Society in 1828; she was elected an Honorary Member of the Society in 1835—an especially high honour at a time when the Fellowship was still restricted to men. In 1838 she was admitted a Member of the Royal Irish Academy, and in 1846 she was awarded the Gold Medal for Science by the King of Prussia. She died in Hanover in 1848 January, only two months before her 98th birthday.

HERSCHEL, Sir William (1738–1822)

Friedrich Wilhelm Herschel was born in Hanover on 1738 November 15, the second son and third child of an oboeist in the band of the Hanoverian Foot Guards. He inherited his father's considerable musical talent, and at the age of 15 was himself appointed a member of the Foot Guards band as a violinist and oboeist. He had been educated at the Garrison School in Hanover, which he left at the age of 14.

Herschel paid his first visit to England in 1756, as a member of the band. Frustrated by the life of a bandsman in a regiment defeated by the French (at Hastenbeck in 1757) he sought his discharge and returned to London in 1757 November. At first he supported himself by undertaking manuscript copying for a London music shop; in 1760 he was appointed instructor to the

band of the Durham Militia and moved to Sunderland. William's musical reputation grew, and he undertook many freelance engagements. In 1762 he became concert manager in Leeds and in 1766 organist at a Halifax church; he soon left the latter post, however, being offered that of organist at the new Octagon Chapel in Bath. His ambition was to be a composer, and he did in fact compose many pieces; much of his spare time however was devoted to the study of languages, mathematics and, later, optics. In 1772 he brought his sister Caroline to England—a step which was to prove an important one to his later astronomical work.

It appears to have been about this time that Herschel developed an interest in astronomy—or at least in astronomical optics. In 1773 he manufactured his first telescope—a refractor of 4 feet in length, using bought lenses which gave a magnification of approximately × 40. He produced a series of such instruments, each larger than the previous one, culminating in a giant 30 feet in length. Deterred by the difficulty of mounting such a monster effectively, he hired a Gregorian reflector in 1773 September in order to compare the advantages and disadvantages of the reflector and the refractor. He seems to have been satisfied of the advantages of the reflector, for he immediately changed to this type of instrument and never reverted. He also began to make his own optical parts, his objective mirrors being mostly constructed from speculum metal. Herschel entered into his new hobby with an enthusiasm bordering on the fanatical—his sister records the conversion of practically every room in their house into a workshop, and that she was sometimes obliged even to feed her brother whilst he continued the grinding of a telescope mirror!

Herschel's first reflectors were of about 2-feet focal length, but he soon produced one of $5\frac{1}{2}$ feet and found it so successful that he immediately commenced building a 7-foot instrument. By the middle of 1776 he had erected 10-foot and 20-foot reflectors also. His achievement was all the more remarkable in that for each instrument he ground several mirrors, so that the best might be selected for use. Between 1773 and 1795 he produced well over 400 mirrors.

As his initial enthusiasm for telescope-making wore off Herschel began to undertake astronomical observation for its own sake, as opposed to making observations for the purpose of testing and adjusting the optics of his telescopes. In about 1779 he commenced his first 'review of the heavens'; this was carried out with a 7-foot reflector and an eyepiece giving a magnification of × 222. The review consisted of a systematic scrutiny of every star of the fourth magnitude or brighter. He concentrated particularly on close double stars, hoping that it would be possible to detect their annual parallax. Herschel followed this with his second review—a most ambitious programme in which he used a new and excellent 7-foot reflector having an aperture of 6·2 in. and an eyepiece giving a power of × 227. The second review took Herschel two years to complete; at the end of it he was able to compile his first *Catalogue of Double Stars*, listing 269 pairs. The catalogue was published by The Royal Society in 1781.

Herschel's interests were now rapidly becoming focused on observational work, making use of the telescopes whose manufacture had earlier been his preoccupation. His principal instrument at this time was the 20-foot reflector (aperture 12-in.), but this was situated some distance from his house and Herschel frequently used the 7-foot on the pavement outside his home instead. This led to a chance encounter one night with Dr (later Sir) William Watson, F.R.S., who introduced Herschel into the Bath Literary and Philosophical Society and later communicated some of his papers to The Royal Society. Herschel's output of observational work was now quite prodigious, resulting in the preparation of no less than 31 papers in a period of 15 months. Ever anxious for the aid of more powerful instruments he now prepared plans for a huge reflector of 48-in. aperture; he was later forced to modify this to a 36-in., and even then was forced to attempt to cast the speculum mirror himself. He spent many months on this attempt but after numerous setbacks was forced to shelve the project.

Meanwhile, however, he had made the discovery that was to make him famous—that of Uranus on 1781 March 13; this was the first occasion on which a new planet had been discovered. Herschel, who was scrutinizing stars in Taurus with his favourite 7-foot telescope as part of the second review of the heavens, thought that his discovery was a comet; only when a number of observations had been amassed could its orbit be computed and its true nature established.

A paper describing Herschel's discovery was read to The Royal Society on 1781 April 26; in May, Herschel himself was received at the Society and presented with its highest award, the Copley Medal; in June he was elected to Fellowship of the Society.

In 1782 May, Herschel was received in audience by King George III, and in July he demonstrated his 7-foot telescope to the Royal Family at Windsor. As a result of this Herschel was granted a pension from the Royal Purse of £200 per annum, to enable him to give up his career as a music-teacher and settle within easy reach of Windsor so that further observing sessions for the Royal Family might be held. Herschel's appreciation for the King's assistance was marked by his wish to name the new planet *Georgium Sidus*—a name which persisted in England for many years, although later superseded by the name 'Uranus' suggested by Bode. In compliance with the King's request Herschel moved to Datchet later in 1782.

On the completion of his third review of the heavens in 1784 Herschel was able to prepare his *Second Catalogue of Double Stars*, containing 434 new pairs. Herschel regularly observed variable stars, the Moon and the planets; a remarkable feat was his discovery of the solar motion.

Freed from his teaching duties Herschel was also enabled to develop a thriving business in the manufacture and sale of telescopes. By 1783 his observational interests were canalized into the cataloguing of nebulae and clusters and the study of the distribution of the stars—he was thus the pioneer in the study of galactic structure. In 1786 he published his *Catalogue of One Thousand new Nebulae and Clusters of Stars*—all new discoveries additional to those catalogued by Messier and others. These discoveries were made with the aid of a new 20-foot telescope, this one having an aperture of $18\frac{3}{4}$-in.; this was perhaps the most successful of Herschel's larger instruments. Herschel's technique was to search sample areas of the sky by systematic sweeping, recording any nebulae or clusters and counting the number of stars visible in each area. The first results of the star counts (which he termed *star gauges*) were published in 1784 in a paper read to The Royal Society entitled 'Account of some Observations tending to investigate the Construction of the Heavens'; in this paper Herschel first propounded the suggestion that the stellar universe was disk-like in shape, its plane being marked by the Milky Way, the Sun and the solar system being situated somewhere near its centre. Herschel supported this suggestion with a great deal of observational evidence, using the star-gauging technique, in several further papers. In all this laborious observational work, as indeed in all of his observing programmes, Herschel was aided by his sister Caroline as both assistant and recorder.

In 1786 Herschel moved to his last home —*Observatory House* in Slough. Here he was to achieve one of his oldest ambitions with the construction of a 40-foot (48-in. aperture) reflector. Two grants of £2,000 were made by the King towards the cost of construction, and he also contributed the sum of £200 per annum for maintenance and the payment of labourers to manoeuvre the telescope when in use. At this time the King also awarded a pension of £50 per annum to Caroline Herschel as William's assistant. Several attempts were made to cast a speculum blank for the 48-in. mirror; two of the successful blanks were ground and figured by Herschel, assisted by teams of labourers. Following his usual practice of testing the mirror in the telescope on celestial objects, then removing it for any necessary changes to be made to its figure, the final stages occupied many months. Although Herschel was able to discover the sixth and seventh satellites of Saturn with the instrument in 1789, the figuring of the second, thicker, mirror was not finally completed until 1796. The difficuties involved in preparing and manoeuvring such a large instrument for use were very considerable, and Herschel was somewhat disillusioned with the limited use he was able to make of it; he tended to reserve it for the observation only of extremely faint objects beyond the light-grasp of the 'large 20-foot', his favourite instrument. Nevertheless, the giant instrument became the object of wide-spread admiration, and a great many visitors called at *Observatory House* to view the telescope, then the largest ever constructed, and to question its creator. Among the most frequent callers were the King and members of the Court, and many distinguished astronomers from abroad.

In 1787, using the 20-foot telescope, Herschel followed up his discovery of Uranus six years earlier by discovering two of its satellites. Both Uranus and Saturn occupied a great deal of Herschel's observing time, and Venus, Mars, Jupiter and the Moon were also frequently studied. Theories of the 'atmospheric' currents of Jupiter, measures of the rotation periods and polar flattening of both Jupiter and Saturn, studies of the dimensions and structure of the Saturn ring-system, and long series of drawings of the great comets of 1807 and 1811, all feature among his papers on solar-system astronomy, too numerous to be detailed here. In 1789 Herschel published his *Catalogue of a Second Thousand of New Nebulae and Clusters of Stars*.

In 1788, at the age of 50, William Herschel married Mary Pitt, the widow of a friend and neighbour. In 1792 their only child was born—a son, John Frederick William Herschel, destined to become one of his father's most distinguished successors. In 1793 William Herschel became a naturalized Englishman.

In 1800 Herschel discovered and investigated the properties of infra-red radiation—heat. Between 1794 and 1797 he had devoted his observing time to the study of the comparative brightness of the stars, producing six catalogues in which nearly 3,000 stars were arranged in order of apparent magnitude. Four of these catalogies were published by The Royal Society between 1796 and 1799, the other two remaining unpublished until 1905. As Herschel did not allocate a numerical value to the apparent magnitude of each star, the accuracy and utility of these catalogues was not fully realized, but when they were re-examined by E. C. Pickering a century later and compared with his *Harvard Photometry* observations, the derived apparent magnitudes were found to be accurate to within a tenth of a magnitude. In 1802 Herschel's second catalogue of nebulae and clusters was published.

In 1808 Herschel suffered a serious illness, and though he recovered, during the years that followed his health underwent a steady deterioration. Even in 1820, however, he was still engaged in the supervision of the construction of another instrument, an excellent 20-foot reflector later used both in England and at the Cape of Good Hope by his son. The construction of the instrument was actually undertaken, under his father's direction, by John Herschel. As his health failed William was able to observe less and less frequently, and by the middle of 1821 he had been forced to give up this work altogether. He died on 1822 August 25, only three months short of his 84th birthday.

Herschel was, of course, honoured by universities and learned societies throughout the world; in 1816 he was created a Knight of the Hanoverian Guelphic Order

by the Prince Regent. In 1821 he was elected the first President of the Astronomical Society, later to become the Royal Astronomical Society; owing to his failing health he was never able to attend a meeting, but remained President until his death. His son John was also a founder member of the Council of the Society and its first Foreign Secretary.

Sir William Herschel is often described as the 'Father of Sidereal Astronomy', but this implies scant recognition of his great contributions to solar-system astronomy; such was the breadth of his work that he must surely be regarded as one of the most versatile as well as one of the greatest observational astronomers of all time. It is very fitting that the crest of the R.A.S. is a representation of Herschel's great 40-foot reflector, based upon a contemporary engraving.

HERSCHEL, Sir John, Bart. (1792–1871)
John Frederick William Herschel was born at Slough on 1792 March 7, the only child of Sir William and Lady Mary Herschel. Educated at Eton and privately, John Herschel went up to St. John's College, Cambridge, in 1809. After a most distinguished university career he graduated in 1813 as Senior Wrangler and Smith's Prizeman. His early mathematical work was of such high standard that he was elected a Fellow of The Royal Society at the extraordinarily early age of 21. Nevertheless, he was not wholly determined upon a scientific career at this stage; his father hoped he would enter the Church, but John leant towards the law and in 1814 he enrolled as a student at Lincoln's Inn. He gave up his legal studies in 1816, however, and returned to Slough to take over most of his father's observational work and assist him in the manufacture of his telescopes. He also continued his work in pure mathematics, for which The Royal Society awarded him the Copley Medal, its highest award, in 1821. This must have given great satisfaction to his aged father, who had been similarly honoured 40 years earlier.

From 1821–23 John Herschel carried out a programme of double-star measurements in collaboration with James South. In 1925, using the new 20-foot reflector he had constructed to his father's design, he commenced a re-survey of the heavens, especially the nebulae and clusters discovered by his father during his great surveys. John was greatly assisted in this work by the zone-catalogue prepared by Caroline Herschel after her brother's death.

In 1826 John was awarded the Gold Medal of the Royal Astronomical Society for his work on double stars. His re-examination of the northern heavens was completed in 1833 and led to the publication of a catalogue of more than 2,300 nebulae and clusters, including 750 discovered by John himself. For this important work he was awarded a Royal Medal of The Royal Society in 1836, and also a second Gold Medal of the R.A.S. In 1824 he had become Secretary of The Royal Society, and he was knighted by King William IV in 1831. He married in 1829.

It had long been John Herschel's ambition to extend his father's reviews and star-gauge counts to the southern sky, and thus complete the coverage of the heavens. Accordingly, in 1833 he moved to the Cape of Good Hope with his wife and three children. He took a house close to the foothills of Table Mountain, and in its grounds set up the 20-foot reflector (aperture 18¾-in.) and a good refractor. With great diligence he commenced the systematic sweeping of the southern constellations, completing it in four years; he thus became probably the only observer ever to have systematically scanned the entire heavens. While at the Cape he discovered more than 1,200 double stars and more than 1,250 nebulae and clusters. He also studied the Magellanic Clouds and catalogued 1,200 stars, nebulae and clusters contained in them. Whilst in South Africa he was fortunate in witnessing the return of Halley's Comet, and made a long series of detailed drawings recording its changing structure.

John Herschel returned to Slough in 1838; he was created a Baronet on the occasion of Queen Victoria's coronation. In 1839 he was forced to have his father's great 40-foot telescope dismantled, as the wooden mounting had become unsafe. In 1840 he moved to Collingwood, a large country house at Hawkshurst, Kent. For nine years he devoted himself to the compilation of his *Results of Astronomical Observations at the Cape of Good Hope*, published in 1847. This brought him another Copley Medal from The Royal Society. He did no further observing following his return from the Cape, his time being fully occupied by the analysis and preparation of his work for publication, and in meeting the many calls upon his time made by pressing demands to serve on scientific and government advisory committees, etc. He was a Member of the Council of The Royal Society for many years, (and was offered the Presidency which he refused) and a Trustee of the British Museum. He was three times President of the R.A.S., in 1827–29 (when he was the fourth President, his father having been the first), 1839–41 and 1847–49. He was the first Foreign Secretary of the R.A.S. (1820–27) and served again in that capacity in 1846–47. In 1849 he published a text-book of general astronomy, *Outlines of Astronomy*, which became the standard text for many decades. In 1855 he retired from public service and devoted himself to realizing another of his life's ambitions—the compilation of his *General Catalogue of Nebulae and Clusters of Stars of the Epoch 1860*; this work, published in 1864, included every such object then known—most of them discovered during the great sky surveys by his father and himself, a total of 5,079 objects. This great compilation was revised by Dreyer and re-published as the *New General Catalogue of Nebulae and Clusters of Stars* in 1888—the famous 'N.G.C.', still the standard reference catalogue of these objects.

John Herschel's next task was similarly ambitious—the compilation of a catalogue embodying all the double stars discovered by his father and himself; this was published three years after his death as the *General Catalogue of 10,300 Multiple and Double Stars.*

Sir John Herschel died on 1871 May 11, aged 79. Endowed with a superb intellect he also proved himself to be an observer of the highest class; it was both remarkable and fortunate that William Herschel's own son should have proved such a worthy successor to him: it was surely unique that between them the Herschels dominated English astronomy for no less than a century. It was fortunate too that, no doubt thanks to his father's flourishing business as a telescope manufacturer, John Herschel was comfortably off and had no need to be restricted to a salaried post; he was thus free to complete and catalogue the vast observational programmes commenced by his father.

HERTZSPRUNG, Ejnar (1873-1967) Danish astronomer, one of the founders of modern astrophysics. Was for many years Director of the Leiden Observatory, Holland. In 1905, while at the Potsdam Observatory, Hertzsprung discovered the existence of giant and dwarf stars and carried out pioneer work which was to be developed by H. N. Russell and to provide the astrophysicist with one of his most powerful tools—the **Hertzsprung–Russell diagram,** *q.v.*

HERTZSPRUNG GAP The gap in the giant sequence of the **Hertzsprung–Russell diagram,** between spectral types *Ao* and *Go*; it arises from the fact that very few giant stars of these spectral types are known.

HERTZSPRUNG–RUSSELL DIAGRAM A graph demonstrating the relationship between the luminosity of a star and its spectral type, which has for many years been an important aid to the study of stellar constitution. The name is often abbreviated to 'H–R diagram', occasionally to 'Russell diagram'.

The H–R diagram may be said to have had its origin in an anomaly noticed by

Ejnar Hertzsprung of the Potsdam Observatory, of which he published details in 1905. From his studies of red stars Hertzsprung noticed that if near stars were ranged in order from type *B* (white) to type *M* (red) their absolute magnitudes decreased progressively towards the red, but that distant red stars were much more luminous than near red ones—comparable in luminosity to the white stars. Hertzsprung therefore suggested that there were two distinct types of star—one group, which he termed 'dwarf' stars, whose luminosity varied with spectral type, and another group, which he termed 'giants', whose members were all bright stars and showed no variation of luminosity with spectral type. Hertzsprung was later able to distinguish the two types by means of slight differences in their spectra. Dwarf stars were found to greatly outnumber giant stars.

The Director of the Princeton Observatory, H. N. Russell, independently discovered the same differentiation during a study of the absolute magnitudes of the stars he was observing in a parallax programme. Russell, with Shapley, carried out an ambitious programme of stellar density determinations, which also confirmed the existence of the two types of star. In 1911 Russell demonstrated that the stars in many of the open clusters showed the same properties, almost all of the stars proving to be dwarf type; some giants were however found in two of the clusters.

The original H–R diagram was published by Russell in 1913; a great many stars have since been added to those plotted by Russell, so that modern versions of the H–R diagram are based on data for thousands of stars (Fig. 52). It will be noted that a plot of luminosity *vs.* spectral type is, effectively, a plot of surface temperature *vs.* absolute magnitude.

The variation in luminosity for dwarf stars is the dominant feature of the diagram, showing a decrease in their absolute magnitudes from about -3 for *Bo* stars to about $+9$ for *M* stars. This 'stream' on the H–R diagram was later termed by Edding-

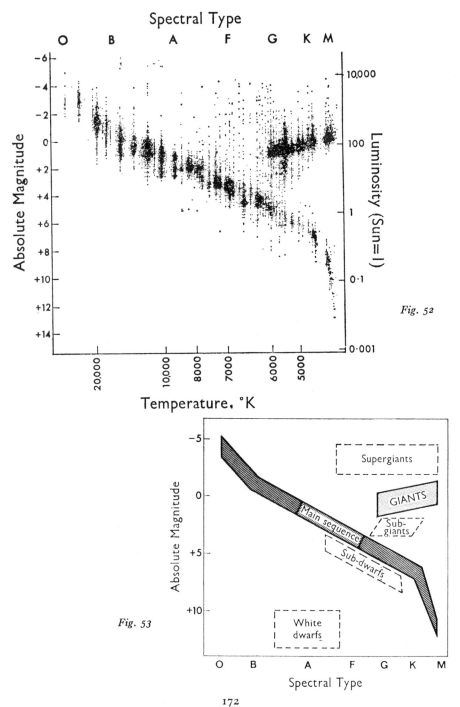

Fig. 52

Fig. 53

ton the *main sequence*. The giant stars form a stream with constant luminosity for all types, ranging between +1 and 0, the majority being in classes *G*, *K* and *M*. The term 'dwarf' is now reserved for true dwarf stars and is not used for the majority of main-sequence stars.

It will be noted that both giant and main-sequence stars abound in classes *G* to *M*, but that very few giants are found in classes *A* and *F* (this is now known as the *Hertzsprung gap*).

As more data became available over the years several new groups have appeared on the diagram. A number of stars in classes *F* to *M*, particularly in class *G*, are found to be very much larger than the conventional giants and to have much greater

less in luminosity, and the so-called 'sub-dwarfs', very small and dense stars some two magnitudes fainter than the main-sequence stars.

The **white dwarfs** form a class of their own; they are very small stars of very little luminosity but exceptionally dense. The location of the principal streams on the H–R diagram is shown in Fig. 53.

Stars in the globular clusters were found by Shapley to depart significantly from the usual pattern in the H–R diagram, the most luminous stars being very red (class *M*) and the luminosity steadily decreasing with spectral type towards type *B* with a remarkable division in the sequence at about *K0* (Fig. 54.)

The discovery by Baade that stars exist in

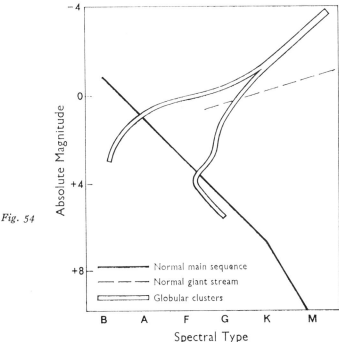

Fig. 54

Absolute Magnitude

—— Normal main sequence
— — — Normal giant stream
▭ Globular clusters

Spectral Type

luminosities—between −2 and −4. These are the 'supergiants', including such stars as *Antares*, *Betelgeuse* and *Rigel*.

Two further streams are now known, the 'sub-giants' which are similar to the giants of classes *G* to *M* but some two magnitudes

two Populations led to a comparative study of the H–R diagrams of the variable stars in each Population. Population I stars are mostly blue-white stars of types *O* and *B* and occur mainly in the 'arms' of spiral galaxies; Population II stars are found in the galactic nuclei and are mostly red stars. Schematic H–R diagrams for the intrinsic variables in Population I and II are given in Fig. 55; it will be noted that the intrinsic variables are all stars of high luminosity, none of them appearing in the lower half of the H–R diagram.

it crosses the mountain spur north of Cichus and sweeps on, curving slightly, until it terminates at a mountain arm from Capuanus at ($\xi - 390$, $\eta - 535$). Immediately to the east there is a network of fine rilles surrounding the crater Ramsden, which are probably associated faults.

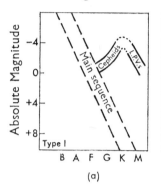
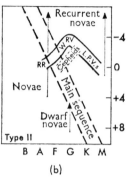

(a)   (b)

Fig. 55

The Hertzsprung–Russell diagram is an invaluable aid to the collation and analysis of astrophysical data, and has been the starting point for several theories of stellar evolution; its development marks a major milestone in the history of the interpretation of astronomical observations.

(See also **Stars—spectral classification of; Stellar evolution.**)

HESIODUS Lunar surface feature, co-ordinates $\xi - 245$, $\eta - 490$. A crater 28 miles in diameter, with rather rugged walls, on the southern boundary of the Mare Nubium. Adjoins the eastern wall of Pitatus, to which it is connected by a mountain pass.

HESIODUS CLEFT A long lunar valley or cleft, associated with the crater Hesiodus. It commences as a very narrow fissure running from the north-eastern rampart of Pitatus ($\xi - 209$, $\eta - 471$) to the northern wall of Hesiodus at ($\xi - 240$, $\eta - 477$). The cleft reappears, much wider (about 2 miles) from the north-east wall of Hesiodus (at $\xi - 260$, $\eta - 482$) and runs approximately south-eastwards. At about ($\xi - 320$, $\eta - 510$)

HESPERIA Martian surface feature, approximate position Ω 240°, $\Phi - 20°$. Diagonal lightish area between the parallel Mare Cimmerium and Mare Tyrrhenum.

HESTIA Proposed name of satellite VI of Jupiter, *q.v.*

HEVEL, Johann (1611–1687) Better known as **Hevelius**, *q.v.*

HEVEL (alternatively **Hevelius**) Lunar surface feature, $\xi - 923$, $\eta + 038$. A crater 70 miles in diameter, close to the eastern limb, just to the north of Grimaldi. The walls rise to 6,000 ft. in the west, are terraced on the inside and broken by small craters in the east. There is a small central mountain and a bright craterlet (Hevel A) in the north-eastern part of the floor. Usually rather difficult to observe, owing to its general brightness and proximity to the limb.

HEVELIUS (1611–1687) Johann Hevel (otherwise Hewelcke), a notable astronomer of Danzig. Compiled a catalogue giving the places of some 1,500 stars, based upon his own observations; these were remarkably accurate, especially in view of the fact that he used only naked-eye sighting instruments, firmly believing that the telescope was not suitable for precise, positional observations. He did however use the long refracting telescopes of the day for non-positional work, and made one of the earliest maps of the surface of the Moon to show reasonable accuracy when compared with modern observations. A few of the names he allocated to lunar surface features are still in use.

HEVELIUS Lunar surface feature, co-ordinates $\xi - 923$, $\eta + 038$. Usually designated **Hevel,** *q.v.*

HIDDEKEL Martian surface feature, approximate position Ω 345°, $\Phi + 15°$. Canal running north-eastwards from the eastern point of Furca, towards the Ismenius Lacus.

HIGH ALTITUDE OBSERVATORY, CLIMAX The High Altitude Observatory of Harvard University and the University of Colorado, situated at 11,000 ft. at Climax, Colorado, U.S.A.; one of the world's leading solar physics observatories.

HIGH-VELOCITY STAR Name given to the members of a group of stars which do not share the rotation of the Sun and most other stars in the Galaxy around the galactic centre, and consequently appear to have large proper motions and high velocities *relative to the Sun*. They are mostly Population II stars including the stars comprising the globular clusters, some moving clusters and the planetary nebulae. They do, as a group, have a rotational motion around the galactic centre, but the individual members of the group are moving in galactocentric orbits which are both highly eccentric and highly inclined to the galactic plane, hence their apparent high velocities which are in reality due to their direction of motion rather than a measure of their actual velocity. *Arcturus* is perhaps the best-known example.

HIPPARCHUS OF NICAEA (190–120 B.C.) The greatest astronomer of ancient Greece, who has been referred to as 'the founder of systematic observational astronomy'. Most of his observational work was carried out at an observatory he built on the island of Rhodes. He collected many observational records of his predecessors and compared them with his own, and was able to discover many of the fundamentals of observational astronomy by this means, among them the **precession of the equinoxes**. He confirmed the value of the **obliquity of the ecliptic** obtained by Eratosthenes, and established that the then accepted value of the length of the Tropical Year ($365\frac{1}{4}$ days) was too long by several minutes.

Hipparchus also produced the first star catalogue, containing the celestial latitude and longitude and apparent magnitude of 1,080 stars; this was to remain the standard catalogue of the heavens for over 1,500 years. Hipparchus also produced a geocentric theory of the motions of the heavenly bodies.

HIPPARCHUS Lunar surface feature, $\xi + 085$, $\eta - 090$. A plain near the apparent centre of the Moon's disk, 100 miles in diameter. Owing to the ruined condition of the walls, Hipparchus is very difficult to see as a connected whole, except when on the terminator. There is a small but well-formed crater (Horrocks) in the north-western part of the floor, and there are many other small features breaking up the interior.

HISTORIA CŒLESTIS BRITANNICA A catalogue of 2,935 stars, compiled by **Flamsteed** from his own observations. It was completed after his death by his assistants Crosthwaite and Sharp, and published in three volumes in 1725.

HÖRBIGER Lunar surface feature, co-ordinates $\xi - 080$, $\eta - 530$. A vast ruined ring, more than 100 miles in diameter, adjoining the **eastern ramparts of Walter**

and Regiomontanus. There is much fine detail on its surface.

HORIZON, CELESTIAL The great circle cut on the celestial sphere by the plane through the observer that has the zenith and nadir as its poles; hence in all directions the celestial horizon has a zenith distance of 90°.
(See also **Celestial sphere**.)

HORIZONTAL PARALLAX The geocentric parallax of a body observed on the horizon. (See **Parallax, stellar**.)

HOROLOGIUM (The Clock. *Genitive* Horologii, *I.A.U. abbreviation* Hor.) A rather insignificant, partially circumpolar, constellation in the southern sky; contains no bright stars, even the brightest (α Hor) being the only one of the fourth magnitude.

HORSEHEAD NEBULA One of the best-known absorption nebulae, situated in the gaseous nebulosity covering the central region of Orion, a little to the south of ζ Ori; so-called because of its characteristic shape.

HOUR ANGLE The angle between the declination circle of an object and the meridian.
(See also **Celestial sphere**.)

HOYLE, Frederick Contemporary English astronomer and one of the world's leading cosmologists; played an important part in the development of the steady-state theory, now producing a new theory based upon a new concept of gravitation.

HUBBLE, Edwin P. (1889–1953) Brilliant American astrophysicist, and one of the greatest exponents of observation with large apertures. Born in Marshfield, Missouri, Hubble graduated from the University of Chicago in 1910; he spent three years at Queen's College, Oxford, as a Rhodes Scholar, and obtained a B.A. in Jurisprudence in 1912. (He also gained a blue for athletics.) On his return to the

U.S.A. in 1913 he practised successfully as an attorney for a year but then returned to the University of Chicago in order to revert to his first love, astronomy. He undertook a research programme at the Yerkes Observatory in the photography of faint nebulae. After war service in the United States Infantry he accepted Hale's offer of a post at the Mount Wilson Observatory and recommenced his study of the nebulae.

In 1923 he discovered a Cepheid variable in the Great Nebula in Andromeda, and was thus enabled to establish that it was far outside our own Galaxy; Hubble proceeded to discover Cepheids in numerous other nebulae and proved them to be extragalactic objects. He also studied the distribution of the extragalactic nebulae by the photography of 1,300 selected areas of the sky with the Mount Wilson 100-in. and 60-in. reflectors, and established that their distribution is uniform.

Hubble was the first to institute a system of classification of the galaxies, and his system is still in use today. He made many important contributions to the study of galactic evolution.

In 1929 he used the spectrograms of galaxies obtained by V. M. Slipher at the Lowell Observatory, and M. L. Humason at Mount Wilson, and established that the recessional velocities of all galaxies, indicated by the red shift of their spectra, are directly proportional to their distance. Arising from this he propounded that all the galaxies had been receding from an original starting point (at which they must all have comprised a densely packed mass) for a constant length of time—very approximately, some 7,000 million years; their rates of recession being linked by a constant factor (the *Hubble Constant*) which Hubble gave as about 500 km/sec per million parsecs. Hubble was actively engaged in furthering his studies of the galaxies to within days of his death, both at Mount Wilson and with the 200-in. Hale telescope at Mount Palomar. Only four months before he died he delivered a memorable George Darwin Lecture to the

Royal Astronomical Society on *The Law of Red Shifts*. He also published a very readable popular account of his work in *The Realm of the Nebulae*.

He was widely honoured for his pioneering work, receiving the Barnard, Bruce and Franklin gold medals in his own country and the Gold Medal of the Royal Astronomical Society in 1940.

(See also **Galactic evolution; Galactic recession; Red shift**.)

HUBBLE CONSTANT Hubble demonstrated that the rate of recession of all galaxies is directly proportional to their distances, and that there is a constant interval, for all galaxies, that they have been receding from a common point of origin; this interval is about 7,000 million years. The rates of recession of the individual galaxies are related by the Hubble Constant—the value of which was determined by Hubble as approximately 500 km/sec per million parsecs. The latest determination is about 530 km/sec per million parsecs.

(See also **Galactic recession; Red shift**.)

HUBBLE EFFECT The red shift in galactic spectra, interpreted by Hubble as being due to the recession of the galaxies.

HUGGINS, Sir William (1824–1910) Very distinguished English scientist, who made great contributions to the development of astrophysics and was one of the pioneers of stellar spectroscopy. In 1865 he established that the Moon possessed no atmosphere worth speaking of, by observing the spectrum of a star whilst it was being occulted by the Moon, and noting that light of all wavelengths was cut off simultaneously. In 1864 Huggins obtained the first spectogram of a diffuse nebula, and confirmed their predominantly gaseous nature. He also discovered the first moving cluster, by confirming that the five stars in the Plough shown by Proctor to have a common proper motion (ζ, ϵ, δ, γ and β UMa) also shared a common line-of-sight velocity of recession.

Although Huggins worked at his own private observatory in Tulse Hill, London, he was regarded as one of the leading scientists of the day and was widely honoured. He was President of the Royal Society (1900–1905) and of the British Association (1891). He was President of the Royal Astronomical Society (1876–1878) and was twice awarded its Gold Medal, in 1867 and 1885; he also served the R.A.S. as Secretary (1867–1873) and Foreign Secretary (1873–1876). He was created a Knight Commander of the Order of the Bath (K.C.B.) in 1897, and became the first scientist to receive the O.M. when the Order of Merit was founded in 1902.

HULST, H. C. van de Contemporary Dutch astronomer; famous for his prediction (in 1944) of the 21-cm hydrogen radiation, of which he was also a co-discoverer in 1951.

HUNTER'S MOON The Full Moon following the **Harvest Moon** (*q.v.*) which also results in a sequence of several moonlit evenings. In the southern hemisphere the Hunter's Moon occurs in April/May.

HUYGHENS, Christian (1629–1695) A Dutchman, and one of the leading practical astronomers of the seventeenth century. He constructed the first successful pendulum clock, and made many improvements to the telescope. His two-lens eyepiece proved to be one of the most successful ever designed and is still in wide use today.

He discovered satellite VI of Saturn (*Titan*) in 1655, and established the nature of Saturn's ring system in the following year.

(See also **Eyepiece, Huyghenian.**)

HYADES A splendid open cluster in Taurus, less striking than the other galactic cluster in Taurus (the **Pleiades**) but nevertheless a most rewarding sight with a small telescope. They tend, unfortunately, to be overshadowed by the bright orange *Aldebaran* which is almost on the line-of-sight from the Hyades but is, in fact, much closer to us and quite unconnected with the cluster.

HYDRA (The Water Snake. *Genitive* Hydrae, *I.A.U. abbreviation* Hya). An enormously long constellation, straggling almost a third of the way around the southern sky, from Canis Minor to Libra. In all it is bounded by thirteen other constellations.

There are no very bright stars; α Hya is second-magnitude and there are six third- and numerous fourth-magnitude stars. There are a number of double and variable stars, and there is a small planetary nebula (27 Hya) about 2° south of μ Hya.

HYDROGEN The simplest and lightest of all chemical elements, and the most abundant element in the cosmos. It is gaseous at normal temperatures, and is in fact extremely difficult to liquefy. Its atomic weight is 1·0078.

HYDROGEN-ALPHA LINE The third most conspicuous absorption line in the solar spectrum is at a wavelength of 6563 Ångstroms, and is the first of a series of lines due to hydrogen known as the Balmer series; it is the Fraunhofer *C* line. The prominence of this line in the red part of the spectrum is the reason for the pinkish colour of the chromosphere as seen at total solar eclipses. Light of this wavelength is that most frequently chosen for monochromatic studies of the Sun's activity with the spectroheliograph.

(See also **Sun—spectrum of.**)

HYDROGEN RADIATION, 21 CENTI-METRE In 1944 van de Hulst predicted that neutral hydrogen should emit radiation, albeit very weakly, of wavelength 21 cm, and that the integration of this weak radiation from the vast numbers of atoms in interstellar hydrogen clouds should render it detectable to terrestrial radio-observers. The radiation was de-tected independently in 1951 by three teams of radio astronomers, in Australia, the U.S.A. and Holland—the latter team including van de Hulst himself.

The 21-cm hydrogen line has since proved a most valuable aid in observations of the distribution of interstellar hydrogen, and of galactic structure. With its aid, the structure of the Galaxy has been positively established, with the deter-mination of the distance of the galactic centre and the delineation of several spiral arms—the Sun being near the edge of one of them.

(See also **Galactic structure.**)

HYDROGEN—SPECTRUM OF The spectrum of an atom of an element com-prises a number of lines, indicating that the substance is emitting radiation of several different wave-lengths. In order to emit radiation at all an atom must have electrons passing from one energy state to another, lower, energy state, the excess energy being emitted as radiation. The wavelength of this quantum of radiation is determined by the particular change of energy states which causes it to be emitted. When a substance is in a normal excited state it has numerous electrons passing between a series of energy states, each causing radiation of a characteristic wave-length to be emitted. It is possible to predict these wavelengths for a substance, by means of an analysis of the possible transitions of electrons between energy states, and thus the spectral lines produced can be identified.

The formation of the spectrum of hydrogen, the simplest atom of all (one nucleus, one orbiting electron), has been studied in considerable detail. The spectral lines produced occur in series, each con-taining many lines. The five principal series of lines in the spectrum of hydrogen are termed the Lyman, Balmer, Paschen, Brackett and Pfund spectra; the positions of the first five lines in each of these series are plotted in Fig. 56 against a logarithmic wavelength scale. These lines would nor-mally be identified by Greek letters for each

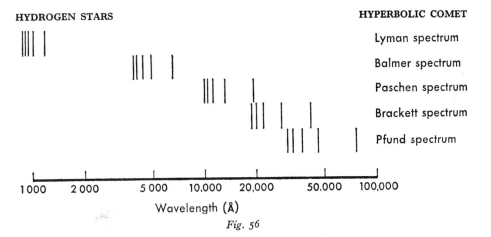

Fig. 56

series, commencing with the lines of longest wavelength (i.e. reading from right to left in Fig 56); thus the longest wavelength shown in Fig. 56 would be the Pfund-a line, and the shortest shown would be the Lyman-ε line.

Many lines due to hydrogen occur in the spectra of a star, so that very careful identifications have to be made, based upon theoretical predictions of their wavelengths, before lines due to other substances can be positively identified. In the spectrum of *Deneb* obtained with the 100-in. reflector at Mount Wilson, for instance, 29 Balmer lines have been identified.

HYDROGEN STARS Name sometimes used to denote stars of spectral class *A*, owing to the prominence of hydrogen absorption lines in their spectra. (See **Stars—spectral classification of.**)

HYDRUS (The Little Snake. *Genitive* Hydri, *I.A.U. abbreviation* Hyi.) A small, southern circumpolar constellation containing three third-magnitude stars.

HYGINUS Lunar surface feature, co-ordinates $\xi + 109$, $\eta + 135$. A large crater-pit, some 4 miles in diameter, with a low raised rim. It is situated in the centre of the great **Hyginus Rille,** in a region adjoining the Sinus Medii in the centre

of the apparent disk. This whole area abounds with clefts, including the complex network of clefts associated with the crater Triesnecker. [Plate 6(f, g).]

HYGINUS RILLE A striking lunar surface formation, centred on the crater-pit Hyginus. It commences at a craterlet north-west of Agrippa (at $\xi + 196$, $\eta + 082$) and swings north-east and east to Hyginus ($\xi + 109$, $\eta + 135$); at this point it changes direction abruptly, again heading north-east until it runs into the Mare Vaporum (at $\xi + 080$, $\eta + 190$), a total length of 194 miles.

When observed with a high power the cleft reveals a very detailed structure, and appears to be a fracture that has developed along a chain of small craterlets. Such fault-lines are important in considerations of the nature and origin of the surface features. [Plate 6(f, g).]

HYPERBOLA The conic section having an eccentricity greater than 1; it is an open curve.

HYPERBOLIC COMET Approximately 11 per cent of all comets observed are found to have hyperbolic orbital elements; i.e. their orbits have eccentricities greater than 1·0. It must not be assumed, however, that all these bodies have an origin outside the solar system, although a few of them may have; the comets are only observable over a very short arc of their orbit around perihelion, and the orbital elements cannot be determined with sufficient accuracy to distinguish reliably between elliptical, parabolic and hyperbolic arcs. This problem is further complicated by the fact that on the journey towards aphelion, when invisible from Earth, the comet may pass close to one or more of the major planets and be subjected to colossal perturbations.

(See also **Comets—orbits of.**)

HYPERBOREUS LACUS Martian surface feature, approximate position Ω 60°, $\Phi + 75°$. Dark spur radiating southwards from the border of the north polar cap.

HYPERION Satellite VII of Saturn, *q.v.*

HYSCUS Martian surface feature, approximate position Ω 130°, $\Phi - 35°$. Dusky streak connecting the eastern end of the Mare Sirenum and the Aonius Sinus, alternatively known as Icaria.

I

I.A.F. The International Astronautics Federation, the world co-ordinating body for astronautical research.

I.A.U. The International Astronomical Union, *q.v.*

I.A.U. ABBREVIATIONS The standard abbreviations for the constellation names, adopted by the International Astronomical Union in 1922 and 1932 (see **Constellation names and abbreviations**).

I.A.U. CATALOGUE OF RADIO SOURCES A catalogue of discrete radio sources sponsored by Commission 40 (Radio Astronomy) of the International Astronomical Union, published in 1955 as *A Catalogue of Reliably Known Discrete Sources of Cosmic Radio Waves.*

The catalogue is in two parts, *List 1* which gives the data for the eight sources for which really reliable data had been determined, and *List 2* containing provisional data for a further 30 sources. The eight sources included in *List 1* are listed in Table 31 on page 355 of this book.

The system of nomenclature adopted by the I.A.U. is used for all discrete sources; it comprises two digits indicating the hours of Right Ascension of the source, N or S to indicate north or south Declination, a digit indicating the 10°-belt of Declination in which the source is located, and a serial letter. Thus, the catalogue number for the source Cassiopeia A is 23N5A, indicating that it is the first source identified in the 23rd hour of R.A. and between 50° and 60° north Declination.

In recent years it has become widespread practice to adopt the designations of the very comprehensive **Cambridge catalogues of radio sources,** *q.v.*

(See also **Radio astronomy.**)

I.C. Abbreviation for the *Index Catalogues,* supplements to Dreyer's **New General Catalogue,** *q.v.*

I.U.A.A. The International Union of Amateur Astronomers, founded at Bologna in April 1969.

IAPETUS Satellite VIII of Saturn, *q.v.*

IAPYGIA Martian surface feature, approximate position Ω 295°, $\Phi - 20°$. Dark area south of the Syrtis Major; the Hadriacum Mare, running south-eastwards, and Hellespontus, running south-westwards from Iapygia, form the northern boundary of Hellas.

ICARIA Martian surface feature, approximate position Ω 130°, $\Phi - 35°$. Dusky streak connecting the eastern end of the Mare Sirenum and the Aonius Sinus.

IGNEOUS THEORY A theory that the majority of the lunar surface features were formed by igneous activity (see **Moon—origin of surface features**).

IMMERSION Term sometimes used for the disappearance phase of an eclipse or occultation.

IMPACT THEORY A theory that the majority of the lunar surface features were formed by meteoric impact (see **Moon—origin of surface features**).

IMPERIAL SYSTEM The system of units of measurement traditionally used in the United Kingdom. Scientists normally use the **metric system** (*q.v.*), under which heading conversion factors will be found.

IMPERSONAL ASTROLABE The **prismatic astrolabe,** *q.v.*

INCLINATION (AXIAL) The angle between the axis of rotation of a planet and the perpendicular to the plane of its orbit; it can also be regarded as the angle between the equatorial plane and the orbital plane. The axial inclinations for the planets of the solar system are as follows (those for Mercury, Venus and Pluto being unknown):

Earth: 23° 27′	Saturn: 26° 44′
Mars: 23° 59′	Uranus: 97° 53′
Jupiter: 3° 04′	Neptune: 28° 48′

(See also **Planetary motion; Solar system.**)

INCLINATION (ORBITAL) The angle between the orbital plane of a planet and the plane of the Ecliptic; it is one of the fundamental elements of a planetary orbit, and is usually designated i. The orbital inclinations of the planets of the solar system are as follows:

Mercury:	7° 00′ 14″8
Venus:	3° 23′ 39″5
Earth:	0° 00′ 00″0
Mars:	1° 50′ 59″6
Jupiter:	1° 18′ 18″1
Saturn:	2° 29′ 22″7
Uranus:	0° 46′ 23″1
Neptune:	1° 46′ 23″5
Pluto:	17° 10′ 11″7

(See also **Planetary motion; Solar system.**)

INDUS (The Indian. *Genitive* Indi, *I.A.U. Abbreviation* Ind.) A southern, circumpolar constellation containing few bright stars; the brightest are two of the third magnitude.

INFERIOR CONJUNCTION That position of an inferior planet between the Sun and the Earth where its geocentric longitude is the same as that of the Sun. (See **Planetary motion.**)

INFERIOR PLANET Term used to describe a planet closer to the Sun than the Earth—i.e. Mercury or Venus.

INFRA-RED SPECTRA Spectrograms obtained with the aid of a suitable filter or other means of selecting a part of the infra-red region of the spectrum, i.e. in the range of wavelengths between, approximately, 20,000 Å and 7,700 Å. This technique is an important research tool of the astrophysicist.

INGRESS Term used to denote the commencing stage of a transit or shadow-transit of a planetary satellite.
　　(See **Satellite phenomena.**)

INNER PLANET Arbitrary description given to those planets having orbits inside that of the Earth—i.e. Mercury and Venus—which are also termed the **inferior planets.**

INNES, Robert T. A. (1861–1933) Notable astronomer who specialized in the study of double stars. Born in Scotland he went to Australia and achieved notable success as an amateur observer and theorist; he was later invited by Gill to become Secretary of the Royal Observatory, Cape of Good Hope. The remainder of his career was spent in South Africa; in 1903 he was appointed Director of the Transvaal Observatory at Johannesburg; this became the Union Observatory in 1912 when Innes was appointed Union Astronomer, which post he held until his retirement at the end of 1927.
　　His most lasting achievement was the publication, in 1926, of the *Southern Double Star Catalogue, q.v.*

INTERFERENCE If two beams of light, originating from the same source and hence having identical waveforms, are combined, they will 'interfere' with each other, the effect upon the resulting combined beam depending upon the phase-relationship of the two beams at the point of combination.
　　If the beams are in phase, the amplitude of the resultant beam is equal to the sum of the amplitudes of the separate beams, as in Fig. 57; if, however, the beams are

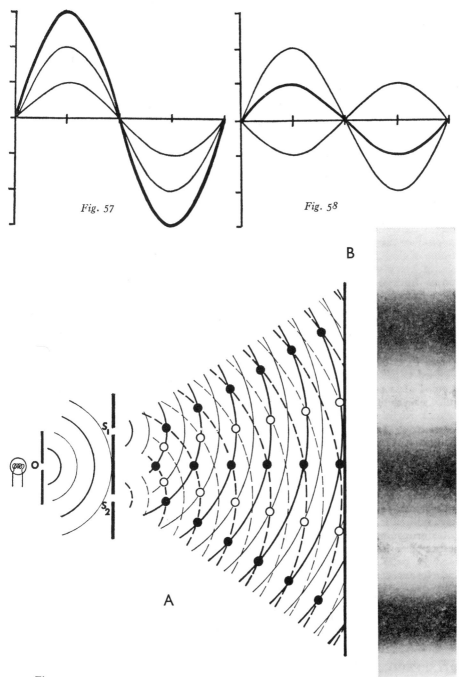

Fig. 57

Fig. 58

B

A

Fig. 59

exactly out of phase, the amplitude of the resultant waveform is equal to the difference of the amplitudes of the component beams (Fig. 58). Thus, whereas the separate beams will be of equal intensity, the image produced by the combined beam will consist of a 'fringe' comprising a regular pattern of images of intensity varying between the sum and the difference of the intensities of the separate beams. This is best illustrated by the principle of a simple interferometer, such as Young's double-slit interferometer. In this instrument (see Fig. 59 (a)), a light from one source O is divided by a screen containing two slits (S_1, S_2) so as to produce two separate beams; the wavefronts of these are shown, maxima being shown heavy and minima light, and the waves from S_1 being shown solid and those from S_2 dotted. It will be seen that there will be points of maximum interference ($\bullet$) and of minimum interference ($\bigcirc$); the image on the screen will be a fringe as shown in Fig. 59 (b).

One form of 'beam-splitter' which can be used to produce interference fringes is a ruled glass screen or a grating; if two ruled screens are used together, with their rulings slightly inclined, a pattern of interference fringes known as **Moiré fringes** is produced; this principle has been widely applied in recent years to precise measuring devices (some of them used in astronomy), but little use had previously been made of the principle of interference—except by astronomers who have utilized it in the form of the **stellar interferometer** since 1920. In more recent times the same principle has been used at radio frequencies. (See **Radio interferometer**.)

INTERFERENCE FILTER Optical element utilizing the principle of interference to isolate a narrow band of the spectrum.
(See also **Lyot birefringent filter**.)

INTERFEROMETER, STELLAR An instrument used to measure the angular diameter of a distant object, or the angular separation of two distant objects, by means of the interference of light. They are commonly used in the following two forms.

Beam interferometer. This type is usually used with very large reflecting telescopes, for the measurement of the angular diameters of stars. In this case, as illustrated in Fig. 60, the division of the light-beam from the star is achieved by means of two small plane mirrors M_1, M_2 carried on a beam (hence the name) or girder,

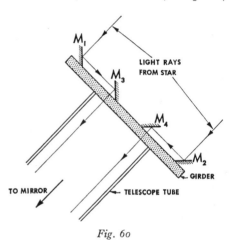

Fig. 60

and whose separation can thus be made greater than the aperture of the objective mirror of the telescope. The light-beams from M_1 and M_2 are reflected into two similar mirrors M_3 and M_4, and hence onto the main mirror. They meet at the focus of the telescope, producing interference fringes.

Parallel-slit interferometer. This type is usually used with refracting telescopes, the beam of light from the object under observation being split by means of a diaphragm containing two narrow parallel slits whose separation is adjustable; the diaphragm is usually placed over the O.G. (Fig. 61), but may under certain conditions be sited within the telescope tube. This type has been successfully used for the measurement of close double stars.

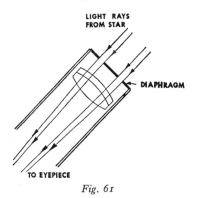

Fig. 61

Operation. The separation of the auxiliary mirrors (M_1 and M_2), or of the parallel slits, is adjusted until a point is found at which the interference fringes disappear; this separation (D) can be used to obtain the angular separation of the components of a double star (d) from the formula

$$D = 1 \cdot 22 \ \lambda/d$$

where λ is the mean wavelength of the light from the star.

If the observation is the determination of the angular diameter of a star (a), this is obtained from the similar expression

$$D = 1 \cdot 22 \ \lambda/a$$

if it is assumed that there is no limb-darkening effect for the star concerned; if it is desired to take account of limb-darkening by assuming that the falling off in intensity towards the limb will be similar to that observed in the case of the Sun, the formula to be used is

$$D = 1 \cdot 33 \ \lambda/a.$$

History. The use of this principle to measure angular diameters was suggested by Fizeau in 1868, but was only developed by Michelson who, with Pease, made the first determination in 1920 using a 20-ft. beam interferometer attached to the 100-in. reflector at Mount Wilson. The smallest diameter measurable with this instrument was about 0″02, and a second instrument was therefore constructed specially for the purpose, comprising a 50-ft. beam interferometer and a 40-in. reflector.

A number of stellar diameters were measured, but the observations proved to be exceptionally difficult to make successfully; stellar diameters can be calculated theoretically from the magnitude and spectral type, and as those measured with the interferometer agreed closely with the theoretical values, the accuracy of the theoretical method was demonstrated and the use of the interferometer was not continued to any great extent. This fact must not be allowed to cloud, however, the great and lasting importance of these original measures made with the instrument.

(See also **Radio interferometer; Stars, diameter of.**)

INTERLOCKING RING-STRUCTURES

Lunar ring-structures which overlap each other, but where the existence of the walls of both rings indicates that they were formed contemporaneously. (See **Moon— surface features of.**)

INTERNATIONAL ASTRONOMICAL UNION (I.A.U.)

The world co-ordinating body for astronomical research, founded in 1920. General Assemblies are held, in a different member country each time, normally once in three years; special colloquia are held on specific topics from time to time. National Committees are appointed in each member country as the liaison with the Union, and Standing Commissions are appointed to conduct the scientific work of the Union. Each of these is responsible for a given field, and co-ordinate research work and negotiate international co-operation and standardization in that field. The members of the Standing Commissions are leading workers in the field concerned, from all parts of the world.

The Union has a superb record of international co-operation in all branches of astronomy, set out in the substantial volumes of the *Transactions of the International Astronomical Union.*

INTERNATIONAL COUNCIL OF SCIENTIFIC UNIONS (I.C.S.U.) The co-ordinating body for the numerous international Unions for the various scientific disciplines, of which the International Astronomical Union is one.

INTERPOLATION A mathematical process whereby intermediate values of a tabulated function—such as an astronomical ephemeris—may be calculated from the figures tabulated. It is based upon the premise that however the tabulated function may vary, a study of successive differences will determine the exact correction to be applied to the earlier tabulated value so as to ensure that the interpolated value is correct. In practice, the process is cut off after only a few differences, when accuracy sufficient for the purpose has been secured.

Notation. The notation used is set out in the following scheme; this shows in the second column the value of the tabulated function appropriate for the given arguments (points of entry) shown in the first column. The third, fourth, fifth and sixth columns show the first-, second-, third- and fourth-order differences respectively. It will be seen that the term δ is used to indicate a difference, followed by a superior index which indicates its order; thus δ^2 is a second difference. The term f is used to indicate a function, and is followed by a subscript indicating the argument to which it refers; thus f_2 is the

function value appropriate to the argument $+2$. The same subscript series are used for differences, but it will be noted that alternate differences apply to points midway between arguments; thus the first difference between the functions f_1 and f_2 is denoted $\delta_{1\frac{1}{2}}^1$, or simply, $\delta_{1\frac{1}{2}}$, whereas the second-order difference between $\delta_{\frac{1}{2}}$ and $\delta_{1\frac{1}{2}}$ is δ_1^2. It will be found easier to follow this notation if it is noted that the subscripts are constant along any horizontal line of the table.

A numerical example is given alongside the notational scheme, and study of this may assist in understanding the notation used.

Linear interpolation. This method uses the first difference only; such an approximation is often sufficient to achieve the accuracy required. The method may be expressed in the form

$$f_p = f_0 + p\,\delta_{\frac{1}{2}} \qquad (1)$$

where f_p is the function required to be interpolated for argument p.

If, for the example tabulated above, f_p is required for $p = 0.75$, we obtain by substitution of the appropriate quantities in equation (1):

$$\begin{aligned} f_{0.75} &= 46373 + 0.75\,(+4139) \\ &= 46373 + 3104 \\ &= 49477. \end{aligned}$$

Besselian interpolation. Where greater accuracy is required, a method utilizing second- and higher-order differences is

Argument	Function	DIFFERENCES			
		First	Second	Third	Fourth
-2	f_{-2}				
		$\delta_{-1\frac{1}{2}}$			
-1	f_{-1}		δ_{-1}^2		
		$\delta_{-\frac{1}{2}}$		$\delta_{-\frac{1}{2}}^3$	
0	f_0		δ_0^2		δ_0^4
		$\delta_{\frac{1}{2}}$		$\delta_{\frac{1}{2}}^3$	
$+1$	f_1		δ_1^2		δ_1^4
		$\delta_{1\frac{1}{2}}$		$\delta_{1\frac{1}{2}}^3$	
$+2$	f_2		δ_2^2		
		$\delta_{2\frac{1}{2}}$			
$+3$	f_3				

Argument	Function	DIFFERENCES			
		First	Second	Third	Fourth
-2	36682				
		$+5115$			
-1	41797		-539		
		$+4576$		$+102$	
0	46373		-437		-25
		$+4139$		$+77$	
$+1$	50512		-360		-20
		$+3779$		$+57$	
$+2$	54291		-303		
		$+3476$			
$+3$	57767				

adopted; that most commonly used was devised by **F. W. Bessel.**

Bessel's formula (expressed here to the fifth term, i.e. utilizing fourth differences), is as follows:

$$f_p = f_0 + p\delta_{\frac{1}{2}} + B_2\left(\delta_0^2 + \delta_1^2\right) + B_3\,\delta_{\frac{1}{2}}^3$$
$$+ B_4\left(\delta_0^4 + \delta_1^4\right) + \ldots \qquad (2)$$

It will be noted that the first two terms of equation (2) are identical to equation (1). B_2, B_3 and B_4 are the Besselian Interpolation Coefficients, and are conveniently tabulated in the literature—notably in *Interpolation and Allied Tables* (Her Majesty's Stationery Office, London, 1956).

To use again the numerical example tabulated above, we derive by Besselian interpolation the function f_p for $p = 0.75$. The coefficients B_2, B_3 and B_4 for $p = 0.75$ are -0.046875, -0.00781 and $+0.0085$. Therefore, by substitution in (2),

$$f_{0.75} = 46373 + 0.75(+4139)$$
$$- 0.046875(-797)$$
$$- 0.00781(+77) + 0.0085(-45)$$
$$= 46373 + 3104 + 37.36 - 0.60 - 0.38$$
$$= 49513 \text{ (to the nearest whole number)}.$$

It will be noted that the difference in the figure obtained for f_p by linear interpolation and by Besselian interpolation is 36, less than one per cent of the first difference; this underlines the fact that Besselian interpolation need only be used where the highest accuracy is required, and then only as many differences as are really necessary should be used. In the present example the result would have differed by only 1 in the last place if second differences only had been used.

INTERSTELLAR MATTER The space between the stars has long been known to be far from empty; because of its effect on the light from more distant objects the presence of some obscuring matter had long been suspected, and the dark 'absorption' nebulae found in many parts of the sky, especially near the galactic plane, were regarded as further evidence of it. Careful quantitative studies of the light from distant stars, especially those in the

globular clusters, have confirmed the presence in interstellar space of clouds of gas molecules and dust particles. This material has a tendency to transmit red light, but to absorb and scatter the shorter wavelength blue light; there is thus a reddening effect of stars in the distant globular clusters, which increases with distance.

Absorption lines attributable to the interstellar matter appear in the spectra of distant spectroscopic binaries; from a study of these sodium, calcium, iron, titanium and other elements are known to be present, in addition to large quantities of hydrogen. Although the hydrogen does not reveal itself in these spectra, its presence can be inferred with certainty from its universal abundance, and was confirmed by the discovery of its radio emission on the 21-cm wavelength in accordance with the prediction of van de Hulst.

(See also **Absorption, galactic; Hydrogen radiation, 21 centimetre.**)

INTRINSIC VARIABLE Term used to denote a variable star whose radiation is in fact varying, as opposed to extrinsic variables such as the eclipsing binaries. Intrinsic variables include both regular and irregular variables, novae, etc.

INVERSION, OPTICAL Certain image-forming elements in optical systems produce an image that is inverted relative to the object; this inversion may be lateral (i.e. left-to-right) as well as vertical. A notable example is the refracting telescope, which in a simple form such as the astronomical telescope produces an image both laterally and vertically inverted. To produce an erect image it is necessary to introduce additional lenses, as in the terrestrial telescope.

(See also **Eyepiece, terrestrial; Optics; Telescope, astronomical; Telescope, refracting; Telescope, terrestrial.**)

IO Satellite I of Jupiter, *q.v.*

IONIZATION This is the term used for the deprivation of an atom of one or more of the electrons from its outer shell. The affected atom is said to be 'ionized'. The terms 'doubly ionized' or 'triply ionized' are used to indicate the state of having lost two or three electrons respectively, etc.

(See **Atom.**)

IONOSPHERE A stratum of the Earth's atmosphere, some of whose constituent atoms are ionized by the effect of ultra-violet radiation received from the Sun. The height of the ionospheric layers varies, but it lies, approximately, between 50 and 250 miles above the Earth's surface.

It comprises in the main three electrically conductive layers of different characteristics. The F-layer, usually above 150 miles high, has the power to reflect short-wave radio signals; the E-layer, usually 60–120 miles high, reflects the medium wavebands; the D-layer, usually 50–70 miles high, reflects long-wave radiations. These powers are used to facilitate long-range broadcasting, but unfortunately the state of the ionized layers is easily disturbed by solar activity such as sunspots, flares, etc., which can therefore cause considerable disruption to broadcast services.

(See also **Atmosphere (of the Earth); Solar–terrestrial relationships.**)

IRIS DIAPHRAGM A diaphragm composed of a number of separate blades, usually constructed of metal and so shaped as to produce an approximately circular central aperture; the diameter of this aperture depends upon the relative position of the blades, which can be varied by rotating a peripheral control ring.

Apart from its well known use in the camera, the iris diaphragm is also used to control the amount of light passing through certain optical instruments used in some branches of astronomy.

IRRADIATION An effect which introduces errors into telescopic observations of bright objects (e.g. determinations of planetary diameters), since the eye sees bright objects larger than they really are. The effect is physiological in origin. It can be reduced, but not eliminated, by the use of a telescope of large aperture and by illuminating the field of the eyepiece so as to reduce contrast between the bright object and the background field.

IRREGULAR VARIABLE A variable star whose light variation does not follow any predictable pattern; there are various types, notably the U Geminorum, R Coronæ Borealis and RV Tauri stars.

(See **Variable stars.**)

ISAAC NEWTON TELESCOPE In his Presidential Address to the Royal Astronomical Society in 1946, Professor H. H. Plaskett propounded the desirability of providing a giant telescope in the United Kingdom. Following from this a submission with the backing of the entire Society was made to the British Government, which was strongly supported by The Royal Society and by the then Astronomer Royal, Sir Harold Spencer Jones. As a result of this the Government agreed to provide a 100-in. telescope to be erected in Great Britain for the use of all British astronomers. The instrument was to be named the Isaac Newton Telescope, in honour of the man who founded the great tradition of British astronomy three centuries ago.

The long period required to finalize the design details of an instrument sufficiently modern in its conception and versatile in its function to remain useful for at least the remainder of the century, together with inevitable delays arising from problems of national economy, have delayed the implementation of this decision, already twenty years old. The instrument has now been erected, however, in the grounds of the Royal Greenwich Observatory at Herstmonceux, which body will be responsible for its maintenance. It is administered by a Large Telescope Users' Panel, set up by the Science Research

Council in 1968 to administer all large telescopes under the Council's control. The Panel will allocate the observing time of the instrument to suitably qualified British astronomers (not solely members of the Royal Observatory staff), on the relative merits of their proposed research.

The blank for the primary mirror was cast by Messrs Corning during the preparations for the casting of the blank for the 200-in. Hale telescope on Mount Palomar; it was presented by the Trustees of the McGregor Fund to Sir Harold Spencer Jones for use in the Isaac Newton Telescope.

The new instrument has an aperture of 98 inches, and will be used at the prime focus at a focal ratio of $f/3$, at the Cassegrain focus at $f/15$ and at the coudé focus at $f/32$. It will be an extremely versatile instrument, and is likely to be used for stellar spectroscopy and photometry and for radial-velocity and proper-motion determinations. It is hoped also to use it for astrometric programmes. [Plate 31(b).]

ISIDIS REGIO Martian surface feature, approximate position $\Omega\,275°$, $\Phi+20°$. A prominent light ochre area, enclosed to the west and south by the Syrtis Major and to the east by the Nepenthes-Thoth. Adjoins, in the north, the Neith Regio.

ISLAND UNIVERSE Term sometimes used in the past to describe the objects now known as galaxies or (less correctly) as 'extra-galactic nebulae'.

ISMENIUS LACUS Martian surface feature, approximate position $\Omega\,330°$, $\Phi+40°$. A dark 'oasis' adjoining the southern edge of the north temperate band, to which it is connected by the canal Arnon. A number of often prominent canali radiate from it; Protonilus to the east, Deuteronilus to the west, Euphrates and Hiddekel to the south.

J

JACKSON, John (1887–1958) One of the most notable British astronomers of recent times; after a brilliant career at Cambridge he became a Chief Assistant at the Royal Observatory, Greenwich, in 1914. In 1933 he succeeded Spencer Jones as H.M. Astronomer at the Cape, where he remained until his retirement in 1950.

He made many notable contributions to fundamental astronomy, including analyses of double-star observations, important stellar parallax and proper motion programmes, and led three solar eclipse expeditions from Greenwich. He was appointed a Commander of the Order of the British Empire (C.B.E.) in 1950. He was awarded the Gold Medal of the Royal Astronomical Society in 1952, and was also its President (1953–1955) and Secretary (1923–1929); he was elected a Fellow of the Royal Society in 1938.

JAMUNA Martian surface feature, approximate position Ω 40°, Φ + 10°. Canal radiating north-eastwards from Auroræ Sinus, separating Xanthe and Chryse.

JANSSEN Lunar surface feature, co-ordinates ξ + 460, η − 705. A huge walled plain, about 100 miles in diameter, situated in the south-western limb-region. The mountain walls are prominent but very broken by newer formations—notably the north-western wall, a length of which has been obliterated by the 55-mile crater Fabricius. Many clefts and other fine detail can be observed on the floor of this feature, and there is a smallish central mountain.

JANUS Proposed name for satellite X of Saturn, discovered on 1966 December 15. (See **Saturn—satellites of.**)

JEANS, Sir James Hopwood (1877–1946) One of the best known British astronomers of the early twentieth century; one of the leading theoretical cosmologists and, at the same time, famous as a popularizer of astronomy and cosmology. His many books, including such works as *The Stars in Their Courses, The Mysterious Universe, The Universe Around Us*, etc., brought knowledge and pleasure to thousands, and are still widely read today. He was a leading observer, being a Research Associate of Mount Wilson Observatory; it was for his theoretical work, however, that he received the greatest recognition. Among his many honours were the Royal Medal of the Royal Society, of which he was elected a Fellow in 1906, and the Gold Medal of the Royal Astronomical Society. He was President of the latter body from 1925–1927. He was knighted in 1928, and later appointed to the Order of Merit.

JEFFREYS, Sir Harold Contemporary theoretical astronomer and the leading geophysicist of modern times; former Plumian Professor of Astronomy in the University of Cambridge, and President of the Royal Astronomical Society 1955–1957. Has been awarded many honours, including the Copley and Royal Medals of the Royal Society, the Gold Medal of the Royal Astronomical Society and the Wollaston Medal of the Geological Society

JODRELL BANK The Cheshire location of the **Nuffield Radio Astronomy Laboratories** of the University of Manchester, *q.v.*

JOLIOT-CURIE Name given by the Russian Academy of Sciences to a dark patch on the far side of the Moon, discovered on photographs taken by **Lunik**

III. The patch is situated on the floor of a great walled plain, some 90 miles in diameter, situated close to the Mare Marginis, part of which is on the visible face of the Moon. The crater has been photographed as an extreme limb feature at the Pic-du-Midi Observatory.

(See also **Moon, far side of.**)

JONES, Sir Harold Spencer (1890–1960) The tenth Astronomer Royal; not only one of the world's leading astronomers, but one of the most eminent scientists of modern times. It is impossible to indicate the vast range of his achievements in this brief note, but it can perhaps be inferred from the following summary of his appointments and interests.

Spencer Jones had a brilliant career at Cambridge, where he obtained a first in both the Mathematical Tripos and the Natural Sciences Tripos. When Eddington left the Royal Observatory to become Plumian Professor of Astronomy at Cambridge the Astronomer Royal, Sir Frank Dyson, selected Spencer Jones to replace him as Chief Assistant. He served with great distinction in this capacity, making important contributions in many fields, notably the variation of latitude and stellar proper motions.

In 1933 Spencer Jones was appointed H.M. Astronomer at the Royal Observatory, Cape of Good Hope. While in South Africa he expanded and reorganized the Royal Observatory, completing many important programmes initiated by Gill and launching many more, including determinations of proper motions, photographic magnitudes, radial velocities and stellar parallaxes, and the completion of the 2nd and 3rd Cape Catalogues.

During this period the principal interest of his career was being developed—the rotation of the Earth and the motions of the Sun, Moon and planets. As President of the Solar Parallax Commission of the I.A.U. he directed the great international programme of observations of **Eros** during its close approach of 1931, and was personally responsible for supervising the measurement of the plates and for the analysis of the results. After ten years' effort he was able to announce a new value of the solar parallax, then exceeding in accuracy any previous determination.

In 1933 Spencer Jones returned to Greenwich, having been appointed H.M. Astronomer Royal on the retirement of Dyson.

Among his first tasks as Astronomer Royal was the supervision of the erection of two important new instruments—the Yapp 36-in. reflector and the Cooke Reversible Transit Circle. The Yapp reflector was launched on an important series of colour–temperature determinations directed by W. M. H. Greaves. Following the installation of the Cooke R.T.C., a long programme of precise measurement was necessary in order to determine the division errors of its declination circles; Spencer Jones took a close personal interest in both the measurements and their analysis.

Spencer Jones also reorganized the Time Service provided by the Royal Observatory. In 1939 he published a classic paper on 'The rotation of the Earth, and the secular accelerations of the Sun, Moon and planets'; in this paper, the culmination of his years of research in this field, he proved conclusively that observed discrepancies in the motions of the other bodies were in fact due to irregularities in the axial rotation of the Earth.

Perhaps Spencer Jones' most lasting contribution was the realization that the deterioration in observing conditions at Greenwich, due to the encroachment of modern street-lighting and to atmospheric pollution, necessitated the complete removal of the Royal Observatory to a more favourable location. He obtained Admiralty approval for such a move, and immediately after the Second World War a number of possible sites were examined and Herstmonceux Castle selected. Spencer Jones took up residence in the Castle in 1948, and the various departments of the Observatory were transferred in a number of stages, the move being finally completed in 1958, three years after Spencer Jones' retirement on 1955 December 31. To commemorate his contributions to fundamental astronomy, and his administrative achievement in removing the Observatory, the group of meridian instruments at Herstmonceux have been named the 'Spencer Jones Group'.

Another long-term project to which Spencer Jones gave a great deal of his time was the proposal for the Isaac Newton Telescope, and his short 'retirement' was fully occupied, being principally devoted to the furtherance of international co-operation in science in his capacity as Secretary General of the International Council of Scientific Unions and Director of the I.C.S.U. Publications Office. He received the highest honours, awards and honorary degrees from many lands; he was knighted in 1943, and created a Knight Commander of the Order of the British Empire (K.B.E.) in 1955. He was awarded the Royal Medal of the Royal Society, and the Gold Medal of the Royal Astronomical Society, in 1943; he was President of the Royal Astronomical Society from 1937–1939, and a member of its Council for over 30 years; he was President of the British Astronomical Association (1934–1936), of the Institute of Navigation (1947–1949) and of the British Horological Institute (1937–1960); he twice served as Master of the Worshipful Company of Clockmakers. From 1945 to 1948 he was President of the International Astronomical Union.

(See also **Astronomer Royal; Isaac Newton Telescope; Royal Greenwich Observatory; Solar parallax.**)

JOVIAN PLANETS Name sometimes given to the group of **major planets**.

JULES VERNE Prominent dark circular formation on the far side of the Moon, discovered on photographs taken by *Lunik III*. (See **Moon—far side of.**)

JULIAN CALENDAR The system of calendar reckoning introduced by Julius Caesar in 46 B.C., based upon a year of 365·25 days. The odd quarter of a day was ignored for three years and an extra full day added to the fourth (known today as a 'Leap Year').

(See also **Calendar.**)

JULIAN DAY A system of date reckoning providing a continuous sequence of days throughout the B.C. and A.D. periods; it must not be confused with the Julian Calendar invented by Julius Caesar. Julian Day numbers were so called by their inventor Joseph Scaliger (1540–1609), after his father Julius.

Julian Day Numbers are simply a count of the number of mean solar days that have elapsed since a definitive epoch—chosen by Scaliger as mean noon on B.C. 4713 January 1. The Julian Day Numbers for each day of the year are tabulated in the astronomical almanacs; they are particularly useful in computations involving the comparison of observations with a time-scale, such as the light-variation of variable stars, eclipse cycles, etc.

The Julian date of an observation consists of the Julian Day Number for the previous mean noon at Greenwich, followed by the interval of mean solar time that has elapsed since that moment; the latter part is usually given in decimal form. Thus the Julian Date of an observation made at 6 p.m. on 1965 May 22 was 2438903·25, the Julian Day Number for that day being 2438903.

Tables to facilitate the determination of Julian Day Numbers are published in the *Astronomical Ephemeris* each year; the Julian Day Numbers for the first of each month for the decade 1965–1975 are given in Table 14 (opposite).

(See also **Calendar.**)

JULIUS CAESAR Lunar surface feature, co-ordinates $\xi + 257$, $\eta - 156$. A well-defined but imperfect crater ring just north of the Ariadæus cleft and close to the eastern borders of the Mare Tranquillitatis. The western wall is completely

Table 14. Julian Day Numbers 1970–1980

DATE YEAR	Jan. 1	Feb. 1	Mar. 1	Apr. 1	May 1	Jun. 1
1970	244 0588	0619	0647	0678	0708	0739
1971	0953	0984	1012	1043	1073	1104
1972	1318	1349	1378	1409	1439	1470
1973	1684	1715	1743	1774	1804	1835
1974	2049	2080	2108	2139	2169	2200
1975	244 2414	2445	2473	2504	2534	2565
1976	2779	2810	2839	2870	2900	2931
1977	3145	3176	3204	3235	3265	3296
1978	3510	3541	3569	3600	3630	3661
1979	3875	3906	3934	3965	3995	4026
1980	244 4240	4271	4300	4331	4361	4392

DATE YEAR	Jul. 1	Aug. 1	Sep. 1	Oct. 1	Nov. 1	Dec. 1
1970	244 0769	0800	0831	0861	0892	0922
1971	1134	1165	1196	1226	1257	1287
1972	1500	1531	1562	1592	1623	1653
1973	1865	1896	1927	1957	1988	2018
1974	2230	2261	2292	2322	2353	2383
1975	244 2595	2626	2657	2687	2718	2748
1976	2961	2992	3023	3053	3084	3114
1977	3326	3357	3388	3418	3449	3479
1978	3691	3722	3753	3783	3814	3844
1979	4056	4087	4118	4148	4179	4209
1980	244 4422	4453	4484	4514	4545	4575

broken up into a series of isolated mountains. The floor is dark, especially in the north, and has a modest amount of fine detail.

JUNIOR ASTRONOMICAL SOCIETY

An organization formed in 1954 to promote and encourage an interest in astronomy, and to provide instruction and assistance for beginners in this study.

JUNO Minor planet number 3, discovered by Harding in 1804; it has a diameter of only 118 miles, scarcely larger than

Jupiter's fifth satellite, and an apparent magnitude of about + 10.

(See **Minor planets**.)

JUPITER The fifth planet in order of distance from the Sun, the first of the major planets and the largest body in the solar system with the exception of the Sun itself.

Is a conspicuous naked-eye object, at favourable oppositions vies even with Venus and is capable (like Venus) of casting shadows. The disk can be seen with a small telescope or even powerful binoculars, together with the four brightest ('Galilean') satellites.

With a telescope of moderate aperture a wealth of surface detail is visible, much more readily observable than that of Mars, and constantly changing; careful and regular observation is both interesting and useful, and it is therefore one of the most rewarding subjects for study within reach of the amateur astronomer. The phenomena of the Galilean satellites also provide a source of useful observation with small instruments.

JUPITER—DIMENSIONS AND PHYSICAL DATA

The apparent equatorial diameter of Jupiter at mean opposition distance is 46″86, corresponding to an actual equatorial diameter of 88,760 miles (about eleven times that of the Earth). The planet is an oblate spheroid, its polar diameter being only 82,970 miles.

The density is only 1·33 times that of water, which is very approximately one quarter that of the Earth; it follows from this very low figure that, despite the considerable volume (1,319 times that of the Earth), the mass is only 317·9 times the Earth's mass. These facts have stimulated much discussion of the probable constitution of Jupiter and the other major planets.

The force of gravity at the surface of Jupiter is 2·64 times that of the Earth; the resulting velocity of escape is therefore very high—about 37·4 miles per second.

The albedo is 0·73, almost identical to that of Saturn; this high value supports the idea that the major planets have a gaseous nature.

JUPITER—OBSERVATION OF

Some types of useful observation of Jupiter and the other outer planets require the use of advanced instruments that are not usually available to the amateur observer; for this reason fewer programmes than is desirable are carried out, the professional observatories having many other demands on their resources. Among these types of observation may be mentioned high-resolution photography in several wavelengths of light (see Plate 12, Jupiter photographed with the 200-in. reflector at Mount Palomar, a in blue light and b in red light); comparisons of such photographs greatly assist in the deduction of the physical activity causing the observed features. The advanced studies also include spectrography, radio observation, meridian observations, etc.

In the case of Jupiter there is, however, the opportunity for amateur observers using comparatively modest equipment to make an important contribution to the study of the planet by careful and regular visual observation. The aim of this is to continue the records of the changing positions and appearance of the surface detail, including determinations of the longitudes and latitudes of surface detail, and the colours and relative intensities of the belts and zones.

By far the most important and valuable aspect of this work is the determination of longitude by the method of central-meridian transits; this consists of recording the times at which the various surface markings cross the **central meridian** of the disk. The position of the central meridian is usually determined by visual estimation, although it can be measured by the use of a filar micrometer. The times of transit are recorded, to the nearest minute, for all the markings that can be individually recognized; as the rate of rotation of the planet is known, the longitude (in System I or System II as appropriate) can be calculated. It is from series of longitudes determined in this way that our knowledge of the rotation periods of the various surface currents has been obtained.

The latitudes of the boundaries of the belts and zones tend to be variable, and should therefore be determined from time to time during an apparition; this can be done approximately by visual estimation—either at the telescope or by drawing for subsequent measurement—or by the measurement of high-resolution photographs. The most valuable method is micrometrical measurement at the telescope; this can only be carried out, however, by a skilled observer using a powerful telescope on a good, clock-driven equatorial mounting and equipped with a high quality filar micrometer.

The recording of the colours and intensities of the belts and zones is usually done by visual estimation at the telescope. The general appearance of the planet's disk should be recorded by means of a whole-disk drawing, but such drawings should be regarded as supplementary to the timing of central-meridian transits. It is rarely necessary to make whole-disk drawings more frequently than, say, every two hours; it is sometimes useful to make additional detail drawings showing the structure of any particularly complex feature, etc. (See also **Jupiter—observed features and notable phenomena; Jupiter—satellites, phenomena of; Jupiter—telescopic appearance.**)

JUPITER—OBSERVED FEATURES AND NOTABLE PHENOMENA

The telescopic appearance of Jupiter (described below) is a very striking one, and with a moderate aperture shows more surface detail than any other planet. It is also by far the most rewarding of the planetary surfaces to study, since owing to the gaseous nature of the observed surface its fine detail is in a constant state of flux, and cumulative observations of this detail permit deductive analysis of the physical activity of the surface layers.

Whilst the various currents described here have well-defined boundaries which remain constant in latitude, the edges of the belts are often 'ragged'; the belts also tend to vary in width and complexity of detail, sometimes split into two wholly or partially separate components, and vary in intensity even to the point of fading away completely on occasion. 'Outbreaks' of light and dark spots occur, and whilst the majority of such markings conform closely to the mean rotation period for their current, both dark and light spots have appeared having very abnormal motions—i.e. travelling along the current. Belts have

been seen to vary in colour as well as intensity, and attempts have been made to correlate such variations with changes in the rotation periods.

Red Spot. One of the best known and most permanent of the surface features is the Great Red Spot—a vast oval marking, about 30,000 miles long and 10–15,000 miles wide, which is on occasion the most obvious feature of the planet's surface. It is comparatively rarely seen to be truly red, more often seeming to be a dull grey or pale pink.

A Red Spot was first recorded by R. Hooke in 1664; after fading and even disappearing sometimes during the next half-century it ceased to be visible in 1713 and did not reappear for nearly 120 years. It was re-observed by H. Schwabe in 1831, and has been regularly seen since. From its rediscovery it gradually intensified from pale pink to a deep brick red colour which it maintained until 1882. Since then it has faded almost to invisibility several times and has revived again, particularly in 1920, 1926 and 1936. Only in 1936 did it attain the deep red of 1878–1882. Its colour has been variable in recent years, very often a dull grey and rarely deeper than a very pale pink. It generally appears as a dark peripheral ellipse with a pale interior. It is situated in a well-defined bay in the southern edge of the SEB, known as the *Red Spot Hollow*; the Hollow is usually plainly visible even at times when the Red Spot itself is absent. It has been noted that when the Spot appears particularly dark, the Hollow appears to be almost obliterated by some kind of white obscuration, which also seems to intensify the whiteness of the STrZ; the presence of this obscuring matter has been verified by ultra-violet photography.

The Red Spot and its Hollow often display considerable motion relative to the other surface features; although there is evidence of some movement in latitude at times this is very slight, whereas its movements back and forth in longitude totalled over 1,000 degrees in a hundred years, equivalent to almost three circuits of the planet. There is no evidence of periodicity in the motion of the Spot; however an interesting correlation between its motion and its colour was discovered by B. M. Peek in 1939. Peek pointed out that in every known instance a conspicuous darkening of the Spot had been accompanied by a lengthening in its rotation period; its greatest intensity was reached in 1880 and 1936, and in those two years its rotation periods were the longest recorded. The rotation period of the Spot during this century has averaged about 9 hr 55 min 38 sec. [Plate 12(a, b, c, d, g, h)].

South-Tropical Disturbance. On 1901 February 28, P. B. Molesworth observed a grey ligament across the STrZ, connecting the SEB$_s$ and the STB; this feature rapidly expanded in longitude, suggesting an injection of dark material into the surface current being diffused along it by the rotational flow. Bright spots appeared at its ends, forming the concave ends which remained one of the permanent characteristics of the feature. The Disturbance achieved great length, stretching half-way around the planet for much of its life. Its central portion faded, leaving the ends dark and well defined. [Plate 12(e, f).]

The rotation period of the Disturbance has tended to lengthen by a few seconds during the present century, and has averaged about 9 hr 55 min 30 sec; as this rotation period is slightly shorter than that of the Red Spot, the Disturbance has tended to overtake the Spot from time to time, and their behaviour on these occasions has been of much interest. At the first observed conjunction in 1902 the preceding end of the Disturbance broke up on reaching the following end of the Red Spot Hollow, and the dark matter flowed past on either side of the area of the Spot without actually encroaching upon it; the preceding end of the Disturbance reformed at the preceding end of the Hollow and continued on its way. Even more remarkable was the speed at which this manœuvre was accomplished, a few days instead of the six weeks that would

have been required at the normal rates of motion.

Although not always so readily observable, the succeeding conjunctions of the Disturbance and the Red Spot area seem to have followed much the same pattern.

Having varied in length and structure for many years the Disturbance finally disappeared in 1940, although minor disturbances in the STrZ which have been observed from time to time may in fact have been new manifestations of this once very prominent feature.

Circulating Current. A remarkable series of events occurred in the STrZ during the apparition of 1919–1920; having faded a year previously, the South Tropical Disturbance returned with considerable turbulence. From the start both of its ends were dark and pronounced, albeit rather lost at first in the confusion of spots appearing in the Zone. As conditions settled two conspicuous, round, dark spots, about 60° apart, appeared in the undisturbed region of the Zone close to the southern edge of the SEB. They were soon found to have a remarkable drift in longitude—about 4° a day in the *following* direction, i.e. against the general flow. The leading spot was last seen some 3° or 4° from the preceding end of the Disturbance, and the second one about twelve days later when about 25° from it. Five days after the last observation of the first spot a rather smaller spot appeared some 10° from the Disturbance, near the other edge of the Zone (adjoining the STB). This spot also had a motion of 4° per day, but *away* from the Disturbance; a second spot also appeared in this higher latitude, following some 55° behind. Both spots faded out before they reached the following end of the Disturbance.

All of this suggested that in some way the Disturbance prevented the passage of these rapidly moving spots, turned them about and sent them back along a parallel route.

Much the same events were observed at the apparitions of 1928, 1931, 1932–1933 and 1934, save that at most of these apparitions a whole series of spots were seen, and at some of them the individual spots were replaced by 'humps' or peaks on the southern edge of the SEB.

Equatorial Belt upheavals. The higher latitude belts are rarely notable for complex detail or rapid changes in structure, and this kind of activity has in the main been restricted to the Equatorial Belts, both of which have on many occasions displayed great turbulence. The normally double SEB in particular has a long history of erratic behaviour. Sometimes its southern component, including the Red Spot Hollow, fades and almost vanishes for up to three years; then comes a great burst of activity in the Belt, followed by a return of the missing features. The principal SEB upheavals occurred in 1919–1920, 1928–1929, 1938, 1943, 1949, 1952 and 1955; they usually take the form of an outbreak of spots, formed at a particular point on the Belt, which rapidly spread along it until they encircle the planet. Many spots, both light and dark, are formed, and there is continual, rapid and often striking change in the Belt's structure. Some evidence has been derived from the records of these outbreaks that they may occur at regular intervals, with a period rather less than three years, but the evidence cannot yet be regarded as conclusive and there are a number of gaps in the sequence.

These are only some of the more notable phenomena observed and analysed in the past 75 years, during which time the planet has been very thoroughly observed. Vast though the volume of observed data is, it still poses more problems about the nature of the surface and sub-surface layers of the planet than it solves, and it may be many years before the full value can be obtained from the efforts of the observers, largely amateur, who have compiled this outstanding collection of information.

JUPITER—ORBITAL DATA The orbit of Jupiter has a semi-major axis of 5·202804 A.U., corresponding to a mean distance from the Sun of 483·6 million miles; owing to the eccentricity of the orbit (0·0484) this distance varies between 460·1 million miles at perihelion and 507·1 million miles at aphelion.

The orbit is inclined to the Ecliptic by $1°18'18''1$; the mean orbital velocity is 8·1 miles per second, giving a sidereal period of 4332·59 days—about 11·86 years.

JUPITER—RADIO EMISSION FROM Early in 1955, Jupiter was discovered to be a source of radio emission at a frequency of 22·2 Mc/s (equivalent to a wavelength of 13·5 metres); during the decade which has elapsed since this discovery, radiation from the planet has been recorded on many occasions. These records have been examined with great care and compared with those of visual observations of the planet's surface detail, and a number of interesting and (in some cases) significant correlations have been obtained; nevertheless the evidence available is not sufficient to demonstrate conclusively that the radiation originates in visually observable features.

Many of the apparently localized sources of radio 'noise' observed on the planet have a rotation period significantly shorter than that adopted for non-equatorial visible features (System II, 9 hr 55 min 40.632 sec); a new System III, based upon a rotation period of 9 hr 55 min 29 sec has therefore been adopted for radio observations.

It has been suggested that the radiation may originate in an ionized layer of the upper atmosphere; an alternative hypothesis is that the radiation is in fact of solar origin and received from Jupiter by reflection.

JUPITER—SATELLITES OF Jupiter, with twelve, has more known natural satellites than any other planet. Of these twelve, the four brightest were discovered by Galileo whilst he was testing, in January 1610, the performance of his epoch-making instruments; they are thus among the earliest telescopic discoveries. These four satellites, usually termed the 'Galilean Satellites', are particularly interesting for the phenomena they display due to the Earth being almost in their orbital plane; the other satellites are small and insignificant, and (with one exception) were discovered photographically.

Satellite V was discovered by Barnard visually, using the 36-in. refractor of the Lick Observatory with an occulting bar to hide the glare of the planet.

The known data relating to the satellites is presented in Table 15. The numbering of Jupiter's satellites is rather confusing; satellites I–IV are numbered in order of distance from the planet, and V–XII in order of their discovery.

It is also regrettable that no names have been adopted by the International Astronomical Union for the eight satellites discovered in recent times; names have been proposed for these satellites, however, and are given here for information.

The eighth satellite was discovered by P. J. Melotte, who photographed it with the 30-in. reflector at the Royal Observatory, Greenwich.

The Galilean satellites are known to have axial rotation periods equal to their revolution periods, and hence present the same face constantly towards the primary; it is possible to observe surface markings on them, but this work can only be carried out with powerful instruments in first-class observing conditions. Our knowledge of the surface detail is due largely to the splendid series of observations obtained by Lyot, Camichel and Gentili at the Pic-du-Midi Observatory high up in the French Pyrénées.

JUPITER—SATELLITES, PHENOMENA OF

The orbital inclinations of the four Galilean satellites, referred to the equatorial plane of Jupiter, are extremely small:

Satellite	Orbital inclination
I	$0 \cdot 0°$
II	$0 \cdot 5°$
III	$0 \cdot 2°$
IV	$0 \cdot 2°$

Table 15. Satellites of Jupiter

Satellite	Discoverer	Year of discovery	Mean distance from primary (miles)	Synodic Period				Orbital inclination	diameter (miles)	Mean apparent magnitude
				d	h	m	s	°		
V Amalthea	Barnard	1892	112,251	00	11	57	27·6	0·4	100	13·0
I Io	Galileo	1610	262,219	01	18	28	35·9	0·0	2,000	4·8
II Europa	Galileo	1610	417,217	03	13	17	53·7	0·5	1,800	5·2
III Ganymede	Galileo	1610	665,499	07	03	59	35·9	0·2	3,100	4·5
IV Callisto	Galileo	1610	1,170,545	16	18	05	06·9	0·2	2,800	5·5
VI Hestia*	Perrine	1904	7,135,239	265	22	43		28	60	13·7
VII Hera*	Perrine	1905	7,296,315	275	17	09		29	10	18·6
X Demeter*	Nicholson	1938	7,367,181	276	04	56		28	20	16·0
XII Adastrea*	Nicholson	1951	13,184,889	551				147†	10	18·8
XI Pan*	Nicholson	1938	14,027,525	597				163†	10	18·1
VIII Poseidon*	Melotte	1908	14,619,600	635				148†	10	18·8
IX Hades*	Nicholson	1914	14,740,500	645				157†	10	18·3

* Proposed name, not yet adopted by the I.A.U.
† Revolution retrograde.

Further, the inclination between the orbital planes of Jupiter and the Earth is also very small ($1°18'18''3$); because of this the orbital planes of the satellites are practically edge-on to the Earth. This results in the regular occurrence of four types of phenomenon; *eclipses* of the satellites by the shadow-cone of Jupiter; *occultations* by Jupiter itself; *transits* of satellites across the visible disk of Jupiter and transits of the *shadows* of satellites.

Satellites I, II and III are eclipsed by Jupiter during every revolution; the orbital inclination is sufficient to enable the satellite farthest from Jupiter (IV) to escape eclipse during certain revolutions, but one more often than not takes place.

It will be appreciated that eclipses cannot be observed when Jupiter is at conjunction or opposition, as the shadow-cone is then hidden directly behind the planet. Conversely when Jupiter is at quadrature the entire eclipse (of satellites II, III and IV) is visible to one side of the disk of the planet. At other times the satellite may disappear into eclipse and reappear from occultation, or vice versa. Between opposition and the following conjunction satellites are occulted by the preceding limb of Jupiter, and reappear from eclipse beyond the following limb; between conjunction and the next opposition they are eclipsed before reaching the preceding limb and reappear from occultation at the following limb.

Satellite I is so close to Jupiter that the whole eclipse can never be observed; the combined duration of the eclipse and occultation is approximately $2\frac{1}{4}$ hr.

It is also rare to see both immersion and emersion in the case of satellite II; the combined duration of eclipse and occultation is about $2\frac{3}{4}$ hr. in this case.

Eclipses of satellite III can usually be observed in full, except near opposition; their duration is very variable, but averages about $3\frac{1}{4}$ hr.

Eclipses of satellite IV are also visible in full, except at opposition, and last (on average) for about 4 hr.; during each sidereal period of Jupiter ($11\cdot86$ years) there are two intervals of about three years when no eclipses of satellite IV occur.

Transits and shadow-transits occur, of course, in pairs, but may be well separated in time—by up to several hours in the case of outer satellites when Jupiter is near conjunction. Between opposition and the following conjunction the shadow follows the satellite; between conjunction and the next opposition the shadow precedes the satellite. The disks of the satellites themselves are normally very difficult to observe in transit except with large apertures, the shadow-transit being a much easier observation. Satellite IV sometimes passes above or below the disk of Jupiter, no transit taking place.

Very occasionally all four satellites are simultaneously eclipsed, occulted or in transit, and are therefore absent from the background sky; this situation will occur five times during the remainder of the present century, on 1980 April 9 (twice) 1990 June 15, 1991 January 2 and 1997 August 27.

For a few months every six years or so, as the Earth passes through the orbital planes of the satellites, mutual eclipses and occultations occur; these are, however, rather difficult to observe without moderately large apertures.

The mean daily motions (n) of satellites I, II and III are such that the following relation holds:

$$n_{I} - 3n_{II} + 2n_{III} = 0;$$

from this it follows that these three satellites can never experience the same phenomenon simultaneously, although it is possible for any two of them to do so.

The accurate timing of all contacts of these phenomena enable comparisons to be made between the observed and computed times, which are of great value in dynamical astronomy. It is also of interest to recall that it was timings of the eclipses of Jupiter's satellites which enabled Römer to make the first determination of the finite velocity of light.

JUPITER—STRUCTURE AND CONSTITUTION

Although a great deal of progress has been made by theorists in developing a concept of the structure of Jupiter that agrees with observed data, it has not yet proved possible to confirm many of the theoretical conclusions in a positive manner.

Following on the early work of Jeffreys, Rupert Wildt published in 1930 a proposed model for Jupiter that was widely accepted for a quarter of a century, but has recently been superseded. Using the known mass, volume and mean density, Wildt deduced a model comprising material in three quite different states; a solid core of radius about 18,500 miles, a mantle of frozen material 17,000 miles thick, and a gaseous layer 8,000 miles deep (Fig. 62).

Although only very imperfect spectra were then available, Wildt deduced theoretically that the prominent absorption bands present in the spectrum of Jupiter but not that of the Sun must be due to methane (CH_4) and ammonia (NH_3). This brilliant interpretation of poor material was subsequently confirmed entirely by the infra-red spectra obtained by Dunham at Mount Wilson. [Plate 13(f).]

Wildt predicted that methane and ammonia should be present in approximately equal amounts, but the lower vapour pressure of ammonia would result in its condensing at lower levels and therefore methane should be the most abundant compound at the observable level. Wildt also stated that the hydrogen content did not exceed 10 per cent by mass. This composition agreed with the observed data, but would be a very surprising one from the cosmogonal point of view, since all theories presuppose that the planets were originally formed from solar or quasi-solar material, and the Sun contains more than 90 per cent hydrogen. Whereas the inner planets, with their low gravitational attractions, would be expected to have lost most of this hydrogen, it should have been retained by the massive outer planets.

The problem was reconsidered by W. H. Ramsey about 1950; he showed that the mean densities previously assumed for the core and frozen layer were too low, and the deduced amount of heavy elements too large. He suggested that the increase in density towards the centre of the planet was not due to chemically different layers formed by gravitational separation, but to phase changes in a completely homogeneous mixture. This theory arose from the then recent studies of phase-changes under high pressure; a number of non-metals had been found to undergo a change of molecular structure at high pressure, and to become dense and metallic. Hydrogen can assume the properties of an alkali metal, but this form is only stable at very high pressures. The pressure at the centre of Jupiter, however, is approximately 40 times as great as the critical pressure for the formation of metallic hydrogen.

Ramsey concluded that the hydrogen content of Jupiter must be between 76 and 84 per cent by mass, probably less than 10 per cent of this existing in the normal molecular phase at the upper (observable) levels of the planet.

The nature of the observed surface features is difficult to deduce, especially in view of the lack of agreement between the boundaries of the belt–zone system and of the currents deduced from spot observations. The dark coloration of the belts has been variously attributed to clouds of ammonia droplets and to the presence of nitrogen dioxide (NO_2).

The ever-changing structure of the belts obviously arises from turbulences in the gaseous surface layers, but it is probable that this is only the manifestation at the visible surface of disturbances taking place much deeper in the 'atmosphere'.

There has been much speculation as to the nature of the Red Spot; most of these have assumed it to be a solid body of some kind floating in the atmosphere, although it seems equally possible that it too is a purely atmospheric effect caused by some form of disturbance at a lower level.

It is to be hoped that continued careful

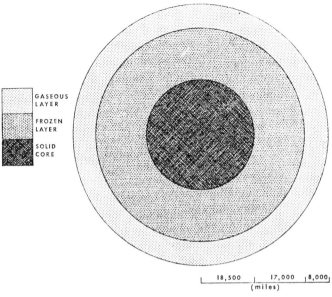

GASEOUS
LAYER

FROZEN
LAYER

SOLID
CORE

| 18,500 | 17,000 | 8,000 |
(miles)

Fig. 62

analysis of the nature and motions of the features observed by both optical and radio methods will eventually lead to a fuller understanding of the constitution of this interesting but mysterious planet; meanwhile it is obviously essential that these observations be continued on as large a scale as possible. (See also **Planets, major—constitution of.**)

JUPITER—TELESCOPIC APPEAR-ANCE The apparent diameter of Jupiter is 46″86 at mean opposition distance, and is never less than 30″; it therefore presents a sensible disk with telescopes of quite modest aperture; little detail can be detected, however, except at particularly favourable oppositions, with apertures smaller than a 6-in. reflector or 4-in. refractor. For really detailed study of the surface features substantially larger apertures than this are necessary.

On examining the telescopic image it is seen immediately to comprise a disk noticeably flattened at the poles, and displaying a number of dark, parallel, longitudinal *belts* interspersed with lighter

zones; the relative widths and intensities of the belts vary from one apparition to another, and the equatorial belts (in particular) are sometimes seen to be composed of two narrower components. In order to facilitate reference to the various areas of the disk, a standard nomenclature was devised and has been in use for many years; the approximate location of the belts and zones, and their usual abbreviations, are shown in Fig. 63, together with the poles, direction of apparent rotation and the preceding (*p*) and following (*f*) limbs. It should be pointed out that the positions of the belts in latitude are not constant, neither are their widths, so that Fig. 63 can only be regarded as a guide. It must also be remembered that this figure shows the telescopic (inverted) view. There may be further belts visible in high latitudes on occasion—e.g. an NNNNTB; the highest latitude belts detectable in each hemisphere are usually merged into the dusky polar regions. Any of the belts, even the most prominent, may on occasion fade into insignificance or even disappear

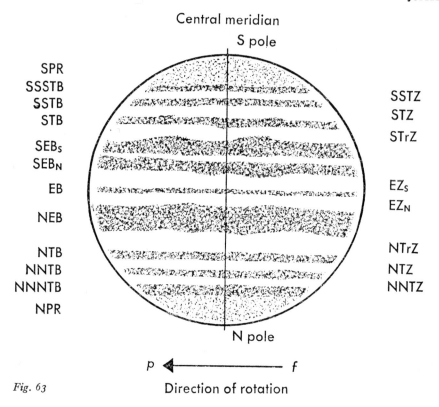

Central meridian
S pole

SPR
SSSTB
SSTB
STB

SEBs
SEBn

EB

NEB

NTB
NNTB
NNNTB

NPR

SSTZ
STZ

STrZ

EZs
EZn

NTrZ
NTZ
NNTZ

N pole

p ◄─────────── f

Fig. 63   Direction of rotation

completely for a time.

The full descriptions of the belts and zones are as follows:

SPR	South Polar Region
SSSTB	South South South Temperate Belt
SSTB	South South Temperate Belt
STB	South Temperate Belt
SEBs	South Equatorial Belt (South component)
SEBn	South Equatorial Belt (North component)
EB	Equatorial Band
NEB	North Equatorial Belt
NTB	North Temperate Belt
NNTB	North North Temperate Belt
NNNTB	North North North Temperate Belt
NPR	North Polar Region
SSTZ	South South Temperate Zone
STZ	South Temperate Zone
STrZ	South Tropical Zone
EZs	Equatorial Zone (South)
EZn	Equatorial Zone (North)
NTrZ	North Tropical Zone
NTZ	North Temperate Zone
NNTZ	North North Temperate Zone

The zones are generally of a creamy or light grey colour, and the belts grey, dark brown or reddish-brown. A number of colours have been reported on occasion, by various observers, but such coloration is usually extremely slight and very difficult to assess quantitatively.

From a study of individual condensations in the fine structure of the belts, and of any 'spots' or 'wisps' observed in the zones, it is found that the surface is divided into a number of parallel currents in which most features share an apparent rotation period different from that obtaining in other currents. The rotation periods in the various currents (Fig. 64) do not indicate the simple pattern of differential rotation that would be expected for a body

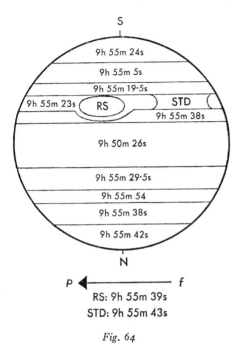

RS: 9h 55m 39s
STD: 9h 55m 43s

Fig. 64

whose outermost layers, at least, are gaseous; instead there is a broad equatorial current having a rotation very much faster than that in all the other currents, whose rotation periods differ only by seconds. It is to be noted that the boundaries of the currents do not, in general, coincide with the belt–zone boundaries.

For the purposes of defining the positions of surface features it was therefore necessary to adopt two systems of longitude; System I (the 'Great Equatorial Current', containing the SEB$_N$, EZ and NEB$_S$), and System II for the remainder of the planet. The zero of longitude, in both systems, was defined as the longitude of the Central Meridian (on the basis then in use) at the epoch 1897 July 14·0; at this moment the longitudes were 47°·31 (System I) and 96°·58 (System II), and these were adopted, together with sidereal rotation periods of 9 hr 50 min 30·003 sec

(System I) and 9 hr 55 min 40·632 sec (System II). Tables of the longitude of the central meridian, in both systems, are published in *The Astronomical Ephemeris*, *The Handbook of the British Astronomical Association*, *The Observer's Handbook* published annually by the Royal Astronomical Society of Canada, etc.

Radio observations of localized sources of radiation on the planet's disk have tended to fit a rotation period of 9 hr 55 min 29 sec, which has been tentatively used as the basis of a new System III for the use of radio observers.

JUPITER—VISIBILITY FROM EARTH

The opposition distance of Jupiter from the Earth is, of course, very variable, depending upon the position of Jupiter in its orbit; it can be as little as 367 million miles at a favourable perihelic opposition, but may be as much as 600 million miles at an aphelic opposition.

The mean synodic period is 398·88 days, and hence oppositions occur at intervals of 13 months; the planet is observable, on average, for about ten months at each apparition. There is great variation, however, in the observing conditions which obtain at the several apparitions during a synodic period, owing to the fact that the planet may be situated at declinations ranging from 25°N to 25°S.

The most favourable apparitions for observers located in the United Kingdom are those centred on December oppositions; on these occasions the planet can be observed for up to 16 hours a night, and is at the high altitude necessary for satisfactory observation; at the other extreme, when the opposition occurs in June, the planet is observable only for an hour or two and its altitude is so low as to render really useful observation almost impossible.

JUVENTÆ FONS Martian surface feature, approximate position Ω 63°, $\Phi - 5°$. A small but very dark oasis connected to the Auroræ Sinus by the canal Bætis.

K

K STARS Stars of spectral class K; they are orange stars with surface temperatures of 3,000–4,000 °K (giants), 4,000–5,000 °K (dwarfs). *Aldebaran* and *Arcturus* are notable examples.

KAPTEYN, Jacobus C. (1851–1922) Dutch astronomer who discovered in 1904 the effect of star-streaming, now known to be the observed effect of the rotation of the Galaxy. He devised a plan in 1906 for the photographic observation of 206 sample areas of the sky; examinations were made of the plates obtained of these 'Selected Areas', from which Kapteyn was able to deduce, very approximately, the structure of the Galaxy. Although far from accurate by modern standards, this was the first analysis of the structure of the Galaxy and paved the way for the more sophisticated investigations which have been carried out since.

KAPTEYN SELECTED AREAS The sample areas of the sky—206 in number—which Kapteyn selected in 1906 for photographing by large instruments in all parts of the world, so that star-counts and other measurements could be made on the plates obtained, leading to a statistical determination of the distribution of stars throughout the Galaxy. This was the first real attempt to obtain observational evidence of the structure of the Galaxy, and as such was of far greater importance than the rather imprecise and inaccurate result perhaps indicated.

KEPLER, Johann (1571–1630) A brilliant mathematical astronomer, famous for his discovery of the laws of planetary motion. Born in Wurtemberg, he became—after graduating—a high-school teacher special-izing in mathematics and astronomy. During a visit to Prague he met Tycho Brahe, and returned there to take up the position of Imperial Mathematician and become Tycho's assistant. He worked with Tycho for the last few years of his life, and succeeded him as Imperial Astronomer in 1601.

Using the great volume of accurate positional observations of the planets made by Tycho, Kepler discovered after an exhaustive analysis the three fundamental laws of planetary motion which now bear his name, and which were the greatest of his many contributions to the development of theoretical astronomy.

KEPLER Lunar surface feature, co-ordinates $\xi - 609$, $\eta + 141$. A very prominent bright crater in the Oceanus Procellarum, the centre of an important ray system. Named, of course, after the great German astronomer, Kepler has a diameter of 22 miles. Fine detail and dark bands are occasionally observed, but the brightness of the surrounding ray system makes observation of Kepler difficult at high angles of illumination.

KEPLER'S LAWS OF PLANETARY MOTION The fundamental laws which govern the motion of a planet in its orbit, discovered by Kepler from an analysis of the observations made by Tycho Brahe. Kepler published the first two laws in 1609 and the third in 1618; they are as follows:

1. A planet's orbit is an ellipse, with the Sun at one of the foci;
2. A planet travels in its orbit at speeds such that its radius vector sweeps out equal areas in equal intervals of time;

3. The square of the revolution period of a planet is proportional to the cube of its mean distance from the Sun. (See also **Planetary motion.**)

KILOMETRE Metric unit of length or distance, equivalent to 1000 metres. The equivalent in Imperial units is 0·6214 miles. (See **Metric system.**)

KILOPARSEC Unit of distance used by astrophysicists; it is equal to 1,000 parsecs, or approximately 3,260 light years.

KIRCHHOFF'S LAWS A series of laws defining some of the properties of propagation of radiant energy, formulated by G. Kirchhoff in 1860. Of particular importance to the astrophysicist is the law of absorption, which states that the power of a substance to absorb radiation is greatest for the wavelength the substance itself emits when radiant.

KIRKWOOD, Daniel (1815-1895) American astronomer remembered for his work on commensurabilities and resonance effects in the solar system; he pointed out in 1866 that at certain mean distances from the Sun there were gaps in the minor planet zone, and that the period of a planet orbiting at any of these distances would be a simple fraction of that of Jupiter; he suggested that the repetitive maximal perturbation due to Jupiter would force such a planet into a new orbit. In 1867 he suggested that a similar mechanism might account for Cassini's Division in Saturn's rings, the ring particles being pulled out of this area by the perturbing effect of the satellites—especially Mimas, whose period is twice that of a body at the distance of the Division. This principle has since been satisfactorily used to account for the other divisions in the ring system.

(See also **Minor planets; Saturn—rings of.**)

KIRKWOOD'S GAPS Name given to the divisions in the ring system of Saturn, attributed by Kirkwood to the resonance effect of perturbations by the satellites upon the ring particles.

(See **Saturn—rings of.**)

KUIPER, Gerard P. Contemporary American astronomer, one of the leading experts in the study of the nature of the surfaces of the Moon and planets, and also one of the most successful observers with 'giant' telescopes. Using the 82-in. reflector of the McDonald Observatory, Kuiper discovered the fifth satellite of Uranus (*Miranda*) in 1948 and the second satellite of Neptune (*Nereid*) in 1949.

L

L.P.V. Usual abbreviation for a **long-period variable**, *q.v.*

LACERTA (The Lizard. *Genitive* Lacertae, *I.A.U. abbreviation* Lac.) A small northern constellation which reaches midnight culmination at the beginning of September. It is situated between Cygnus and Andromeda, and adjoins the northern boundary of Pegasus. Contains no stars brighter than the fourth magnitude.

The constellation contains a fine open cluster (N.G.C. 7243) and the sites of two novae; one of these, CP Lac, lies at the northern boundary of the constellation, adjoining Cepheus. At its outburst in 1963 this nova attained a visual magnitude of +2.

LACUS SOMNIORUM A small lunar *mare* of irregular shape, adjoining the north-west corner of the Mare Serenitatis, into which it runs through a break in the mountain wall of the Mare north of Posidonius.

LÆSTRYGON Martian surface feature, approximate position Ω 200°, Φ 0°. Canal crossing the equator, running due south from Trivium Charontis to Læstrygonum Sinus.

LÆSTRYGONUM SINUS Martian surface feature, approximate position Ω 200°, $\Phi - 20°$. Dark condensation projecting from the northern edge of the Mare Cimmerium. Connected to Trivium Charontis by Læstrygon.

LAGRANGE, Joseph L. (1736–1813) One of the greatest mathematicians of the eighteenth century; Lagrange was born in Italy, although of French descent. He succeeded Euler as Head of the Mathematics Department of the Berlin Academy in 1766, and remained there until 1787 when he moved to Paris. He was a contemporary of Laplace, with whom he dominated the spheres of mathematical and astronomical theory for many years. He made many contributions to our knowledge of the solar system.

LANGRENUS Lunar surface feature, co-ordinates $\xi + 863$, $\eta - 155$. A magnificent crater, 85 miles in diameter, close to the western limb of the Moon. One of the meridional chain of great formations including Furnerius, Petavius, Vendelinus, Cleomedes and Endymion. Appears very bright against the dark floor of the Mare Fœcunditatis, on whose western boundary it is situated. The walls are terraced and rise to 9,000 ft. in the east; there is a central mountain with twin peaks, the higher being 3,300 ft. [Plates 4(b); 5(b).]

LANTHANIDE ELEMENTS Name sometimes given to the series of rare-earth elements having atomic numbers from 57 to 71 inclusive; the name derives from the first element in the series—lanthanum. (See **Chemical elements.**)

LAPLACE, Pierre S. (1749–1827) The great French mathematician, who with Lagrange led the development of theoretical astronomy for many years. He was a prolific writer, not only for the learned journals but also for popular consumption; most of his major contributions are summarized in his book *Mécanique Celeste*, which was published in five volumes during the period 1799–1825.

Laplace made many notable contributions to the dynamics of the solar system; perhaps he is best remembered, however, for his famous **nebular hypothesis** published in 1796. In this Laplace suggested a mechanism for the common origin of the bodies comprising the solar system, suggesting that the planets and satellites were formed as local condensations in a vast, cooling, nebula. (See **Cosmogony— theories of.**)

LASSELL, William (1799–1880) English amateur astronomer, one of the leading planetary observers of his day.

Lassell was the first to adopt Fraunhofer's equatorial mounting for a reflecting telescope of any size—his 9-in. Newtonian erected near Liverpool in 1840. Following a visit to the Earl of Rosse's workshops at Parsonstown, where the Earl's mammoth 6-ft. reflector was then being erected, Lassell constructed a 24-in. reflector which was brought into use in 1845. With this instrument, on 1846 October 10, Lassell discovered a satellite of Neptune (*Triton*) only 17 days after the discovery of the planet itself. In 1848 he discovered the eighth satellite of Saturn (*Hyperion*), also discovered independently by G. P. Bond, and in 1851 he discovered the two innermost satellites of Uranus (*Ariel* and *Umbriel*).

In 1852 Lassell re-erected his 24-in. reflector in Malta, in order to take advantage of the superior observing conditions; in 1859–1860 he constructed a 48-in. equatorial reflector which was shipped to Malta and erected in 1861. With this very powerful instrument Lassell made a large number of valuable observations of the planets, nebulae and double stars.

Lassell returned to England in 1864 and settled in Maidenhead, where he re-erected the 24-in. telescope; failing eyesight had caused him to give up observing by 1870 and the instrument was then little used until after Lassell's death when it was moved to Greenwich. The 48-in. was never re-erected; Lassell offered it to the Melbourne Observatory, but his offer was rejected in favour of a new instrument and Lassell's instrument was finally scrapped.

LAST QUARTER The phase of the Moon at western quadrature, half of the illumin-

ated hemisphere being visible from the Earth. The phase is the characteristic 'half-moon' shape. (See **Phases of the Moon.**)

LATITUDE, CELESTIAL The latitude of a heavenly body is its angular distance from the Ecliptic, measured along a secondary to the Ecliptic.

LATITUDE, TERRESTRIAL The latitude of a point on the surface of the Earth, i.e. its angular distance from the equator, measured along a meridian.

Latitude is measured in degrees, from 0° to 90° N or S of the equator.

LATITUDE VARIATION As the Earth's axis of rotation is not that about which the figure of the Earth is symmetrically distributed, but is slightly inclined to it (see Fig. 65), the actual axis of the geoid (N'S') has a circular motion around the axis of rotation (NS). The resulting effects

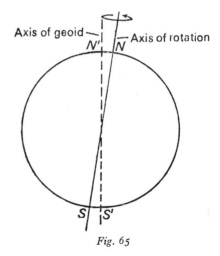

Fig. 65

are a wandering of the Earth's poles around a mean position and a variation in the observed latitude of any place.

This effect was predicted on theoretical grounds by Euler, and was first detected by Kustner in 1888, in the form of a variation in the latitude of Berlin.

The movement of the pole is the resultant of two distinct motions. The first of these stems directly from the asymmetry of the geoid and has a period of 432 days (about $14\frac{1}{2}$ months); this motion of the pole has an amplitude of $0\rlap{.}''36$ (equivalent to about ± 30 ft.).

The second movement has a period of 1 year, being due to seasonal shifts of airmasses; it has an amplitude of $0\rlap{.}''18$ (about ± 15 ft.). The pole may thus depart from its mean position by up to 45 ft. when the two effects are in phase, and by no more than 15 ft. when they are entirely out-of-phase.

The latitude variation is determined from series of observations of the declinations of selected stars specially obtained at a chain of fundamental observatories.

LAW OF EQUAL AREAS The second law of planetary motion. (See **Kepler's Laws of planetary motion.**)

LEAP YEAR The tropical year is equal to 365 d. 5 hr. 48 min. 45·98 sec.; thus the adoption of a civil year equal to 365 days results in a deficit of 23 hr. 15 min. 3·92 sec. in 4 years. To counteract this the **Julian Calendar** was based upon every fourth year containing an extra day (i.e. 366 days). Such years are termed leap years. As this correction results in a surplus of 3 d. 2 hr. 53 min. 30 sec. every 400 years, the principle was amended slightly in the **Gregorian Calendar** so as to reduce the number of leap-year days in a 400-year period by 3; this is achieved by ruling that century years (i.e. those years exactly divisible by 100) are not leap years, except where the century is also divisible by 4. Thus 1900 was not a leap year but 2000 will be.

(See also **Calendar.**)

LEIDEN OBSERVATORY The observatory of the University of Leiden, and the major astronomical establishment in Holland.

LEMURIA Martian surface feature, approximate position $\Omega\,200°$, $\Phi+70°$. Lightish area in north polar region, north of Panchaiä.

LENS An optical element which functions by **refraction**; it is in fact a piece of a refracting substance—often glass—bounded by two opposing surfaces, at least one of which is usually spherical.

LENS, ACHROMATIC A lens so designed as to minimize **chromatic aberration**; the most common means of achieving this is by the use of a doublet whose components are manufactured from different types of glass. Glasses are chosen having refractive indexes such that light of two carefully selected wavelengths is brought to a common focus, the wavelengths being chosen so as to compress the residual aberration as much as possible. Thus, 'achromatic' telescope objectives are often constructed as a doublet having one component of crown glass and the other of flint glass.

LENS, ASPHERICAL A lens having one curved surface aspherical, usually in order to reduce or eliminate a specific aberration.

LENS, BICONCAVE A negative, diverging lens bounded by two opposing concave surfaces (Fig. 66).

LENS, BICONVEX A positive, converging lens bounded by two opposing convex surfaces (Fig. 67).

LENS, CONCAVO-CONVEX A positive, converging lens bounded by one convex surface and a concave surface of greater radius of curvature (Fig. 68).

LENS, CONVERGENT A positive lens having a converging effect upon any pencil of rays transmitted by it; thus, the divergence of a divergent beam is reduced, whilst a parallel beam will be converged and brought to a focus, etc.

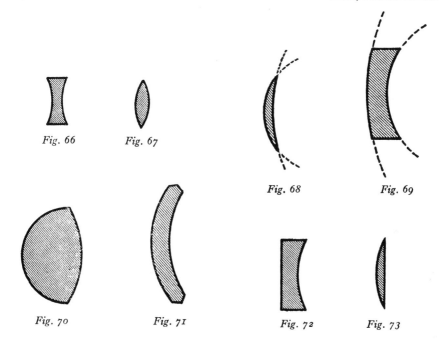

Fig. 66

Fig. 67

Fig. 68

Fig. 69

Fig. 70

Fig. 71

Fig. 72

Fig. 73

LENS, CONVEXO-CONCAVE A negative, diverging lens bounded by one convex surface and a concave surface of lesser radius of curvature (Fig. 69).

LENS, CROSSED A biconvex lens having a first surface of radius of curvature some six times that of the second; in such a condition the **spherical aberration**, for a parallel incident beam, is minimal (Fig. 70).

LENS, DIVERGENT A negative lens having a diverging effect upon any incident pencil of rays; thus a convergent beam will be parallelized or rendered divergent.

LENS, DOUBLET A lens comprising two components, which may be cemented together or separated by an air-space; lenses are normally manufactured in this form in order to minimize **chromatic aberration**. The objectives of refracting telescopes are normally of this form.

LENS, EYE The magnifying component of a two-lens **eyepiece**, situated nearest to the eye.

LENS, FIELD The light-gathering component of a two-lens **eyepiece**, situated farthest from the eye.

LENS, MENISCUS A lens bounded by two spherical surfaces of approximately the same radius of curvature, one convex, the other concave (Fig. 71).

LENS, OBJECTIVE The light-gathering element of a refracting telescope or similar instrument; also known as the **object-glass**.

LENS, PLANO-CONCAVE A negative diverging lens bounded by one plane and one concave surface (Fig. 72).

LENS, PLANO-CONVEX A positive, converging lens bounded by one plane and one convex surface (Fig. 73).

LENS, TELEPHOTO A camera lens of extra long effective focal length, thus resulting in a greater linear magnification in photographs obtained with it than in those obtained with a normal camera lens.

LENS, VARIFOCAL A versatile form of telephoto lens, consisting of a positive lens or lens system in front of a negative lens or system; the separation between the systems is variable so as to vary the size of the image obtained.

LENS, WIDE-ANGLE A camera lens designed to receive an incident beam of very wide angle, thus enabling large areas to be photographed at short operating distances. Not widely used in astronomy, although the night-sky camera may be said to employ the principle.

LENS, ZOOM A camera lens so constructed that the angle of view may be varied whilst preserving a constant focal length, thus enabling the size of the image obtained to be changed without altering the focus. Used mainly in cinematography.

LENS STOP A diaphragm containing a circular aperture, placed at advantageous positions in a lens system. It is usually painted matt black to prevent unwanted reflections. Its function may be to restrict the effective aperture or field of view of the instrument, or to eliminate stray internal reflections. It is also frequently used to confine the rays utilized to those close to the optical axis, a process which reduces the illumination but greatly improves definition.

LEO (The Lion. *Genitive* Leonis, *I.A.U. abbreviation* Leo.) A zodiacal constellation reaching midnight culmination in early March. Contains one first-magnitude star (*Regulus*), three of the second magnitude and a large number of fainter stars. The constellation is situated between Cancer and Virgo; to the north of it lie Leo Minor and Ursa Major.

The constellation is a splendid sight,

and is easily recognizable, many of its brighter stars forming the well-known 'Sickle' of which *Regulus* forms the handle.

LEO MINOR (The Lesser Lion. *Genitive* Leonis Minoris, *I.A.U. abbreviation* LMi.) A small northern constellation south of Ursa Major and north of Leo. Contains no stars brighter than the fourth magnitude.

LEONIDS One of the major meteor showers, normally lasting from about November 14–18 at the present time, and reaching a maximum on November 16 or 17. The stream is associated with Comet P/Tempel-Tuttle (1866′ I) and gives rise to very heavy showers at 33-year intervals The shower that occurred on the night of 1833 November 12–13 was the heaviest ever recorded, with an hourly rate of about 35,000; observers described it as reminiscent of a snowstorm. Another magnificent display occurred in 1866, but subsequent maxima have been very poor by comparison, the main swarm having been diverted by the perturbative effects of Jupiter and Saturn so as to miss the Earth. [Plate 16(f).]

It is usual for heavier than usual activity to be observed for some years before each maximum; at maximum the hourly rate is still likely to be well in excess of 60. The radiant of the shower is situated in the Sickle of Leo.

LEPUS (The Hare. *Genitive* Leporis, *I.A.U. abbreviation* Lep.) A small southern constellation at the foot of Orion, between Eridanus and Canis Majoris. Contains one second- and four third-magnitude stars.

LETRONNE Lunar surface feature, co-ordinates $\xi - 662$, $\eta - 182$. A broken ring formation on the eastern border of the Oceanus Procellarum, to the north of Gassendi. Forms a meridional chain with Gassendi and the ring adjoining Flamsteed; shows a notable resemblance to the latter, and like it is only a partial remnant of a once well-formed feature. There is also a fragment of a central peak. The whole appearance is of a crater formation that has been largely submerged by the *mare* surface material.

LEVEL, GEODETIC An instrument used in surveying to determine differences in height between points on the Earth's surface; it usually consists of a telescope which can be accurately levelled by means of a spirit bubble.

LEVEL ERROR The difference between the apparent elevation and true elevation of a celestial body, the apparent elevation being measured above the apparent horizon and the true elevation being measured above a plane passing through the centre of the Earth and parallel to the apparent horizon. The magnitude of the level error depends upon the altitude of the body observed; it is greatest for a body on the apparent horizon.

LEVEL ERROR OF A TRANSIT IN-STRUMENT The angle by which the east–west (mechanical) axis of a transit instrument departs from the horizontal. (See **Transit circle—errors of.**)

LE VERRIER, Urbain J. J. (1811–1877) Distinguished French mathematical astronomer, whose analysis of the perturbations of Uranus enabled him to predict the position of Neptune so accurately that it was discovered by Galle and D'Arrest within a degree of the predicted position. Le Verrier also determined a revised value of the solar parallax and calculated the orbit of the Leonid meteor stream.

(See also **Neptune—discovery of.**)

LIBRA (The Balance. *Genitive* Librae, *I.A.U. abbreviation* Lib.) A southern zodiacal constellation, reaching midnight culmination in early May. There are few bright stars, the brightest being one of the second and two of the third magnitude. δ Lib is an interesting *Algol*-type variable.

LIBRATION It is usually stated that the Moon always presents the same face towards the Earth, but this is in fact an over-simplification. The Moon is subject to 'wobbling' effects as a result of which the visible hemisphere is variable and some 59% of the Moon's surface can be directly observed from Earth at one time or another. This is of considerable value to lunar observers, as features close to the limb can be studied in much more detail at times of 'favourable libration'—i.e. when that particular limb region is tilted towards the Earth. There are three components of optical libration, which will be discussed separately.

Libration in longitude. This arises from the fact that the Moon rotates on its axis at a uniform rate, whilst its orbital motion is variable, in accordance with Kepler's **law of equal areas**; thus at times the eastern limb, and at other times the western limb, is turned towards the Earth. The maximum libration in longitude is a little more than $6\frac{1}{4}°$.

Libration in latitude. This arises from the fact that the Moon's axis of rotation is inclined to the perpendicular to the plane of its orbit by about $6\frac{1}{2}°$, but remains pointing in a fixed direction in space throughout its orbital revolution. This results in the northern and southern limb regions being alternately tilted towards the Earth, the maximum value of the libration in latitude being, of course, about $6\frac{1}{2}°$.

Diurnal libration. This is a small libratory effect depending upon the position of the observer on the Earth's surface; thus two observers in different parts of the world, studying the Moon simultaneously, would have slightly different hemispheres of the Moon presented to them. The maximum value of the diurnal libration is a little under $1°$.

LIBYA Martian surface feature, approximate position Ω 270°, Φ 0°. A small but prominent ochre area, situated on the equator to the east of Syrtis Major. Bounded to the north by Mœris Lacus and to the south by Syrtis Minor and the northern end of the Mare Tyrrhenum.

LICK OBSERVATORY The Lick Observatory was endowed by James Lick, a Californian millionaire; it is situated on Mount Hamilton (4,250 ft.) in central California. The greater part of Lick's gift was used to provide a giant telescope; although a large reflector was seriously considered, the final choice was a 36-in. refractor for which the objective was made by Alvan Clark and the mounting designed and constructed by Messrs. Warner and Swasey, machine tool manufacturers of Cleveland, Ohio, and later to become one of the leading telescope-makers in the world. The giant refractor was completed in 1888; it was the largest refractor in existence until the Yerkes 40-in. was completed in 1897, and is today still the second largest. The Lick 36-in. is a visual refractor, but a 33-in. correcting lens was later provided so that it can be converted for photographic use. The telescope was used by J. E. Keeler for an important programme of radial-velocity determinations of distant galaxies; and in 1892 Barnard discovered the fifth satellite of Jupiter with its aid; it was also used for a major survey of double stars, leading to the publication of the *New General Catalogue of Double Stars*.

In 1895 Edward Crossley, of Halifax, presented the 36-in. Calver reflector manufactured for and mounted by Common, to the Lick Observatory; many magnificent photographs of nebulae, galaxies and the planets have been obtained with this instrument.

For the past few years the Lick Observatory—already housing the second largest refractor—has also been the home of the second largest reflector in the world: a 120-in. instrument in a huge fork-type mounting. The mirror was originally the final test-blank cast for the 200-in. reflector at Mount Palomar. [Plate 31(a).]

LIFE ON OTHER PLANETS One of the most frequently asked questions concerning astronomy is 'Does life exist elsewhere in the universe?' In the present state of knowledge it is not possible to give a categorical answer; it is however possible to discuss the possibilities to some extent, if we first make certain assumptions.

It is first of all necessary to consider what we mean by 'life'; to this the answer usually given is 'life as we know it'. This is perhaps the only definition of life that we could adopt for this purpose, owing to the impossibility of conceiving what other forms of life might exist elsewhere in the universe, but it is a very narrow definition and may greatly reduce the probability of life-forms occurring elsewhere which we seek to determine. It has the merit, however, of limiting the discussion to forms of life that we can both envisage and make reasonable assumptions about, and which we could conceivably detect by observation and experiment. We may consider, then, the possibility of life existing elsewhere in the universe, in a form similar to the animal or vegetable life known on Earth. We must bear in mind that all known forms of life are adaptive—that is to say they have developed in forms most suited to their environment and have changed in order to remain so suited despite changes in their environment. It is only reasonable to assume that any form of life elsewhere in the universe would similarly have adapted itself to its environment.

A number of factors have affected the development of life on Earth: the composition of the Earth's atmosphere, the distance of the Earth from the Sun and the resulting change of temperatures experienced on the Earth; the chemical nature of the Earth's crust, the presence of a high percentage of water both on the Earth's surface and in its atmosphere, etc. The inclination of the Earth's axis and the obliquity of its orbit give rise to seasonal variations in temperature and general climatic conditions; life-forms have adapted to these, and also to local circumstances dependent upon location on the Earth's surface—e.g. the life-forms which survive in polar regions are quite different from those flourishing in the tropics. The development of certain life-forms is in itself a factor governing the environmental adaptation of other life-forms: thus the development of certain forms of vegetable life has stimulated the development of fauna adapted to the use of such vegetation as food; similarly the development of some forms of animal and insect life has been followed by the development of other species to prey upon them.

In order to consider the possibility that life-forms similar to those on Earth have developed elsewhere in the universe we must look for conditions likely to provide a similar environment; we must neverthe-less remember the equal possibility that other environments may well have developed their own life-forms.

It is clear that any form of life envisaged in this discussion could exist only on a planet (or a planetary satellite) in a gravitational system centred on a star: any known type of star is much too hot a body to support such life on itself; equally the necessary environment could not exist on a planetary body without the benefit of the radiation from the central star—just as our own existence depends upon the Sun.

It is virtually certain that planetary systems similar to the solar system must be fairly common throughout the universe; they would however be undetectable at the distance of most stars. Spectroscopic evidence has been obtained which confirms the presence of at least one companion of planetary size in association with several stars (e.g. 61 Cyg and 70 Oph). If we accept that such systems exist it is reason-able to assume that some of them would include planets comparable to the Earth in terms of the environment they would offer to any life-forms present. The age of the system would not seem to be an important parameter, for it has been established from a study of their fossil remains that some primitive forms of invertebrate marine life developed on Earth quite shortly after the formation of its solid crust, and life-forms have con-tinued to develop ever since.

In recent years some attention has been paid to the possibility of establishing the presence of intelligent life-forms com-parable to *Homo sapiens* on distant planets, if in fact they do exist, by direct com-munication with them. Visual observation would seem to offer little prospect of success in this, owing to the huge distances involved (although an early suggestion was the setting-out of huge geometrical patterns in the Sahara desert, in the hope that Martian beings would 'reply' in the same way!). The development of radio-astronomy, however, has made possible (if not very practicable) the idea of radiating simple sequences of radio waves into space on selected wavelengths. Experiments of this type have been attempted in both the U.S.A. and Russia. There would seem to be little prospect of success, however, at least until such times as a specific star, known to have a planetary system and at a known distance, can be selected as a specific target. A further difficulty is that even at the speed of light (the velocity at which any form of electro-magnetic radiation can be propagated in space) the 'messages' might take centuries to cover the intervening distance, even in the case of comparatively close stars. Such experiments are not therefore likely to produce evidence of the existence of other civilizations in the foreseeable future, and the possibility of life existing on planets associated with stars other than the Sun must remain a matter of pure speculation.

In the case of the solar system we are rather fortunate, for we can at least examine the environments offered by the other planets and consider the possibilities of their proving to be life-supporting.

On the basic of 'life as we know it' we can immediately rule out the outer planets (too cold, no solid surface) and their satellites, and probably Mercury also (too hot, no atmosphere).

Perhaps the most direct evidence exists in the case of the Moon—recent photo-graphs obtained by means of space-probes clearly show features only a few feet in diameter—but there is a total absence of any indication that animal or vegetable life exists, which conclusion is supported by the virtual lack of an atmosphere. It seems equally unlikely that life could exist on the very tiny satellites of Mars or on the minor planets.

We are left, therefore, with the two planets closest to the Earth and most similar to it—Venus and Mars.

Venus is very comparable to the Earth in both size and mass; it has a deep cloudy atmosphere which may also contain dust particles. Certainly the atmosphere is very opaque, and absorbs much of the solar radiation falling upon it, thus preventing it from reaching the solid surface of the planet; the surface temperatures are therefore probably much more similar to those obtaining on earth than we might conclude from the proximity of Venus to the Sun. It has been suggested from theoretical considerations that there should be a considerable amount of water on Venus, but no spectroscopic evidence of water vapour in the atmosphere has been obtained; neither is there any evidence of oxygen. The principal constituent of the Cytherean atmosphere seems to be carbon dioxide. The Earth's vegetation lives by means of a process which involves its absorbing carbon dioxide from which to draw its energy, and emitting oxygen; the high proportion of oxygen in the Earth's atmosphere is probably due to the action of its abundant vegetation. It is to be expected that any planet of similar constitution to Venus or the Earth would have an atmosphere containing a high proportion of carbon dioxide during the period following the formation of its crust; if we assume that, being closer to the Sun, the crust of Venus formed more recently than that of the Earth, we might expect to find a greater amount of carbon dioxide, which coupled with the lack of oxygen might be regarded as suggesting that Venus has not yet developed a comparable amount of vegetation. Such a deduction would be rather dangerous, however, as a comparable portion of oxygen may in fact be present on Venus but its presence may be masked by the impenetrable atmosphere.

To sum up, it would seem quite feasible

for some forms of both animal and vegetable life, specially adapted to the Cytherean environment, to exist on Venus; until sophisticated space-probe vehicles can be 'soft'-landed on the planet or placed in a very low orbit around it, however, it seems unlikely that any concrete evidence is likely to be obtained one way or the other.

In the case of Mars the circumstances are very different: except for its smaller size Mars is probably much more similar to the Earth than Venus. It is believed to have a very similar constitution, and has a rarified atmosphere which is opaque to short-wave-length (e.g. violet) light but transparent to light of longer wavelength (e.g. red); both the solid surface and cloud formations in the upper atmosphere can therefore be studied in detail. Observations of the solid surface reveal, *inter alia*, dark markings which vary with the Martian seasons and are believed by some to be vegetation; environmental considerations suggest however that it must be a rather primitive form of vegetation, probably akin to terrestrial lichens. Direct observations of the surface reveal no markings that might be expected were there a highly developed civilized form of animal life on the planet—large connurbations, etc., should be detectable. It is not possible to say at present, however, whether or not less intelligent forms of animal life exist, but the transparent atmosphere should enable this to be established within the immediate future by means of space-probe vehicles, with far more certainty than in the case of Venus. If animal life exists on Mars, however, it must be in a form adapted to an environment which would be quite inadequate to support terrestrial life, for the atmosphere of Mars is almost wholly inert, comprising nearly 94 per cent nitrogen and nearly 4 per cent argon; the remainder about 2·3 per cent, is almost entirely carbon dioxide. There is some evidence that water may be present, although not in large quantities, on the surface—probably it exists mainly in association with vegetation in the form of bogs, rather than areas of open water.

It seems probable, then, that some form of vegetable life can exist on Mars, and possible that some specially adapted fauna could also exist there; there is also reasonable prospect of obtaining confirmatory evidence in the near future.

LIGHT In the past light was incorrectly believed to consist of a stream of tiny corpuscles which, on striking the eye, caused the sensation of vision. It is now known to be a form of electromagnetic radiation. It is produced by bodies at high temperatures, and also by some living organisms—bacteria, luminous fish, etc.

Provided that there is no interrupting body in its path, light is radiated equally in all directions; since like other forms of radiation it has a wave-form, at any given moment the light from a source is thus a series of concentric circular waves. A popular analogy of this condition is the series of concentric waves formed by dropping a stone into water. It will therefore be clear that the light impinging on an object in its path will have a wavefront which is an arc of a circle; this fact can be ignored for most purposes, however.

Light constitutes that part of the electromagnetic spectrum having wavelengths between about 4,000 Å (violet light) and 7,200 Å (red light).

It is convenient, when considering the behaviour of light, to regard it as travelling in an infinite number of separate rays, radial to the source; this permits the behaviour of a single ray to be considered, which greatly simplifies most optical studies. It is particularly helpful when studying the path of a beam of light through an optical instrument.

It is axiomatic that any ray of light travels in a straight path (the concept of the *rectilinear propagation of light*), unless it passes from one medium into another of different density when its direction will be changed by **refraction** (*q.v.*). The direction of a ray of light can also be changed by **reflection** from a polished surface.

An important consequence of the rectilinear propagation of light is that if an opaque object is placed in its path it may be either reflected or absorbed, but cannot pass around the object, and therefore an area of shadow is formed beyond the object. This has important consequences in astronomy—notably the occurrence of eclipses.

A number of parallel rays of light are said to form a *beam* or *pencil*. A beam of 'white' light comprises rays of light of all the visible wavelengths; these may be separated by **dispersion,** using a prism or diffraction grating.

LIGHT CURVE A graph in which the variation of intensity of illumination is plotted against time. This is the usual means of recording the fluctuating brightness of a variable star. The light curve is obtained by plotting determinations of the apparent magnitude obtained either by visual estimate or by photometric means.

LIGHT YEAR One of the fundamental units used in the measurement of astronomical distances. It is the distance that would be travelled in one year by a particle travelling at the velocity of light. This is taken to be $9·4605 \times 10^{13}$ km, or very approximately 5,879,000,000,000 miles.

LIGHT-TIME The time taken by the light from a distant object, travelling at its finite velocity of 186,282 miles per second, to reach the Earth. If the object is observed at time T and the light-time is t, the position and state of the object as observed will be, of course, those that obtained at time $(T-t)$.

LIMB Term used to denote the apparent edge of a body having a detectable disk, e.g. the Sun, Moon or a planet. Regions close to the limb, especially of the Moon, are termed 'limb regions'.

LIMB DARKENING An effect present in observations of the disk of the Sun and other heavenly bodies, wherein the bright-

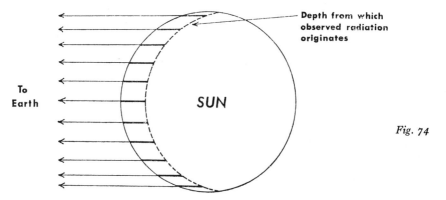

Depth from which observed radiation originates

To Earth

SUN

Fig. 74

ness diminishes towards the limb, resulting in the appearance of an annular shadow. The phenomenon arises from the fact that the light-rays from the central portion of the disk leave almost radially and originate from a comparatively low level; those from the limb regions leave almost tangentially, and would have a much greater depth of atmosphere to penetrate from an equivalent depth: those that we see originate, in fact, from a higher, cooler level than those in the centre of the disk, since the optical depth is constant in the line of sight over the entire disk (see Fig. 74).

A similar effect is observed in the case of planets with deep atmospheres, notably Jupiter and Saturn; it is due to the same cause, save that the light does not originate in the planet but is sunlight scattered by atmospheric particles.

LINE PROFILE A graph of the intensity of radiation versus its component wavelengths; more specifically the shape of the 'peaks' and 'troughs' representing the spectral lines in such a graph.

LINES, SPECTRAL When the light from an astronomical object is passed through a spectroscope a spectrum is produced which consists of a background continuum against which a number of lines are seen. These are usually the dark absorption lines, but in some cases may be the bright lines of the emission spectrum.

(See **Spectra**.)

LINE-OF-SIGHT VELOCITY Velocity in the observer's line of sight, or **radial velocity**, *q.v.*

LINEAR INTERPOLATION Simple means of obtaining intermediate values of a tabulated function from the values given. (See **Interpolation**.)

LINNÉ Lunar surface feature, co-ordinates $\xi + 18$, $\eta + 465$. Prominently situated on the eastern floor of the Mare Serenitatis, Linné is one of the most interesting and enigmatic formations on the Moon. In the early nineteenth century it was recorded as a deep crater, 5 miles in diameter; in 1866 Julius Schmidt could detect no crater at all, merely a white, cloud-like marking. Later observers agreed with this description, but did detect a shallow depression, containing a tiny pit, within the bright area. Early in the present century leading observers recorded it as a shallow crater-ring with a small crater cone on the east rim and a small peak on the west.

These varying descriptions were carefully studied by W. H. Pickering, who concluded that they constituted definite evidence of changes in the structure of the feature. Pickering also detected changes in the overall size of the white area, which he interpreted as a patch of hoar-frost.

Contemporary observations with fairly large telescopes show a low mound in the centre of the white area, with a deep pit at its summit.

Whilst observations of this feature are difficult to make with accuracy, and all the records must therefore be regarded with considerable reserve, it nevertheless seems to be very probable that this feature has undergone substantial changes in its appearance over the years and should be carefully observed with powerful instruments whenever possible.

If further changes are observed the history of Linné will be of the utmost importance to theorists considering the nature and formation of the lunar surface features.

LITTROW SPECTROSCOPE A form of long-focus spectroscope which, although quite unsuitable for attachment to a telescope, is a very convenient means of achieving high dispersion in a fixed, laboratory spectroscope. It can, however, be used for astronomical spectroscopy with the addition of a cœlostat, and forms the basis of many spectroheliographs. It is an autocollimating instrument, the same lens being used to collimate the light before it reaches the grating and as the objective of the camera or visual telescope used to observe the spectrum after diffraction.

LOBACHEVSKII A prominent dark feature on the far side of the Moon, discovered on photographs taken by *Lunik III.*

LOCAL GROUP The cluster of galaxies of which our own Galaxy is a member; the type, size and distance of the major members of the group are given in Table 16.

(See also **Galaxies; Galactic structure.**)

LOCKYER, Sir J. Norman (1823–1920) One of the earliest English astrophysicists. In 1887 he proposed a theory of stellar evolution to explain the observed differences in spectral type; this ranks as a great step forward, although it is now known that the premises upon which Lockyer built his theory were unsound. He was one of the pioneers of solar spectroscopy.

Table 16. The local group of galaxies

SYSTEM	CONSTELLATION	TYPE	DIAMETER (kpc)	DISTANCE (kpc)
M31	And	Sb	26·2	457
The Galaxy	—	Sb	24	—
M33	Tri	Sc	11·6	479
Nubecula Major	Men	I	9·2	44
Nubecula Minor	Tuc	I	7·0	50
NGC 205	And	E	3·4	457
NGC 6822	Sgr	I	1·8	316
NGC 221	And	E	1·6	457
NGC 185	And	E	1·6	398
IC 1613	Psc	I	3·0	457
NGC 147	And	E	2·0	398
Wolf–Lundmark system	Aqr	I	2·0	501
Fornax system	For	E	2·1	144
Sculptor system	Scl	E	1·0	69

LOMONOSOV Lunar surface feature, located on the far side of the Moon and discovered on photographs taken by the Soviet 'interplanetary station', Lunik III. (See also **Moon, far side of.**)

LONG-PERIOD VARIABLES A general term embracing all variable stars having periods greater than 40 days, with the exception of Cepheid and eclipsing variables. (See **Variable stars.**)

LONGITUDE, CELESTIAL The longitude of a heavenly body is the angular distance between the secondary to the Ecliptic containing the body and the First Point of Aries (♈); it is measured eastwards from ♈.

LONGITUDE, TERRESTRIAL The longitude of a point on the surface of the Earth, i.e. the angular distance between the meridian on which the point is situated and the Prime Meridian. Longitude is measured in degrees, from 0° to 180° E or W of the Prime Meridian.

LORENTZ, H. A. (1853–1928) Eminent Dutch physicist, who devised a set of equations which expressed the variations in measurements in time and mass in bodies moving through space at velocities significant when compared with the speed of light. These equations are known as the **Lorentz transformations**, and arise from the **Lorentz–Fitzgerald contraction**, *q.v.*

LORENTZ TRANSFORMATIONS The set of equations developed by H. A. Lorentz to define the variations in measurements of time and mass in bodies moving at very high velocities, due to the Lorentz–Fitzgerald contraction.

LORENTZ–FITZGERALD CONTRACTION At the end of the nineteenth century it was suggested by G. F. Fitzgerald that the results of the Michelson–Morley experiment could be explained if a body, moving in space at a high velocity significant compared with the velocity of light, were contracted in the direction of its motion. It was shown by H. A. Lorentz that such a contraction was predictable on the basis of the atomic theory of the nature of matter, and he formulated the equations governing the contraction (the **Lorentz transformations**). It was later shown by Albert Einstein that the contraction was a fundamental consequence of special relativity.

The Lorentz–Fitzgerald contraction is sometimes abbreviated to the 'Lorentz contraction'.

LOWELL, Percival (1855–1916) A wealthy American amateur astronomer, who built the Lowell Observatory at Flagstaff, Arizona, specifically for the observation of the surface features of Mars. The principal telescope was initially an 18-in. refractor, but this was replaced in 1896 by a fine 24-in. refractor.

Lowell became famous for his observations of Mars, in which he depicted the canali as linear markings, and for his belief that they are an irrigation network created by intelligent beings. His dogmatic pronouncements to this effect did much to lose him the support of other scientists, and prevented him from receiving the credit his considerable scientific and mathematical ability deserved. The Lowell Observatory has contributed a great deal of valuable observational evidence to our knowledge of the solar system, and stands as a living memorial to Lowell's great devotion and personal contribution to this cause, which should not be overshadowed by the more doubtful aspects of his interpretation of observation.

Lowell spent many years analysing residual perturbations of Uranus extra to those due to Neptune, with a view to discovering a trans-Neptunian planet; photographic searches based upon Lowell's calculations were carried out at the Lowell Observatory from 1905–1916 without avail, and discontinued only on Lowell's death. The search was resumed in 1929 and early in 1930 Pluto was discovered; it proved to have an orbit remarkably similar to that predicted by Lowell, but also proved to be incapable of causing the perturbations to Uranus upon which his prediction was based! (See **Pluto—discovery of.**)

LUMINOSITY FUNCTION A measure of the distribution in space of stars according to their luminosities. It is usually expressed as the number of stars per cubic parsec for each unit of absolute magnitude; this is termed the general luminosity function. If the luminosity functions for each spectral class are determined separately, they can be plotted on the **Hertzsprung–Russell diagram,** *q.v.*

(See also **Stars—luminosity of.**)

LUMINOSITY, STELLAR The total radiative flux of a star, i.e. the total amount of energy radiated from its entire surface, per second. (See **Stars—luminosity of.**)

LUNA Name given to a series of lunar-probe vehicles launched from the Soviet Union. The early vehicles in the series were better known by the popular name 'Lunik', derived from *Luna* (Moon) and *Sputnik* (literally 'Fellow traveller'—the name given to the first Russian artificial earth satellites). The vehicles launched in the programme are listed in Table 17.

Lunik I was the first successful attempt at a close approach to the Moon; launched on 1959 January 2 it passed within 4,000 miles of the Moon on January 4 when it was 370,000 miles from Earth. Among the scientific results obtained with this probe was the fact that the Moon lacks a magnetic field of significant strength.

Lunik II landed on the Moon, in the western part of the Mare Imbrium, on 1959 September 13 after a 34-hour flight—the first lunar landing to be achieved (albeit a 'heavy' one).

The most spectacular results of the early *Luna* vehicles were the first photographs of the averted face of the Moon obtained by *Lunik III* on 1959 October 10 when it passed the Moon at a distance of some 3,850 miles.

After an interval of $3\frac{1}{2}$ years *Luna 4* was launched, it is believed as as attempt to achieve a soft landing on the Moon but this has never been officially confirmed. In fact the probe vehicle passed more than 5,000 miles from the Moon and was lost in its solar (i.e. heliocentric) orbit.

After a further gap of more than a year the programme was resumed in 1965 with the launching of four vehicles in a period

Table 17.   Luna programme

Vehicle	Launched	Result	(date)
Luna 1 (Lunik I)	1959 Jan. 2	Passed app. 3,730 miles from Moon,	1959 Jan. 4
Luna 2 (Lunik II)	1959 Sep. 12	Heavy landing on Moon,	1959 Sep. 13
Luna 3 (Lunik III)	1959 Oct. 4	Passed app. 3,850 miles from Moon,	1959 Oct. 10
Luna 4	1963 Apr. 2	Passed app. 5,280 miles from Moon,	1963 Apr. 6
Luna 5	1965 May 9	Heavy landing on Moon,	1965 May 12
Luna 6	1965 Jun. 8	Missed Moon by app. 99,400 miles,	1965 Jun. 11
Luna 7	1965 Oct. 4	Heavy landing on Moon,	1965 Oct. 7
Luna 8	1965 Dec. 3	Heavy landing on Moon,	1965 Dec. 6
Luna 9	1966 Jan. 31	First soft landing on Moon,	1966 Feb. 3
Luna 10	1966 Mar. 31	First orbit of Moon,	1966 Apr. 2
Luna 11	1966 Aug. 24	Orbit of Moon,	1966 Aug. 27
Luna 12	1966 Oct. 22	Orbit of Moon,	1966 Oct. 25
Luna 13	1966 Dec. 21	Soft landing on Moon	
Luna 14	1968 Apr. 7	Soft landing on Moon	
Luna 15	1969 Jul. 13	Crash landing,	1969 Jul. 21

of less than seven months, three of them achieving heavy landings (*Luna 5* in the Mare Nubium, *Luna 7* and *Luna 8* in the Mare Tranquillitatis). Owing to an instrumental failure a motor started to correct the course of *Luna 6* could not be stopped, and the vehicle went wildly off course, missing the Moon by almost 100,000 miles.

At last, with *Luna 9*, the Russians achieved the first ever 'soft' landing on the Moon's surface. The vehicle followed the planned course exactly, and landed under complete control in the Oceanus Procellarum. This proved immediately that the lunar maria have a solid surface capable of supporting the weight of a space vehicle and disproved the theory proposed some years ago that they were covered by very deep layers of dust. Some minutes after landing the probe's radio transmitter commenced operation; in all seven periods of communication with the probe were recorded, totalling more than eight hours.

The television camera carried by the probe vehicle was arranged so as to obtain a 360° panoramic view of the surrounding surface, and some historic photographs were obtained, showing a very rough, porous surface bearing a marked resemblance to lava from terrestrial volcanoes, thus greatly strengthening the arguments in favour of some form of vulcanism for the mechanism of formation of most of the lunar surface features.

LUNABASE The basic rocks forming the dark areas of the Moon's surface, sometimes termed 'marial' rocks or 'marebase'.

LUNÆ LACUS Martian surface feature, approximate position Ω 65°, $\Phi + 15°$. Moderately dark oasis in the north tropical region of the planet, south-west of the Mare Acidalium, to which it is connected by Nilokeras. The prominent canal Ganges runs south-east from Lunæ Lacus, into the Auroræ Sinus.

LUNAR FAULT A deformation of the crustal rocks of the Moon.

LUNAR ORBITER American lunar probe project. A contract was placed by N.A.S.A. with the Boeing company in 1964, for the production of 8 probe vehicles to be placed in circumlunar orbits. The principal experimental object is the photographic study of the lunar surface; unlike the earlier *Ranger* and *Surveyor* spacecraft, the *Orbiter* vehicles carry cameras which record images on film in the usual way; these are processed and then scanned and telemetered back to Earth over a lengthy period, thus permitting very high resolution. Other experiments to be carried out with the *Orbiter* vehicles include radiation measurement, micro-meteorite detection, magnetic and spectroscopic studies of the Moon and the study of the corpuscular radiation from the Sun.

Orbiter 1, established in a very low lunar orbit in 1966 August, produced a series of magnificent photographs of the lunar surface of a quality and resolution never previously attained.

During the following twelve months *Orbiters 2, 3, 4* and *5*—the last two being in polar orbits—provided photographic coverage of such high resolution as to supersede entirely all previous mapping of the lunar surface from Earth-based observations.

LUNAR RAY SYSTEMS Hundreds of the ring-structures on the Moon's surface are surrounded by a quantity of highly reflective material; in many cases this takes the form of bright streaks approximately radial to the ring-structure. These streaks are termed *rays*, and the streaks associated with one ring-structure are collectively termed its *ray system*. In some cases only the inner walls of the ring are bright, the ray system appearing as a bright ring, but most ray systems are composed of bright streaks outside the walls of the ring. It is usual for ring-structures having a bright ray system to have a bright interior also.

There are two main types of ray systems: those in which the rays are long streaks, and those in which many short, filamentary streaks form a complex network of bright matter surrounding the ring-structure.

The streaks comprising the former type are usually long and linear; the largest are those associated with the great mountain-walled plain Tycho, some of which can be traced across the lunar surface for more than a thousand miles. At a casual glance such systems of rays appear to be radial to the centre of the ring-structure concerned, but closer inspection reveals that this is not strictly the case; they do however appear to radiate from a number of points all of which are contained within the ring.

A number of ring-structures have a rather different form or ray: these appear at first sight to be curved, but otherwise similar to the Tycho type of ray. On closer examination, however, it appears that the curved streaks are formed by a number of short sections of ray, each in itself radial to the parent ring, but which are spread along a curved path. The great ray-system centred on Copernicus is of this type, and can be clearly seen on any good photograph of the Full Moon [e.g. Plate 4(a)].

The second type of ray system is found surrounding many of the smaller ring-structures; it generally appears as a bright nimbus, usually termed a *halo*, surrounding the crater. Probably the finest example of this type of ray system is the halo surrounding Euclides, a small crater (7 miles in diameter) situated some 250 miles south-east of Copernicus. (Euclides is the tiny crater close to the top right-hand corner of Plate 4(c), in which its halo-type ray system can be compared with the long curved streaks of the Copernicus system.)

Some examples of this type of ray system can be resolved under favourable conditions, and appear to be composed of a great number of short, filamentary rays, superimposed on each other. They are less uniformly radial to the parent ring than in the case of the long rays of the Tycho type.

The general appearance of both types of ray system suggests that they are some form of splash-mark; originally this was used as evidence in favour of the theory that the lunar ring-structures were formed by meteoritic impact. Recent studies, however, have indicated that the existence of the ray systems is in fact quite compatible with the theory, now much more widely accepted, that most of the lunar surface features are igneous in origin. It has been suggested that the rays may mark fault-lines in the lunar crust, being matter extruded through small craterlets; it is significant that many rays appear to commence at a craterlet, and that many other craterlets can be found along their lengths. Another suggested mechanism for the formation of the ray systems is the bombardment of the surface around the parent ring-structure by matter erupted during the formation of the ring by volcanic activity. (See also **Moon—surface features of; Moon—surface features, origin of.**)

LUNAR 'SEAS' See **Mare**.

LUNAR SURFACE FEATURES—CO-ORDINATES OF

The positions of crater rings and other features of the lunar surface are usually given in selenographic co-ordinates. These may be in the form of selenographic latitude (β) and longitude (λ), but are more often expressed in Cartesian co-ordinates referred to the centre of the mean sphere of the Moon, owing to their greater convenience for observers.

The selenographic latitude (β) of a point is the angle between the point and the lunar equator, measured in a meridian; the selenographic longitude (λ) is the angular distance between the point and the **first lunar meridian**, measured in the equator. β is considered to be positive in the northern hemisphere and negative in the southern hemisphere; λ is considered positive in the western and negative in the eastern hemisphere.

The framework of the more usual rectangular co-ordinates is shown in Fig. 75; the origin of the system is the centre of the mean sphere of the Moon, and the radius of the mean sphere is taken to be 1. It will be seen that the co-ordinates of the point P in the third

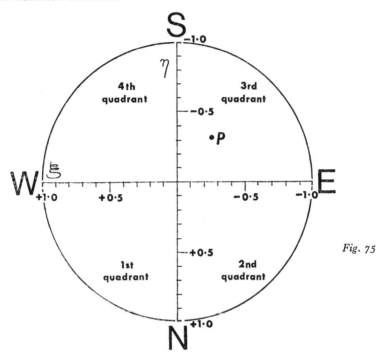

Fig. 75

quadrant are $\xi - 0.250$, $\eta - 0.330$; in practice these are usually abbreviated to the form $\xi - 250$, $\eta - 330$; the co-ordinates of all lunar surface features listed in this book are given in this form.

Descriptions of the general location of a feature are given in the classic usage of the compass directions as shown in Fig. 75; i.e. a feature near the limb in the 2nd quadrant is described as being in the north-eastern limb region. In 1961 the International Astronomical Union adopted an alternative convention for use in 'astronautical' maps, where south remains at the top but east and west are interchanged; some recent charts follow the new convention, and it is therefore important to ascertain the convention adopted for the chart used before attempting to locate the features described in this book. Maps intended for lunar explorers are printed with north at the top.

(See also **Moon—surface features of.**)

LUNAR THEORY General term for the theoretical study of the motion of the Moon. (See **Moon—motion of.**)

LUNARITE The rocks forming the bright areas of the Moon's surface, sometimes termed 'continental' rocks. They are of lower density than the **lunabase,** *q.v.*

LUNATION The interval between repetitions of the same phase of the Moon, e.g. New Moon to New Moon; also termed the Moon's 'synodic period' or 'synodic month'. Its mean value is about $29\frac{1}{2}$ days.

LUNE A geometrical figure; it is the area enclosed by two arcs. It may be used to describe the area of the Moon visible at a narrow crescent phase, or during eclipse, etc.

LUNIK Popular name for the early lunar-probe vehicles of the Russian Luna programme, notably *Lunik III* which obtained the first photographs of the far side of the Moon. (See **Luna**.)

LUNI–SOLAR PRECESSION The main component of the precession of the equinoxes, due to the gravitational effects of the Sun and Moon upon the oblate geoid. (See **Precession**.)

LUPUS (The Wolf. *Genitive* Lupi, *I.A.U. abbreviation* Lup.) A southern constellation lying between Centaurus and Scorpius. Rather small in area but contains a considerable number of third- and fourth-magnitude stars.

LYMAN SPECTRUM One of the series of lines in the spectrum of hydrogen due to transitions between various energy levels. It is the series of lines of shortest wavelength. (See **Hydrogen—spectrum of**.)

LYNX (The Lynx. *Genitive* Lyncis, *I.A.U. abbreviation* Lyn.) A northern constellation reaching midnight culmination in mid-January. Covers a large area of the sky but contains very few bright stars. Situated between Ursa Major and Auriga and Gemini.

LYOT, Bernard (1897–1952) The leading French astronomer of his time, Lyot spent his entire career on the staff of the Meudon Observatory near Paris. He made notable contributions to the study of the Moon and planets, especially in the field of polarization studies. His greatest work, however, was devoted to the study of the Sun's corona. To facilitate this work Lyot invented first the **coronograph** (in 1930) and later the birefringent monochromator (popularly known as the 'Lyot filter'). Lyot was elected a member of the Académie des Sciences de Paris in 1939, and in the same year was awarded the Gold Medal of the Royal Astronomical Society; in 1947 he received the Bruce Medal of the Astronomical Society of the Pacific.

LYOT BIREFRINGENT FILTER One of the most important instruments developed for solar research. The principle was developed independently by Bernard Lyot in 1933 and Y. Öhman in 1938, and developed for use in solar observation by Lyot and others.

The device makes use of the fact that certain crystalline minerals, notably quartz (SiO_2) and calcite ($CaCO_3$), are *birefringent*: that is to say, a beam of light refracted by a crystal of the substance is split into two emergent refracted rays which are polarized perpendicularly to each other. (Glass, by contrast, is *mono-refringent*, the incident ray emerging as a single refracted ray.) If a quartz plate is sandwiched between two sheets of Polaroid it acts as an interference filter producing alternative bands of the continuous spectrum and dark interspaces of equal width, the Polaroid filters allowing only one of the two emergent beams to pass.

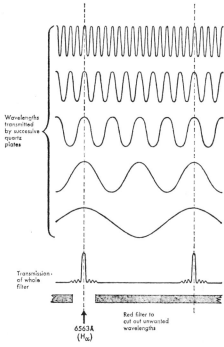

Wavelengths transmitted by successive quartz plates

Transmission of whole filter

6563Å
(Hα)

Red filter to cut out unwanted wavelengths

Fig. 76

In the Lyot filter a series of quartz plates are used, each exactly twice the thickness of the previous one. The wavelength of light transmitted by each quartz plate being dependent upon the thickness of the plate, the cumulative effect of the series of plates is to transmit only an extremely narrow band at intervals along the spectrum. An ordinary red glass or gelatin filter is then used to cut off all of these save for one at the long wavelength end. The dimensions of the quartz plates are selected to ensure that this final beam has the wavelength of the hydrogen-alpha line at 6563 Å (see Fig. 76).

The optical properties of the quartz plates vary with only very slight changes in temperature, so that they have to be enclosed in an insulated tube with a thermostatically controlled heating element to maintain the desired temperature within fine limits.

The use of such an instrument with a conventional equatorial refractor (usually with an aperture of 4–6 in.) permits the Sun to be observed in Hα light without the problems introduced by the scanning slits or Anderson prisms of the **spectro-heliograph.** The birefringent filter is however an expensive instrument to construct and requires to be used under very carefully controlled conditions; consequently only a few are in use, in leading solar physics observatories.

The instrument is usually termed the *Lyot filter* for brevity; it is also variously known as the *interference–polarization filter*, the *birefringent monochromator*, etc.

LYRA (The Lyre. *Genitive* Lyrae, *I.A.U. abbreviation* Lyr.) A small northern constellation between Hercules and Cygnus. Contains one first-magnitude star (*Vega*) and two of the third magnitude. ϵ^1 and ϵ^2 Lyr are an interesting pair of binaries known as the 'double-double'.

β Lyr is a typical example of the 'Lyrid' or bright-eclipsing variables.

One of the best-known planetary nebulae is located in this constellation—the 'Ring Nebula' (M57, or N.G.C. 6720), between β and γ Lyr.

LYRIDS An important meteor shower occurring about April 22. The radiant is on the border of Lyra and Hercules, about 8° west of *Vega*. The shower is regular and predictable, but not heavy, the hourly rate usually being about 7–10. Records of the shower can be traced back for over 2,500 years. The swarm is associated with Comet Thatcher (1861 I).

LYTTLETON, R. A. Contemporary mathematical astronomer and one of the leading theorists of the present time; was one of the pioneers of the concept of the steady-state universe. Lyttleton is also an expert in the study of the physics of comets.

M

M STARS Stars of spectral class M; they are red stars having surface temperatures of about 3,000 °K (giants), 3,400 °K (dwarfs). The best-known example is *Betelgeuse*.

MK-SYSTEM (or MKK-SYSTEM) A classification system for stellar spectra developed at the Yerkes Observatory by Morgan, Keénan and Kellman, which takes into account the luminosity of the star as well as its spectral type; it is therefore a quantitative refinement of the more familiar Harvard–Draper sequence, and is of greater value to the theoretical astrophysicist.

(See **Stars—spectral classification of.**)

MACROBIUS (Lunar surface feature, co-ordinates $\xi+674$, $\eta+363$); a walled plain, 42 miles in diameter, near the north-eastern border of the Mare Crisium. The walls rise to 13,000 ft. There is a double-peaked central mountain.

MÄDLER, J. H. von (1794–1874) Collaborator of Wilhelm Beer at his Berlin observatory, where they produced in four parts between 1834 and 1836 the most accurate map of the Moon's surface then in existence, the result of more than a decade of patient observation, which was to inspire selenographers and be the starting point for their own studies for many years. The map was followed in 1837 by their descriptive volume *Der Mond*. Beer and Mädler also collaborated to produce the first systematic chart of the surface features of Mars, as observed by them during the apparition of 1830.

Mädler became director of the Dorpat Observatory in Estonia in 1840.

MAGELLANIC CLOUDS The Large and Small Magellanic Clouds are two irregular, diffuse nebulae, visible to the unaided eye as two detached portions of the southern Milky Way. They are, in fact, satellite nebulae to our own Galaxy.

They are very important sources of astrophysical data, being the nearest extragalactic systems. Many Cepheid variables, globular clusters and gaseous nebulae have been discovered in them. [Plate 20(a, b).]

MAGINUS (Lunar surface feature, co-ordinates $\xi-085$, $\eta-770$); a large mountain-walled plain, 110 miles in diameter, situated in the mountainous southern region of the Moon, near Clavius and Tycho.

MAGNETIC FIELD The area surrounding a magnet (i.e. any body exerting magnetic force), over which the magnetic force is effective. The magnetic field of the Earth is similar to that of a bar magnet oriented almost, but not quite, along the axis of rotation.

The Earth's magnetic field influences the direction of arrival of charged particles of the Sun, and hence **Aurorae** are most common in polar regions.

MAGNETIC STORM See **Storm, geomagnetic.**

MAGNETIC VARIATION The inclination of the axis of the Earth's magnetic field to its axis of rotation; it is slowly varying. It is the angle between the direction of magnetic north as shown by a magnetic compass and true north.

MAGNETISM, TERRESTRIAL The properties of the magnetic field of the Earth, which has the general form of the field surrounding a simple bar magnet. The magnetic axis is inclined to the Earth's axis of rotation by a small angle, which is subject to slow change (the *magnetic variation*).

MAGNITUDE A number assigned to a star or other body to indicate its brightness relative to other bodies.

MAGNITUDE, ABSOLUTE A measure of the actual luminosity of a star, taking into account its distance from the Earth. It can be calculated for any star whose **parallax** (and hence distance) can be determined; it is expressed in the same scale as that used for **apparent magnitude**, and is in fact the apparent magnitude the star would have if situated at a standard distance from the Earth of 10 parsecs. This is the distance at which a star would have a parallax of $0''.1$.

The absolute magnitude (M) may be derived from the apparent magnitude (m) and the parallax (π) by the formula

$$M = m + 5 - 5 \log \pi.$$

In Table 18 are given the apparent and absolute magnitudes of a number of the brightest stars, together with an indication of their true brightness relative to that of the Sun.

MAGNITUDE, APPARENT The numerical system of indicating the relative apparent brightness of stars was first adopted by the Greek astronomer Hipparchus (190–120 B.C.). Hipparchus selected about 20 of the brightest stars visible to the naked eye which he called the first-magnitude stars, and all those barely visible he designated sixth-magnitude stars. Between these rather arbitrary limits Hipparchus divided stars into second, third, fourth and fifth magnitude, according to their apparent brightness. This approximate scale of magnitudes was used for centuries until the growth of telescopic observation, and the refinement of the techniques used for the estimation of the brightness of stars necessitated adoption of a more precise scale.

Table 18.   *The apparent and absolute magnitudes of some bright stars*

	Parallax (π)	Apparent Magnitude (m)	Absolute Magnitude (M)	True Brightness (Sun = 1)
Sirius (α CMa) .	$0''.375$	-1.58	$+1.3$	26.3
Canopus (α Car) .	.005	-0.86	-7.4	80,000
Vega (α Lyr) . .	.121	$+0.14$	$+0.5$	52
Capella (α Aur) .	.071	$+0.21$	-0.5	140
Arcturus (α Boo) .	.085	$+0.24$	-0.1	100
α Cen . . .	.758	$+0.33$	$+4.7$	1.0
Rigel (β Ori) . .	.003	$+0.34$	-7.4	78,000
Procyon (α CMi) .	.288	$+0.48$	$+2.9$	6.0
Achernar (α Eri) .	.023	$+0.60$	-2.6	950
β Cen . . .	.016	$+0.86$	-3.1	1,500
Altair (α Aql) . .	.198	$+0.89$	$+2.4$	9.5
Betelgeuse (α Ori) .	.005	$+0.92$	-5.6	15,000
Aldebaran (α Tau) .	.046	$+1.06$	-0.6	150
Pollux (β Gem) .	.093	$+1.21$	$+1.1$	32
Spica (α Vir) . .	.021	$+1.21$	-2.2	660
Antares (α Sco) .	.019	$+1.23$	-2.4	790
Fomalhaut (α PsA) .	.143	$+1.29$	$+2.1$	13
Deneb (α Cyg) .	.004	$+1.33$	-5.7	16,000
Regulus (α Leo) .	.041	$+1.34$	-0.6	150

Sir John Herschel (1792–1871) discovered that the apparent luminosities of a first-magnitude star and one of the sixth magnitude were in the ratio of about 100 to 1. It was decided to adopt a scale where this ratio would be exactly 100:1; on this scale a star of a given numerical magnitude is exactly 2·512 times as bright as one a whole magnitude fainter. This ratio may be expressed in the form

$$\frac{I_1}{I_2} = 2\cdot512 \ (m_2 - m_1)$$

where I_1, I_2 are the apparent luminosities of the stars and m_1, m_2 their numerical magnitudes. The theory of the scale of visual magnitudes was adjusted so that the mean magnitude of stars near the sixth magnitude agreed with their mean magnitude as given in the *Bonner Durchmusterung*. Many determinations of visual magnitudes have since been made, principally at the observatories of Harvard and Potsdam.

The basic scale of magnitudes can be extended in both directions, stars one magnitude brighter than first magnitude have been designated magnitude 0 and brighter ones magnitude −1, etc. The brightest star visible, *Sirius*, has a magnitude of −1·6; on this scale the magnitude of the Sun is −26·7.

By means of comparison with stars of known magnitude, the magnitudes of variable stars and planetary satellites, etc., can be estimated with a high degree of accuracy.

Apparent magnitude, however determined, is based purely upon the apparent brightness of the object as observed, and is no indication of its true, intrinsic brightness.

MAGNITUDE, BOLOMETRIC

A theoretical figure representing the total amount of radiation, in all wavelengths, emitted by the body. It cannot be determined by observation, but can be calculated from the visual magnitude. Using laboratory determinations of the energy required in different wavelengths to give the same amount of light, Eddington computed a table of the differences between bolometric and visual magnitudes, as follows:

Table 19.   The difference between visual and bolometric magnitudes

Effective temperature of star °C	Magnitude difference (visual − bolometric)
2,540	+2·59
3,000	+1·71
3,600	+0·95
4,500	+0·35
6,000	0·00
7,500	+0·02
9,000	+0·12
10,500	+0·31
12,000	+0·53

MAGNITUDE, PHOTOELECTRIC

A magnitude determined by the use of a photoelectric photometer attached to a telescope. This is the method most widely used today for the accurate determination of stellar magnitudes.

Many of the determinations made by this method are on the UBV system. The photometric measurement of the brightness of the star is measured in turn through three filters, the U filter giving a magnitude in the ultra-violet spectrum, the B filter giving a magnitude in the same spectrum as photographic magnitudes and the V filter giving a magnitude in the spectrum of photovisual magnitudes. The use of this technique permits intercomparison of magnitudes determined by various methods. In recent years photoelectric magnitude determinations have also been carried out using six filters, the six regions observed covering the entire spectrum from red to violet.

MAGNITUDE, PHOTOGRAPHIC

A magnitude determined from photographs made using emulsions sensitive to blue light; the wavelengths currently used are between 4,000 and 5,000 Ångstroms.

MAGNITUDE, PHOTOVISUAL Magnitude determined from photographs made with an isochromatic emulsion and a filter transmitting only the longer wavelengths between 5,000 and 6,000 Ångstroms. Photovisual magnitudes determined in this way are almost identical with visual magnitudes.

MAGNITUDE, VISUAL A magnitude determined from observations made visually. The observations may be made with the unaided eye or with the assistance of a telescope. Visual magnitudes are always determinations of the apparent magnitude.

MAIN SEQUENCE The lower branch of the **Hertzsprung–Russell diagram** (in which absolute magnitude is plotted against spectral type), along which the majority of dwarf stars of all types are distributed. The absolute magnitude of main-sequence stars varies according to their spectral type, the luminosity being progressively less for stars of the redder types, unlike the giant stars whose luminosity does not appear to vary significantly with spectral type.

MAJOR PLANET Arbitrary description given to the four giant planets—Jupiter, Saturn, Uranus and Neptune.

MAKSUTOV CAMERA A form of Schmidt camera devised by D. D. Maksutov of the State Optical Institute, Moscow, in 1941. The aspherical correct-

ing plate of the conventional Schmidt camera is replaced by a meniscus lens having spherical surfaces; the layout is shown in Fig. 77. Fig. 78 shows two possible variations of the type: (a) with the Meniscus corrector combined with a

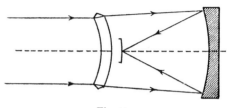

Fig. 77

right-angle prism, enabling the Newtonian focus to be used, and (b) with a Gregorian-type elliptical mirror, enabling the conventional 'eye-end' observing position to be used. This design showed certain advantages, notably in the simplicity of manufacture of the optical parts and the short tube-length, and led to a number of useful variants of the Meniscus–Schmidt camera. [Plate 29(c).]

MALUS (The Mast). Ancient name for the constellation now known as **Pyxis** *q.v.*

MANILIUS (Lunar surface feature, coordinates $\xi+153$, $\eta+250$); a beautiful crater 25 miles in diameter, on the northwestern corner of the Mare Vaporum.

MANY-BODY PROBLEM A major fundamental aspect of celestial mechanics,

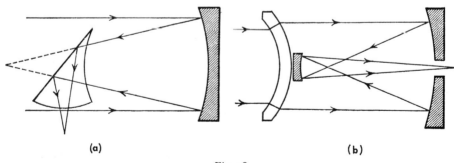

(a)   (b)

Fig. 78

which seeks to predict the future relative motions of a number of bodies in space as a result of their mutual gravitational influence. (See also **Three-body problem; Two-body problem.**)

MARE (Plural Maria). Literally meaning 'Sea', this name was incorrectly given to the dusky areas on the Moon visible to the unaided eye, and has become accepted by usage; also used by Schiaparelli when naming some of the dusky areas on Mars.

MARE ACIDALIUM (Martian surface feature, approximate position Ω 25°, $\Phi + 50°$). Dusky area, one of the most northerly features normally observable.

MARE AUSTRALE (Southern Sea); a dark area on the Moon, seen greatly foreshortened on the south-west limb.

MARE BOREUM (Martian surface feature, approximate position Ω 85°, $\Phi + 58°$), A dusky streak running westwards from the northern edge of the more prominent Mare Acidalium; like most of the higher latitude features is frequently difficult to observe or missing altogether.

MARE CHRONIUM (Martian surface feature, approximate position Ω 210°, $\Phi - 60°$). A long, dusky area, one of the most southerly observable features on Mars.

MARE CIMMERIUM (Martian surface feature, approximate position Ω 210°, $\Phi - 30°$). A long, dusky region, parallel to the Mare Tyrrhenum, with several important canali radiating from its northern end, such as Cyclops, Cerberus II and the Tritonis Sinus. These vary, being prominent at some apparitions and almost invisible at others, and sometimes varying significantly during the apparition. The outline of the western end of the Mare Cimmerium is therefore very changeable.

MARE CRISIUM (Sea of Crises); an oval dark area, of some 65,000 square miles, near the north-west limb of the Moon. Of considerable interest to lunar observers; some of the better-substantiated possible changes in the lunar landscape have been reported in this area. Obscuration of the surface has also been recorded in parts of the Mare. There are many small features on its surface, notably the craterlets Picard and Pierce.

MARE ERYTHRÆUM (Martian surface feature, approximate position Ω 25°, $\Phi - 30°$). A large, dusky area in the south temperate zone of Mars.

MARE FŒCUNDITATIS (Sea of Fertility); a large, dark area near the western limb of the Moon, south of the Mare Crisium and adjoining the Mare Tranquillitatis, and covering more than 150,000 square miles. Its boundary is not very well defined, and there are few objects of interest in it, other than Messier and Pickering.

MARE FRIGORIS (Sea of Cold); a long, ill-defined, dusky area spreading across the north polar region of the Moon.

MARE HUMBOLDTIANUM (Humboldt's Sea); a small, dusky area on the north-west limb of the Moon. It is difficult to observe owing to the severe foreshortening.

MARE HUMORUM (Sea of Moisture); a dusky plain near the south-east limb of the Moon, adjoining the Oceanus Procellarum.

MARE IMBRIUM (Sea of Showers); the best defined of the lunar maria, almost circular in form and covering more than 350,000 square miles of the north-east quadrant of the Moon. Surrounded by mountains for two-thirds of its perimeter, the Mare Imbrium contains numerous features of interest including large crater formations such as Archimedes and Aristillus, and isolated mountain peaks such as Pico and Piton. In its north-east boundary lies the huge 'Bay of Rainbows' (the **Sinus Iridum**). [Plate 5(d).]

MARE INGENII An extensive area of dark lunabase in the southern part of the far side of the Moon, discovered on photographs obtained by *Lunik III*. (See **Moon —far side of.**)

MARE MARGINIS (Marginal Sea); a small, dusky plain on the western limb of the Moon. It is difficult to observe owing to the foreshortening.

MARE MUSCOVIENSE (Moscow Sea); the name given by the Academy of Sciences of the U.S.S.R. to a large, dusky plain, some 200 miles in diameter, discovered on the averted face of the Moon by means of photographs taken by *Lunik III*.

MARE NECTARIS (Sea of Nectar); a near-circular, dusky plain in the south-west quadrant of the Moon, adjoining the southern end of the Mare Tranquillitatis. Broken into at its southern end by the giant ruined walled-plain Fracastorius.

MARE NUBIUM (Sea of Clouds); a very large, ill-defined dusky plain, adjoined to the east by the Oceanus Procellarum and to the north by the Mare Imbrium, with which features it almost fills the eastern half of the Moon's visible hemisphere.

MARE SERENITATIS (Sea of Serenity); a large, well-defined dusky plain in the north-west quadrant of the Moon, running into the Mare Tranquillitatis and linked to the Mare Imbrium by a narrow, dusky strait. Notable for the bright ray from Menelaus which appears to bisect it and which is visible to the naked eye at Full Moon.

MARE SERPENTIS (Martian surface feature, approximate position Ω 320°, $\Phi - 20°$). A prominent dusky area in the south temperate zone of Mars, adjoining the southern end of the **Sinus Sabæus.**

This region is frequently observed to undergo a seasonal change, being faint or missing altogether during the Martian winter, developing during the spring and becoming very dense in midsummer.

MARE SIRENUM (Martian surface feature, approximate position Ω 160°, $\Phi - 30°$). A very prominent dusky band stretching diagonally across the south temperate region of the planet, almost parallel to the Mare Cimmerium and the Mare Tyrrhenum.

MARE SMYTHII (Smyth's Sea); a dusky plain on the Moon's western limb, difficult to observe owing to foreshortening.

MARE SOMNII (Sea of Sleep); name allocated by the Academy of Sciences of the U.S.S.R. to a large dusky plain on the averted face of the Moon, discovered from photographs taken by *Lunik III*.

MARE SPUMANS (Foaming Sea); a small dusky plain near the western limb of the Moon, between the Mare Smythii and the Mare Fœcunditatis. Difficult to observe owing to foreshortening.

MARE TRANQUILLITATIS (Sea of Tranquillity); a vast dusky plain dominating the north-west quadrant of the Moon with the adjoining Mare Serenitatis. There are few interesting features on its surface.

MARE TYRRHENUM (Martian surface feature, approximate position Ω 245°, $\Phi - 30°$). A prominent, dark band running diagonally across the south temperate zone of Mars, parallel to the Mare Cimmerium. At its northern end runs into the most prominent surface feature of the planet, the **Syrtis Major.**

MARE UNDARUM (Sea of Waves); a small dusky plain near the western limb of the Moon, north of the Mare Spumans. Difficult to observe owing to the considerable foreshortening.

MARE VAPORUM (Sea of Vapour); a small dusky area just north of the centre of the Moon's visible hemisphere. Adjoins the western border of the Mare Nubium.

MAREBASE The basic rocks constituting the dark areas of the Moon's surface, usually known as *lunabase*.

MARGARITIFER SINUS (Martian surface feature, approximate position Ω 20°, Φ 0°). An important 'canal' running across the Martian equator.

MARINER Name given to a series of space-probe vehicles launched from the U.S.A.; the six vehicles launched by the time of writing are listed in Table 20. The first attempted launching (*Mariner 1*—an intended Venus probe) was unsuccessful. The first Mars probe—*Mariner 3*, could

bright during favourable apparitions. At these times it can approach to within 30 million miles of the Earth, closer than any other planet except Venus. Mars probably bears a closer resemblance to the Earth than any other planet.

MARS—DIMENSIONS AND PHYSICAL DATA The apparent diameter of Mars, at mean opposition distance, is 17″87, which indicates that the actual equatorial diameter is 4,220 miles—rather more than half the diameter of the Earth. Like the Earth, Mars is an oblate spheroid, the polar diameter being only 4,200 miles; this small difference is not, of course, obvious to visual observers. The mass of Mars is 0·108 times that of the Earth, and the volume 0·150 times that of the Earth. This corresponds to a mean density of

Table 20.   Mariner space-probe vehicles

Vehicle	Date launched	Purpose	Result	(date)
Mariner 2	1962 Aug. 27	Venus probe	Passed app. 25,500 miles from Venus.	1962 Dec. 14
Mariner 3		Mars probe	Failed.	—
Mariner 4	1964 Nov. 28	Mars probe	Passed app. 6,200 miles from Mars.	1965 Jul. 15
Mariner 5	1967 Jun. 14	Venus probe	Passed app. 6,300 miles from Venus.	1967 Oct. 19
Mariners 6, 7	1969 Mar., Apr.	Mars probes	Passed app. 2,000 miles from Mars.	1969 Jul., Aug.

not be contacted after being placed in a heliocentric orbit, owing to component failures. The second Mars probe, *Mariner 4*. was however outstandingly successful, it obtained and telemetered back to Earth 19 high-quality photographs of the Martian surface, covering an arcuate belt from Phlegra ($\Phi + 40°$), across the Mare Sirenum to Aonius Sinus ($\Phi - 50°$). The photographs reveal a Moon-like surface with many ring-structures. [Plate 10(f, g).]

MARS The fourth known planet in order of increasing distance from the Sun, and the first with an orbit outside that of the Earth. To the unaided eye Mars appears as a reddish star, and can be extremely

3·96 times that of water, only 70% that of the Earth; this is believed to indicate that the planet has a rocky constitution, similar to the other terrestrial planets, but that the dense central core of iron, etc., is proportionately smaller and therefore contributes less to the mean density of the planet.

The gravitational attraction at the surface of Mars is only 0·38 that of the Earth; thus an object weighing 1 lb on Earth would weigh only 6 oz on Mars. Future space-travellers able to jump 6 ft on Earth will be able to clear nearly 16 ft on Mars. A further consequence of the low gravitational attraction is that the velocity of escape for gases is similarly low, only 3·1 miles per second (compared with 7·0 for the Earth).

The albedo is 0·16; this accords well with our knowledge of the planet, being much less than the values for Venus and the Earth, which have denser atmospheres, and more than for rocky bodies having little or no atmosphere (such as the Moon and Mercury).

MARS—NATURE AND ATMOSPHERE

The mean density of Mars is 3·95 times that of water; this is less than two-thirds that of the Earth, and very similar to that of the Moon. It is believed that the internal constitution of Mars is broadly similar to that of the Earth—a rocky spheroid with a dense, iron-bearing core, surrounded by a gaseous atmosphere. The atmosphere is more tenuous than that surrounding the Earth, and the dense central core of the planet must be proportionately smaller than that of the Earth; these factors explain the lower mean density.

The composition of the Martian atmosphere is rather different from that of the Earth, which contains about 78% nitrogen and 21% oxygen; in the case of Mars there is about 94% nitrogen and practically no oxygen. Three constituents account for almost the entire composition of the atmosphere: nitrogen (N_2), 93·8%; argon (A), 3·9%; carbon dioxide (CO_2), 2·2%.

The atmospheric pressure at the surface of Mars is about 85 millibars—compared with about 1,000 millibars at the surface of the Earth. The fall-off in pressure with height takes place at a different rate, however, and at a height of approximately 20 miles the atmospheric pressure equals that of the Earth and above this height is greater than the pressure at corresponding heights above the Earth's surface.

The upper layers of the Martian atmosphere have been photographed in ultra-violet and blue wavelengths, and the surface of the planet has been photographed in the more penetrative red and infra-red wavelengths; from comparisons of such photographs [Plate 10(a, c, e)] much has been learnt about the distribution of various types of cloud in different levels of the Martian atmosphere.

Although a possible explanation of the polar caps of Mars suggests the presence of a considerable amount of water on the planet, it has been established by exhaustive spectroscopic analysis over many years that any water vapour present in the atmosphere must be much less than 1 per cent, and probably no more than 0·1 per cent. The clouds seen must therefore be formed, in the main, by a different mechanism from terrestrial clouds. The large, high-altitude clouds seen in photographs in blue and ultra-violet light are believed to be areas of high pressure; the large, yellowish clouds seen visually and in longer wavelength photographs (e.g. in red light) are believed to be dust-storms, 2 to 3 miles above the surface. There have also been white clouds observed from time to time, especially near aphelion, which are fairly high (10–15 miles) and may be composed of ice-crystals, similar to terrestrial cirrus clouds.

MARS—OBSERVATION OF

Useful positional observations of Mars can only be made with highly refined equipment, and are therefore made only in suitably equipped professional observatories. Photographic and spectrographic analysis are also beyond the scope of most amateurs, but there is a great deal of useful work which can be carried out by amateur observers. It should be remembered that even now a very large part of our present knowledge of this planet has been obtained by amateur workers.

Telescopes of moderate aperture are necessary—a 6-in. reflector or 4-in. refractor is about the absolute minimum required to do useful work; to record extensive detail, and to carry out useful work at apparitions other than the two or three most favourable in each cycle, larger apertures, say 10- to 15-in., are necessary.

As for all planetary work, a rigid equatorial mounting is a necessity; setting circles and a clock drive are desirable but not essential. A range of good eyepieces is required, giving magnitudes from, say, ×120 to ×450; as the detection of subtle colouring is important in the study of Mars, it is desirable that any eyepiece used is achromatic.

The most useful form of observation the amateur can make is a drawing of the detail visible; this should be of the entire disk, except on rare occasions when a particular region is a subject of special interest. It is desirable to examine the disk thoroughly for some minutes, fixing the main features in one's mind, and then to sketch in faintly the outlines of these fairly rapidly, noting the time (in hours and minutes of G.M.T. or G.M.A.T.); the detailed shading and other refinements can then be added at a more leisurely pace.

Drawings should be made on a prepared blank; a scale of 2 inches to the planet's diameter is usually adopted, although at the beginning and end of an apparition, when the visible disk is small, a diameter of 1 inch may be found more suitable. At times when the **defective illumination** (phase effect) is considerable, it will be found helpful to construct the terminator on the blanks before commencing observation.

It is not desirable to study maps or drawings of the planet prior to an observing session; since much of the observable detail is at the limit of visibility this would increase the possibility of recording features that one expected to see but which are not, in fact, detectable.

It is important to fix the relative positions and intensities of the various features as accurately as possible, and to search carefully for any variations in the colour of the dark areas, any obscuring clouds, etc., etc. As much additional information as possible should be attached to the drawing in the form of brief notes. It is usual to add the observer's name, type of instrument, aperture and magnification(s) employed, and also the central meridian longitude (ω) and centre-of-disk latitude (ϕ). Reliable observations from experienced observers are welcomed by the Director of the Mars Section of the British Astronomical Association.

Prominent features should be accurately timed at central-meridian transit (the method is fully detailed in **Jupiter— observation of**), so that their longitude may be determined.

Observers fortunate enough to have the use of a filar micrometer should measure whenever possible the position angle and diameter of the polar cap(s), and the positions of the major features visible.

MARS—OBSERVED FEATURES AND NOTABLE PHENOMENA The most obvious features observed are the large dusky grey areas, the light (orange or ochre) areas and, on occasion, the polar caps. Less obvious features seen are the canali and atmospheric clouds of various kinds. Most of these features are subject to variations in shape and intensity from time to time, some on a seasonal and others on a random basis. It is therefore important that the surface detail should be carefully studied throughout each apparition, and any changes carefully recorded, as they are most important evidence in speculations as to the nature of the surface of the planet.

Map of the surface features. The principal features observed are shown in Plate 11. This does not represent the features seen at a particular apparition, but is a composite map of all the major features seen at one apparition or another. Although the relative intensities of the various features have been preserved as far as possible, at a given apparition many of the features would appear lighter or darker than shown here, and some of the fainter markings might be absent altogether.

The positions of surface features are normally defined by the use of **planetographic co-ordinates**; in the case of Mars these are termed **areographic co-**

ordinates. Areographic longitude is usually indicated by Ω, areographic latitude by Φ. The meridian passing through the feature formerly named 'Dawes' Forked Bay' has been universally adopted as the zero of areographic longitude, and this prominent feature is accordingly known to contemporary observers as the **Sinus Meridiani**.

Nomenclature. The first map of Mars was published by Beer and Mädler in 1840; this was followed by those of Proctor (based upon the invaluable observations of W. R. Dawes) in 1869, Kaiser in 1872 and N. E. Green, one of the foremost British observers, in 1877. Most of the names allocated to the principal features were the work of Green. At the favourable apparitions of 1877, 1879 and 1881, however, Schiaparelli—working with a new 8¾-in. refractor in Milan—detected hundreds of new surface features; he carefully measured their positions on the surface of the planet, and consequently produced maps that far exceeded all previous ones in both complexity and accuracy. He also allocated a new series of names to the principal features, using the names of lands and seas in the Middle East and names of biblical and mythological significance. These names, augmented by later workers (principally Lowell, Fournier and Antoniadi) have become universally adopted (despite their Latin form—rather clumsy for use in observatory conditions!). and were adopted, with some rationalization, by the International Astronomical Union in 1958. Although they are patently features of a dry surface, the dark areas have continued to be called 'seas', as have those of the Moon. The various sizes and shapes of dark areas are called Mare (sea), Sinus (bay), Lacus (lake) and Fretum (strait). Most of the large ochre areas were given names suggesting that they were continents.

The Polar caps. The polar regions of Mars were first reported white in 1666, by Gian–Domenico Cassini, who suggested that they were snow caps as on the Earth. They are, however, much more extensive than those of the Earth—a fact which early observers sought to explain as being due to the fact that Mars is so much farther from the Sun and consequently much colder. In 1719 Giovanni Maraldi drew attention to the fact that the polar caps were not diametrically opposite, suggesting that as in the case of the Earth the areas of greatest cold are not situated exactly at the poles.

In 1784 Sir William Herschel pointed out that the polar caps were largest during the Martian winter and grew steadily smaller during the spring and summer, reaching a minimal area in late summer and rapidly growing again during the following winter. He proposed the first properly reasoned theory that the caps consisted of ice and snow. This proposition was frequently opposed, especially during the early years of the present century. It was suggested by Ranyard and Storey that the caps consisted of solid carbon dioxide. In the late 1940s and early 1950s Kuiper, working with the infra-red spectrometer attached to the 82-in. reflector at the McDonald Observatory, proved that this could not be the case and obtained evidence that the polar caps consisted of water, in the form of a very thin layer of hoar-frost.

Among the early workers whose theories were thus vindicated was Percival Lowell, who had based his conclusion upon his observations of the **'blue band'**—a dark, bluish fringe surrounding the cap as it shrinks during the Martian summer. Lowell pointed out that a cap of solid carbon dioxide would sublimate at the atmospheric pressure obtaining on Mars, and that the blue band must therefore be an area wetted by water from the melting cap. This moisture would gradually disperse, by evaporation and soaking into the surface dust, which would dry in a few days and return to its normal colour.

It has been suggested that the band is merely an optical illusion, due to the effects of contrast between the bright cap and its less bright surroundings. The band is observed only during the melting periods, however, and at such times is easily observed even with quite small telescopes; there is thus no question that it must be regarded as a real phenomenon.

That the caps must be extremely thin is indicated by the rapidity with which they melt; the southern cap can cover 4 million square miles, and yet has been known to disappear completely during the course of a Martian summer.

The southern cap always becomes very irregular in outline as it shrinks, and develops two dark rifts; these always appear in the same places, and probably represent areas where the ice-layer crosses high ground and melts and disperses more quickly. Both caps have a tendency to break up into a number of small parts towards the end of their shrinkage.

The light areas. These large areas— normally orange or ochre in colour, although some appear more creamy, almost white, on occasion—are believed to be the deserts of Mars; they are probably vast barren plains, of a sandy, eroded nature, quite different (owing to the almost complete lack of water outside the polar regions) from the soil encountered on Earth. Mountains are probably non-existent, and any minor undulations are unlikely to reach more than 2–3,000 ft. above the surrounding surface. The surface material is probably broken down to the form of dust particles in many of these plains, which are easily lifted by air-currents and formed into the yellowish veil which is frequently seen to obscure large areas of the planet's surface.

The dark areas. The dark areas usually appear to be various shades of grey, and occasionally brownish; this rather colour-less effect is partly due to contrast with the surrounding bright regions, and to the comparative faintness of the markings: other colours are often detected, especially with larger telescopes.

Although named 'seas', the dark areas are, in fact, dry land; they may however

be the dried-up beds of seas of long ago— a hypothesis supported by the evidence (of seasonal changes in colour) that they are still the better irrigated part of the non-polar regions of the planet.

The observed seasonal colour changes, described below, strongly suggest that the dark areas are covered by some form of vegetation largely absent from the orange deserts; vegetation as we know it on Earth would not be likely to survive the lack of surface water, the low atmospheric pressure and the extremes of temperature encountered on Mars. Most terrestrial forms of vegetation live by the breakdown of carbon dioxide by photosynthesis; a by-product of this process is oxygen, and it is inconceivable that if such large areas on Mars were producing oxygen in this way we should not be able to detect its presence in the atmosphere.

Analysis of the light reflected from these areas of Mars shows it to be similar to sunlight reflected from certain mosses and lichens, and it is notable that these do not produce free oxygen like the majority of terrestrial vegetation, and are also resistant to extremes of temperature and humidity. It is therefore widely believed that the dark areas of Mars are covered by some form of lichen or moss. Another class of plant with similar characteristics is the algae, which exist in damp conditions. Antoniadi pointed out that the low density of Mars suggests that the surface rocks may be highly porous and these may, therefore, have a fairly high water content; if this is the case, it is also possible that algae figure largely in the dark areas.

Canali. Narrow dusky streaks were observed by both Secchi and Schiaparelli, both of whom continued the convention of naming dark features as if they were stretches of water and consequently designated these streaks **'canali'**—which is Italian for 'channels'. It is most regrettable that this term was misconstrued by many people, and taken to mean 'canals', with its implication of an artificial origin.

Schiaparelli, in fact, discoverer of more of these features than any other observer, preserved a very open mind as to their nature and origin. The fact that a great controversy raged for many years about this very matter is due, not to Schiaparelli who has so often been blamed for it, but to two simple facts. Firstly, Percival Lowell—a most careful observer and enlightened astronomer and a man who devoted a lifetime to the study of the planets—placed on record his belief that the canali were in fact artificial water-ways, built by intelligent Martian beings for purposes of irrigation. Secondly, no two observers interpret alike what they see, neither do they draw it alike. Both Schiaparelli and Lowell saw the faint markings in Mars in geometrical patterns, and represented the canali as thin straight lines; other observers, notably Antoniadi and, later, Phillips, drew them as more diffuse and often composed of a number of component spots.

Schiaparelli's discoveries were received with some scepticism, especially as he later recorded more canals as straight lines, and even as parallel 'tramlines'; many of the more obvious canals began to be confirmed by very experienced and competent observers such as A. Stanley Williams, however, and it is now known that all the principal canals recorded by Schiaparelli and his contemporaries really exist, however inaccurate we may feel them to have been.

The canali should obviously be regarded as a specific type of dusky feature, and in fact many of them are extensions of larger features or borders of bright regions. It is probable that they would resolve into a broken-up, complex structure if observed with a powerful enough telescope, and it is notable that it is the drawings of observers such as Antoniadi which compare best with the high-definition photographs obtainable today. The significance of their linear appearance must not, however, be ignored; even if they can be resolved into a fine structure of separate markings these are nevertheless distri-buted along a straight and comparatively narrow track; as they share in the seasonal colour changes of other dusky features it is possible that they represent vegetation growing along naturally irrigated paths. [Plate 10(d).]

Seasonal changes. Apart from the forma-tion and melting of the polar caps, the most important seasonal effects observed are changes in the colour of the dusky shadings—the maria, canali, etc.

In the late nineteenth century Liais, Trouvelot, Lowell and Douglass recorded a cycle of colour change, from green, through brown, to yellow, during the Martian spring and early summer. During the 1924 apparition Antoniadi, using the 33-in. refractor at Meudon, observed many of the dark areas to be green: he noted however that as the south polar cap shrank a darkening of the adjacent canali and the dark areas occurred, and gradually spread northwards. As this darkening proceeded most of the green areas became brown, and even brownish-lilac or reddish. This darkening often reaches the equator and beyond, so that certain tropical features have a double cycle, being darkened following the shrinkage of both the north and south polar caps alterna-tely. The most obvious explanation of this phenomenon is that the water from the melting polar caps is spreading along the features affected; the dark coloration may be the actual body of water, but is more likely to be a change in the appear-ance of the feature due to the arrival of the water by surface channel or sub-surface percolation. The rate of progress of the darkening is rather remarkable—often between 25 and 50 miles per day.

Many of the dusky features also change in both shape and intensity on a seasonal basis, although the exact details of their structure and of the changes may vary from one Martian year to the next—as such changes are doubtless climatically induced this is not surprising.

Whilst, obviously, they cannot prove or disprove anything unaided, the seasonal changes which ave been observed can be interpreted in ways which tend to support the theory that the dark areas contain a primitive form of vegetation.

Among the more notable seasonal changes observed are those affecting the well-known area containing the Syrtis Major, Mare Serpentis, Pandoræ Fretum and Hellespontus. The Syrtis Major itself generally appears to be quite wide during most of the Martian year, but during summer in the southern hemisphere it appears to narrow, due to the apparent brightening of a lighter area in the eastern part of this feature.

Both the Mare Serpentis and Pandoræ Fretum are faint or invisible during the southern hemisphere winter, but darken during the spring and are usually quite prominent, and often very intense, during Martian summer. The broad streak or canal Hellespontus undergoes one of the most striking seasonal variations, closely associated with the melting of the south polar cap. During the winter Hellespontus is usually visible only as a faint, broad streak; as the polar cap begins to melt during the spring, however, and the blue band forms, an intense dark patch appears at the southern end of the feature, where it adjoins the polar cap. As the cap shrinks during the spring, the dark patch spreads northwards along Hellespontus, becoming a streak which reaches the Mare Serpentis by mid-spring; this feature may also have been darkening, as described above. Hellespontus still continues to narrow until the beginning of summer, however, by which time it appears as a sharply defined dark streak, and frequently appears to be an extension of a dark rift in the polar cap.

Non-seasonal changes. These are too numerous to describe in detail, save for a few of the most notable, but are fully detailed in the literature.

An area of Mars which seems to be constantly undergoing severe changes of form, at quite irregular intervals, is the Solis Lacus region; at times it appears as a simple, oval area with a dark, central 'spot', and at others it is polygonal in outline, with a complex structure of spots and streaks in its border, in the central spot and in streaks connecting the two.

Another feature extremely subject to similar random changes in structure is Trivium Charontis; many of the canali, too, are liable to changes in breadth and intensity. Even so permanent a feature as the Sinus Meridiani, or 'Forked Bay', can undergo remarkable changes.

Atmospheric phenomena. Observed phenomena in the Martian atmosphere are largely cloud formations of various kinds; we are fortunately able to study the atmosphere at all levels, owing to the light-absorbing properties of the violet layer. This is a layer of finely divided matter—dust particles, ice crystals or water droplets, which absorbs light of shorter wavelength (i.e. blue, violet, etc.); hence photographs taken in light of such wavelength photograph the upper atmosphere only, down to this absorbing layer, whereas photographs taken in light of longer wavelength (red or infra-red) penetrate this layer and photograph the surface of the planet. Thus it is possible to observe clouds in those parts of the atmosphere both above and below the violet layer. A further idea of their level can be obtained from a study of their position and movements when seen at or near the limb of the planet.

A considerable amount of effort has gone into the study of the Martian clouds, which have for many years been known to fall into a few fairly well-defined categories.

From time to time vast, yellow obscurations are seen, which cover enormous areas of the planet's surface and on occasion blot out even such prominent markings as the Syrtis Major and Trivium Charontis; particularly large and persistent examples of this type of cloud occurred during the apparitions of 1909 and 1911. (The 1911 cloud persisted for several months.) These clouds are at a very low altitude, and are believed to be vast dust- or sand-storms, rather than clouds in the conventional sense.

More clearly delineated, but smaller and less long-lived, are the white and 'blue' clouds which are frequently seen. The white clouds can be intensely white, and even rival the polar caps on occasion; they are often dense enough to render quite prominent surface features invisible.

Somewhat higher than these are the 'blue' clouds, so called as they are usually bluish-white in colour, and which are usually seen near the limb or terminator. If seen at the sunrise limb they usually break up and disappear in an hour or two; conversely, they are seen to form over areas approaching the sunset limb, and persist until they disappear due to nightfall or the planet's rotation. These are usually less bright than the white clouds and the polar caps; they are believed to be ice-fog or mists—condensations due to the lower night-time temperatures which evaporate soon after sunrise.

Ring formations. On 1965 July 14–15 the American Mars-probe vehicle *Mariner 4* passed the planet at a distance of approximately 6,200 miles. It obtained a series of 19 telemetred photographs covering a belt from Phlegra ($\Phi + 40°$), across the Mare Sirenum to Aonus Sinus ($\Phi - 50°$), and showing far more detail than can be obtained from Earth even with the aid of the largest telescopes. The photographs reveal a surface remarkably similar to that of the Moon, with many ring structures. Studies of the morphology of these ring structures, and of their diameter–frequency distributions, indicate that they are, like those of the Moon, probably of quasi-volcanic origin. [Plate 10(f, g).] Further ring-structures were photographed by *Mariners 6* and *7* in 1969 July.

MARS—ORBITAL DATA The orbit of Mars has a semi-major axis of 1·5236915

A.U., corresponding to a mean distance from the Sun of 141·6 million miles; the actual distance varies considerably, due to the high eccentricity (0·0934), which is greater than that for any planet except Mercury and Pluto. The distance at perihelion is about 129 million miles, and at aphelion about 154 million miles.

The orbit is inclined to the ecliptic by 1° 50′ 59″·6. The mean orbital velocity is 15·0 miles per second, and the sidereal period 686·980 days—about 1 year and 10¾ months.

MARS—SATELLITES OF There are only two known satellites of Mars, *Phobos* (I) and *Deimos* (II). Both were discovered during August 1877 by Asaph Hall, using the new 26-in. refractor of the U.S. Naval Observatory in Washington. Hall had been engaged in a systematic search for possible Martian satellites since the beginning of the month, much beset by fog and generally poor observing conditions; he discovered Deimos on August 11 and Phobos a week later. The satellites are named after the attendants of the God of War (Mars) in Greek mythology—'Fear' (Phobos) and 'Flight' (Deimos). [Plate 10(b).]

Both satellites are very close to the parent planet, the mean distance of Phobos (from the centre of Mars) being 5,800 miles, and that of Deimos 14,600 miles—about 1½ and 3½ diameters of the planet, respectively. The revolution period of Phobos is 7 hr 38 min, and that of Deimos 30 hr 18 min; the effects of the closeness of the satellites to the primary and their short revolution periods compared with the rotation period of Mars (24 hr 37 min 22 sec), would be rather startling to an observer on Mars: he would see one moon (Phobos) rise in the west, rush across the sky and set in the east only 4½ hours later, passing through more than half its cycle of phases in the meantime; meanwhile, Deimos would be seen to rise in the east and remain above the horizon for 2¾ days, and would go through two complete cycles of phases in that time.

Both satellites are extremely small, and their exact sizes are consequently difficult to measure; Phobos is believed to be about 8 miles in diameter and Deimos about 5 miles. The apparent stellar magnitude of both is therefore very small, about 10 or 12. They are only observable when near greatest elongation from the planet, and with powerful instruments.

The Martian satellites are famed for the fact that their existence was apparently predicted by Jonathan Swift in *Gulliver's Travels*, published 151 years before their discovery by Hall; it is inconceivable that they could have been discovered at this time and Swift's reference to them must be taken as inspired guesswork.

MARS—SURFACE FEATURES OF The nomenclature used for many years to designate the observed surface features was introduced by Schiaparelli and modified by later observers. The names and co-ordinates of the more permanent features, together with a specially prepared map, were adopted as standard by the International Astronomical Union in 1955. Apart from one or two anomalous cases, the I.A.U. designations and co-ordinates have been used, wherever applicable, throughout this book.

The co-ordinates used are the areographic longitude (Ω) and the areographic latitude (Φ).

The permanent and many of the semi-permanent or occasionally seen features of the Martian surface are shown on the map in Plate 11. It must be emphasized, however, that one would not expect to see all the features depicted during any one apparition, and that the appearances of most of them vary from one apparition to another.

The features listed below are described by name in individual entries in this book; the numbers refer to Plate 11. (See also **Areographic co-ordinates; Mars—observed features and notable phenomena.**)

1. Achillis Pons
2. Æolis
3. Æria
4. Ætheria
5. Æthiopis
6. Agathodæmon
7. Amazonis
8. Ambrosia
9. Amenthes
10. Aonius Sinus
11. Arabia
12. Araxes
13. Arcadia
14. Argyre I
15. Argyre II
16. Arnon
17. Atlantis
18. Auroræ Sinus
19. Ausonia

20. Bætis
21. Baltia
22. Bathys
23. [Blue band]
24. Boreosyrtis
25. Bosporus Gemmatus

26. Candor
27. Casius
28. Cebrenia
29. Cecropia
30. Ceraunius
31. Cerberus
32. Chalce
33. Chaos Hyblæus
34. Chersonesus
35. Chryse
36. Chrysokeras
37. Claritas
38. Copaïs Palus
39. Coprates
40. Cyclopia
41. Cydonia

42. Deltoton Sinus
43. Depressiones Hellesponticæ
44. Deucalionis Regio
45. Deuteronilus
46. Diacria
47. Dioscuria

48. Eden
49. Edom
50. Edom Promontorium
51. Electris
52. Elysium

53. Eos
54. Eridania
55. Eunostos
56. Euphrates
57. Euripus I
58. Euripus II

59. { Forked Bay
     { Furca

60. Ganges
61. Gehon

62. Hades
63. Hadriacum Mare
64. Hellas
65. Hellespontus
66. Hesperia
67. Hiddekel
68. Hyperboreus Lacus
69. Hyscus

70. Iapygia
71. Icaria
72. Isidis Regio
73. Ismenius Lacus

74. Jamuna
75. Juventæ Fons

76. Læstrygon
77. Læstrygonum Sinus
78. Lemuria
79. Libya
80. Lunæ Lacus

81. Mare Acidalium
82. Mare Boreum
83. Mare Chronium
84. Mare Cimmerium
85. Mare Erythræum
86. Mare Serpentis
87. Mare Sirenum
88. Mare Tyrrhenum
89. Margaritifer Sinus
90. Memnonia
91. Meroe Insula
92. Moab
93. Mœris Lacus

94. Nectar
95. Nectaris Fretum
96. Neith Regio
97. Nepenthes-Thoth
98. Nereidum Fretum
99. Niliacus Lacus

100. Nilokeras
101. Nilosyrtis
102. Nix Olympica
103. Noachis
104. Nox

105. Ogygis Regio
106. Olympia
107. Ophir
108. Orchus
109. Ortygia
110. Oxia Palus
111. Oxus

112. Pambotis Lacus
113. Panchaia
114. Pandoræ Fretum
115. Phæthontis
116. Phison
117. Phlegra
118. Phœnicis Lacus
119. Phrixi Regio
120. Portus Sigeus
121. Promethei Sinus
122. Propontis
123. Protei Regio
124. Protonilus
125. Pyrrhæ Regio

126. Scandia
127. Sinai
59. Sinus Meridiani
128. Sinus Sabbæus
129. Sirenum Sinus
130. Sithonius Lacus
131. Solis Lacus
132. Styx
133. Syria
134. Syrtis Major
135. Syrtis Minor

136. Tanaïs
137. Tempe
138. Tharsis
139. Thaumasia
140. Thoth
141. Thyle I
142. Thyle II
143. Thymiamata
144. Tithonius
145. Tithonius Lacus
146. Tractus Albus
147. Trinacria
148. Tritonis Lacus
149. Tritonis Sinus
150. Trivium Charontis

MARS—TELESCOPIC APPEARANCE

The immediate impression gained when viewing Mars by telescope is of a well-defined, orange-coloured disk. If a particularly dark area, such as the **Syrtis Major**, is in the visible hemisphere at the time, it may be noticed immediately as a grey smudge. If the observation is made at a time when the **phase** effect is substantial, the deformed outline of the disk will also be obvious (the minimum fraction of the disk visible is 84 per cent).

The principal features visible will be seen after a minute or so as the eye accommodates—these will be the denser of the dark areas and possibly one or two of the most prominent **canali**; any particularly light areas will also begin to stand out from the ochre areas at this stage.

The remaining features, i.e. fine structure in the grey areas, fainter canali, faint traces of colour in the grey areas, etc., will only be seen by careful scrutiny, the finer details being seen only during brief moments of better seeing. Experienced observers will be able to detect and record more fine detail than the novice, and will be able to use numerous observing techniques to increase the amount of detail recorded (e.g. **averted vision**).

The image is subject to severe *boiling* (due to disturbance in the Earth's atmosphere) almost constantly.

The polar gap tilted toward the Earth at the time will normally be quite prominent, except during the Martian midsummer period when it is quite small.

The majority of the dusky areas form a rough south temperate belt, and the principal orange or ochre areas a sort of north tropical zone.

The axial rotation is not obvious, being very similar to that of the Earth (24 h. 37 m. 23s.); thus the same features will be seen centrally about forty minutes later each successive night. The inclination of the axis of rotation is also similar to that of the Earth, being 23° 59′.

On occasion large areas of the planet's surface are obscured by vast yellow clouds, believed to consist of sand, or dust. These low altitude observations often persist for several weeks. Other atmospheric phenomena can sometimes be detected, notably the higher altitude white and bluish-white clouds, these are usually smaller and of shorter duration.

(See also **Mars—observation of; Phase of superior planet.**)

MARS—VISIBILITY FROM EARTH

The distance of Mars from the Earth at opposition is a very variable quantity, depending upon how close Mars is to perihelion at the time of opposition. At aphelic oppositions Mars can be as much as 63 million miles from the Earth, but may be as close as $34\frac{1}{2}$ million miles at the most favourable perihelic oppositions; these are experienced when the date of opposition occurs on or close to August 23. Thus the closest approach of the nineteenth and twentieth centuries occurred on 1924 August 22.

The positions of the oppositions from 1939 to 1986, relative to the aphelion and perihelion points of Mars' orbit, are shown in Fig. 79, from which it will be seen that the next close approach will occur during the opposition of 1971.

Unfortunately for observers in the Northern Hemisphere, Mars has a high southern declination at autumnal oppositions, and is thus better placed for observation from the Southern Hemisphere during very favourable oppositions.

The mean synodic period of Mars (the average interval between oppositions) is the longest in the solar system: 779·94 days. This is rather less than 26 months, and hence oppositions occur, on average,

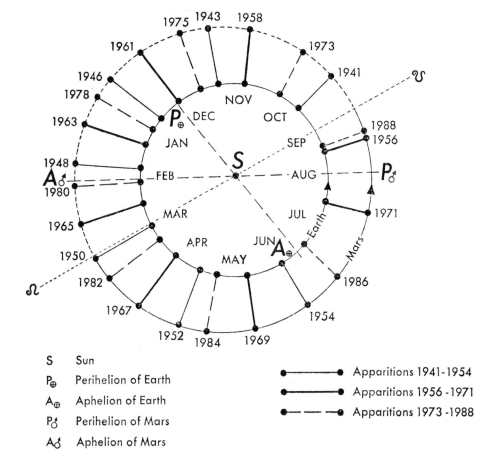

S — Sun
P⊕ — Perihelion of Earth
A⊕ — Aphelion of Earth
P♂ — Perihelion of Mars
A♂ — Aphelion of Mars
☊ — Ascending node of orbit of Mars
☋ — Descending node of orbit of Mars

●————● Apparitions 1941-1954
●————● Apparitions 1956-1971
●— — —● Apparitions 1973-1988

Fig. 79

some two months earlier every alternate year.

Being the closest of the planets having orbits outside that of the Earth, Mars has the largest 'loop' of **retrograde motion**; in fact, it retrogresses through an arc of about 18°, and takes some two months to do so.

The effect of **phase** is also more obvious in the case of Mars than for the more distant superior planets; Mars presents a full phase at both opposition and con-junction, but is distinctly gibbous at the quadratures. The fraction of the illumin-ated disk of Mars visible from Earth is, however, never less than 84 per cent.

MASKELYNE, Rev. Nevil (1732–1811)
The fifth Astronomer Royal, from 1765–1810. Voyaged to St. Helena in 1761 to observe the transit of Venus. Appointed Astronomer Royal on the death of Bliss. Instituted a programme at Greenwich of accurate positional observations of the

Sun, Moon, planets and 36 fundamental reference stars, and introduced new methods of reduction and tabulation of the observed results. Made many improvements to the Greenwich instruments, and specified the Troughton 6-ft. mural circle which was completed and brought into use in 1816, five years after Maskelyne's death, and used for the determination of declinations until the **Airy Transit Circle** commenced work in 1852. In 1774 Maskelyne made an expedition to Scotland for the purpose of determining the mean density of the Earth.

Shortly after becoming Astronomer Royal Maskelyne arranged with the Royal Society for the establishment of a fund to provide for the annual publication of the Greenwich Observations—a series which has continued up to the present day.

Maskelyne's greatest achievement was the foundation in 1767 of the *Nautical Almanac*, of which he was the Superintendent for 44 years.

MASS A mechanical concept, indicative of the amount of matter of which a body is comprised. Mass is not the same as the more familiar concept of weight, since weight varies according to the environment whilst the mass would be the same in any environment. It was demonstrated by Einstein that the energy in a body is proportional to its mass, which he expressed in his classic formula $E = mc^2$.

MASS–LUMINOSITY RELATIONSHIP
It was demonstrated by Sir Arthur Eddington in 1924 that a simple relationship exists between the mass of a star and its total luminosity. The stars used in determining the relationship were component stars of binary systems whose masses have been determined by dynamical analysis of their relative motions, and whose absolute luminosity could be calculated since their parallax was also known. Eddington found from a careful study of these stars that the absolute luminosity is proportional to the logarithm of the mass; the proportion may be

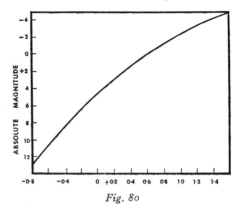

Fig. 80

expressed in the form $L \propto M^x$, where x varies from $4\frac{1}{2}$ for stars whose mass does not exceed half that of the Sun to $3\frac{1}{2}$ for stars with masses greater than $1\frac{1}{2}$ times that of the Sun.

The relationship is shown graphically in Fig. 80 and seems to apply to all main-sequence stars, whose observed masses seldom differ from the figures predicted by the mass–luminosity curve by more than 20 per cent.

White-dwarf stars figure prominently among exceptions to this rule, but these stars seem to be exceptions to most general rules.

MASS RATIO The ratio of the masses of the components of a **binary system**, *q.v.*

MAUNDER, E. Walter (1851–1928) A member of the staff of the Royal Observatory at Greenwich for many years, Maunder is perhaps best remembered for his demonstration of the change in sunspot latitudes during a solar cycle by means of the so-called **'Butterfly diagram'** (Fig. 144, p. 456); he was, however, a pioneer in solar physics, and played a considerable part in the establishment of the Solar Department of the Royal Observatory—which remains to this day one of the leading centres of solar research.

In addition to his professional activities, Maunder worked without respite to create a situation in which amateur astronomers could play a useful part alongside the professionals; he was the principal founder of the British Astronomical Association, its President from 1894–1896 and first Editor of its Journal, from 1890–1894 and again 1896–1900. Maunder also served the B.A.A. at various times as Secretary, Director of the Mars Section and (for 15 years) Director of the Solar Section. His wife was also a stalwart of the B.A.A., and was its Editor from 1916–1929.

MAUROLYCUS (Lunar surface feature, co-ordinates $\xi + 180$, $\eta - 663$); a rugged and rather broken walled plain, 75 miles in diameter, in the very mountainous south polar region. The mountain walls rise in places to over 14,000 ft. There is a central peak, which is connected to the south-east wall by a ridge.

McDONALD OBSERVATORY Situated at over 7,000 ft. on Mount Locke, near Fort Davis in Texas, and operated jointly by the Universities of Chicago and Texas. The main instrument is the 82-in. reflector completed in March 1939. [Plate 30(b).]

McMATH–HULBERT OBSERVATORY One of the world's leading solar physics observatories, built and equipped by two highly skilled amateur observers, Robert R. McMath and H. S. Hulbert. The observatory, situated on Lake Angelus, Michigan, U.S.A., is now a branch of the University of Michigan Observatory. Much pioneering work in the observation of the Sun has been carried out there— notably the development of **spectrohelio-cinematography.**

MEAN ANOMALY See **Anomaly, mean.**

MEAN MOTION A hypothetical concept in celestial mechanics being the velocity a planet (or similar orbiting body) would have were it moving in a circular orbit of radius equal to its mean distance from the Sun in a period equal to its actual revolution period.

MEAN PLACE The position of a star on the celestial sphere, as seen from the Sun, referred to the mean equator and equinox at the commencement of a year; it is thus the apparent place corrected for annual parallax, proper motion, precession, aberration and nutation. All observations of the apparent place of a star made during a particular year may be reduced to the mean place for the beginning of that year, so that they may be intercompared; in practice, however, all observations made over a period of several years are reduced to a common epoch, e.g. 1950·0. (See also **Apparent place; True place.**)

MEAN TIME Time based upon the motion of a hypothetical Mean Sun, which moves around the celestial equator at a uniform rate, whereas the true Sun moves along the Ecliptic at a variable rate.

MEASURING MACHINE An important piece of observatory equipment, used for determining the relative positions of images recorded on photographic plates. The simplest form consists of a low-power microscope containing cross wires, below which the plate is mounted in a carriage which can be traversed by means of a micrometer screw. A less accurate screw is provided to give the plate carriage motion in the perpendicular direction to that of the micrometer screw.

The desired object is positioned centrally on the cross wires and the position of the plate carriage relative to the microscope can be read off by means of the micrometer screw head and vernier provided. Provision is usually made for the plate carriage to be rotated through 90° for measurements in the other co-ordinate to be made. There is usually a source of light beneath the plate.

MEGAPARSEC A unit of distance equal to one million parsecs, approximately 3,260,000 light years.

MELOTTE, Philibert Jacques (1880–1961) Member of the staff of the Royal

Observatory at Greenwich (and in war-time exile at Abinger) for 53 years from 1895–1948. For half of this time he was in charge of the Astrographic Department.

Best known for his discovery in 1908 of the eighth satellite of Jupiter, his outstanding ability as a photographic astronomer may be judged from the prints of the Greenwich zone of the *Carte-du-Ciel* programme and of the Franklin–Adams Charts, both still in use in observatories and to be found in the major astronomical libraries. Melotte also took charge of the measurement and reduction of the 2,847 plates used by Spencer Jones in the redetermination of the solar parallax.

He was elected a Fellow of the Royal Astronomical Society in 1909, and in the same year was awarded the Jackson–Gwilt Medal & Gift of the Society in recognition of his discovery of Jupiter's eighth satellite. Secretary of the British Astronomical Association from 1913–1921 and 1926–1930, and its President from 1944–1946.

MEMNONIA (Martian surface feature, approximate position Ω 145°, Φ − 20°. A large, ochre area in the equatorial zone of Mars.

MENDELEEV Prominent dark object on the far side of the Moon, discovered on photographs taken by *Lunik III*. (See **Moon—far side of.**)

MENELAUS (Lunar surface feature, co-ordinates $\xi + 264$, $\eta + 280$); a very bright crater, 20 miles in diameter, with well-defined, terraced walls rising 8,000 ft. above the floor. There is a mountain peak just off-centre, from which a ridge runs to the south-east wall. The crater lies on the southern boundary of the Mare Serenitatis, and is the origin of a brilliant ray which runs right across the Mare, engulfing the crater **Bessel**.

MENISCUS LENS A lens having two spherically curved faces, one convex and the other concave.

MENISCUS–SCHMIDT CAMERA A variation of the original form of Schmidt Camera, in which the aspherical correcting plate is replaced by a Meniscus lens. This principle was first developed, independently, by D. D. Maksutov in Moscow and A. Bouwers of Delft, Holland, in the early 1940's. A number of refinements have been added by later workers.

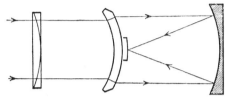

Fig. 81

This type of instrument has found a number of uses at small focal ratios, notably for meteor photography.

If a weak, aspherical doublet is used as an additional correcting plate (see Fig. 81), it is possible to reduce very substantially the spherical and chromatic aberrations.

MENSA (The Table; Originally Mons Mensæ, Table Mountain. *Genitive* Mensae, *I.A.U. abbreviation* Men.) A southern circumpolar constellation, containing no bright stars.

MERCURY Name given to a series of manned artificial Earth satellites launched from the United States as part of a programme for developing spacecraft techniques. Six vehicles were successfully launched (Table 21, p. 246).

MERCURY The innermost known planet of the solar system. Owing to its proximity to the Sun it can only be seen at or near its elongations, and is not easy to observe at all with the unaided eye. When seen it is usually pinkish and twinkling, due to its low altitude.

There is no record of the discovery of Mercury, which has been known from the earliest times despite the difficulty of

Table 21. Mercury manned satellite vehicles

Vehicle	Launched	Duration of flight
Mercury 3 ('Freedom 7')	1961 May 5	1 hr 49 min
Mercury 4 ('Liberty Bell 7')	1961 July 21	3 hr 18 min
Mercury 6 ('Friendship 7')	1962 February 20	4 hr 56 min
Mercury 7 ('Aurora 7')	1962 May 24	4 hr 56 min
Mercury 8 ('Sigma 7')	1962 October 3	9 hr 13 min
Mercury 9 ('Faith 7')	1963 May 15–16	34 hr 30 min

observation, but its appearances as an 'Evening Star' and a 'Morning Star' were not connected by the ancients, who imagined them to be separate objects. Thus the Greeks called it *Hermes* when an evening star but *Apollo* when a morning star. Hermes was the messenger of the gods, the son of Zeus; in Roman mythology he was known as Mercury, after whom the planet is now named.

MERCURY—DIMENSIONS AND PHYSICAL DATA The apparent diameter of Mercury at mean inferior conjunction is $10''.88$, corresponding to a true equatorial diameter of 3,010 miles. There is no detectable polar flattening.

The mass of Mercury is not easy to determine, owing to the proximity to the much more massive Sun and its lack of a satellite, but the latest calculations indicate a mass of 0·054 that of the Earth (about $\frac{1}{18}$). This corresponds to a mean density of 5·41 times the density of water—only a little less than that of the Earth. The volume is 0·06 that of the Earth.

The gravitational attraction at the surface of Mercury is 0·37 that at the Earth's surface; thus a body weighing a pound on Earth would weigh only about $5\frac{3}{4}$ oz on Mercury. Similarly, a high-jumper able to clear 6 ft on Earth would be able to jump over 17 ft on Mercury.

The velocity of escape for gases is very low, only 2·6 miles per second, so that none of the lighter gases could be retained by the planet.

The albedo is 0·06, slightly less than that of the Moon; this supports the inference from the planet's mean density that it has a rocky constitution, fundamentally similar to that of the Earth.

MERCURY—NATURE AND ATMOSPHERE The density of Mercury (5·07 times that of water) suggests that it must be a spheroid of rocky constitution, very similar to that of the Earth (q.v.). Its surface is probably very rugged, which will account for the low albedo. [The mean albedo (0·06) is very close to that of the Moon (0·07), and shows the same variation with phase. This suggests that the nature of the surfaces of the two bodies must be very similar. It was also found by Lyot that polarization measurements of the two bodies gave very similar results.]

As the greater part of one hemisphere is permanently subjected to the Sun's heat (at only one-third of the Earth's distance from the Sun), it must have a surface temperature of more than 400°C. The 'dark' hemisphere, conversely, must be extremely cold, probably only a few degrees above the **absolute zero**, since there appears to be no significant atmosphere to conduct the heat from the sunlit side. Due to the effects of **libration**, there is an intermediate zone at the junction of the light and dark hemispheres which will alternately be exposed to the Sun's heat and cut off from it; such extremes of temperature must result in colossal stresses and fracturing of the surface rocks, which may even be reduced to dust in consequence.

The low **velocity of escape** means that Mercury is not capable of retaining any of the lighter gases for long. Observations of Mercury in transit across the Sun's disk confirm that there can be little atmosphere, although it has been thought for some time that there may be a very thin atmosphere composed of heavy gases; possible evidence of such an atmosphere was obtained by Dollfus at the Pic-du-Midi Observatory a few years ago. No evidence of oxygen or water vapour has been found. In April 1963 Nikolai Kozyrev took advantage of the favourable elongation of the planet and obtained a series of spectrograms with the 50-in. reflector of the Crimean Astrophysical Observatory; from an examination of these spectrograms Kozyrev has discovered an atmosphere of hydrogen—the lightest known gas. The density of this atmosphere, however, is only about one-thousandth of the density of the Earth's atmosphere. Kozyrev points out that loss of hydrogen molecules due to the low velocity of escape would result in this atmosphere being entirely dissipated 'within several hundred thousand years', but explains its continued existence by the suggestion that the planet's nearness to the Sun results in its atmosphere being constantly replenished by the fluxes of hydrogen nuclei (protons) shot towards it by the Sun.

MERCURY—OBSERVATION OF Positional observations of Mercury are of considerable value, as its orbit is highly eccentric; due to this fact and to the proximity of the planet to the Sun they are, however, difficult to obtain. This aspect of observing the planet is therefore best left to the professional observatories, who can make determinations of its position by transit-circle observations in daylight.

Observations of the surface features are extremely difficult, owing to their faint, diffuse nature and the unfavourable circumstances in which this planet—never more than 28° from the Sun—must be observed. Owing to the lack of contrast they are best observed with a comparatively low-power eyepiece, and hence a large aperture is almost essential. Under most conditions they are unlikely to be observable with an instrument much smaller than an 8-in. reflector, using a ×150 eyepiece.

The limbs of the planet are usually fuzzy and **'boiling'**, owing to the disturbed atmosphere close to the Sun; where conditions permit, however, careful note should be taken of the apparent shape of the terminator, which sometimes has indentations and irregularities.

MERCURY—ORBITAL DATA The orbit of Mercury has a semi-major axis of 0·387099 A.U., a mean distance from the Sun of 36 million miles; the actual distance varies from about 28½ million miles at perihelion to about 43½ million miles at aphelion. As this variation indicates, the eccentricity of the orbit is very high, the actual figure being 0·2056. The orbit is inclined to the Ecliptic by 7° 0′ 14″.6. These are by far the greatest eccentricity and orbital inclination of any of the planets, the eccentricity being more than double the next highest (that of Mars) and the inclination more than double that of the next greatest (Venus). Only certain of the planetary satellites, minor planets, etc., have greater eccentricities and orbital inclinations.

The velocity of the planet in its orbit is also very variable, again due to the high eccentricity of the orbit; the maximum value (at perihelion) is about 35 miles per second and the minimum (at aphelion) about 23 miles per second. The mean orbital velocity is taken as 29·8 miles per second, giving a sidereal period of 87·969 days.

MERCURY—TELESCOPIC APPEARANCE In the telescope Mercury appears as a diffuse, whitish object, its shape depending upon its phase at the time, with no obvious surface detail. Very faint and diffuse grey markings can, however, be seen from time to time. These are important for the establishment of the axial rotation period of the planet; in 1800 Schröter derived a rotation period of 24 hr 5 min, but this was not confirmed. In 1882 Schiaparelli commenced a careful study of the surface markings and in 1889 announced that the rotation period was equal to the orbital revolution period of 88 days, with the result that the planet always presents the same face to the Sun; subsequent observations of surface markings support this view, as do observations of heat radiated from the sunlit face. This situation probably arose through the tidal forces set up by the gravitational attraction of the massive and close Sun, which would have the effect of slowing down the axial rotation of the planet.

The markings mapped by Schiaparelli were fairly well substantiated by the diligent observations made in the 1930s by Antoniadi, using the 33-in. refractor at the Meudon Observatory, Paris. Antoniadi also allocated names to those markings that appeared to be permanent. His chart is reproduced in Plate 9(b).

MERCURY—TRANSITS OF

If Mercury is at or near one of its nodes when at inferior conjunction, it may pass directly between the Sun and the Earth and be seen to pass, as a tiny black dot, across the face of the Sun. This can only occur when inferior conjunction takes place within a few days of May 7 or November 9. Owing to the eccentricity of its orbit, which brings Mercury closer to the Earth in May than in November, the likelihood that a transit will occur is greater in November.

Twenty-two synodic periods of the planet are roughly equal to 7 years and 41 periods to 13 years, or more accurately, 145 synodic periods almost exactly equal 46 years; transits are therefore possible after intervals of 7, 13 or 46 years, although transits at 7-year intervals are not possible in May.

The first recorded observation of a transit of Mercury was made by Gassendi on 1631 November 7, and numerous observations have been made since. Observations of transits can be used to determine more accurately the elements of Mercury's orbit.

Transits are due to occur this century as follows: 1970 May 9; 1973 November 9; 1986 November 12 and 1999 November 14.

MERCURY—VISIBILITY FROM EARTH

Owing to its small distance from the Sun, Mercury can only be seen at or near its elongations, in the eastern sky shortly before sunrise when at western elongation and in the west shortly after sunset at eastern elongation. The angular distance of Mercury from the Sun varies, owing to the eccentricity of its orbit, but its average value is only 23°. The planet can never rise before the Sun, or set after it, by much more than two hours; taking into account the glare of the Sun for a substantial part of this time, and the very low altitude of the rising (or setting) planet, it will be understood that the planet is only observable for brief periods, and with difficulty. It can of course be more easily observed during daylight with a powerful telescope equipped with accurate setting-circles which will permit location of the planet using tables of its position.

The path of the planet makes varying angles with the horizon at different times of the year, from which it is found that morning elongations occurring in September and October and evening elongations in March and April are the most favourable for observers in the northern hemisphere. The stellar magnitude of Mercury at greatest elongation varies between $-1 \cdot 2$ and $+1 \cdot 1$. The mean synodic period, i.e. the interval from one inferior conjunction to the next, is 116 days; greatest elongation East occurs about 22 days before inferior conjunction and greatest elongation West about 22 days after. The interval between eastern and western elongations is thus about 44 days, and between western and eastern elongations about 72 days.

The apparent diameter of Mercury as observed from Earth varies between 4·7 and 12·7 seconds of arc, depending upon its distance. The planet also undergoes a

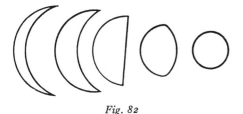

Fig. 82

complete cycle of phases, due to its orbit being within that of the Earth (see **Phases of inferior planet**). The comparative size of the disk at the different phases is shown in Fig. 82.

MERIDIAN A circle around the surface of a planet, all points on which lie in one plane in which the axis of rotation also lies; if the planet is spherical a meridian will be a great circle passing through its poles.

MERIDIAN ASTRONOMY That branch of astronomy concerned with observations made only in the plane of the observer's meridian; these include all observations made for the purposes of time determination and most of the positional observations made visually—both of fundamental importance to astronomers. This arises from the fact that the Right Ascension of a body can be simply obtained from the sidereal time of its meridian transit, and the converse that a determination of the sidereal time can be made by timing the meridian passage of a fundamental star whose position can be assumed. For positional work the other co-ordinate, Declination, can be calculated from the observed meridian altitude of the body. Finally, it should be noted that if bodies of accurately known position are observed with the aid of accurately known time, the observer's position on the surface of the Earth can be determined—an important basis of astronomical navigation.

The principal instrument used in meridian astronomy is, of course, the **transit circle** (*q.v.*); the small transit instrument and the **photographic zenith tube** are mainly used for time-determination observations.

MERIDIAN, CELESTIAL The great circle of the **celestial sphere** (*q.v.*) which passes through the north and south celestial poles, the zenith and the nadir.

MERIDIAN CIRCLE The **transit-circle**, *q.v.*

MERIDIAN PHOTOMETER An instrument developed by E. C. Pickering to compare the apparent magnitudes of two stars which are on or close to the meridian simultaneously, but at different altitudes. This was achieved by the use of two objectives, each with a plane mirror capable of being set at the appropriate angle to bring the light from two stars widely separated in Declination to a common focus. To facilitate this one star selected was a close circumpolar—this star was then used constantly as one of each pair of stars observed, in the interests of consistency and simple reduction.

The two beams were then passed through two Nicol polarizing prisms to an eyepiece; by contra-rotating the prisms the observer equalized the apparent brightness of the two images. The difference in magnitude could be calculated from the amount of rotation of the prisms necessary to equalize the images. With an instrument of this type Pickering and his assistants at Harvard carried out the enormous series of photographic magnitude determinations leading to the publication of the *Harvard Photometry* in 1884, followed by *Revised Harvard Photometry* and its *Supplement*—a total of more than 50,000 stars. The circumpolar used was formerly *Polaris*, later superseded by λ UMi. (See **Harvard Photometry**.)

MERIDIAN, PRIME A meridian defined as the zero of longitude of a planet. That for the Earth was defined by an international conference held in Washington in 1884 as the meridian passing through the centre of the Airy Transit Circle of the Royal Observatory at Greenwich.

Although observation with the Airy Transit Circle ceased in 1953, it has been preserved *in situ* to mark permanently the Prime Meridian. It is now surrounded by other important positional instruments from the past and forms part of the new astronomical section of the National Maritime Museum housed in the former Royal Observatory buildings.

MERIDIAN TRANSIT The passage of a star or other body across the observer's meridian, due to the rotation of the Earth. (See **Meridian astronomy**.)

MEROE INSULA (Martian surface feature, approximate position Ω 290°, $\Phi + 30°$). An ochre area in the north temperate region of Mars.

MERSENIUS (Lunar surface feature, co-ordinates $\xi - 709$, $\eta - 368$); a walled plain, 45 miles in diameter, in the eastern limb region of the Moon. The terraced walls rise to 7,000 ft. in the west, higher in the north. The floor is convex, and has a central craterlet.

MESOSPHERE Term sometimes used to denote the upper part of the **stratosphere**, between about 33 and 48 miles above the Earth's surface. (See also **Atmosphere, terrestrial; Ionosphere.**)

MESSIER, Charles (1730–1817) A prominent French discoverer of comets in the late eighteenth century, Messier drew up a catalogue of nebulous objects in the northern sky in order to facilitate the identification of new comets, but this catalogue proved so useful to other astronomers that it is now the work by which he is remembered.

MESSIER (Lunar surface feature, co-ordinates $\xi + 738$, $\eta - 033$); a deep crater 9 miles in diameter, named after the famous French astronomer; it is the westernmost of a very well-known pair of craters, the other being **Pickering**. It is situated on a light band crossing the Mare Fœcunditatis. There is a double streak streaming eastwards from this pair of craters, known as the **Comet's Tail**.

MESSIER CATALOGUE One of the earliest astronomical catalogues of importance, Messier's catalogue was the first reliable tabulation of nebulous objects, many of which are still known by their Messier designation (M31, M33, etc.).

It was compiled by Charles Messier, an assiduous observer of comets, and was no doubt intended primarily to assist him in this work by preventing the mis-identification of nebulous objects as new comets.

The catalogue was published in three parts, in 1771, 1780 and 1781, and the complete catalogue was republished in 1784; it contained 103 objects. Most of the later objects were Messier's own discoveries, but some of the later ones may have been discovered by his contemporary, Méchain.

The well-known 'Sombrero Hat' nebula in Virgo was added by hand to Messier's own copy of his catalogue, and is now often designated M104.

It will be noted from the following list of the Messier objects that M47, M48, M91 and M102 have never been positively identified. As the New General Catalogue designations are the most commonly used today, these are given in the table where appropriate. The table is reprinted by permission from the *Handbook of the British Astronomical Association, 1964*. Positions given are for the epoch 1950·0; constellations are given in standard I.A.U. abbreviations; distances are given in parsecs (pc), kiloparsecs (kpc) and Megaparsecs (Mpc), *q.v.*

Table 22. *The Messier Catalogue*

M	NGC	R.A. (1950·0)	Dec.	Mag. (Vis)	Distance	Const.	Description
		h m	° ′				
1	1952	5 31·5	+21 59	8·4	1950 pc	Tau	Crab nebula; supernova remnant and radio source.
2	7089	21 30·9	−01 03	6·3	16 kpc	Aqr	Globular cluster.
3	5272	13 39·9	+28 38	6·4	14 kpc	CVn	Globular cluster.
4	6121	16 20·6	−26 24	6·4	2·3 kpc	Sco	Globular cluster.
5	5904	15 16·0	+02 16	6·2	8·3 kpc	Ser	Globular cluster.
6	6405	17 36·8	−32 11	5·3	630 pc	Sco	Galactic cluster.
7	6475	17 50·6	−34 48	4	250 pc	Sco	Galactic cluster.
8	6523	18 00·1	−24 23	6	1·5 kpc	Sgr	Gaseous nebula; 'Lagoon' nebula.
9	6333	17 16·2	−18 28	7·3	7·9 kpc	Oph	Globular cluster.
10	6254	16 54·5	−04 02	6·7	5·0 kpc	Oph	Globular cluster.
11	6705	18 48·4	−06 20	6·3	1·7 kpc	Sct	Galactic cluster.
12	6218	16 44·6	−01 52	6·6	5·8 kpc	Oph	Globular cluster.
13	6205	16 39·9	+36 33	5·7	6·9 kpc	Her	Globular cluster.
14	6402	17 35·0	−03 15	7·7	7·2 kpc	Oph	Globular cluster.
15	7078	21 27·6	+11 57	6·0	15 kpc	Peg	Globular cluster.
16	6611	18 16·0	−13 48	6·4	1·8 kpc	Ser	Gaseous nebula; has embedded star cluster.
17	6618	18 17·9	−16 12	7	1·8 kpc	Sgr	Gaseous nebula; 'Omega' nebula, a radio source.
18	6613	18 17·0	−17 09	7·5	1·5 kpc	Sgr	Galactic cluster.
19	6273	16 59·5	−26 11	6·6	6·9 kpc	Oph	Globular cluster.
20	6514	17 58·9	−23 02	9	1·6 kpc	Sgr	Gaseous nebula; 'Trifid' nebula.
21	6531	18 01·7	−22 30	6·5	1·3 kpc	Sgr	Galactic cluster.
22	6656	18 33·3	−23 58	5·9	3·0 kpc	Sgr	Globular cluster.
23	6494	17 54·0	−19 01	6·9	660 pc	Sgr	Galactic cluster.
24	6603	18 15·5	−18 26	4·6	5·0 kpc	Sgr	Galactic cluster.
25 IC	4725	18 28·8	−19 17	6·5	600 pc	Sgr	Galactic cluster.
26	6694	18 42·6	−09 27	9·3	1·5 kpc	Sct	Galactic cluster.
27	6853	19 57·4	+22 35	7·6	200 pc	Vul	Planetary nebula; 'Dumb-bell' nebula.
28	6626	18 21·5	−24 54	7·3	4·6 kpc	Sgr	Globular cluster.
29	6913	20 22·1	+38 22	7·1	1·2 kpc	Cyg	Galactic cluster.
30	7099	21 37·5	−23 25	8·4	13 kpc	Cap	Globular cluster.
31	224	00 40·0	+41 00	4·8	700 kpc	And	Galaxy; the 'Great' nebula; member of local group; radio source.
32	221	00 40·0	+40 36	8·7	700 kpc	And	Galaxy; elliptical companion of M31.
33	598	01 31·0	+30 24	6·7	700 kpc	Tri	Galaxy; member of local group.
34	1039	02 38·8	+42 34	5·5	440 pc	Per	Galactic cluster.

Table 22.   *The Messier Catalogue (continued)*

M	NGC	R.A. (1950·0)	Dec.	Mag. (Vis)	Distance	Const.	Description
35	2168	06 05·8	+24 21	5·3	870 pc	Gem	Galactic cluster.
36	1960	05 32·0	+34 07	6·3	1·3 kpc	Aur	Galactic cluster.
37	2099	05 49·1	+32 32	6·2	1·3 kpc	Aur	Galactic cluster.
38	1912	05 25·3	+35 48	7·4	1·3 kpc	Aur	Galactic cluster.
39	7092	21 30·4	+48 13	5·2	250 pc	Cyg	Galactic cluster.
40	—						Probably 2 faint stars in position given by Hevelius.
41	2287	06 44·9	−20 41	4·6	670 pc	CMa	Galactic cluster.
42	1976	05 32·9	−05 25	4	460 pc	Ori	Orion nebula.
43	1982	05 33·1	−05 18	9	460 pc	Ori	Orion nebula.
44	2632	08 37·4	+20 00	3·7	158 pc	Cnc	Galactic cluster; 'Præsepe'.
45	—	03 44·1	+23 58	1·6	126 pc	Tau	Galactic cluster; 'The Pleiades'.
46	2437	07 39·5	−14 42	6·0	1 8 kpc	Pup	Galactic cluster.
47	—						Possibly NGC 2422.
48	—						Possibly NGC 2548.
49	4472	12 27·2	+08 16	8·6	11 Mpc	Vir	Galaxy.
50	2323	07 00·6	−08 16	6·3	910 pc	Mon	Galactic cluster.
51	5194	13 27·8	+47 27	8·1	2 Mpc	CVn	Galaxy.
52	7654	23 22·0	+61 19	7·3	2·1 kpc	Cas	Galactic cluster.
53	5024	13 10·5	+18 26	7·6	20 kpc	Com	Globular cluster.
54	6715	18 52·0	−30 32	7·3	15 kpc	Sgr	Globular cluster.
55	6809	19 36·9	−31 03	7·6	5·8 kpc	Sgr	Globular cluster.
56	6779	19 14·6	+30 05	8·2	14 kpc	Vir	Globular cluster.
57	6720	18 51·7	+32 58	9·3	550 pc	Lyr	Planetary nebula; the 'Ring' nebula.
58	4579	12 35·0	+12 05	8·2	11 Mpc	Vir	Galaxy.
59	4621	12 39·5	+11 55	9·3	11 Mpc	Vir	Galaxy.
60	4649	12 41·1	+11 49	9·2	11 Mpc	Vir	Galaxy.
61	4303	12 19·4	+04 45	9·6	11 Mpc	Vir	Galaxy.
62	6266	16 58·1	−30 03	8·9	6·9 kpc	Oph	Globular cluster.
63	5055	13 13·6	+42 18	10·1	4 Mpc	CVn	Galaxy.
64	4826	12 54·3	+21 57	6·6	6 Mpc	Com	Galaxy.
65	3623	11 16·3	+13 22	9·5		Leo	Galaxy.
66	3627	11 17·6	+13 16	8·8		Leo	Galaxy.
67	2682	08 47·8	+12 00	6·1	830 pc	Cnc	Galactic cluster; famous old cluster, of great importance for theories of stellar evolution.
68	4590	12 36·8	−26 29	9	12 kpc	Hya	Globular cluster.
69	6637	18 28·1	−32 23	8·9	7·2 kpc	Sgr	Globular cluster.
70	6681	18 40·0	−32 21	9·6	20 kpc	Sgr	Globular cluster.
71	6838	19 51·5	+18 39	9	5·5 kpc	Sge	Globular cluster.
72	6981	20 50·7	−12 44	9·8	18 kpc	Aqr	Globular cluster.
73	6994	20 56·4	−12 50			Aqr	Is just 4 stars.

Table 22. The Messier Catalogue (continued)

M	NGC	R.A. (1950·0) Dec.		Mag. (Vis)	Distance	Const.	Description
74	628	01 34·0	+15 32	10·2		Psc	Galaxy.
75	6864	20 03·2	−22 04	8·0	24 kpc	Sgr	Globular cluster.
76	650	01 38·8	+51 19	12·2	2·5 kpc	Per	Planetary nebula.
77	1068	01 40·3	−00 13	8·9		Cet	Galaxy.
78	2068	05 44·2	+00 02	8·3	500 pc	Ori	Gaseous nebula.
79	1904	05 22·2	−24 34	7·9	13 kpc	Lep	Globular cluster.
80	6093	16 14·1	−22 52	7·7	11 kpc	Sco	Globular cluster.
81	3031	09 51·5	+69 18	7·9	3·0 Mpc	UMa	Galaxy; radio source.
82	3034	09 51·9	+69 56	8·8	3 Mpc	UMa	Galaxy.
83	5236	13 34·2	−29 37	10·1	4 Mpc	Hya	Galaxy.
84	4374	12 22·5	+13 10	9·3	11 Mpc	Vir	Galaxy.
85	4382	12 22·9	+18 28	9·3	11 Mpc	Com	Galaxy.
86	4406	12 23·7	+13 13	9·7	11 Mpc	Vir	Galaxy.
87	4486	12 28·3	+12 40	9·2	11 Mpc	Vir	Galaxy; giant elliptical, radio source, with peculiar jet.
88	4501	12 29·5	+14 42	10·2	11 Mpc	Com	Galaxy.
89	4552	12 33·1	+12 50	9·5	11 Mpc	Vir	Galaxy.
90	4569	12 34·3	+13 26	10·0	11 Mpc	Vir	Galaxy.
91	—						Possibly a comet, or identical with M 58.
92	6341	17 15·6	+43 12	6·1	11 kpc	Her	Globular cluster.
93	2447	07 42·4	−23 45	6·0	1·1 kpc	Pup	Galactic cluster.
94	4736	12 48·5	+41 24	7·9	6 Mpc	CVn	Galaxy.
95	3351	10 41·3	+11 58	10·4		Leo	Galaxy.
96	3368	10 44·1	+12 05	9·1		Leo	Galaxy.
97	3587	11 12·0	+55 18	12·0	800 pc	UMa	Planetary nebula; the 'Owl' nebula.
98	4192	12 11·3	+15 11	10·7	11 Mpc	Com	Galaxy.
99	4254	12 16·3	+14 42	10·1	11 Mpc	Com	Galaxy.
100	4321	12 20·4	+16 06	10·6	11 Mpc	Com	Galaxy.
101	5457	14 01·4	+54 35	9·6	3 Mpc	UMa	Galaxy.
102	—						Identical with M 101.
103	581	01 29·9	+60 27	7·4	2·6 kpc	Cas	Galactic cluster.
104	4594	12 37·4	−11 21	8·7	4·4 Mpc	Vir	Galaxy; the 'Sombrero Hat' nebula.

METAGALAXY Term used to denote the entire universe, comprising all the heavenly bodies both known and assumed, together with the space containing them.

METEOR General name given to those particles of rock, very small by planetary standards, which the Earth encounters during its passage around the Sun. They range from very large bodies weighing many tons to tiny particles of dust. Friction with the air molecules in the Earth's atmosphere heats them to incandescence as they plunge towards the Earth under the influence of its gravitational attraction, which enables the larger ones to be seen at night as glowing particles streaking across the sky; owing to persistence of vision, the impression is of a luminous trail. This is, of course, the phenomenon popularly termed a 'shooting star'.

Most meteors are burnt up before reaching the Earth's surface, but occasionally very large ones are not completely destroyed and survive to strike the surface —these are termed **meteorites**. **Micro-meteorites**—very fine dust particles—are able by virtue of their lightness to float down through the atmosphere and settle on the surface.

Meteors observed are of two kinds, **sporadic meteors** and **shower meteors**. The latter are of some importance owing to their probable association with comets, and are widely observed. The heavier showers are usually well observed by amateur, visual observers, but regular photographic patrols are carried out all the time at a number of observatories, using specially developed Meniscus–Schmidt cameras. The passage of a meteor through the atmosphere leaves a trail of ionized particles along its path; these can be observed by radar (by day as well as by night), and the path determined very accurately if observations are made from two radar stations separated by some distance.

All meteors are found to have elliptical orbits and are hence permanent members of the solar system.

METEOR, SHOWER A meteor which shares a common direction of arrival at the Earth with others, all travelling in close, similar orbits around the Sun (a **meteor stream**). They occur in large numbers for a short period, and their trails, if produced back, all appear to originate from a small area of the sky (the **radiant**).

METEOR, SPORADIC A meteor not belonging to a shower; sporadic meteors occur quite randomly and in all parts of the sky; they have no common direction of arrival at the Earth.

METEOR STREAM A number of meteoric bodies circling the Sun in close, similar orbits. When the Earth, in its own passage around the Sun, crosses this stream many of these bodies are encountered and plunge towards the Earth. These are seen by observers on Earth as a meteor shower, their luminous trails all appearing, if produced back, to originate from a common radiant. If the radiant is determined by observation, and measurements of the motion of the individual meteors are made, it is possible to calculate the original orbit of the stream. This has enabled a number of the principal streams to be related to the orbits of known comets, from which one may infer that the meteors are débris left along its path by a comet, or that comet and meteors share a common origin.

The meteors are in many cases not evenly distributed along the stream, and hence the number of meteors seen in a shower may vary from year to year. Observations are also adversely affected

Table 23. Some typical meteor showers

Shower	Date of Maximum	Normal Limiting Dates	Typical (1965) Zenithal Hourly Rate	Remarks
Quadrantids	Jan. 3	Jan. 3–5	45	
Aquarids	Jul. 29	Jul. 15–Aug. 10	40	
Perseids	Aug. 12	Jul. 27–Aug. 15	50	Associated with Comet 1862 III
Orionids	Oct. 21	Oct. 15–25	20	Associated with Halley's Comet
Taurids	Nov. 7	Oct. 26–Nov. 15	10	Associated with Encke's Comet
Leonids	Nov. 16	Nov. 14–17	30	

by the presence of moonlight. The most notable shower is the **Perseids**, which last for several days; on occasion 50 to 60 meteors an hour can be observed. Some typical showers are listed in Table 23. See also Plate 16(f).

METEORIC THEORY A theory that the majority of the lunar surface features were formed by meteoric impact (see **Moon—origin of surface features**).

METEORITE A meteor which is not completely destroyed during its passage through the Earth's atmosphere, and which survives to reach the Earth's surface. Meteorites are of particular interest as they are the only bodies of celestial origin which can be studied in the laboratory. There are four main types of meteorite: **aerolites**, containing mainly rocky material; **siderolites**, containing mainly rocky material and also some metal, principally iron and nickel; **siderites**, consisting almost entirely of iron and nickel; **tektites**, globules of a silicaceous nature. A very large majority of known meteorites are aerolites.

Meteorites are known in many different weights and dimensions; many are preserved in museums all over the world. Some of them weigh many tons; among meteorites found in Greenland by Peary, discoverer of the North Pole, is one measuring 11 ft × 6¾ ft × 5¼ ft and weighing about 36 tons. Some of the largest craters in the Earth's surface are attributed to the impact of meteorites, e.g. the crater measuring over 4,000 ft. in diameter and 570 ft. deep, near Cañon Diablo in Arizona. [Plate 17(b).]

The largest known meteorite was found near Grootfontein in South-West Africa, and weighs some 60 tons; it is estimated from the amount of iron in the surrounding terrain, however, that it must originally have weighed more than 70 tons. The smallest known meteorites are the micrometeorites; these are particles so small that they are able to settle slowly through the atmosphere and arrive intact on the

Earth's surface. They are sometimes known as meteoritic dust. On land micrometeorites are very difficult to separate from dust originating on the Earth's surface, but they are easily separated from silt dredged from the ocean floor. Under the microscope they may be recognized by the air holes formed in their surface whilst it was in a molten state during their fall through the Earth's atmosphere. [Plate 17(a).]

(See also **Tektites**.)

METEORITIC THEORY Theory that the surface features of the Moon were formed by the impact of meteorites. (See **Moon—origin of surface features**.)

METHANE A gaseous hydrocarbon, CH_4, one of the main constituents of the major planets. A poisonous gas, frequently encountered in coal mines where it is known as 'fire damp' and in bogs where it is known as 'marsh gas'.

METON (born approx. 460 B.C.) An astronomer of Athens, who deduced the lunar cycle now known as the Metonic Cycle from his observations of the summer solstice of 432 B.C.

METONIC CYCLE A period, discovered by Meton of Athens in 432 B.C., after which the phases of the Moon recur on the same days of the same months. It arises from the fact that 19 Tropical Years of 365·2422 days total 6939·602 days, while 235 lunations (each of 29·5306 days) total 6939·689 days. Thus the mean phases of the Moon will recur on the same calendar date 19 years later, and within about 2 hours of the same time. (The date may, in fact, differ by 1 day, depending upon the number of Leap Years in the cycle.)

The Greeks used the Metonic Cycle to fix the dates of their religious festivals, which had to take place at certain phases of the Moon.

Whilst the **Saros** can be used to predict the occurrence of eclipses with certainty, they will be visible from different parts of the Earth's surface; the Metonic Cycle can be used to predict the repetition of an eclipse visible from a given part of the Earth. (See also **Saros; Golden Number.**)

METRE Metric unit of length or distance, equivalent to 0·001 kilometres or 100 centimetres. (See **Metric system.**)

METRIC SYSTEM A system of units of measurement employing only multiples of ten. It is normal practice these days for scientists to use metric units of size and weight, although the conventional units of time are retained. In astronomy the units most concerned are, of course, those of distance. In this book the more familiar 'Imperial' units have been used, but the conversion to metric units can be performed quite simply by anyone who so desires, using the following information, which is not a complete tabulation but includes the units occurring most frequently in this book.

$$1 \text{ kilometre (km)} = 1000 \text{ metres (m)}$$
$$1 \text{ m} = 100 \text{ centimetres (cm)}$$
$$1 \text{ cm} = 10 \text{ millimetres (mm)}$$

$$1 \text{ km} = 0·6214 \text{ miles}$$
$$1 \text{ m} = 39·37 \text{ inches (in.)}$$

$$1 \text{ mile} = 1·609 \text{ km}$$
$$1 \text{ foot (ft)} = 30·48 \text{ cm}$$
$$1 \text{ in.} = 2·54 \text{ cm}$$

MEUDON OBSERVATORY The French Observatory of Physical Astronomy, situated near Paris. The principal instrument is the 32·7-in. visual refractor, which has a 24·4-in. photographic refractor coupled to it on the same mounting.

MIAPLACIDUS The southern star β Car, magnitude 1·80.

MICHELSON–MORLEY EXPERIMENT An experiment conducted in 1887 by A. A. Michelson and E. W. Morley, to measure the velocity of the Earth relative to the 'æther'; the experiment comprised the measurement of the velocity of light

in two perpendicular directions, one of which was parallel to the direction of the Earth's orbital motion at the time. The result was negative, demonstrating the absence of the interstellar medium envisaged up to that time and known as the 'æther'. The experiment was an important contribution to cosmological thought, leading directly to the work of Fitzgerald and Lorentz.

MICROMETEORITE Name given to a tiny particle of meteoritic dust which floats slowly through the atmosphere to settle on the Earth's surface.

MICROMETER An instrument for the accurate measurement of small distances by the movement of a precision-made screw having a calibrated head and, often, a vernier scale.

MICROMETER, CROSS-BAR A simple device for measuring the position of a comet or other object relative to a star of known position. It consists of two bars, set accurately at right angles to each other;

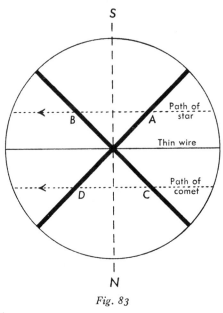

Fig. 83

the telescope is set so that the bars are inclined to the east–west path of the stars by 45°. This is achieved, in the case of a micrometer equipped with a position circle, by adjusting the micrometer until the stars' motions are parallel to one bar, then turning through 45° measured by the circle. Micrometers without a position circle are equipped with a fine wire set at 45° to the bars, along which a star is made to trail in order to set the micrometer (see Fig. 83).

The observation is very similar to that with the ring micrometer; it consists of recording the times at which the star crosses the bars at *A* and *B* and the comet or other body at *C* and *D*. From these times the differences between the two bodies in both Right Ascension and Declination can be calculated, so that if the co-ordinates of the star are known those of the comet can be simply determined.

(See also **Micrometer, ring**.)

MICROMETER, FILAR A device for measuring the apparent separation of two objects, or the diameter of a single object, in the field of view of a telescope. The layout is shown in Fig. 84. It consists of two wires, separately moveable; the frame bearing one of them has a micrometer screw attached and the amount of movement may therefore be read off from the micrometer head. The whole micrometer is usually held on a rotating plate, which can be locked at any angle, and the position angle read off on a circular scale.

Fig. 85 shows the method of positioning the wires on the object being observed before the readings are taken. It is usual to take a number of readings, moving the wires off and resetting them, and using the mean of the values obtained.

Fig. 85(a) shows the micrometer setting to determine the separation of a double star; Fig. 85(b) that used to determine the apparent diameter of a planet.

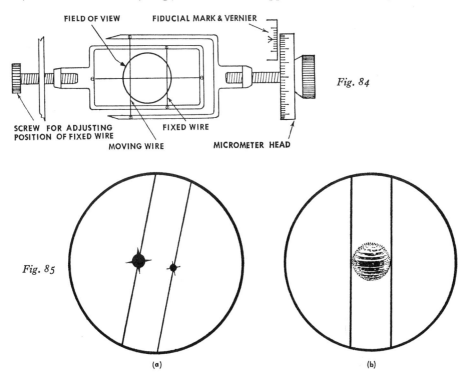

FIELD OF VIEW   FIDUCIAL MARK & VERNIER

Fig. 84

SCREW FOR ADJUSTING POSITION OF FIXED WIRE

FIXED WIRE

MOVING WIRE   MICROMETER HEAD

Fig. 85

(a)   (b)

MICROMETER, IMPERSONAL A device used in observations with the transit circle in order to minimize errors due to the observer's personal equation. It consists of a vertical wire in the focal plane of the telescope, which can be traversed across the field of view by means of a screw having a handle at either end; these are rotated by each hand alternately, thus permitting a smooth motion, the observer meanwhile keeping the wire in such a position that it bisects the star. An agate disk with electrical contact studs set in it rotates with the screw, by means of which impulses are sent to a recording chronograph, together with second pulses from the observatory clock. There are several fixed wires in the field also, enabling a number of positions of the star in the field of view to be related to times determined from the chronograph record.

Use of the impersonal micrometer has reduced errors due to personal equations to the order of 6 hundredths of a second.

In a modern refinement the smooth movement is imparted to the wire by an electric motor drive, the observer having a remote speed control to enable him to keep the star image bisected; with this refinement the personal errors have been reduced to the order of only 2 hundredths of a second.

MICROMETER, RING A simple device for measuring the position of a comet or other object relative to a star of known position. It consists of a flat ring, usually of metal or produced photographically on a glass plate, mounted in the focal plane of the telescope; it is thus coplanar with the image produced by the telescope objective, and both can be observed simultaneously by means of a positive eyepiece.

The telescope is set so that both objects cross the field well away from its centre; ideally one should be north and one south of the centre of the field (see Fig. 86). The observation consists of recording the times at which both objects cross the ring. The mean of the times at which the star

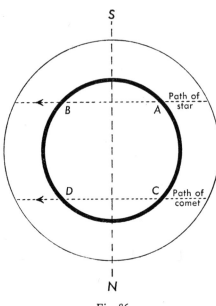

Fig. 86

crosses the ring at A and B gives its time of crossing the central meridian SN; similarly the mean of the times at which the comet crosses the ring at C and D gives its time of central meridian transit. The difference between the two transit times is the difference in Right Ascension between the bodies.

Similarly the difference in Declination between the bodies can be determined from the times taken by the bodies to traverse the chords AB and CD respectively, provided that the scale value is known, that is to say the time required for an equatorial star to cross the ring centrally (i.e. along a diameter). When the differences in R.A. and Dec. have been determined the co-ordinates of the unknown body can be calculated from the known co-ordinates of the star.

(See also **Micrometer, cross-bar.**)

MICRON A unit of length used for measuring extremely small distances. It is equal to 10^{-6} metres, i.e. 1/1,000 mm or 10,000 Å. The usual abbreviation is μ.

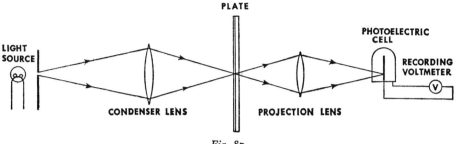

PLATE

LIGHT
SOURCE

PHOTOELECTRIC
CELL

RECORDING
VOLTMETER

CONDENSER LENS   PROJECTION LENS

Fig. 87

MICROPHOTOMETER An instrument for measuring the relative density of images on a photographic plate, from which the relative brightness of the sources photographed may be deduced.

The instrument consists basically of a light-source (usually a straight, uncoiled filament, tungsten lamp) and an optical system which focuses the light transmitted by the photographic plate being scanned onto a light-sensitive element, usually a photoelectric cell or photomultiplier tube. The varying output from this element is passed through a voltmeter, and the changing voltage may be read off from a dial or, more usually, recorded as a continuous graph on a paper strip.

A simplified layout for a microphotometer is shown in Fig. 87.

MICROSCOPIUM (The Microscope. *Genitive* Microscopii, *I.A.U. abbreviation* Mic.) A small constellation in the southern sky, adjoining Sagittarius. Contains no bright stars.

MILKY WAY Popular name for the band of faint luminosity extending around the sky along the line of the galactic equator; it is, in fact, the visible manifestation of the **Galaxy**. [Plate 20(c, e).]

MILLIMETRE Metric unit of length or distance, equivalent to 0·001 metres or 0·1 centimetres.

MILLISECOND A unit of time measurement, widely used in observatories for the

purposes of time measurement and clock comparisons. It is equal to 1/1,000 sec.

MIMAS Satellite I of Saturn, *q.v.*

MIMOSA The star β Cru, magnitude 1·50; makes one 'corner' of the **Southern Cross**.

MINOR PLANETS Term used to denote the large group of planetary members of the solar system of comparatively small dimension, and having mean distances from the Sun between those of Mars and Jupiter. Alternative names sometimes used are 'asteroids' and 'planetoids'.

Original discoveries. During the eighteenth century astronomers hoped to discover a planet with an orbit in the rather large gap between those of Mars and Jupiter. Instead, four dwarf planets were discovered in this area, each of them less than 500 miles in diameter—'Ceres', 'Pallas', 'Juno' and 'Vesta'. The brightest of these was Vesta, which is occasionally visible to the unaided eye. Pallas was notable for the inclination of its orbit to the Ecliptic—nearly 35°. These four objects could be seen as disks only with the aid of very powerful telescopes, and otherwise appeared to have normal 'stellar' images (hence the frequently used name 'asteroid').

A German amateur astronomer, Olbers, who had discovered both Pallas and Vesta, suggested that the minor planets might be the fragments of a single, disrupted planet

259

Table 24.   The original asteroids

No.	Name	Year of Discovery	Dis- coverer	Diameter (miles)
1	Ceres	1801	Piazzi	485
2	Pallas	1802	Olbers	304
3	Juno	1804	Harding	118
4	Vesta	1807	Olbers	243

formerly orbiting the Sun between Mars and Jupiter.

No doubt owing to the lack of sufficiently accurate star-charts, no further asteroids were discovered for 15 years—he next being 'Astræa' discovered by Hencke in 1845. New star-charts—in fact those used by Galle in the first identification of Neptune—were used in the discovery of five further minor planets, all of them having diameters of less than 100 miles, between 1847 and 1849.

When four further minor planets were discovered in 1850, the Royal Astronomical Society was led to comment that this rate of increase 'could hardly be expected to continue very long'; by 1870, however, there were 109 asteroids with known orbits, and by 1890 there were 287.

Nomenclature. The usual practice of allotting names from classical mythology was adopted at first, but there were soon departures from this; the twelfth asteroid was discovered in London by Hind in 1852, and he named it 'Victoria', but Americans preferred to adopt the name 'Clio'—greatly to the indignation of Airy, the then Astronomer Royal. In more recent times asteroids have been named 'Chicago', 'Pittsburghia' and 'Rockefellia'.

In 1891 Max Wolf at Heidelberg discovered minor planet number 323 by photography; this began what might be termed the age of mass production of minor planets, as these objects will trail on a photograph of the star field in exposures of only an hour or so, due to their orbital motion. In ten years Wolf and Charloi both discovered more than

100, Palisa more than 80 and Peters over 50. Later Reinmuth at Heidelberg amassed 980, including rediscoveries and some not subsequently re-observed. Of this vast total, however, only 189 were finally numbered, compared with 228 out of Wolf's ultimate total of 582; both naming and numbering had now been abandoned, in view of the great numbers involved. Definitive numbering was reserved only for those minor planets whose orbits could be computed, although numbers allotted earlier continued to be used. [Plate 16(e).]

Several systems of provisional designation were tried, but rapidly became redundant because of the rate of discovery. When designations consisting of the year followed by a letter (e.g. 1965A) were tried, the alphabet was used up in a few months. When a double alphabet was started (e.g. AA, AB, etc.) it was used up in 15 years; the year was then added as a suffix, to enable it to be re-used (e.g. AA 1895, DF 1905, etc.), but the double alphabet had been used three times over by 1925. Since then a double alphabet has been started each year (e.g. 1965 AA, 1965 AB, etc.) in which the first letter used indicates the half-month of discovery, and the second indicates the order of discovery within the period, thus:

Time of discovery   Designations adopted
1965 January (1st half): 1965 AA, AB, etc. ...
        (2nd half): 1965 BA, BB, etc. ...
  February (1st half): 1965 CA, CB, etc. ...
        (2nd half): 1965 DA, DB, etc. ...

This system allows for the discovery of minor planets at a rate of more than two per day.

In 1938 a series of plates was exposed at the Mount Wilson Observatory, in an attempt to discover extra satellites of Jupiter; two new satellites were indeed discovered, but so were 31 new asteroids! The total of minor planets whose orbits had been determined had reached 1,489 by 1939 and is now about 1,600.

Orbits. Most of the known minor planets are in near-circular orbits, with mean distances from the Sun between 150 and 450 million miles; the average of the known mean distances is about 270 million miles. Three reliable positional observations are required to determine an orbit, and nearly all the current discoveries are of very faint asteroids, with apparent magnitudes averaging about 15; for this reason only about a fifth of the asteroids discovered are sufficiently well observed for an orbit to be determined.

It is therefore not unknown for a minor planet to be lost—the classic example of this being 'Aethra' which was lost for 49 years, from 1873 to 1922. This is partly due to the severe perturbations caused by Jupiter and Saturn; in recent years computers have proved very useful in analysing the complex orbital motions.

Orbital periods range mostly between $3\frac{1}{2}$ and 6 years. The average orbital inclination is 9°·7—greater than any of the planets except Pluto. Some asteroid orbits lie almost in the plane of the ecliptic, however, and a few have inclinations exceeding 30°. No cases of retrograde motion are known. The commonest direction of minor planet perihelia is that of Jupiter's perihelion, and they are fewest in the direction of Jupiter's aphelion; this confirms the great influence of Jupiter upon the minor planets (Fig. 88).

The orbits are often rather eccentric compared with those of the planets, resembling more those of the shorter-period comets. The average eccentricity is 0·15; the maximum about 0·9. A few of the highly eccentric asteroid orbits lie partly inside the orbit of the Earth, and the asteroids can therefore pass fairly

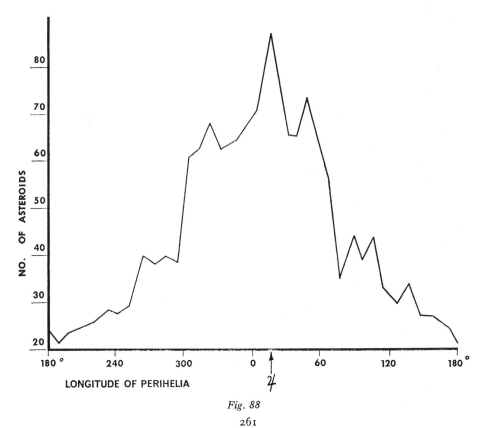

Fig. 88

close to the Earth on occasion.

In 1898 Witt in Berlin discovered an asteroid with a mean distance from the Sun of 136 million miles—then the smallest known—which was originally designated DQ and later known as number 433 (Eros). The orbit of Eros is such that it can approach to within 14 million miles of the Earth; the close approaches of 1901 (30 million miles) and 1931 (16 million miles) were widely observed for the purpose of redetermining the **solar parallax**. Some of the more recently discovered asteroids pass much closer to the Earth than Eros; 'Amor' was only 10 million miles away at the time of its discovery in 1932; 'Adonis' has an orbit extending from just outside the orbit of Mercury to twice the mean distance of Mars. 'Icarus' passes even closer to the Sun than Adonis, yet is 183 million miles from it at aphelion. 'Hermes', discovered and photographed by Reinmuth in 1937, approached to within 400,000 miles of the Earth, less than twice the distance of the Moon. Its relative movement was so fast that it appeared to traverse the entire sky in 9 days. Objects such as these move too quickly for accurate orbits to be determined; Adonis, Apollo and Hermes are all 'lost' and may only be rediscovered when they once again cross the Earth's orbit at a point close to the position of Earth itself at the time.

Groups and gaps. It has been shown that many of the asteroids are members of 'groups', five of which contain some hundreds of members. In particular there are two groups having the same mean solar distance as Jupiter, 483 million miles, but situated 60° ahead of and 60° behind the planet in its orbit. These are known as the 'Trojan' groups. The leading Trojan group contains 'Achilles' and six asteroids, and the following group 'Patroclus' with four others. Names from Homer's *Iliad* have been given to all the asteroids in these groups, although unfortunately Greeks and Trojans have been mixed in each group! The fact that the

Trojan groups maintain their positions relative to Jupiter indicates that despite their not insignificant mass and the perturbations caused by the other planets, principally Saturn, they are behaving in accordance with a solution of the three-body problem propounded by Lagrange.

Most of the remaining groups may be accounted for by dynamical considerations; from an analysis of their orbits Hirayama found five groups of asteroids within which orbital similarities suggested a common origin; this offers some support to Kuiper's refinement of the disrupted planet theory, referred to below.

It was shown by Kirkwood in 1866 that there were gaps, comparatively free from minor planets, at distances from the Sun where their orbital periods would be simple fractions of that of Jupiter; this suggested that the effect of Jupiter's gravitational pull reaching a maximum at regular and frequent intervals had been to pull any asteroids present into other orbits. The gaps are most noticeable at solar distances corresponding to revolution periods $\frac{1}{3}$, $\frac{2}{5}$, $\frac{3}{7}$, $\frac{1}{2}$ and $\frac{3}{5}$ of that of Jupiter (Fig. 89). There is here an obvious similarity to Saturn's ring system. It is particularly notable that there is a gap in the minor planet zone at the position corresponding to a rotation period $\frac{1}{2}$ that of Jupiter, and an enormous group (the 'Hecuba' group, containing more than 400 asteroids) just outside this gap, with a mean period slightly less than half of Jupiter's: a close parallel with **Cassini's Division** and Saturn's Ring B.

Light variation. The light received from many asteroids displays considerable variation; the variation is often of an irregular nature, especially in the case of Eros. This remarkable object was seen by Von Oppolzer in 1900 to undergo a rapid drop of $1\frac{1}{2}$ magnitudes in less than 1 hour and 20 minutes; he watched it for some time, and established that it was undergoing a complete cycle of two maxima and two minima in 5 hours 16 minutes. This variation gradually became less marked,

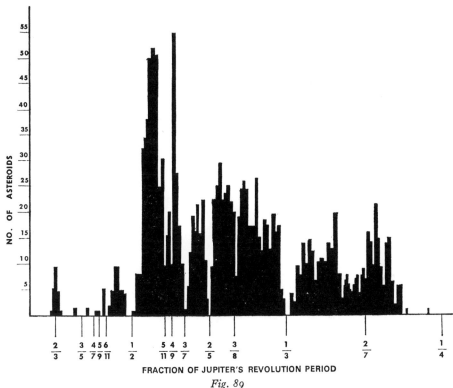

FRACTION OF JUPITER'S REVOLUTION PERIOD

Fig. 89

however, and in a few months ceased altogether. Observations at subsequent apparitions showed that the light variation was sometimes present to a greater or lesser extent, sometimes absent altogether. It was believed that these effects were due to Eros having a most unusual shape for an astronomical body, being a long, thin object rotating about its shorter axis; depending upon the relative positions of the Earth and Eros, the observer on Earth would sometimes be looking at the rotating top, or bottom, of Eros only—in which case no light variation would occur—whereas on other occasions he would see the long sides and short ends in turn as they rotate; thus presenting a variable surface area and, hence, a variable amount of reflected light.

This theory was confirmed by observations made during the very close approach of 1931 by Finsen and van den Bos at Johannesburg, two of the world's leading variable-star observers, who were able to measure the size of Eros and observe its changing apparent shape as it rotated (in the same direction of rotation as the other planets—anti-clockwise in the sense North Pole uppermost). From these observations Eros was shown to be about 14 miles long and 4 miles wide.

Origin. This evidence of Eros's 'rotating splinter' shape supports the theory that the asteroids may be fragments of a disrupted planet; F. G. Watson has estimated, however, that all the minor planets known would together make up a body of only some 600 miles in diameter and about 1/4,000 of the Earth's mass. Kuiper considers the most likely cause of disruption to be collision with another body, rather than explosion or tidal forces. Kuiper has also suggested that the largest asteroids may have been some five or ten planets originally formed in the zone in lieu of one larger body, and that recurring mutual collisions of some of these have led to their breaking up into the hundreds of small objects known.

An earlier theory is that of Leuschner who suggested in 1927 that short-period comets that lose their gases by solar radiation pressure may become asteroid groups; our present knowledge of asteroid orbits does not tend to support this suggestion, however.

(See also **Kepler's Laws of planetary motion; Saturn—Rings of.**)

MINUTE (OF ARC) A unit of angular measure, being one sixtieth part of one degree, or 1/21,600 of a full circle.

MINUTE (OF TIME) A unit of time measurement, being one sixtieth part of one hour.

MIRA The star o Cet, sometimes known as *Mira Ceti*. It is an interesting long-period variable. It is visible to the naked eye only for four months around its maximum, and a telescopic object for the remaining seven months. The actual period is rather variable, but averages 331 days. The magnitude range is also variable; maxima are usually of third or fourth magnitude, but may on occasion be as high as the second or as low as the fifth magnitude. Minima usually lie between 8·5 and 9·5. The rise is more rapid than the fall—a typical light-curve is shown in Fig. 90.

Mira is an *M*-type supergiant, and has a faint companion which is believed to be a white dwarf.

The first regular observations of this variable were carried out by Holwarda, a seventeenth-century Dutch observer, but it was seen as a fourth-magnitude star by Bayer and plotted in his *Uranometria* as o Ceti; the earliest recorded observations of the star were made by Fabricius in 1596.

MIRANDA Satellite V of Uranus, *q.v.*

MIRROR In optics, a highly polished boundary between two media. Mirrors may be made of glass or metal; in the case of glass mirrors they are normally (but not necessarily) 'silvered'.

Many astronomical telescopes are of the reflecting type; these embody a concave mirror as the primary, light-gathering element. Plane mirrors or 'flats' are also frequently used in astronomical instruments.

MIZAR The star ζ UMa, magnitude 2·40; a multiple star, being a spectroscopic binary and also having an optical companion (**Alcor**, magnitude 4·0) at a separation of 15 seconds of arc.

MOAB Martian surface feature, approximate position Ω 350°, Φ+20°. Light area south of Ismenius Lacus, bounded by the canals Euphrates to the east and Hiddekel to the west.

MOCK SUN A phenomenon caused by refraction of the Sun's light by ice crystals as it passes through the upper atmosphere. It has the appearance of a bright, rather diffuse, image of the Sun, and is usually separated from the true Sun by an angular distance of 22°.

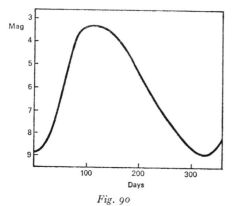

Fig. 90

MOERIS LACUS Martian surface feature, approximate position Ω 270°, $\Phi + 8°$. Dark projection from eastern edge of the Syrtis Major; connected to Tritonis Lacus by the curving Nepenthes-Thoth. Separates Libya from the Isidis Regio.

MOLECULE The smallest unit in which a chemical substance can exist without losing its identity.

MONOCEROS (The Unicorn. *Genitive* Monocerotis, *I.A.U. abbreviation* Mon.) A constellation containing mainly faint stars, situated on the Galactic equator. Reaches midnight culmination in early July.

MONOCHROMATIC LIGHT Light of a single wavelength; in practice light of a narrow band of wavelengths and consequently of one colour.

MONOCHROMATOR A device for selecting light of a narrow band of wavelength from light of many wavelengths, for the purposes of optical or photographic observation. Hence the prism or diffraction grating of a spectrograph is a monochromator. (See also **Lyot birefringent filter**.)

MOON Popular term for a planetary satellite.

MOON, THE The only known natural satellite of the Earth. It is however very much larger and more massive, relative to its primary, than any of the other planetary satellites, and it is perhaps more realistic to think of the Earth and the Moon as a double planet rather than as planet and satellite.

The Moon is the closest of the heavenly bodies and has, therefore, been observed in the greatest detail. Its surface is a most rewarding subject for telescopic examination, for more than half of it is covered by gigantic mountain ranges and crater-like ring formations. As the Moon's periods of axial rotation and orbital revolution around the Earth are equal, it constantly presents the same face towards the Earth; due to **libration,** however, rather more than half the total surface (about 59 per cent) is observable from the Earth at one time or another. [Plate 4(a–c).]

The Moon, beautiful to the naked eye, is a magnificent telescopic object; small wonder that it has inspired generations of astronomers, amateur and professional alike, to devote themselves to the study of the heavens. Many of the greatest astronomers of all time have devoted at least some part of their endeavours to the study of the Moon and the attempted solution of the many problems which it poses.

MOON—DIMENSIONS AND PHYSICAL DATA The apparent diameter of the Moon at mean distance from the Earth is $31' 5''2$, corresponding to an actual diameter of 2,160 miles. There is no significant polar flattening; there is however a slight 'bulge' in the direction of the Earth, the length of the diameter in the Moon–Earth direction being 1·00063 times the polar diameter, equivalent to a bulge 1·37 miles in height.

The mass of the Moon is 0·0123 times that of the Earth, corresponding to a mean density of 3·342 times that of water, 0·606 times the mean density of the Earth. The acceleration due to gravity at the surface of the Moon is 5·32 ft/sec², 0·165 times that at the surface of the Earth. The velocity of escape is consequently very low, 1·48 miles/sec. only 0·213 times that for the Earth.

The period of axial rotation is 27·322 days—the same as the sidereal period of orbital revolution. The Moon thus permanently presents almost the same face towards the Earth, subject only to the effects of **libration.** The Moon's equatorial plane is inclined to the plane of its orbit by 6° 41'; as the orbital plane is inclined to the plane of the Ecliptic by 5° 09' the equatorial plane is inclined to the plane of the Ecliptic by 1° 32'. The mean inclination between the orbital plane and the equatorial plane of the Earth is 23° 24′.

The equivalent stellar apparent magnitude at mean opposition distance is − 12·7; the albedo is very low indeed, 0·07; only Mercury has a comparable figure.

MOON—FAR SIDE OF For almost three and a half centuries after the discovery of the 'crater' formations by Galileo, studies of the lunar surface were restricted to only slightly more than half the total surface, due to the equality of the Moon's synodic period and period of axial rotation. As a result of the Moon's librations, however, only 41 per cent is permanently visible to Earth-bound observers, a further 18 per cent being visible in addition from time to time.

In 1959 this situation was dramatically changed, photographs of a large part of the permanently hidden surface being obtained by the Russian lunar-probe vehicle *Lunik III*, now termed *Luna 3*. This historic achievement occurred on 1959 October 7. [Plate 7(a).]

Although the definition of these first photographs of the far side of the Moon was rather poor, they were of sufficiently good quality for useful conclusions to be drawn from careful analysis by skilled assessors. Interpretations of the surface details revealed were made by both Russian and American astronomers; it is clear that the far side, predictably, has surface features very similar to those of the visible face. The distribution of lunabase (the basic rock of the maria) and lunarite (the more acidic rock of the mountainous regions) is rather different, however, the latter predominating over practically the whole of the newly photographed territory, which is thus very similar to the southern third of the visible hemisphere.

Naturally the various interpretations of the photographs differ regarding many of the less well defined features, but a number of the more prominent objects can be identified with reasonable certainty; some of these are listed below, their approximate

positions being shown in Plate 7(a). The numbers are as listed in **Moon—principal features of.**

45. Giordano Bruno
59. Joliot-Curie
61. Jules Verne
66. Lomonosov
68. Lobachevskii
78. Mare Muscoviense
80. Mare Ingenii
93. Mendeleev
122. Sinus Astronautarum
126. Sovietskii Mountains
131. Sklodowska-Curie
137. Tsiolkovskii

MOON—MAPS OF The first attempt to record the relative positions of the lunar surface features was made by Galileo in 1610; since that time a long series of charts has been prepared by the leading selenographers of each generation.

The first map worthy of the name was that of Hevelius (1647); this was shortly followed by that of Riccioli (1651) and a splendid map constructed on the basis of measured positions by Cassini in 1680. A most accurate, though small, map by Tobias Mayer was published in 1775. The leading observer of the late eighteenth century was J. H. Schröter, often described as the 'founder of modern selenography'; unfortunately, though he produced hundreds of detailed drawings of specific regions and measured the heights of many lunar mountains, Schröter never produced a chart of the entire lunar surface.

One of the landmarks in the history of selenography was the *Mappa Selenographica* of Beer and Mädler, published in 1837. This was only superseded in usefulness by the map produced by Julius Schmidt in 1874. Schmidt's map had a diameter of 73¾ in., almost double the size of Beer and Mädler's map.

Among the most important maps published this century were those of W. Goodacre (77 in., 1910) and H. P. Wilkins (60 in., 1924; 200 in., 1932; 300 in., 1946, 1951, 1955).

In 1909 M. Loewy and P. Puiseux of

the Paris Observatory published an excellent photographic atlas of the lunar surface; since then a number of important photographic atlases have appeared, in addition to the superb photographs of selected regions of the Moon obtained with the giant instruments of the Lick, Mount Wilson and Mount Palomar Observatories.

In 1903 W. H. Pickering published a valuable photographic atlas of the Moon, each region photographed under five different angles of illumination with a specially constructed 12-in. photographic refractor.

All of these atlases, both visual and photographic, have now been surpassed by a series of atlases produced by G. P. Kuiper and colleagues, initially at the Yerkes Observatory and now at the Lunar and Planetary Laboratories of the University of Arizona, Tucson, Arizona, U.S.A. The first part was a superb portfolio of 230 photographs covering the visible surface of the Moon in 44 areas; this collection was published in 1960 as the *Photographic Lunar Atlas*. Two supplements have since been published, the *Orthographic Atlas of the Moon* in 1960, giving orthographic projections of the 44 areas, and the *Rectified Lunar Atlas* in 1962; in the latter lunar photographs are projected onto a white-painted globe and rephotographed from an 'overhead' direction, so that the effect of foreshortening of the features recorded in the original photographs, due to the curvature of the Moon's surface, is removed.

MOON—MOTION OF The apparent motion of the Moon against the background stars is very rapid—the average daily motion being about 13°, compared with about 1° for the Sun. The motion relative to the stars is very obvious from one night to the next, and is easily detectable over a few hours. Another effect of the Moon's rapid motion is the fact that the time of moonrise is, on average, some 50 min later each night.

Ephemerides predicting the Moon's position are extremely difficult to compile, owing to the very complex nature of the Moon's motion due to the severe perturbations caused by the Sun and the planets, and other causes.

One important cause of non-uniform orbital motion is the high average eccentricity of the Moon's orbit, 0·0549. The eccentricity is variable, due to the severe perturbations caused by the Sun, its full range of values being 0·0549 ± 0·0117.

The Moon moves around its eccentric orbit with a varying velocity, in accordance with Kepler's second law of planetary motion. If we imagine a 'mean Moon' moving with a constant orbital velocity and completing one orbit in the same sidereal period as the true Moon, we can consider the effect of the eccentricity of the orbit upon the Moon's motion. If the true Moon and the mean Moon leave perigee together, we find that the true Moon lags behind at first, reaching a maximum of 6° 17′ behind the mean Moon some 7 days after perigee; it then begins to catch up, reaching apogee simultaneously with the mean Moon, and then overtakes it, reaching a maximum lead of 6° 17′ about 7 days before the next perigee, then losing this lead to reach perigee at the same time as the mean Moon. This inequality in the Moon's motion is termed the *equation of the centre;* its mean value is thus ± 6° 17′, but its value actually varies between ± 5° 3′ and ± 7° 31′, due to the varying eccentricity. This variation in the value of the equation of the centre is termed the *evection.* The period of the evection is 31·81 days.

A further inequality in the Moon's motion is caused by the difference in the effect of the Sun's gravitational attraction upon the Earth and the Moon as their relative distances from the Sun vary during the synodic month. The result of this is that the Moon is accelerated from Last Quarter to New Moon and retarded from New Moon to First Quarter; from First Quarter to Full Moon the Moon is again accelerated and retarded from Full Moon to Last Quarter. This inequality has a maximum value of ± 19′·5 and its period is half the synodic month, i.e. 14·77 days; it is termed the *secular variation* of the Moon.

The secular variation is also subject to a second-order effect, the Sun's attraction on the Moon being greater when the Moon is at conjunction (New Moon) than at opposition (Full Moon); the difference is known as the *parallactic inequality*, and has a maximum value of about 2'.

The distance of the Earth (and hence the Earth–Moon system) from the Sun varies during a year, and this also introduces an inequality into the Moon's motion, termed the *annual equation;* its value is ± 5' 38".

The equation of the centre, evection, lunar variation and annual equation are termed the *principal inequalities* in the motion of the Moon.

The prediction of the Moon's motion is complicated by several other factors; the plane of the Moon's orbit is inclined to the plane of the Ecliptic by approximately 5° 09', and the nodes are slowly rotating; the period of a complete revolution of the nodes is 6793·5 days, about 18⅔ years. The inclination of the orbital plane is also slightly variable, with an amplitude of about 18' in a period of 173 days. The rate of regression is also slightly variable, the actual rate differing from the mean rate by up to ± 1° 40.'

A further slight inequality in the motion of the Moon, which for many years baffled astronomers, is the *secular acceleration*. It was first discovered by Halley in 1695, from a comparison of then current observations of the Moon's position with ancient eclipse observations. The Moon is found to be accelerating by about 11 seconds of arc per century. The problem was partially solved by Laplace, following his discovery of a similar effect in the motions of the great satellites of Jupiter; Laplace showed that the eccentricity of the Earth's orbit is slowly decreasing, due to the perturbations of the other planets, and that this would result in a corresponding acceleration in the Moon's motion. It was shown by Adams in 1880, however, that his explanation would account only

for an acceleration of 5″7 per century. The difference (5″3) between this figure and the observed acceleration remained a mystery, until it was shown by Jeffries and Taylor in 1922 that it is probably due to a gradual lengthening in the Earth's period of axial rotation, due to the friction between tidal currents and the ocean floor.

The first attempt to develop a dynamical theory of the motion of the Moon was made by Newton in his *Principia* of 1686; the first tables of the Moon's motion were produced by Clairaut in 1752. Numerous theories of the motion were developed by leading astronomers, culminating with that evolved by the British-born astronomer E. W. Brown during 30 years work on the problem. Brown's *Tables of the motion of the Moon*, published in 1919, are the most complete ever produced and were used as the basis of lunar ephemerides until 1960, when they were only superseded by the direct calculation of ephemeris positions from theory by computer, without recourse to tables at all. The theory used is still essentially that developed by Brown.

It is now realized that accurate positions of the Moon cannot be predicted far in advance, owing to uncertainties in the rotation of the Earth, which is subject to small erratic variations. The lunar ephemeris is therefore calculated from theory and corrected in the light of the most recent observations of the Earth's rotation, prior to its publication in *The Astronomical Ephemeris*.

MOON—OBSERVATION OF Determinations of the Moon's place are of great importance, owing to the complexity of its motion and the constant need for accurate observations to improve its ephemeris; they can only be made with positional instruments of an accuracy not normally encountered outside the professional observatory.

The study of the features of the lunar surface, however, is one in which amateur observers have traditionally played a leading part, and continue to do so. Although extremely detailed maps exist, based in part upon the study of photographs made with some of the world's most powerful telescopes, the appearance of individual features changes constantly due to the effects of libration and the changing angle of illumination, and invaluable work can thus be done, even with quite modest telescopes. For observational work to be of real scientific value, however, it should be carried out in accordance with a carefully planned programme such as that of the Lunar Section of the British Astronomical Association.

Much of the work for visual observers is now concerned with the study of features in the difficult-to-photograph limb regions; such excellent photographs exist of most of the disk, under all conditions of illumination, that a great deal of the study of features therein is now carried out with the aid of photographs. Telescopic observation of these features is still necessary for checking and cases of doubtful interpretation, and in the search for very fine detail. Statistical studies, e.g. of the distribution of various types of feature, have become very important in recent years in investigations into the nature of the features and the general structure of the Moon's surface layers.

Other important work is concerned with the measurement of the relative positions and sizes of the surface features, the lengths of shadows (from which the heights of mountains can be derived), the search for evidence of lava flow, etc.

MOON—ORBITAL DATA

The Moon's orbit has a semi-major axis of 0·00257 A.U., a mean distance from the Earth of 238,900 miles. The mean orbital eccentricity being 0·0549, the actual distance varies between 225,600 and 252,300. The Moon's orbit is subject to major perturbations by the Sun in addition to those caused by the planets.

The sidereal period of orbital revolution is 27·322 days; the mean synodic period is 29·531 days. The orbital plane is inclined to the plane of the Ecliptic by 5° 09′.

MOON—ORIGIN OF SURFACE FEATURES

The nature and the mechanism of formation of the various features of the lunar surface have long been favourite subjects for speculation; the many theories propounded fall into two main groups, the *impact theories* and the *volcanic theories*.

Many variants of the impact theory have been formulated over the years, notably by G. K. Gilbert, R. B. Baldwin and H. C. Urey; sometimes termed *meteoric* or *meteoritic* theories, they seek to account for the formation of the ring structures by the impact of enormous meteorites or small satellites of the Earth–Moon system, smaller formations being attributed to secondary impacts, ricochets, etc. There are a number of vital problems which the impact theories leave unsolved, but for many years they were supported by a substantial majority of astronomers— although it is perhaps significant that these were mostly experts in fields other than lunar study; recent observational evidence has proved to be wholly in support of the volcanic theories and acceptance of volcanism as the principal cause of the surface features is rapidly spreading.

The volcanic theories, often described as *igneous* and sometimes as *plutonic* theories, attribute the various features to volcanic eruptions and subsidences and lava flow when the lunar rock was plastic; they have been developed by many selenologists, notably J. E. Spurr and G. Fielder. They account very satisfactorily for the formation of ring structures of all sizes, the smaller craters by eruptions similar to terrestrial volcanoes of the Vesuvius type and the larger ring plains by volcanic collapse, as in terrestrial calderas. The morphology of the maria and the wrinkle ridges and other features of the lunabase is entirely consistent with the suggestion that they are plains of solidified lava.

Studies of the faulting of the lunar surface and of the rilles and other surface features show a pronounced radial pattern to the Mare Imbrium, and a well-defined over-all grid pattern. The former has been used as evidence of a colossal meteoritic impact in the Mare Imbrium, but both can be satisfactorily explained by tectonic movement during the cooling phase following an era of plutonic activity.

The close-up photographs of the surface obtained by lunar-probe vehicles show surface detail far smaller than was hitherto detectable, and are quite consistent with the volcanic theory. It is interesting that the photographs of the surface of Mars obtained by the *Mariner 4* spacecraft revealed ring structures similar to those of the Moon. J. F. Simpson has shown that the size–frequency ratios of both lunar and Martian ring structures are consistent with those of terrestrial volcanic craters and calderas, but are not consistent with those of terrestrial meteorite craters.

Clearly no one theory can be expected to account for all the observed features of the lunar surface—both mechanisms must have contributed. The arguments as to the mechanism responsible for the majority of the observed features continue, but the evidence now seems to be almost overwhelmingly in favour of the volcanic theory. Some of the minor pitting is no doubt due to meteoric impact, and a few huge, broad chasms such as the Alpine and Rheita valleys are almost certainly due to grazing impact by meteorites. [Plate 6(a).]

Close-up photographs of the lunar surface obtained by the recent *Orbiter* and *Apollo* spacecraft provide additional support for the view that the surface features were mainly formed by volcanic activity.

(See also **Moon—principal surface features of.**)

MOON—PRINCIPAL SURFACE FEATURES OF

Many of the more notable features of the lunar surface are shown in the maps (Figs. 91 and 92); they are described by name in individual entries in this book. The numbers in the following list of features refer to Figs. 91 and 92. Names marked with an asterisk (*) are of features on the far side of the Moon (See **Moon—far side of.**) [Plates 4–8.]

1. Albategnius
2. Alpetragius
3. Alphonsus
4. Altai mountains
5. Anaxagoras
6. Anaximander
7. Appenines
8. Archimedes
9. Ariadæus
10. Ariadæus Rille
11. Aristarchus
12. Aristillus
13. Aristoteles
14. Arzachel
15. Atlas
16. Autolycus

17. Bailly
18. Bessel
19. Birt
20. Bullialdus

21. Capella
22. Carpathian mountains
23. Cassini
24. Catharina
25. Caucasus mountains
26. Clavius
27. Cleomedes
28. Copernicus
29. Cyrillus

30. Darwin
31. Dionysius
32. Doppelmayer
33. Dörfel mountains

34. Endymion
35. Eratosthenes
36. Eudoxus

37. Fabricius
38. Firmicus
39. Flamsteed
40. Fracastorius
41. Furnerius

42. Gassendi
43. Gauss
44. Geminus
45. Giordano Bruno *
46. Grimaldi

47. Hæmus mountains
48. Hercules
49. Herodotus

50. Herodotus Valley
51. Hesiodus
52. Hesiodus Rille
53. Hevel
54. Hevelius
55. Hipparchus
56. Horbiger
57. Hyginus
58. Hyginus Rille

59. Janssen
60. Joliot-Curie *
61. Jules Verne *
62. Julius Cæsar

63. Kepler

64. Lacus Somniorum
65. Langrenus
66. Letronne
67. Linné
68. Lobachevskii *
69. Lomonosov *

70. Macrobius
71. Maginus
72. Manilius
73. Mare Australe
74. Mare Crisium
75. Mare Fœcunditatis
76. Mare Frigoris
77. Mare Humboldtianum
78. Mare Humorum
79. Mare Imbrium
80. Mare Ingenii *
81. Mare Marginis
82. Mare Moscovianum *
83. Mare Nectaris
84. Mare Nubium
85. Mare Serenitatis
86. Mare Smythii
87. Mare Somnii
88. Mare Spumans
89. Mare Tranquillitatis
90. Mare Undarum
91. Mare Vaporum
92. Maurolycus
93. Mendeleev *
94. Menelaus
95. Mersenius
96. Messier
97. Moretus
98. Newton

99. Oceanus Procellarum
100. Olbers

101. Palitzsch
102. Palus Somnii
103. Petavius
104. Philolaus
105. Piccolomini
106. Pickering
107. Pico
108. Pitatus
109. Piton
110. Plato
111. Plinius
112. Posidonius
113. Proclus
114. Ptolemæus
115. Purbach
116. Pythagoras

117. Regiomontanus
118. Rheita
119. Rheita Valley
120. Riccioli

121. Scheiner
122. Schickard
123. Schiller
124. Scott
125. Shackleton
126. Sinus Æstuum
127. Sinus Astronautarum *
128. Sinus Iridum
129. Sinus Medii
130. Sinus Roris
131. Sklodowska-Curie *
132. Sovietskii mountains *
133. Stadius
134. Stag's Horn mountain
135. Stöfler
136. Straight Range
137. Straight Wall

138. Thebit
139. Theophilus
140. Timocharis
141. Triesnecker
142. Triesnecker Clefts
143. Tsiolkovskii *
144. Tycho

145. Vendelinus

146. Walter
147. Wargentin
148. Werner
149. Wilhelm Humboldt

150. Zagut

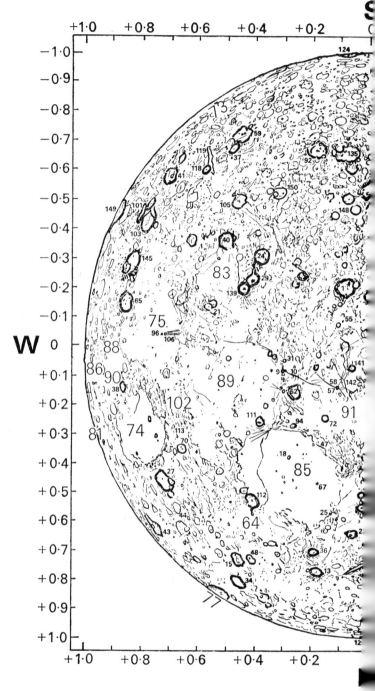

Fig. 91

272

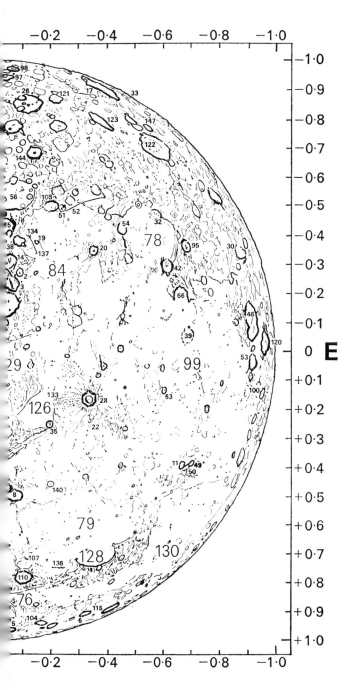

Fig. 92

MOON—TYPES OF SURFACE FEATURE

To the unaided eye it is clear that two types of surface prevail on the Moon, which appear as dark and light areas. With the aid of a small telescope it is seen that the light areas are in fact very mountainous and rugged, whereas the dark areas (*maria*) are comparatively smooth plains broken by only quite minor features. The dark rock of basic composition which forms the maria is termed *lunabase*; in older references it is sometimes described as 'marebase'. The rock of which the mountainous features of the bright regions are composed is believed to be less dense than the lunabase; it is termed *lunarite*. [Plate 4(a).]

Numerous attempts to classify the surface features by their morphology have been made, but until very recently there has been little real effort made to improve the hybrid and inexplicit terminology generally used.

It is usual to refer to the dark grey plains as maria, irrespective of their sizes which range from thousands of square miles to a few hundred square miles.

The most common types of lunar surface are the *ring-structures*; a few occur on the maria, but most of them are found in the bright areas of lunarite. The remaining portions of the bright areas consist of very rugged mountainous terrain.

The ring-structures occur in a diversity of forms and sizes. They are usually loosely referred to as 'craters', but the term *ring-structures* is to be preferred.

A very rough morphological classification of the ring structures has been used for many years, deriving from the work of T. G. Elger, W. Goodacre and others. Large, near-circular plains enclosed by rugged mountain ramparts were termed 'Mountain-walled plains' or simply 'walled plains'. The diameters of these features range from about 60 miles to 180 miles. Their ramparts are often terraced, and are usually very broken, often by vast chasms and ravines and frequently by smaller ring formations. The inner slopes of the ramparts are usually less steep than the outer slopes. Their floors are usually fairly smooth, although small ring structures, clefts, ridges and crater pits do occur in many of them. Typical examples are Bailly, Plato and Ptolemæus.

Rather smaller ring structures, with less broken ramparts and a more nearly circular outline, were usually termed 'ring-plains'; their diameters range from about 30 miles to about 60 miles and they frequently have a large central mountain mass, often with multiple peaks. Such ring structures are very numerous, and include some of the most beautiful objects on the Moon. Among the most striking examples are Copernicus, Eratosthenes, Theophilus and Tycho.

The most numerous type of large ring structure were termed *craters* or *crater rings*—almost circular objects, with steep narrow walls and diameters from 5 to 30 miles. Many of them have small central peaks.

Very small craters, having diameters less than 5 miles, occur in thousands; they are termed *craterlets*. They are often found in the floors of larger features, such as Archimedes and Plato.

Another type of small object of which thousands have been detected are the *crater pits*; these differ from craterlets in that they have no raised wall; they have deep interiors and often very irregular outlines. They are detectable only under low angles of illumination, i.e. when close to the terminator.

In some areas of the Moon *crater cones* are found, steep-sided conical hills, often with a tiny central orifice.

There are numerous mountain ranges on the Moon, notably the Appenines and Alps on the borders of the Mare Imbrium; much of the southern part of the disk is generally mountainous between the many ring structures, and there are also cases of single, isolated peaks such as Pico and Piton.

Many areas of the lunar surface show evidence of local faulting; there is also evidence of large-scale faults and deformations, notably the crater chains and larger rilles.

Contemporary studies of the lunar surface features concentrate particularly upon their relationships with each other; they are found to occur in many interesting configurations, some at least of which will probably prove to be of significance in theories of the structure of the lunar crust and the origin of the surface features. This approach has led to a revision of the nomenclature of the different types of feature on a much more rational basis. Some of the principal types of formation in this scheme, which is largely due to G. Fielder, are briefly described here.

Ring structures

Elementary ring structure. A ring formation having a simple wall of regular cross-section, enclosing a floor which is at the same level as the surrounding surface. Sometimes termed a *simple ring*.

Elliptical ring structure. A ring formation having a peripheral wall elliptical in shape. Elliptical ring structures often occur in crater chains and in bright ray systems.

Multi-ring structure. A ring formation having two or more distinct, concentric walls.

Plateau ring structure. One whose floor is raised above the level of the surrounding surface; the best-known example is Wargentin.

Polygonal ring structure. One whose peripheral wall is polygonal in form: a notable example is Ptolemæus.

Spiral ring structure. A ring formation in which ridges are seen spiralling inwards from the ramparts across the floor.

Concentric ring structures. Two ring structures of different diameter, the smaller being centrally (or near-centrally) placed within the larger. Hesiodus A is a fine example.

Eccentric ring structures. Two ring structures of different diameter where the smaller is within the larger but not centrally situated, touching the wall of the larger ring at one point.

Interlocking ring structures. Ring structures which overlap but with the walls of both in existence, indicating that they were formed contemporaneously.

Consanguineous ring structures. Two or more ring structures of similar form in close proximity; in true consanguineous ring structures the component formations are similar in detailed structure as well as in general shape.

Twin ring structures. Consanguineous ring structures where the component formations are also equal in size.

Contiguous craters. Craters in contact, the walls being low, broken or entirely absent at the point of contact.

Bowl crater. A crater having a concave floor; this property is very common in craters up to 10 miles in diameter.

Rille crater. A crater or craterlet forming part of a rille.

Ringwall crater. A crater situated centrally on the rampart of a larger ring-structure.

Summit crater. A craterlet situated at the top of the central peak of a ring structure or on an isolated mountain peak.

Ghost ring. A ring structure whose ramparts are largely or wholly missing, but whose outline (or part thereof) is marked by wrinkle ridges or other discontinuities of the surface.

Other important surface features

Crater chains. These occur in three main forms: *open chains*, in which the component craters are linearly arranged but not touching; *contiguous chains*, in which the walls of adjacent craters are actually in contact; and *decremental chains*, in which the craters decrease in diameter progressively from one end of the chain to the other. Craters also form curved lines—these are termed *crater arcs*.

Domes. Shallow raised eminences on the lunar surface with a smooth convex cross-section. About a hundred domes have been discovered, with diameters ranging from a few miles up to about 50 miles. Many have small summit craters.

Rilles. This is the term now preferred for the trench-like features previously known as 'clefts', especially for the larger examples. Some of the larger rilles have small craters in them, giving them a resemblance to crater chains. In some cases (e.g. in the vicinity of the crater Triesnecker) a large number of small rilles or clefts form a complicated network. Two superb examples of the large, broad rilles are associated with the ring structures Ariadæus and Hyginus.

Wrinkle ridges. Prominent, sharply defined ridges, so named because of the sinuous nature of many of them. They are normally less than 500 ft. in height, and have gently sloping sides. They are often concentric with the walls of large ring-structures, and often form the 'walls' of ghost rings. They are frequently seen to continue the line of a rille, suggesting that both types of feature shared a common origin during the period of formation of the Moon's crust. Perhaps the best-known example is the great 'serpentine ridge', first recorded by Schröter, in the eastern part of the Mare Serenitatis.

(See also **Lunar ray systems; Moon—principal surface features of.**)

MORETUS (Lunar surface feature, co-ordinates $\xi - 036$, $\eta - 941$); a large walled plain 75 miles in diameter, situated very close to the lunar South Pole. The terraced walls rise to 9,000 ft. There is a beautifully formed central peak rising 7,000 ft. above the floor—the highest known central peak on the Moon.

MORPHOLOGICAL ASTRONOMY In the morphological approach to astronomical research the observed form of the heavenly bodies is studied and an attempt is made to draw conclusions therefrom. The approach lends itself particularly well to some of the large-scale problems of astrophysics, where its conclusions often provide a starting point for further analysis utilizing observational evidence which may be more detailed but which may only be obtainable for parts of the problem. A particularly good example is the study of the galaxies: the morphology of these shows various forms (elliptical, spiral, irregular) and purely morphological reasoning leads to the suggestion of an evolutionary sequence, as proposed by Hubble in 1936. When more sophisticated observational techniques were developed the data they provided was applied to Hubble's first proposal which could then be amplified and amended; the currently accepted sequence of **galactic evolution** (*q.v.*) is in fact the reverse of that originally propounded by Hubble.

The morphological approach has similarly assisted the early creation of a theoretical model to support observed data in a number of other fields, such as stellar evolution, the large-scale distribution of matter in the universe, etc.

MOUNT PALOMAR OBSERVATORY An observatory founded jointly by the Carnegie Institution of Washington and the California Institute of Technology, to house the 200-in. Hale reflector, named after the man whose brain-child it was and whose organizing ability paved the way for its construction. Situated on Palomar Mountain, a 6,000-ft. plateau in the mountains of Southern California, 125 miles from Pasadena. Test observations were commenced in January 1948 and completed in the autumn of 1949; the telescope was formally dedicated to the memory of George Ellery Hale on 1948 June 3. [Plate 31(d).]

The observatory also houses two major Schmidt cameras, the 18-in. × 26-in. $f/2$ Schmidt and the 48-in. × 72-in., $f/2.5$ instrument, at present the largest in the world and employed in the production of the Palomar Sky Atlas. [Plate 29(b).]

MOUNT STROMLO OBSERVATORY The Commonwealth Observatory of

Australia, situated on Mount Stromlo a few miles from Canberra. The principal instrument is a 74-in. reflector; there are also a 30-in. reflector, a 12-in. solar telescope and a 50-in. Gregorian–Schmidt camera.

The Yale–Columbia Southern Station is also situated at Mount Stromlo, the 26-in. photographic refractor having been transferred from its former site at Johannesburg owing to the latter's deteriorating observing conditions.

MOUNT WILSON OBSERVATORY

One of the world's leading centres for observation, established in 1904 by the Carnegie Institution of Washington, on the recommendation of G. E. Hale. Situated on the summit of Mount Wilson (5,886 ft.), a few miles from Pasadena in Southern California.

Principal equipment includes the Hooker 100-in. reflector (mirror by Ritchey), which has been in use since 1917, the earlier 60-in. reflector, also by Ritchey, in use since 1908, 60-ft. and 150-ft. solar tower telescopes, and the Snow coelostat, originally constructed by Hale and Ritchey at the Yerkes Observatory and transferred to the Mount Wilson Observatory on its foundation. [Plates 29(a); 30(c, d).]

MOUNTINGS, TELESCOPE

The principal functions of a telescope mounting are to provide rigidity and freedom from vibration and to permit the instrument to be directed towards the desired part of the heavens.

Small telescopes are usually mounted on a portable tripod; this must be very rigid if the telescope is to be usefully used. The 'pillar and claw' stand with which many small refractors are fitted are generally too unstable to be of use. Larger instruments are normally mounted on a heavy iron pillar. For maximum stability this should be bolted to a large concrete block set into the ground. The observatory floor should be built on separate foundations and there should be clearance of at least an inch between it and the telescope pillar, so as to avoid the transmission of vibration. Observatory instruments are usually supported by heavy steel castings on concrete piers which are themselves usually supported by steel-reinforced concrete piles.

The simplest form of mounting is the *altazimuth mounting*, in which the telescope is permitted movement about two axes— one vertical (giving a motion in azimuth) and one horizontal (giving a motion in altitude). This type of mounting has a major disadvantage: in order to counteract the motion of an observed body across the field, due to the diurnal rotation of the Earth, the telescope must be moved in both altitude and azimuth simultaneously; this is difficult to achieve satisfactorily, especially in the case of larger instruments.

Most telescopes intended for serious observing are therefore provided with an *equatorial mounting*. In this, one axis—the polar axis—can be adjusted so that it is parallel to the Earth's axis of rotation; the other, the declination axis, is perpendicular to the polar axis. The telescope can be driven around the polar axis, in the direction opposite to that of the Earth's rotation, at the rate of one revolution per sidereal day; this drive is provided in many instruments by means of a clockwork mechanism but modern instruments usually have an electric drive. The instrument is moved around the declination axis only when setting; it is then clamped, the drive around the polar axis being sufficient to keep the desired object in the field of view. The observer is usually provided with a remote control to the drive, so that by speeding up or retarding the drive he can keep the object under observation accurately centred on the cross-wires of the guiding telescope.

MULTIPLE STAR

A star system comprising three or more component stars. A considerable number are known, many of them incorporating binary systems. Probably the best known examples are *Mizar* (ζ UMa), with its fainter companion *Alcor*, and *Castor*. *Mizar* and

Alcor were the first-recognized optical double, recorded by Riccioli in about 1650, but *Mizar* itself was discovered by Pickering to be a spectroscopic binary in 1889.

Castor (α Gem) is an optical double, of which both components are spectroscopic binaries; there is also a third fainter spectroscopic binary in the group, which therefore comprises six known components.

Two notable multiple stars are 61 Cygni and 70 Ophiuchi. Both of these are known spectroscopic binaries, but the presence of a third body in each case has been determined from peculiarities in their binary motion. The unseen second companion of 61 Cyg has a mass approximately sixteen times that of Jupiter and the companion of 70 Oph approximately ten times that of Jupiter. Their small masses imply that these small companions are non-luminous bodies, which may therefore be regarded as planets. It is believed that many other stars may have small planetary companions which have not yet been detected because of their greater distance.

MULTI-RING-STRUCTURES   Lunar surface features in which two or more ring-structures are contained within a larger ring-structure. (See **Moon—surface features of.**)

MURAL CIRCLE See **Circle, mural**.

MUSCA (The Fly; originally Musca Australis, the Southern Fly. *Genitive* Muscae, *I.A.U. abbreviation* Mus.) A small southern circumpolar constellation adjoining Crux.

N

N STARS Stars of spectral class N; this is a group of red stars of surface temperature about 2,200° K similar to the M stars but containing rather less oxygen and more carbon.

N.A.S.A. Abbreviation for the National Aeronautics and Space Administration, the United States government agency responsible for the co-ordination of all American earth-satellite and space-probe programmes.

N.G.C. Usual abbreviation for the *New General Catalogue of Nebulæ and Clusters of Stars* by J. L. E. Dreyer.
(See **New General Catalogue.**)

N.P.D. Abbreviation for **North polar distance**, *q.v.*

N.P.S. The **North polar sequence**, *q.v.*

NADIR The point on the celestial sphere vertically below the observer; it is the opposite point to the **zenith**. The zenith and nadir are the poles of the great circle known as the celestial horizon.
(See also **Celestial sphere; Horizon, celestial.**)

NAKED-EYE Term commonly used to describe observations made with the unaided eye, i.e. without the use of a telescope or other optical instrument. Observations made with simple sighting instruments which do not contain optical elements are normally taken to be naked-eye observations.

NASMYTH, James (1808–1890) A British engineer well known for his invention of the steam-hammer; he cast and figured a number of speculum mirrors, notably a 20-in. which he mounted as a Cassegrain–Newtonian on a large turn table carrying both telescope and observer, thus permitting the observer to direct the instrument to any part of the sky without moving from the eyepiece. With this instrument Nasmyth carried out an extensive programme of solar and lunar observation after his retirement from business. His observations of lunar surface features led him to propound the **volcanic theory** of their origin and, with J. Carpenter in 1874, to publish *The Moon*. This book included a chart of the surface features drawn by Nasmyth with a diameter of 12 inches. A notable feature of the book is its use of plates showing lunar-type formations produced in plaster, to illustrate Nasmyth's arguments in support of the volcanic theory.

NATIONAL RADIO ASTRONOMY OBSERVATORY The Federal radio observatory of the United States, situated at Green Bank, West Virginia, U.S.A.

NAUTICAL ALMANAC Shortly before his appointment as Astronomer Royal **Maskelyne** published a handbook for seamen entitled *The British Mariner's Guide* which contained the necessary tables for the determination of the longitude at sea from sextant observations of the Moon's position. Convinced of the need for such a publication, Maskelyne founded *The Nautical Almanac and Astronomical Ephemeris* in the year following his appointment as Astronomer Royal in 1765. In the first issue (for the year 1767) Maskelyne described it as 'a Work which must greatly contribute to the Improvement of Astronomy, Geography and Navigation', a description with which few would disagree. Maskelyne was himself responsible for the preparation of forty-four editions of the 'N.A.'.

The tables of distances of the Moon from adjacent bright stars—the principle content of the first edition—were continued until 1906; additional tables had been added at intervals, the trend being a slow change towards a handbook for astronomers rather than for navigators. The layout of the *Almanac* was completely revised for the issue of 1931. The first part of the *Almanac*, containing the tables of particular use to the navigator, was republished separately from 1896; this was followed by the publication, from 1914, of *The Nautical Almanac, Abridged for the Use of Seamen*. This publication was re-named *The Abridged Nautical Almanac* in 1952.

The Nautical Almanac Office became a separate institution from the Royal Observatory in 1831, but like the Observatory remained under the control of the British Admiralty. It was placed once again under the supervision of the Astronomer Royal, as a department of the Royal Observatory, in 1937.

Throughout the twentieth century there had been a continuing growth of international collaboration in the preparation of the various national ephemerides, especially between the United Kingdom and the United States of America. This culminated with the amalgamation of *The Nautical Almanac* and *The American Ephemeris* from the issue for 1960. The combined volume is published jointly in the two countries, in the U.K. under the new title *The Astronomical Ephemeris*; in the U.S.A. the existing title, *The American Ephemeris and Nautical Almanac*, is retained. From 1960 the British *Abridged Nautical Almanac* was appropriately re-titled *The Nautical Almanac*.

NAUTICAL ALMANAC OFFICE The department of the Royal Greenwich Observatory responsible for the production of *The Astronomical Ephemeris*. (See also **Nautical Almanac**.)

NAUTICAL TWILIGHT The periods during which the depression of the Sun's centre below the theoretical horizon is between 6° and 12°. (See **Twilight**.)

NAVIGATION, ASTRONOMICAL The basic problem of navigation is the determination of one's position on the surface of the Earth at a given time; this means, in effect, the determination of one's terrestrial latitude and longitude. Most of the more precise means of determining these co-ordinates involve positional observations of astronomical objects, although in recent years there has been considerable development of techniques utilizing directional radio beams and the radar principle.

The determination of one's longitude by astronomical means is very simple, for it can be calculated from the observed time at which a star or other body of known position on the celestial sphere transits the meridian; the necessary requirements are therefore only a knowledge of the positions of suitable celestial bodies and accurate time. The former is provided by a suitable compendium of tables, e.g. the *Nautical Almanac*, and the latter requirement was originally solved by the development of the marine chronometer and is now met by wireless time-signals.

There are several means of deducing one's latitude from astronomical observations, most of them based upon the fact that the latitude of the observer is equal to the observed altitude of the celestial pole: thus if the altitudes are measured of two or more stars whose celestial co-ordinates are accurately known, the altitude of the pole and hence the observer's latitude can be determined. The requirements are, therefore, again the *Nautical Almanac* and some means of measuring altitudes—normally a sextant. At sea the marine sextant is used alone, the horizon providing a horizontal reference; on land an artificial horizon must be used in conjunction with the marine sextant. In the air this would be impracticable, and a specially designed self-levelling instrument—the bubble sextant—is used.

NEBULA Term originally used for all celestial bodies having a hazy appearance, including galaxies and star clusters as well as the galactic nebulae to which the term is now restricted. (See **Nebulae—types of.**)

NEBULA, ABSORPTION A galactic nebula whose dust and gas content is not illuminated by the action of an embedded or nearby star, and which is therefore 'visible' only because of its absorption of the light from the background stars which are consequently dimmed or obscured. (See **Nebulae, dark.**)

NEBULA, BRIGHT DIFFUSE Galactic nebulae are concentrations of interstellar matter—a mixture of gas and dust. They are not self-luminous, and many of them are only rendered 'visible' by their obscuration of the background star field; these are the so-called 'dark nebulae'. About a thousand galactic nebulae are known, however, which are actually made visible by the action of nearby stars or stars embedded in the nebula; these fall into two types, the 'reflection' and the 'emission' nebulae. They are generally termed the 'bright diffuse' nebulae.

The *reflection nebulae* are composed largely of cosmic dust and are seen by means of starlight scattered by the individual particles. The adjacent, or embedded, stars are giants or supergiants of spectral type later than *B2*, since hotter stars cause the nebula to emit radiation and hence to be classified as an emission nebula.

The spectrum of a reflection nebula is of course identical to that of the associated star. One of the best-known examples of a reflection nebula is the extensive nebulosity surrounding the stars of the **Pleiades** cluster. [Plate 22(d).]

Emission nebulae also are luminous only by the action of a star; in this case, however, a *B2*-type or hotter star, the ultra-violet radiation from which ionizes the hydrogen gas with consequent radiation; further

radiation arises from the recombination of free electrons and nuclei. The spectrum shows lines due to hydrogen and to ionized forms of nitrogen, oxygen, etc. Particularly notable are the so-called **forbidden lines,** not identifiable with the aid of laboratory-produced comparison spectra but now known to be due to highly ionized forms of oxygen, nitrogen, neon, etc. The most prominent of these lines, formerly attributed to a hypothetical element ('nebulium'), are at wavelengths 4959 Å and 5007 Å; these are in the green part of the visible spectrum, and are responsible for the characteristic greenish hue of the emission nebulae. There is also a prominent doublet at 3727 Å; all of these more prominent forbidden lines are due to ionized oxygen. The Great Nebula in Orion is the best-known and one of the largest of the emission nebulae. [Plate 21(b).]

The bright diffuse nebulae are of great importance in studies of stellar evolution; the majority of *O*- and *B*-type stars are found in or near emission nebulae, which may indicate that the nebulae mark areas where new stars are actually being formed. Small, dark nebulae of globular form, termed 'globules', are common on the outskirts of emission nebulae and may be actual **proto-stars.**

(See also **Evolution, stellar; Nebulae, dark; Nebulae—types of.**)

NEBULA, DARK Galactic nebulae are not self-luminous, the only ones which can be actually seen or photographed being the bright diffuse nebulae whose luminosity is due to the activity of a nearby star. There is a great deal of interstellar gas and dust which is not so illuminated, but the presence of much of it can be detected by its obscuration of the background stars, the light from which is absorbed and scattered by the dust particles and molecules of gas in the nebula. Most of these 'dark nebulae' are in areas containing bright diffuse nebulosity, a fact which emphasizes their similar nature. Among the best-known dark nebulae are the 'Coalsack' adjacent to the Southern Cross and the 'Horse-head' nebula in Orion. [Plate 21(a, c).]

There is a second type of dark nebula which is of considerable importance; this is the group known as *globules*—comparatively small, very dense, absorption nebulae of approximately spherical form. It is believed that globules may in fact be *proto-stars*—new stars in the process of being formed.

(See also **Evolution, stellar; Nebulae, bright diffuse; Nebulae—types of.**)

NEBULA, EMISSION A type of bright, diffuse nebula whose luminosity arises from the excitement of its gases by the ultra-violet radiation from a nearby *O*- or *B*-type star, causing it to emit light. The emission spectrum produced consists mainly of lines due to hydrogen and to ionized forms of oxygen and nitrogen. (See **Nebula, bright diffuse.**)

NEBULA, REFLECTION A type of bright, diffuse nebula whose luminosity arises from the scattering, by the dust particles of which it is partly comprised, of the light from a nearby giant star. This star is always of type *B3* or later, earlier types resulting in *emission nebulae*. (See **Nebula, bright diffuse.**)

NEBULAE, EXTRAGALACTIC Early name, now superseded, for **Galaxies**, *q.v.*

NEBULAE, GALACTIC Term usually used to denote the gaseous nebulae contained within our Galaxy, which comprise the 'bright diffuse nebulae' and the 'dark nebulae'. They are also observed in some of the other nearby galaxies.

NEBULAE, GASEOUS The galactic nebulae, consisting of gas and dust clouds and comprising the 'bright diffuse' and the 'dark' nebulae. [Plate 21(b, e).]

NEBULAE—TYPES OF Many of the objects originally termed nebulae are now known to be quite different from true nebulae; notably the **galaxies** (formerly termed 'extragalactic nebulae'), **star clusters** and **planetary nebulae**, *q.v.*

The true nebulae are those often referred to as 'galactic nebulae'; a more accurate description would be 'intragalactic'. It should be noted that these objects are not confined to our own Galaxy; they have been observed in a number of other galaxies sufficiently close to permit their detection.

The galactic nebulae are also frequently termed 'gaseous' nebulae; it should be remembered however that they are all condensations of interstellar matter, which comprises dust particles as well as gaseous constituents.

The true galactic nebulae comprise the bright diffuse nebulae and the dark, or absorption, nebulae. There are two main types of bright diffuse nebulae, the emission and the reflection nebulae.

(See also **Nebulae, bright diffuse; Nebulae dark.**)

NEBULAR HYPOTHESIS The theory, proposed by Laplace in 1796, that the member bodies of the solar system were formed by the condensation of a hot, rotating, nebular 'atmosphere' surrounding the Sun. (See **Cosmogony—theories of.**)

NEBULAR VARIABLES A class of extrinsic variable stars whose variability seems to be governed by that of nebulae with which they are associated (see **T Tauri stars**).

NEBULIUM Name given to the hypothetical element believed to be the cause of the so-called **forbidden lines** in the spectra of many galactic nebulae, which are now known to be due to highly ionized gases, notably oxygen.

NECTAR Martian surface feature, approximate position Ω 72°, Φ −28°. Canal radiating north-eastward from Solis Lacus, joining eastern border of Thaumasia at the Nectaris Fretum.

NECTARIS FRETUM Martian surface feature, approximate position Ω 67°,

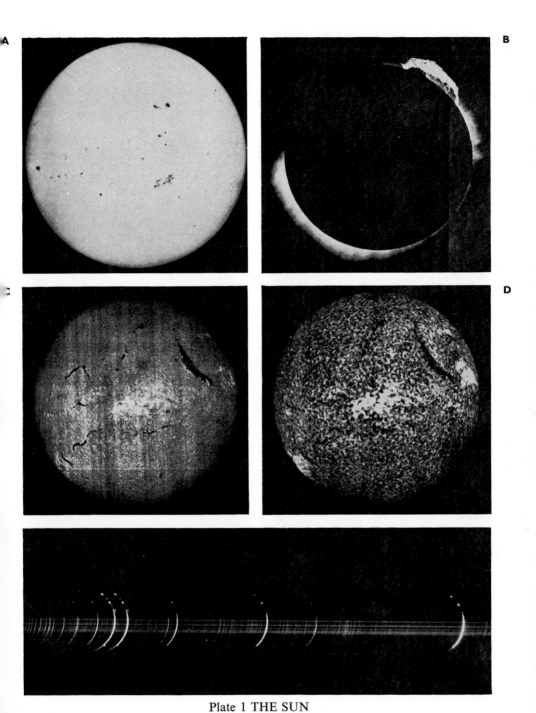

Plate 1 THE SUN

A The whole disk, heavily spotted, 1959 August 29; **B** The total eclipse of 1919 May 29, showing the great 'anteater' prominence.   Spectroheliograms in **C** hydrogen–α light and **D** calcium K₃ light.   **E** Part of the flash spectrum, photographed at the total eclipse of 1925 January 24

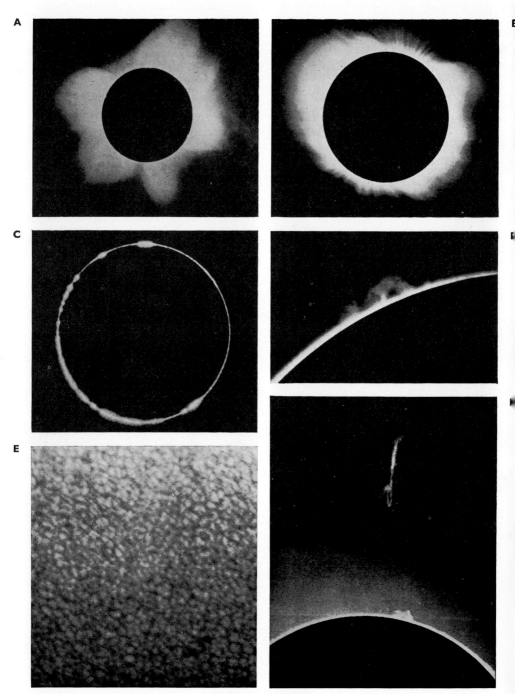

Plate 2 THE SUN

The structure of the corona **A** near sunspot maximum (1936 June 19) and **B** near sunspot minimum (1900 May 28) **C** Baily's beads; **D** Prominence, 1965 August 19, height approx. 30,000 miles; **E** Photospheric granulation, photographed by balloon-borne telescope, 1957; **F** Eruptive prominence, 1928 November 19. (Maximum height reached approx. 600,000 miles)

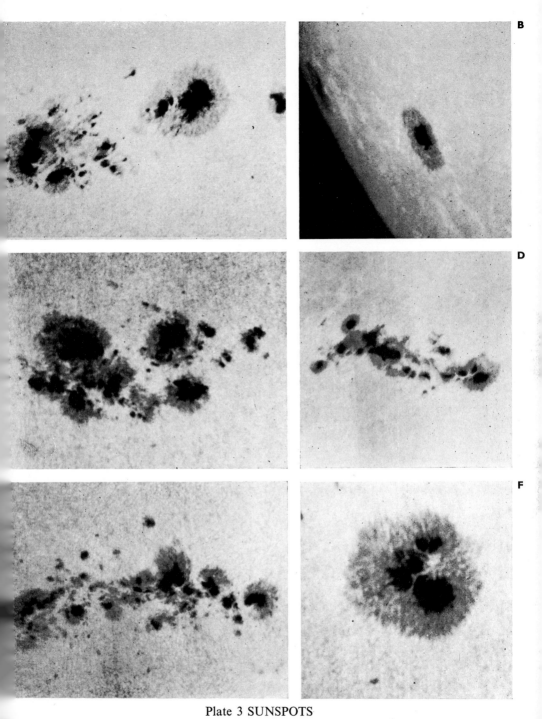

Plate 3 SUNSPOTS

1959 September 10, group almost 100,000 miles long; **B** 1959 October 16, showing the Wilson Effect; **C** 1966 gust 31, group approx. 65,000 miles long; **D** 1967 February 24, group over 100,000 miles long; **E** 1968 October 22, up approx. 90,000 miles long; **F** 1969 April 8, a fine spot more than 25,000 miles in diameter – the largest com-ent of the multiple umbra is equal in diameter to the Earth. [All photographs by W. M. Baxter of Acton, ndon, using a 4-in. refractor]

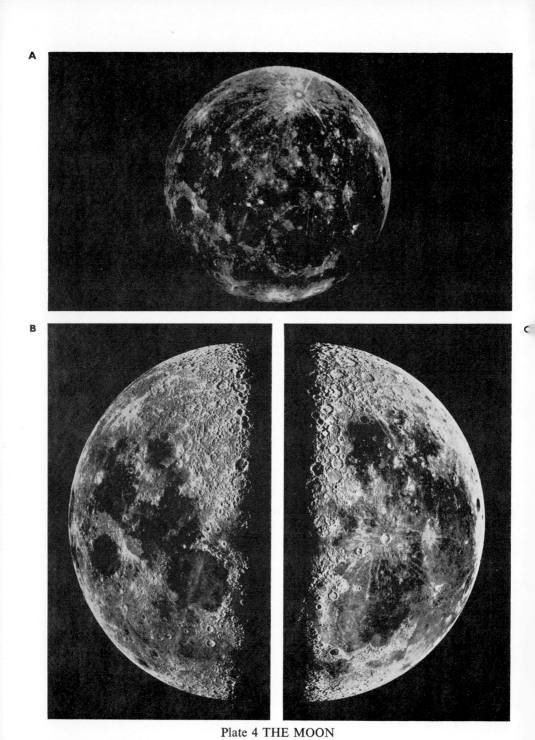

Plate 4 THE MOON

A Age 15 days; **B** age 7 days; **C** age 22 days. (Compare with Figs. 91 and 92, pp. 272–3). [Photographed with the 36-in. refractor at the Lick Observatory]

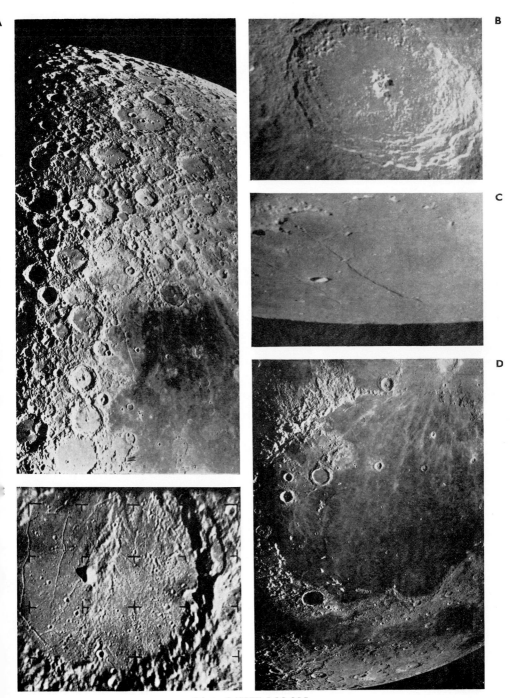

Plate 5 THE MOON

A South pole region to Ptolemaus; **B** Langrenus, photographed from an altitude of 150 miles by the crew of *Apollo 8*, 1968 December 24 [compare with Plate 4 **B**]; **C** Cauchy, with scarp (above) and rille (below); photographed by *Apollo 8* crew, 1968 December 29; **D** Mare Imbrium region; **E** Alphonsus – picture transmitted by *Ranger 9* 1 min. 35 sec. before impact, 1965 March 24 [compare with **A** above]

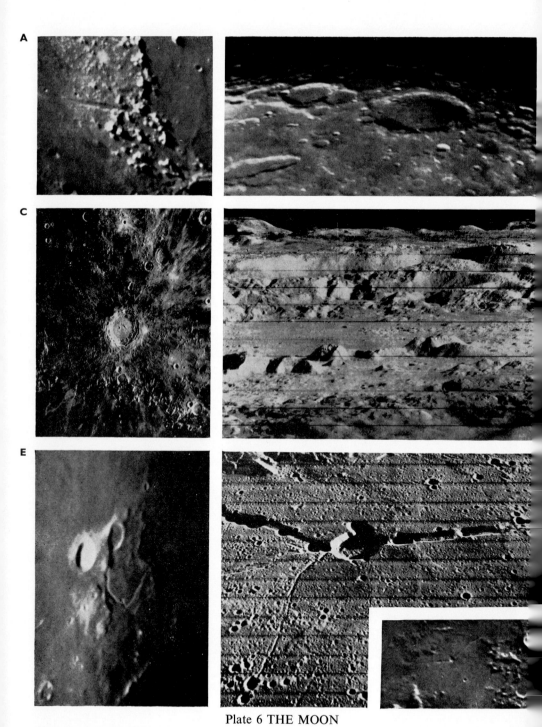

Plate 6 THE MOON

A The Alpine Valley; B Schiller, Phocylides, Wargentin and Schickard. Copernicus – C photographed with 100-i
reflector, Mt Wilson; D close-up looking north across central mountain range, *Orbiter 2* photograph, 196
E Aristarchus, Herodotus and Schröter's Valley. Hyginus and rille, F close-up photograph by *Orbiter 3* an
G normal view from Earth

A

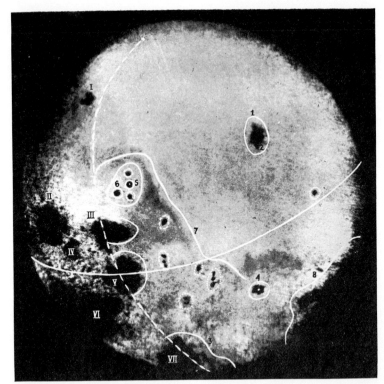

C

Plate 7 THE MOON

A The historic first picture of the far side, obtained by *Lunik 3* in 1957. Key: 1. Mare Muscoviense, including 2. Sinus Astronautarum; 3. part of Mare Australis; 4. Tsiolkovskii; 5. Lomonosov; 6. Joliot-Curie; 7. Sovietskii Mountains; 8. Mare Ingenii. The continuous line is the lunar equator, the broken line marks the limit of the region previously known. Known features: I. Mare Humboldtianum; II. Mare Crisium; III. Mare Marginis; IV. Mare Undarum; V. Mare Smythii; VI. Mare Foecunditatis; VII. Mare Australis. **B** Tycho – close-up photograph by *Orbiter 5*, 1967 [compare with Plate 5 **A**]. **C** The magnificent far-side ring formation Tsiolkovskii, some 200 miles in diameter, photographed by *Orbiter 3*

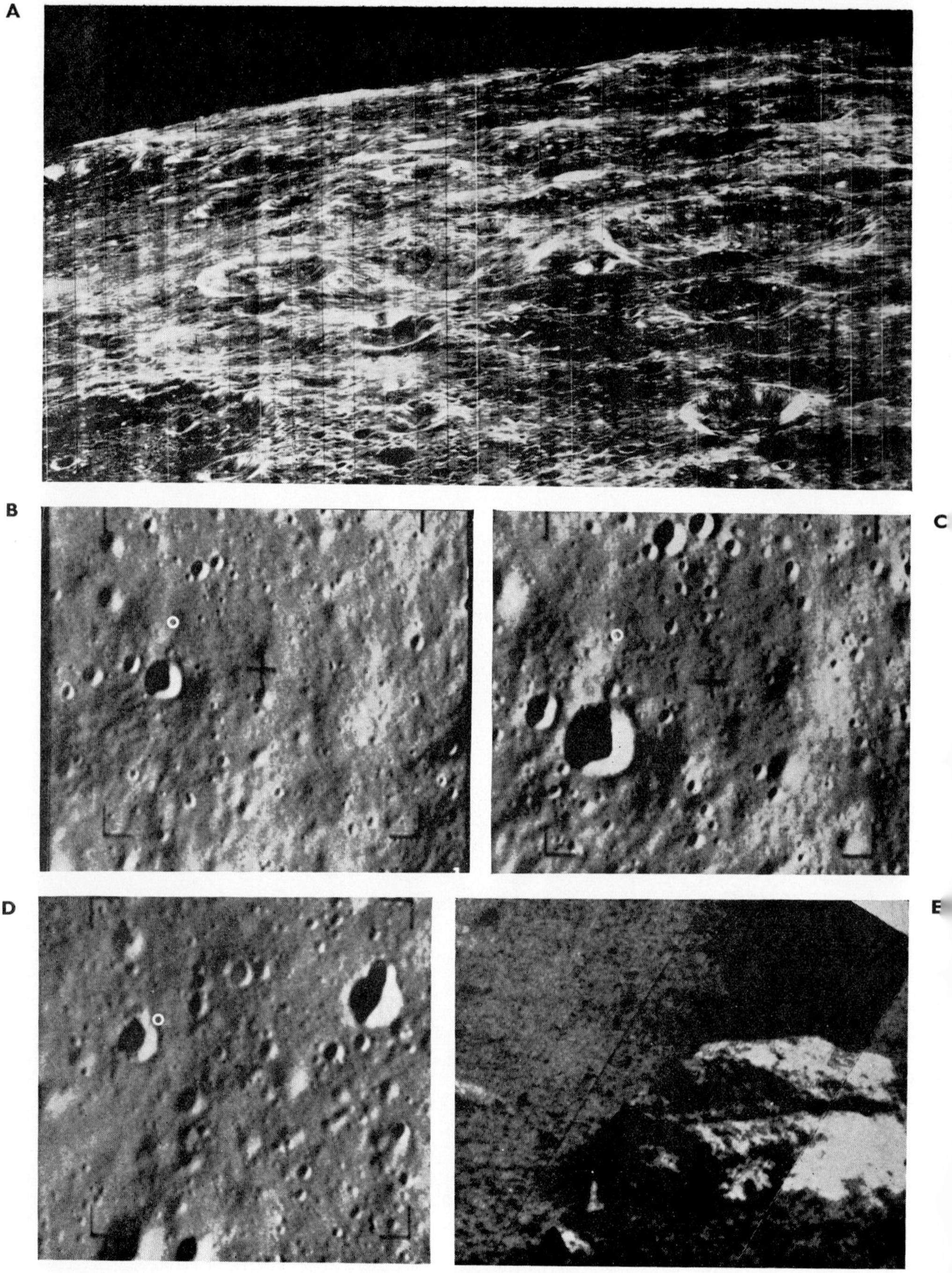

Plate 8 THE MOON

A The lunar landscape – a close-up view by *Orbiter 1*. **B, C, D** Impact area of *Ranger 9* on the surface of Alphonsus, 1966. The last three pictures transmitted by the spacecraft prior to impact. The area of **D** is about 240 feet square; features approx. 20 inches in diameter can be seen. **E** A mosaic of two narrow-angle pictures transmitted by *Surveyor 3* standing on the lunar surface. The grooved stone block is about 20 in. across

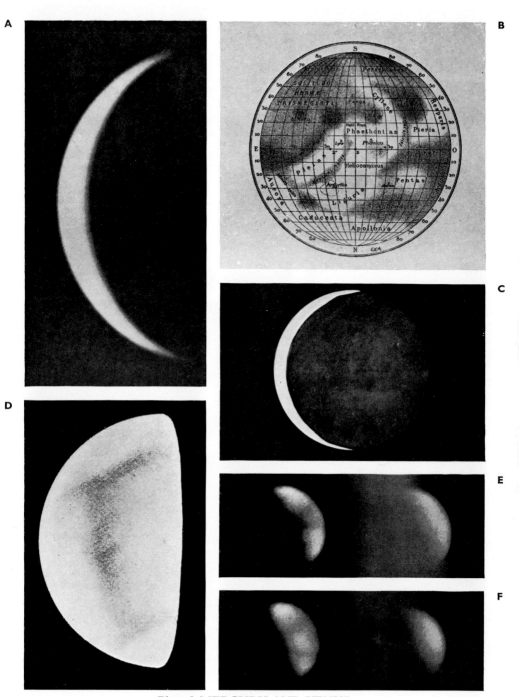

Plate 9 MERCURY AND VENUS

A Venus photographed in blue light, 200-in. reflector, Mt Palomar. **B** Mercury – map of the surface markings drawn by E. M. Antoniadi. **C** Venus – the 'Ashen Light', drawn by Patrick Moore, 1953 March 22; **D** Venus – shadings observed by Patrick Moore, 1954 June 20. Venus photographed in infra-red and ultraviolet light; **E** 1927 November 23, **F** 1927 December 8

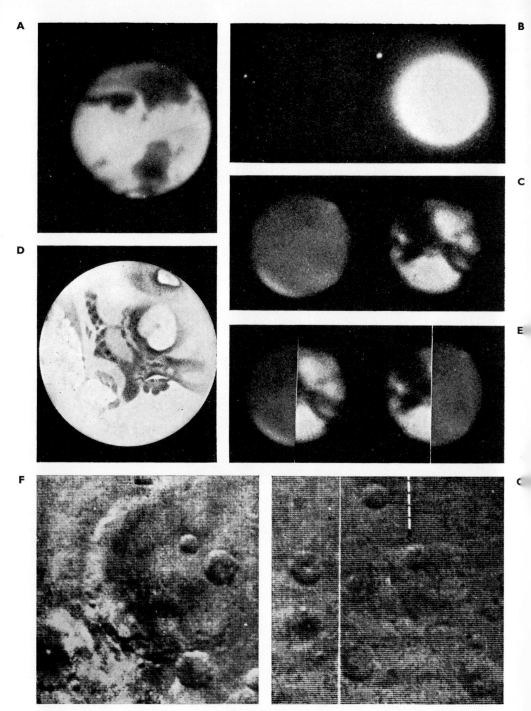

Plate 10 MARS

A Photographed in red light, 200-in. reflector, Mt Palomar; **B** photographed with its two satellites, 82-in. reflector, McDonald Observatory; **C** photographed in ultra-violet and infra-red light, Lick Observatory, 1926; **D** drawn by E. M. Antoniadi, 33-in. refractor, Meudon Observatory, 1909. **E** Infra-red and ultra-violet photographs arranged to show the Wright effect. Close-up pictures of surface showing ring-structures, transmitted by *Mariner 4*, 1965; **F** region of Atlantis; **G** the adjoining region, part of the Mare Sirenum

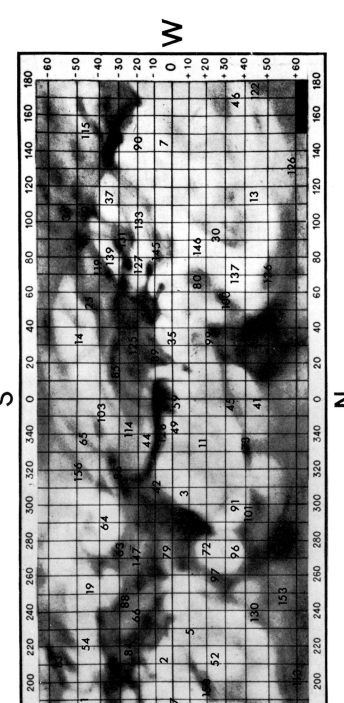

W

S

N

E

Plate 11 MARS

Map of the principal surface features, after G. de Mottoni. The numbers identify
some of the markings listed under the entry Mars – *principal surface features*

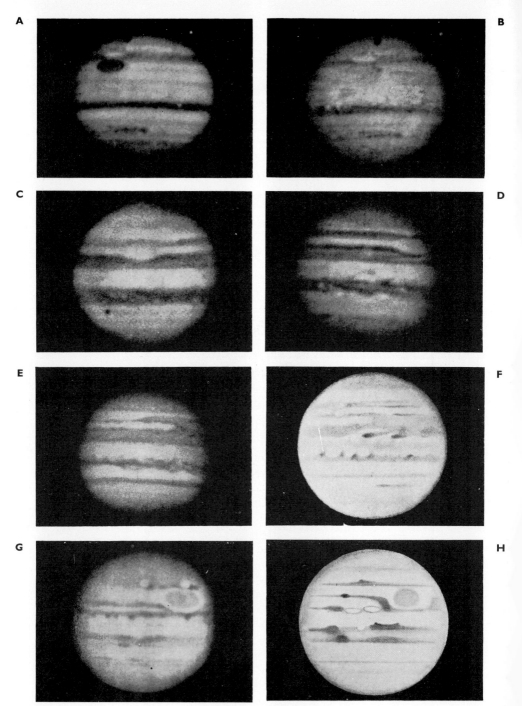

Plate 12 JUPITER

Photographed in **A** blue and **B** red light, 200-in. reflector, Mt Palomar, 1952 October 24; **C** photographed by F. J. Pease, 100-in. reflector, Mt Wilson, 1922 May 29. Photographs by E. C. Slipher, 24-in. refractor, Lowell Observatory: **D** 1915 October 19; **E** 1917 December 19. Drawings by **F** T. E. R. Phillips, 1921 March 7; **G** E. M. Antoniadi, 1911 May 22; **H** the author, 1958 June 8. Note the varying appearance of the Red Spot and its hollow in **A, B, C, D, G** and **H,** and the South Tropical Disturbance in **E** and **F.** The shadow of a satellite is visible on the disk in **A, B** and **C**

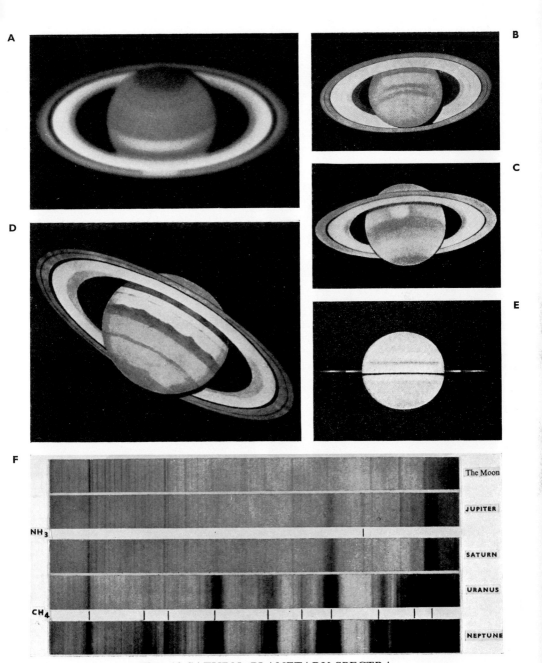

Plate 13 SATURN; PLANETARY SPECTRA

Saturn, **A** photographed with the 100-in. reflector, Mt Wilson; **B** Drawing by E. M. Antoniadi, 1899; **C** W. T. Hay's discovery drawing of the equatorial white spot, 1933 August 3. Drawings by **D** G. Ruggieri, 1955 (rings at open phase) and **E** W. H. Steavenson, 1920 (rings closed). **F** The spectra of the major planets, with that of sunlight reflected off the Moon for comparison. Note the absorption bands due to ammonia (NH_3) and methane (CH_4)

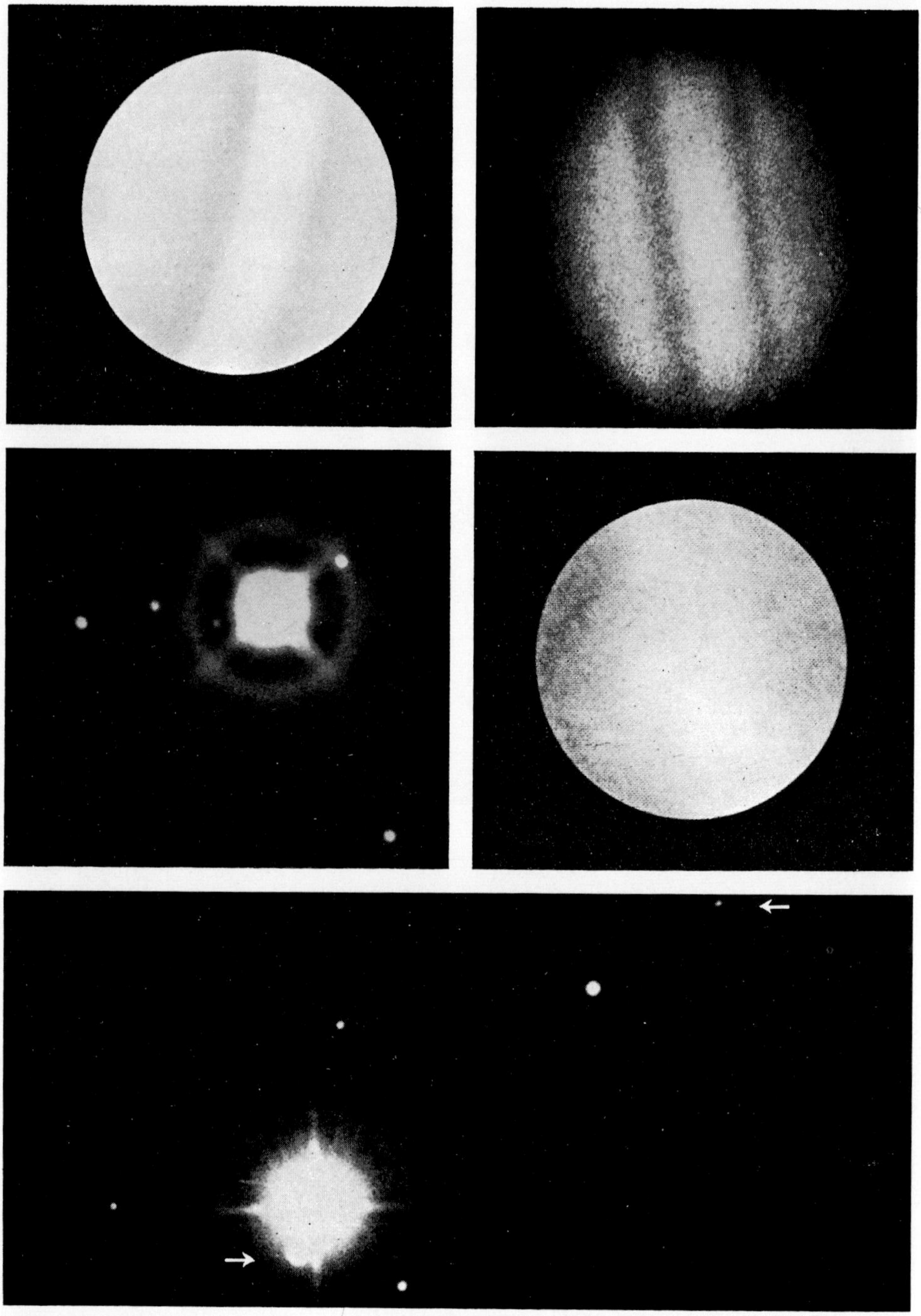

Plate 14 URANUS AND NEPTUNE

Uranus, drawn by **A** W. H. Steavenson, 10-in. refractor, 1915, and **B** E. M. Antoniadi, 33-in. refractor, 1924. **C** Uranus photographed with all five of its satellites by G. P. Kuiper, 82-in. reflector, McDonald Observatory, 1948 (the discovery photograph of the fifth satellite, Miranda). Neptune, **D** drawn by W. H. Steavenson, 1916; **E** photographed with both of its satellites (Kuiper, 82-in. reflector, 1949)

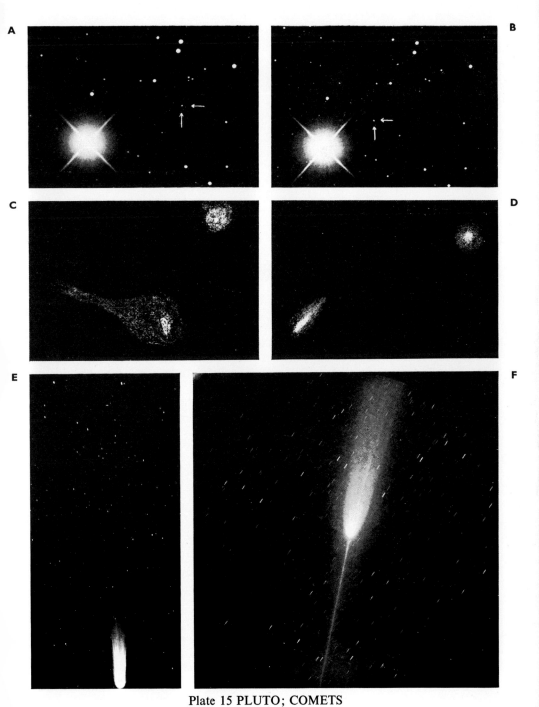

Plate 15 PLUTO; COMETS

Pluto – photographs by Lampland, 42-in. refractor, Lowell Observatory: **A** 1930 March 2; **B** 1930 March 5. The bright star is δ Gem. Biela's Comet: **C** the components shortly after breaking up, 1846, and **D** in 1852. **E** Halley's Comet, 1910; **F** Comet Arend-Roland, 1957

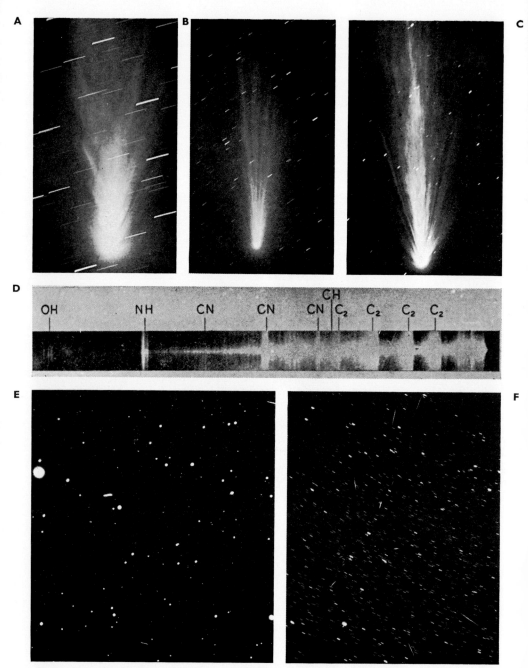

Plate 16 COMETS; MINOR PLANETS; METEORS

Comet Morehouse, photographed by P. J. Melotte and C. R. Davidson with the 30-in. reflector, Royal Observatory, Greenwich: **A** 1908 September 30; **B** 1908 October 29; **C** 1908 November 25. **D** Spectrum of Comet Cunningham, 1940, showing identified emission lines. **E** The trails of three minor planets. **F** Leonid meteors, 1966, showing radiant

Plate 17 METEORITES; AURORAE; GALAXIES

A The great iron meteorite, weighing about 15 tons, found in a forest at Williamette, Oregon, U.S.A. The cavities are due to oxidation; weight at impact must have been more than 20 tons; **B** The great meteorite crater near Cañon Diablo, Arizona, U.S.A., more than $\frac{3}{4}$ mile in diameter and nearly 600 ft deep, photographed from the air by Patrick Moore. **C** The Aurora Australis, observed by Captain R. F. Scott during his British Antarctic Expedition, 1911. **D** The great spiral galaxy in Andromeda (M31)

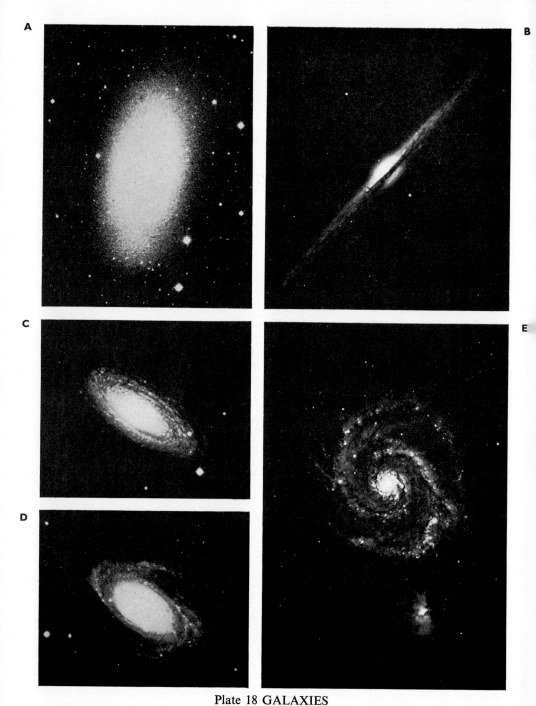

Plate 18 GALAXIES

A The elliptical galaxy N.G.C. 205, a satellite of the great Andromeda galaxy. **B** A spiral galaxy (N.G.C. 4565), seen edge-on; **C** a type Sb spiral galaxy, N.G.C. 2841; **D** the type Sb spiral galaxy in Ursa Major, M81; **E** the great spiral M51 in Canes Venatici, with its satellite galaxy N.G.C. 5195

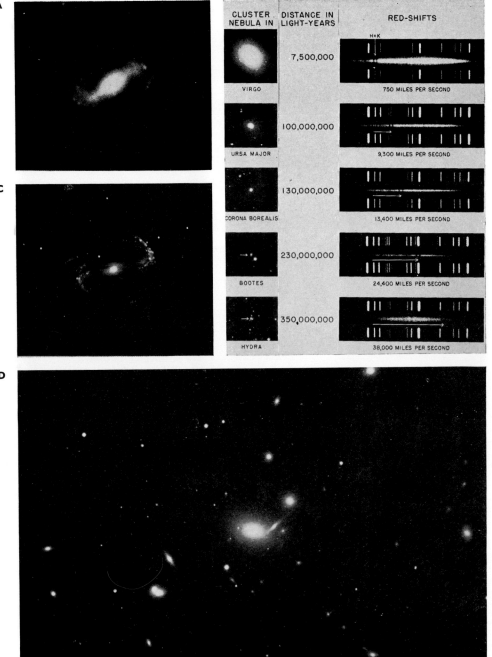

CLUSTER NEBULA IN	DISTANCE IN LIGHT-YEARS	RED-SHIFTS
VIRGO	7,500,000	750 MILES PER SECOND
URSA MAJOR	100,000,000	9,300 MILES PER SECOND
CORONA BOREALIS	130,000,000	13,400 MILES PER SECOND
BOOTES	230,000,000	24,400 MILES PER SECOND
HYDRA	350,000,000	38,000 MILES PER SECOND

Plate 19 GALAXIES

A The barred spiral galaxy N.G.C. 175 (type SBab). **B** The relationship between velocity of recession (measured by the red shift in the spectrum) and distance, for extragalactic objects. Velocities in miles/sec, distances in l.y. Arrows indicate the shift of the H and K lines of calcium. **C** The barred spiral galaxy N.G.C. 1300 (type SBb). **D** The cluster of galaxies in Coma Berenices, approx. 1300 million million million (13×10^{20}) miles distant

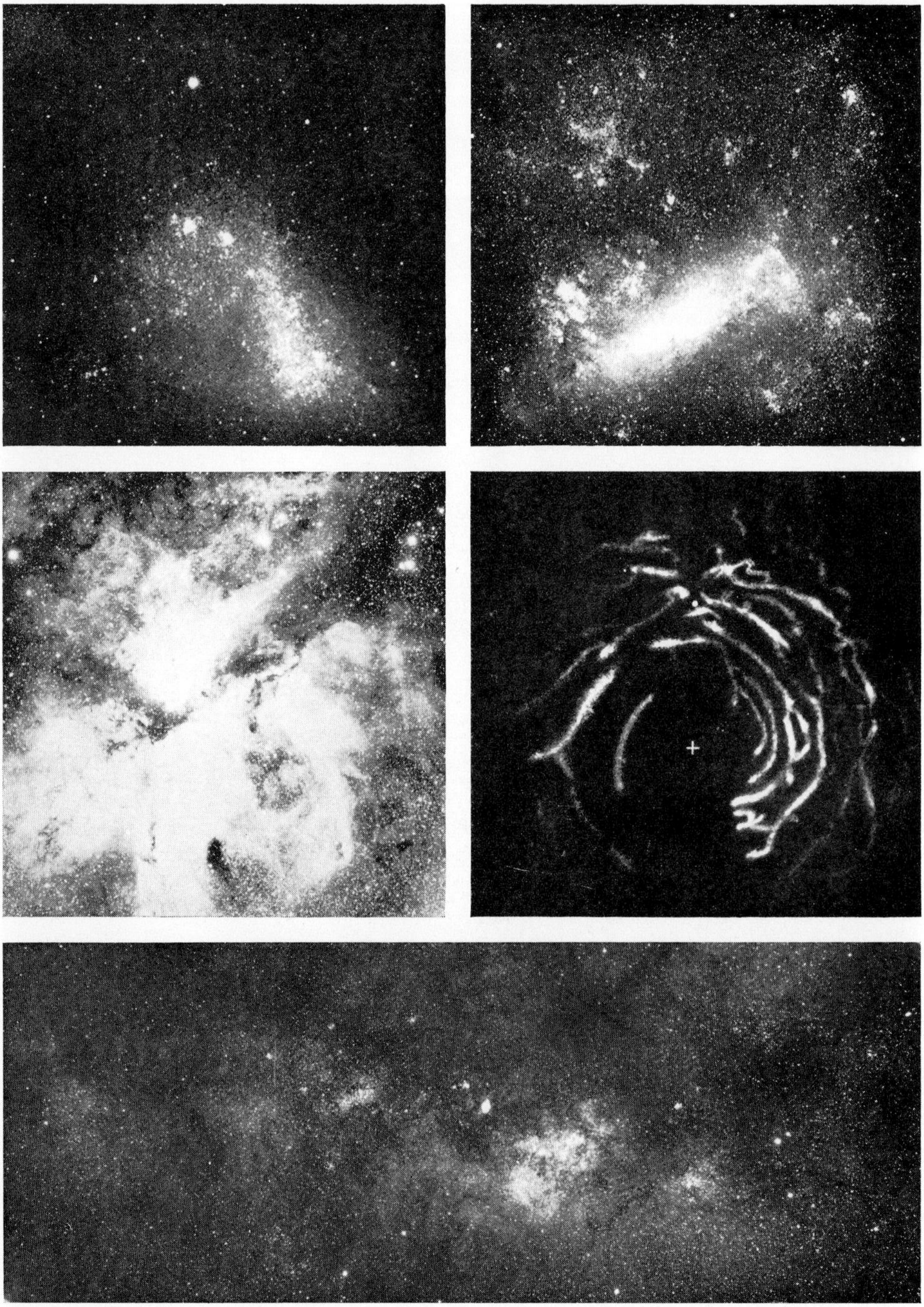

Plate 20 MAGELLANIC CLOUDS; STRUCTURE OF THE GALAXY

The Magellanic Clouds, photographed by E. M. Lindsay with the A.D.H. telescope at the Boyden Observatory: **A** Nubecula Minor, **B** Nubecula Major. The Milky Way: star clouds in the **C** Carina and **E** Scorpio regions. **D** The structure of the Galaxy, after Blaauw and others

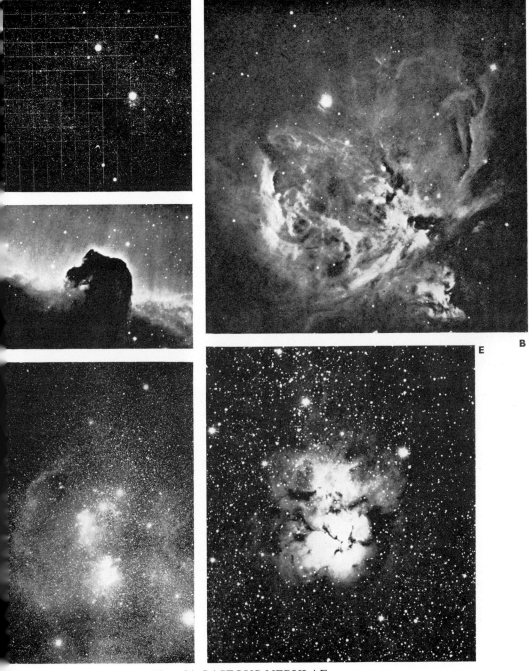

E B

Plate 21 GASEOUS NEBULAE

A The 'Coalsack' absorption nebula in the constellation Crux, the Southern Cross; **B** the great nebula in
Orion, M42; **C** the 'Horsehead' absorption nebula in Orion. **D** The entire constellation of Orion photographed on a blue-sensitive plate, showing the extensive nebulosity. **E** The 'Trifid' nebula, M20

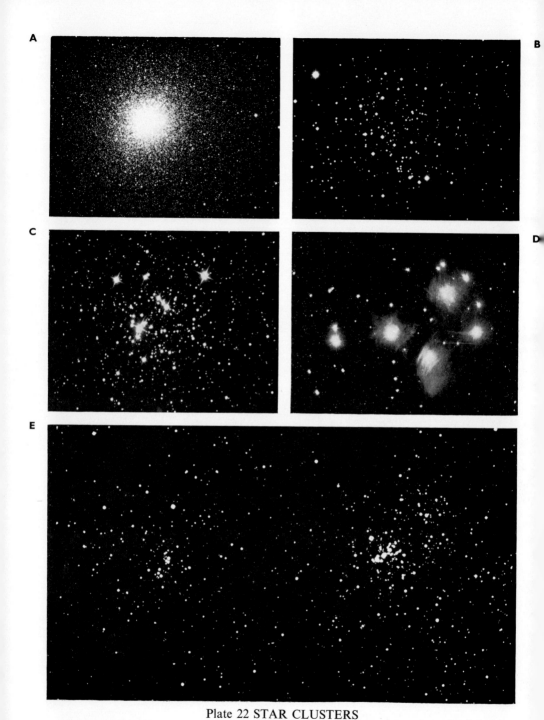

Plate 22 STAR CLUSTERS

A The globular cluster M13 in Hercules. **B** The open cluster M67 in Cancer; **C** the open cluster κ Crucis, the 'Jewel Box'; **D** the Pleiades in Taurus, one of the best known open clusters. **E** The great double cluster in Perseus

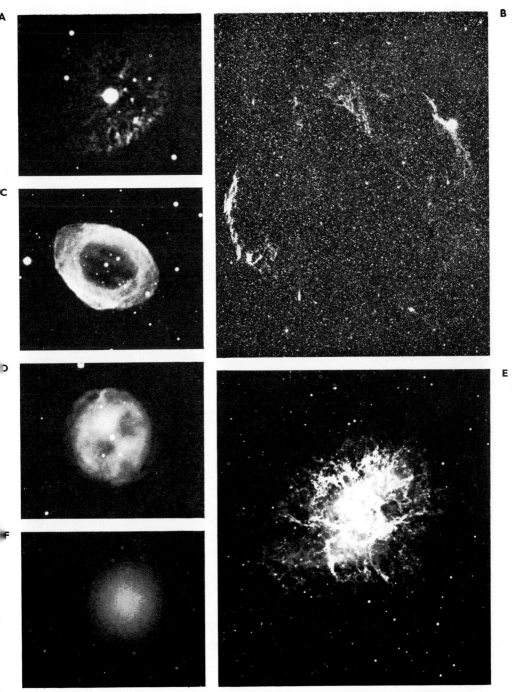

Plate 23 NOVAE; PLANETARY NEBULAE; RADIO GALAXIES

A Nova Persei (1901), showing the expanding nebulosity photographed half a century after the outburst;
B The great filamentary nebulae in Cygnus, probably the remnants of an ancient supernova. Planetary nebulae: **C** the 'Ring' nebula in Lyra and **D** the 'Owl' nebula in Ursa Major. **E** M1, the 'Crab' nebula in Taurus: the remnants of a supernova which exploded in A.D. 1054, and the powerful radio source *Taurus A*. **F** The elliptical galaxy M87 in Virgo, the radio source *Virgo A*

Plate 24 RADIO GALAXIES; PLANETARIA

A Colliding spiral galaxies in Cygnus – the radio source *Cygnus A*; **B** the peculiar galaxy in Centaurus (N.G.C. 5128), probably two galaxies in collision. The radio source *Centaurus A*. Planetarium projectors: **C** a modern Zeiss instrument, developed from the original Zeiss projector; **D** the Japanese Goto projector recently installed in the new planetarium at Armagh, Northern Ireland

A

B

C

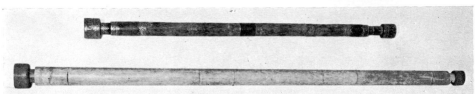

D

E

Plate 25 EARLY ASTRONOMICAL INSTRUMENTS

A A fine 16th century German astrolabe; **B** a 16th century brass armillary sphere; **C** Galileo's refracting telescopes, 1610; **D** mural quadrant installed by Bradley at Greenwich, *c.* 1750; **E** Sir Isaac Newton's reflecting telescope, 1671

Plate 26 TWO HISTORIC INSTRUMENTS

Lord Rosse's 6 ft. reflector, erected at Birr Castle, Ireland: **A** newly completed in 1845, and **B** a contemporary photograph, 1966. **C** The Repsold 7½-in. heliometer, installed at the Oxford University Observatory in 1848

A
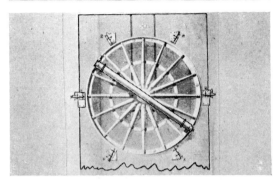

B

C

D

E

Plate 27 MERIDIAN INSTRUMENTS

A The 5-in. transit instrument by Troughton, erected at Greenwich in 1816; **B** The Airy Transit Circle, installed at Greenwich in 1851 where it remains, defining the Prime Meridian of longitude; **C** The Troughton mural circle, erected at Greenwich in 1812; **D** A modern 'broken' transit telescope, in use at the Tashkent Observatory, U.S.S.R.; **E** The Cooke Reversible Transit Circle, erected at Greenwich in 1936 and removed to Herstmonceux in 1955

Plate 28 GREENWICH EQUATORIALS

A The 30-in. Thompson reflector, erected at Greenwich in 1897, transferred to Herstmonceux in 1959;
B the 26-in. Thompson refractor, here seen as erected on the same mounting as the 30-in. reflector at
Greenwich in 1897, since re-erected on a separate mounting at Herstmonceux, 1959; **C** the 28-in. 'Great
Equatorial' refractor, erected at Greenwich in 1894, transferred to Herstmonceux in 1958; **D** the 36-in.
Yapp reflector, erected at Greenwich in 1934, transferred to Herstmonceux in 1959

Plate 29 SPECIAL PURPOSE INSTRUMENTS

A The 150-ft. tower telescope for solar observation, Mt Wilson Observatory; **B** The 48 × 72 in. Schmidt camera, Mt Palomar Observatory; **C** A 30-in. Maksutov camera; **D** The pioneering Cookson Floating Zenith Tube, and **E** its sophisticated successor, the Photographic Zenith Tube (P.Z.T.) at Herstmonceux

Plate 30 SOME 'GIANT' TELESCOPES

A The world's largest refracting telescope, the 40-in. erected at the Yerkes Observatory in 1897; **B** The 82-in. reflector, incorporating many then novel features, erected at the McDonald Observatory in 1939; **C** the 60-in. reflector at Mt Wilson, completed in 1908; **D** the 100-in. Hooker reflector at Mt Wilson, erected in 1918

Plate 31 THE LATEST GIANT TELESCOPES

A The Lick Observatory's 120-in. reflector, completed in 1959; **B** the 98-in. Isaac Newton Telescope, photographed in the maker's factory prior to its erection at the Royal Greenwich Observatory, Herstmonceux, in 1967; **C** the 102-in. reflector of the Crimean Astrophysical Observatory, 1960; **D** the 200-in. Hale reflector, Mt Palomar Observatory, erected in 1948

Plate 32 RADIO TELESCOPES

A The Mark I radio telescope at the Nuffield Radio Astronomy Laboratories, Jodrell Bank; the fully steerable dish is 250 ft. in diameter; **B** One element of the 4C interferometer at the Mullard Radio Astronomy Observatory, Cambridge; **C** The 125 ft. Mark II radio telescope at Jodrell Bank; **D** Part of the one mile radio telescope at Cambridge

$\Phi - 23°$. Dark condensation at eastern end of Thaumasia, south-west of Auroræ Sinus. Connected to Solis Lacus by the canal Nectar.

NEITH REGIO Martian surface feature, approximate position Ω 270°, $\Phi + 35°$. The northern part of the large ochre area adjoining the eastern edge of the Syrtis Major, merging with Isidis Regio to the south. Bounded by Thoth in the east, Casius in the north-east and the eastern part of Nilosyrtis in the south-west. When Nilosyrtis is not visible, merges with Meroe in the west.

NEPENTHES–THOTH Martian surface feature, approximate position Ω 265°, $\Phi + 15°$. Usually one of the most prominent canali, forming the eastern boundary of the Isidis Regio, east of the Syrtis Major. There is a prominent 'oasis'—Tritonis Lacus—in latitude $+20°$; the canal then continues due north to join Casius at the Nodus Alcyonius, this stretch usually being known as Thoth.

The Nepenthes–Thoth proper, south of the Nodus Alcyonius, is frequently seen to be double.

NEPTUNE The eighth planet in order of distance from the Sun and the outer-most of the four major planets.

The second planet to be *discovered*, and the first to be found as a result of a prediction based upon a mathematical analysis of the orbits of the planets already known.

Not visible to the naked eye, but an easy object with binoculars. Owing to its distance and small apparent diameter, however, useful observation is impossible without an extremely large telescope.

NEPTUNE — APPEARANCE AND OBSERVATION OF Though invisible to the unaided eye Neptune can be quite easily observed with binoculars; with moderate apertures it can only be seen as a stellar image, however, and beyond the instructive exercise of plotting its position

relative to the surrounding stars occasionally there is little that can be achieved with such instruments. Under normal circumstances an aperture of 5 or 6 in., with a high power, would be necessary to reveal the disk which has a diameter of $2''12$ at mean opposition distance.

With large apertures the appearance of the planet is a tiny, bluish-white disk; observations made with 'giant' reflectors have revealed the presence of a bright equatorial zone bordered by dusky equatorial belts, similar to Uranus. [Plate 14(d).]

Determinations of the axial rotation period are very difficult, owing to the rarity of long-lived and readily observable discrete markings; it appears to be about 15 hr 48 min. The axis of rotation is inclined to the plane of the orbit by 28° 48′.

NEPTUNE — DIMENSIONS AND PHYSICAL DATA The apparent equatorial diameter of Neptune at mean opposition distance is $2''13$, the actual equatorial diameter being 27,800 miles— rather less than four times that of the Earth.

Like the other major planets, Neptune has a low density, 2·26 times that of water; hence, despite the fact that the volume is 43 times that of the Earth the mass is only 17·5 times that of the Earth.

The acceleration due to gravity at the surface of Neptune is 1·43 times that of the Earth; the resulting velocity of escape is 15·5 miles per second.

Neptune is also similar to the other major planets, and to Venus, in having a high albedo (0·84); this, together with the low density, suggests that Neptune is a largely gaseous body.

NEPTUNE—DISCOVERY OF During the half-century following Herschel's discovery of Uranus, many attempts were made to calculate an accurate orbit for it; its observed positions were found to differ substantially from those predicted for it, however. It was eventually suggested that perhaps the discrepancies were due to the perturbing effect of an undiscovered trans-Uranian planet. Among those who attempted to calculate the position of the unknown planet from the observed motion of Uranus was a young Cambridge mathematical student, John Couch Adams. Adams was the first to reach a solution, his preliminary calculations being completed in 1843.

He then requested Professor J. C. Challis, Director of the Cambridge Observatory, to obtain from the Astronomer Royal (then G. B. Airy) details of the observed discrepancies in the place of Uranus; these were soon forthcoming, and Adams proceeded with his calculations. By September 1845 Adams, then 26 years of age, had derived from his study of the motion of Uranus the orbit, mass and current position of the hypothetical planet. He wished to discuss them with the Astronomer Royal, and Challis wrote to Airy introducing him; owing to Adam's failure to make a firm appointment with Airy, however, he was unable to see him despite his making three separate calls at Greenwich. Misunderstanding the situation, and very disappointed, Adams left a brief statement of his results and returned to Cambridge. A few days later Airy wrote to acknowledge Adams' note, and asked Adams if his solution explained the discrepant motion of Uranus. Unfortunately Adams regarded this question as trivial and superfluous, and as he was by now engaged on a further revision of his calculations he did not reply for a year. In 1846 September he wrote again to Airy, enclosing his improved calculations.

Meanwhile a 35-year-old French mathematician, Urbain Le Verrier, had been independently working on the problem. He published his solution in 1846 June, and when Airy received a copy of Le Verrier's paper he realized that it agreed almost exactly with Adams' result, the predicted positions of the planet being less than a degree apart. Airy immediately instituted a detailed search; he decided that one of the most suitable telescopes for the purpose was the 11¾-in. Northumberland

refractor at Cambridge, and enlisted Challis's co-operation. Airy drew up a search programme, and offered one of the Greenwich staff to assist in the task.

Unfortunately there was no precise chart available of the region concerned (in the constellation Capricornus), and Challis was therefore compelled to construct a chart of all the stars in the region —some 3,000 in all. Before he had had sufficient time to complete this and start to intercompare his observations, the planet had already been discovered, from Berlin.

J. C. Galle, an assistant at the Berlin Observatory, received a letter from Le Verrier on 1846 September 23, giving his calculated position for the new planet and requesting a search. It was pointed out by D'Arrest, a young colleague of Galle, that the area concerned was included in a newly completed star chart, and Galle and D'Arrest therefore commenced a search with the observatory's 9-in. refractor that same evening. Their task was much simpler than that of Challis, Galle simply calling out the positions of the stars and D'Arrest checking them off on the chart. Quite soon the planet was found, and its nature was confirmed by further observations two nights later.

Unfortunately the magnitude of the achievements of both Adams and Le Verrier were dimmed by their becoming the subjects of a heated international controversy. Le Verrier naturally received the credit for the actual discovery, but it was suggested that Adams should have the greater acclaim, as his position had been computed first; both Challis and (especially) Airy were widely blamed for the delay in searching the area indicated by Adam's results, and so losing him the priority; undignified and acrimonious argument raged on both sides of the Channel for a considerable time. Fortunately Adams and Le Verrier themselves did not participate and, in fact, became close friends. As the years have passed reason has prevailed, and the two computers are now accorded equal credit for their contributions to this great achievement.

NEPTUNE—ORBITAL DATA

The orbit of Neptune has a semi-major axis of 30·057852 A.U., corresponding to a mean distance from the Sun of 2,794 million miles. The eccentricity of the orbit is 0·0086, the smallest for a planet in the solar system, with the exception of Venus. The actual distance from the Sun therefore varies from about 2,770 million miles at perihelion to about 2,818 million miles at aphelion.

The orbit is inclined to the Ecliptic by 1° 46′ 23″5; the planet moves in its orbit at a mean velocity of 3·4 miles per second, resulting in a sidereal period of 60,190·0 days—about 164·8 years.

NEPTUNE—SATELLITES OF

On 1846 October 10, less than three weeks after the discovery of Neptune itself, William Lassell was using the 24-in. reflector at his observatory near Liverpool and discovered a large satellite to the planet. This satellite, named 'Triton', is about 2,300 miles in diameter (slightly larger than our own Moon). Its mean distance from the primary is about 220 thousand miles, and it orbits in a period of 5 d 21 hr 3 min 29·8 sec. The mean opposition magnitude of Triton is 13·5.

A satellite of these dimensions might be expected to have retained an atmosphere and this is believed to be the case. Kuiper found possible evidence of the presence of methane in the spectrum of Triton in 1944.

In 1949 Kuiper discovered a second satellite, 'Nereid', on plates obtained with the 82-in. reflector at the McDonald Observatory. It is situated at a mean distance from the primary of some 3,500 miles. It is of interest in that its orbital eccentricity, 0·7493, is greater than that of any other satellite. The synodic period of Nereid is about 362 d 1 hr. Its mean opposition magnitude is only +18·7, and it is believed to be not more than 200 miles in diameter. [Plate 14(e).]

NEPTUNE—STRUCTURE AND CONSTITUTION

As with the other outer planets, much effort has been devoted by theorists to determine the constitution of Neptune, in view of its low mean density. A model was proposed by Wildt in the 1930's which postulated a core of metal-bearing rocks some 12,000 miles in diameter, surrounded by a mantle of frozen material some 6,000 miles thick and a gaseous atmosphere about 2,000 miles deep. Absorption lines due to the presence of methane (CH_4) are prominent in the spectrum of the sunlight reflected by the planet's surface. [Plate 13(f).]

More recently it has been suggested by Ramsey that each of the major planets may be a chemically homogeneous whole, the increase in density towards the centre of the spheroid being due to pressure-induced phase-changes; on the basis of Ramsey's theory a large percentage of the constituent matter of Neptune may be hydrogen.

(See also **Planets, major—constitution of.**)

NEPTUNE—VISIBILITY FROM EARTH

The synodic period of Neptune is 367·49 days; thus, oppositions occur about two days later each year. The planet's movement lies between the declination limits 25° N to 25° S.

The opposition magnitude is about +7·7; the planet cannot therefore be seen with the unaided eye, but can be detected with good binoculars or the smallest telescope. A location chart will be found very helpful, such as that published annually in the *Handbook of the British Astronomical Association*.

NEREID Satellite II of Neptune, *q.v.*

NEREIDUM FRETUM Martian surface feature, approximate position Ω 60°, Φ − 45°. Name now usually adopted for the dark streak formerly known as **Bosporus Gemmatus.**

NEUTRON One of the heavy particles of an atom, which bears no electrical charge.

It is situated inside the atomic nucleus. (See **Atom.**)

NEW GENERAL CATALOGUE The standard catalogue of nebulæ and clusters, being a revision by J. L. E. Dreyer of the *General Catalogue of Nebulæ and Clusters of Stars of the Epoch* 1860 published by J. F. W. Herschel in 1864.

The full title of Dreyer's catalogue is *New General Catalogue of Nebulæ and Clusters of Stars*; it was published by the Royal Astronomical Society in 1888 and is usually referred to as the 'N.G.C.'. The Royal Astronomical Society also published two extensions to the N.G.C., the *Index Catalogue* published in 1895 and the *Second Index Catalogue* published in 1908. The N.G.C. and the two index catalogues were republished as one volume in 1953. Objects are cited in the form 'N.G.C. 6553'.

NEW GENERAL CATALOGUE OF DOUBLE STARS A catalogue of measures of 17,180 binary stars within 120° of the North Pole by the great double-star observer R. G. Aitken, published in two volumes by the Carnegie Institution in 1932. Stars are cited in the abbreviated form 'A.D.S. 6150'.

(See also **Burnham catalogue; Star catalogues.**)

NEW MOON The phase of the Moon when at conjunction, the illuminated hemisphere being invisible from the Earth at that time. (See **Phases of the Moon.**)

NEWCOMB, Simon (1835–1909) One of the foremost names in the history of mathematical astronomy; born in Nova Scotia, Newcomb settled in the U.S.A. and became a computer on the staff of the Nautical Almanac Office of the United States Naval Observatory. In 1861 he became Professor of Mathematics to the United States Navy and in 1877 he was appointed Superintendent of the Nautical

Almanac Office, which post he held for twenty years.

Newcomb was the foremost exponent of celestial mechanics of his time, and made important contributions to our knowledge of the solar parallax, the orbits of the planets and satellites of the solar system (especially the orbits of Uranus and Neptune and the motion of the Moon), the distribution of stars, etc., etc. He was widely honoured, and in 1874 was awarded the Gold Medal of the Royal Astronomical Society.

NEWTON, Sir Isaac (1642–1727) The greatest British-born scientist of all time, who developed the practical and theoretical foundations from which work has developed right up to the present in a remarkable number of fields ranging throughout the physical sciences. Even a cursory study of Newton's work would require a book to itself, and it is necessary to confine ourselves here to a very brief indication of some of his more important contributions in astronomical matters.

Newton was born at Woolsthorpe, Lincolnshire, on 1642 December 25; he was a very delicate child and hardly expected to survive: a remarkable beginning for one who was to live to be an octogenarian and to enjoy excellent health through practically the whole of his life. Leaving school at fourteen in order to help support his twice-widowed mother, Newton was destined to become a farmer. He showed little aptitude for such work, however, and was eventually allowed to return to school to study for entrance to a university. In June 1660 he went to Trinity College, Cambridge, where he concentrated mainly on mathematics. He was forced to return home in 1666, the university being closed owing to an outbreak of plague. He returned to Cambridge in 1667, being elected a Fellow of Trinity College; in 1669, at the age of only 27, he was appointed Lucasian Professor of Mathematics.

Newton had always had a talent for mechanical work as well as for theoretical science and philosophy; thus it is not surprising that some of his most gifted work in astronomy was concerned with optics and the development of optical equipment. In 1666 he conducted his classic experiment with triangular glass prisms, producing and studying spectra from a beam of sunlight: in the years following he was able to explain all the properties of 'refrangibility' (refraction) demonstrated by glass prisms and lenses and explained the true nature of 'white' light. Newton's discoveries in this field explained, *inter alia*, the inefficiency of the refracting telescopes of the day due to chromatic aberration, and this naturally led him to studying the properties of curved mirrors and the construction, in 1668, of the first practicable reflecting telescope. This instrument, prototype of the simple and elegant design known throughout the world as 'Newtonian' and of which countless examples have been made and used by amateur and professional astronomers alike, was in itself a triumph of miniaturization, having an aperture of $1\frac{1}{3}$ inches and a focal length of $6\frac{1}{4}$ inches. The Royal Society requested an opportunity of inspecting the instrument, which Newton met by presenting to the Society in 1671 a similar instrument which is today one of the Society's most treasured possessions. Newton was elected a Fellow of The Royal Society in 1672 January 11. [Plate 25(e).]

Meanwhile, Newton had been far from idle in his theoretical work: during his enforced stay at Woolsthorpe in 1666 he appears to have been primarily concerned to develop a theory of the mechanism responsible for holding together the members of the solar system. Legend has it that the sight of an apple falling in the orchard at Woolsthorpe led him to the concept of gravitation, a force exerted by any body upon any other body: by applying the laws of mechanics he was able to show that the Moon was in a stable situation by virtue of its orbital motion imparting an outward force equal and opposite to the gravitational attraction between the Moon and the Earth (i.e., if the Moon's orbital motion were to cease it would immediately 'fall' towards the Earth). Newton further demonstrated that the gravitational force exerted by a body was proportional to its mass, and that its effect on another body was inversely proportional to the square of the distance between the bodies. Newton applied his conclusions to the planetary system, and found that the theory of gravitation provided a satisfactory explanation for the laws of planetary motion which Kepler had deduced from observations. He went on to explain the tides, and—most important—to develop a theory of the motion of the Moon. He was the first to explain the observed irregularities in the Moon's motion, due largely to the differential effects of the gravitational attraction of the Moon by the Sun and the Earth. He also explained the precession of the equinoxes, arising from the gravitational attraction exerted by the Moon on the equatorial 'bulge' of the oblately spheroidal Earth. Perhaps the most remarkable thing about Newton's gravitational theory is that it remained unpublished for two decades. Newton was by nature a recluse, and had a deep personal dislike of becoming involved in scientific controversy; he preferred to keep his results to himself, and to reconsider and amend them from time to time. In the end his work on gravity was published in the *Philosophiæ Naturalis Principia Mathematica*, published by The Royal Society in 1687; the *Principia* was only published then because of the exertions of Halley, then Clerk to The Royal Society, who also underwrote the entire costs of production of the work.

In 1687 Newton became involved in a dispute between the University of Cambridge and the autocratic King James II who had succeeded Charles II, that great patron of science, in 1685; as a result of this Newton stood, somewhat surprisingly, for Parliament in 1688 and served as a University M.P. for two years. He was then appointed Warden of the Royal Mint, at the time housed in the Tower of London, charged with the replacement of the old hand-struck coinage by the allegedly perfect products of mechanical presses. This technical tour de force Newton achieved with great efficiency, and was rewarded by being appointed Master of the Mint on 1699 December 26 —the day following his 57th birthday.

In 1701 Newton resigned his Chair at Cambridge and his Fellowship of Trinity College, to devote himself to his public service; in 1703, however, he was elected President of The Royal Society, which position he held for the remarkable term of a quarter of a century, until his death. He was further honoured by Queen Anne, who conferred upon him the honour of knighthood during a visit to his old college in 1705.

No reference is made here to Newton's equally great contributions to mathematics, or to his theological writings; posterity has already designated him as the leading scientist of his time, and the greatest natural philosopher this country has ever produced. His contributions to practical optics and to theoretical astronomy have proved to be the biggest single contribution to the development of astronomical science ever made by one man. Newton presided at his last meeting of The Royal Society on 1727 March 2 and died on 1727 March 20; he was buried in Westminster Abbey. His influence on the development of natural science is summed up by the inscription on the bust of him which stands in the Ante-Chapel of Trinity College:

NEWTON

Qui genus humanum ingenis superavit

('Who surpassed all men of genius').

NEWTON Lunar surface feature, co-ordinates $\xi - 061$, $\eta - 973$. An unsymmetrical walled plain, approximately 70 miles in diameter, very close to the limb in the south polar region. Its shape suggests that it was possibly formed by the coalescing of two separate formations. The interior is one of the deepest on the Moon, the wall rising to about 24,000 ft.

NEWTONIAN FOCUS The position at the side of the tube of a reflecting telescope, close to the upper end, at which a primary image is formed, the rays being diverted from the **prime focus** position by the interposition of a prism or inclined flat. (See **Telescope, Newtonian**.)

NEWTON'S LAWS OF MOTION The principles of physical motion were deduced over several centuries by many distinguished mathematicians and astronomers, notably Aristotle, Copernicus, Descartes, Galileo and Kepler; they were first re-examined objectively and rationalized, however, by Newton in his *Principia* published in 1687. In this Newton stated his three classic laws of motion, as follows:

I. Every body continues in its state of rest or of uniform motion in a straight line until subjected to an outside force.
II. When a body is subjected to an outside force the resulting rate of change of momentum acts in the direction of the straight line in which the force is acting, and is directly proportional to the force.
III. To any action there is an equal and opposite reaction.

NICHOLSON, Seth B. (1891–1963) One of the leading American observers of the present century, and one of only four persons who have discovered four planetary satellites (the others being Galileo, William Herschel and Jean-Dominique Cassini), having discovered four satellites of Jupiter —an achievement equalled only by Galileo. Nicholson discovered satellite IX on plates taken with the 36-in. Crossley reflector at the Lick Observatory in 1914, and with the 100-in. Hooker reflector at Mount Wilson photographed satellites X and XI in 1938 and satellite XII in 1951.

In the 1920s Nicholson pioneered, with

E. Pettit, the development of the thermocouple for astronomical purposes; with the aid of the 100-in. reflector they successfully determined the surface temperatures of the Moon and several of the planets. They also used the thermocouple for observations of stars, notably the long-period variables.

NIGHT SKY, ILLUMINATION OF

Although the night sky appears dark it is in fact subject to a faint illumination. This comprises the **airglow**—originating in the Earth's upper atmosphere; sunlight diffused through interplanetary space— sometimes termed **zodiacal light**, although this name is more frequently used for its more concentrated cones in the Ecliptic; **galactic light**—starlight diffused through interstellar space; and **stellar light**—direct light from faint stars invisible to the naked eye. The biggest contribution is the stellar light, especially that from stars of about the twelfth magnitude, whose numbers more than make up for their faintness.

NIGHT-SKY CAMERA

An instrument used in many observatories; it is a simple fixed camera set to record the trails of (usually zenithal) stars caused by the diurnal rotation of the Earth, with a means of relating the position of any breaks in the trails to the time. In this way the reduction, due to cloud, of the effective exposures of astronomical photographs made during the night can be assessed. This is particularly useful where highly automated instruments are in use which are not necessarily manned continuously by an observer.

NILIACUS LACUS

Martian surface feature, approximate position Ω 30°, Φ + 30°. A very dark area at the southern end of the Mare Acidalium, from which it is separated by the Achillis Pons. A number of canali radiate from it, notably Nilokeras to the south-west and Indus to the south-east.

NILOKERAS Martian surface feature, approximate position Ω 55°, Φ + 30°. A prominent canal radiating north-eastwards from the Lunæ Lacus to join the Niliacus Lacus, forming the northern boundary of Xanthe.

NILOSYRTIS Martian surface feature, approximate position Ω 290°, Φ + 40°. Long canal which is often very prominent but which varies considerably from one apparition to another; it runs northward from the tip of the Syrtis Major, between Isidis Regio and Meroe, and then swings westward to become the northern boundary of Meroe to join up with Protonilus in longitude 305°.

NIMBUS A bright 'halo' surrounding a lunar surface feature; it is one of the types of **lunar ray systems, q.v.**

NITROGEN Chemical element and an inert gas. The principle constituent of the Earth's atmosphere, of which it comprises approximately 78%. It is also an important constituent of other planetary atmospheres; it is believed to constitute approximately 98% of the atmosphere of Mars, and in combination with hydrogen as ammonia (NH_3) is very abundant in the atmospheres of the four major planets.

Nitrogen liquefies at about $-196°C$ under normal pressure; it has an atomic weight of 14·008.

NITROGEN SEQUENCE The Wolf–Rayet stars in whose spectra enhanced emission bands due to nitrogen are predominant, constituting the spectral sub-class WN. (See **Stars—spectral classification of.**)

NIX OLYMPICA Martian surface feature, approximate position Ω 130°, Φ + 20°. Dusky area in the northern part of Amazonis.

NOACHIS Martian surface feature, approximate position Ω 350°, Φ − 45°. Large lightish area in the south temperate region of Mars, to the south of the Pandoræ Fretum.

NODAL LINE The line joining the ascending and descending nodes of a planetary orbit; it is the line along which the planes of the orbit and of the Ecliptic intersect. (See **Celestial sphere; Node.**)

NODE One of the two points at which a body in orbit inclined to the Ecliptic crosses the Ecliptic; the point of crossing from south to north is termed the **ascending node** and that from north to south is termed the **descending node.** Usually used with reference to the orbits of the Moon or planets. (See **Celestial sphere; Planetary motion.**)

NODICAL MONTH The interval between successive passages of the Moon through one of its nodes; it is equivalent to about 27 d 5 hr.

NORMA (The Square. *Genetive* Normae, *I.A.U. abbreviation* Nor.) A tiny, southern circumpolar constellation adjoining Lupus and Scorpius. Contains no stars brighter than the fourth magnitude. There is a rich cluster (NGC 6067) just north of κ Nor.

NORTH POINT The point on the celestial sphere, due north of the observer, at which the meridian intersects the horizon.

NORTH POLAR DISTANCE The angular distance, measured in the meridian, between an object and the north celestial pole. Usually abbreviated 'N.P.D.', it is equivalent to 90° minus the declination of the object.

(See also **Celestial sphere; South polar distance.**)

NORTH POLAR SEQUENCE The determination of stellar magnitudes is complicated by difficulties arising from personal, instrumental and atmospheric factors; to reduce these difficulties as much as possible a sequence of reference stars has been adopted as a magnitude standard. The stars selected were all in the region of the north celestial pole (to ensure all-the-year-round visibility in the northern hemisphere); their magnitudes were determined at many observatories, corrected, collated and the mean values determined. This sequence of stars, known as the *North Polar Sequence* (or 'NPS') is now used as the basis to which all magnitude determinations are referred. A number of additional standard sequences have been added from time to time for special purposes.

The NPS comprises 46 stars with photographic magnitudes ranging from 4·47 to 20·96 and twelve red stars of photographic magnitudes 6·69–13·34; there are also other standard sequences of stars near the north celestial pole and stars in the **Pleiades** and **Præsepe** clusters.

In order to link to the NPS southern stars which cannot be directly compared with NPS stars, stars in Selected Areas at Dec. +15° have been observed from Cambridge and Pretoria and adopted as standard intermediate reference stars.

(See also **Stellar magnitudes—determination of.**)

NORTON'S STAR ATLAS The best-known star atlas of all; it comprises eight beautifully drawn charts, covering the entire heavens, which are remarkably clear and simple to use, each accompanied by two pages of detailed lists of the most interesting objects for observation. There is also a 'handbook' section which is a mine of concise and reliable information for novice observers. 'Norton' is, in fact, an indispensable (and inexpensive) aid to all amateur observers. It was first published in 1910, but revised editions are constantly being produced. All naked-eye stars are shown, the limiting magnitude being about 6·4. The charts were drawn by Arthur P. Norton, who was also co-author of the text with J. Gall Inglis. The full title is *A Star Atlas and Reference Handbook, Epoch 1950.*

The rather small scale and the absence

of fainter stars render it inadequate for the purposes of identification or position-estimating, and for serious observation programmes it must therefore be supplemented by Webb's *Atlas of the Stars* or one of the large-scale photographic star charts.

NOTATION It was realized many years ago that it is essential for astronomers from all parts of the world to use a common system of symbols and notation, in order to minimize confusion and permit the proper international exchange of ideas and research results.

Most of the special symbols now in use are those hallowed by tradition, many of them having been in use for centuries. There are only a limited number of special symbols, however, representing the principal members of the solar system, the zodiacal constellations and some of the principal astronomical configurations; for many other quantities italic or Greek characters are used.

The need to standardize the notation used was obvious and the I.A.U. recognized this by appointing a Commission on Notations (Commission 3) immediately the Union was founded in 1920. As a result a provisional notation was soon in use, which was amended and expanded from time to time. An extensive list of the preferred symbols for most branches of astronomy was finally adopted by the General Assembly of the I.A.U. held in Stockholm in 1938, and has been used, with very few changes, ever since. The list was published in 1939 (*Trans. Int. Astron. Un.* **6**, 345–55).

Another important step was the adoption by the first General Assembly of the I.A.U. (Rome, 1922), of a standard list of 3-letter abbreviations for the constellation names; a supplementary list of 4-letter abbreviations was adopted in 1932. Both lists were published in 1933 (*Trans. Int. Astron. Un.* **4**, 221–2).

(See also **Constants, astronomical; Constellation names and abbreviations; Symbols, astronomical.**)

NOVA Not a new star, as the name suggests, but an existing star, usually quite faint, which undergoes a sudden, tremendous increase in its radiative output, the scale of which is indicated by the description often applied to this peculiar type of variable star—'cataclysmic variables'. The increase in the apparent magnitude of a nova is usually of the order of ten magnitudes, indicating a ten-thousand-fold increase in actual luminosity. This increase takes place, in most cases, in a period of only 10–50 hours. A few novae have been observed in which the rise to maximum has required a longer period, e.g. Nova Cygni (1920) which rose from the tenth magnitude to its maximum of 1·5 in a period of 11 days.

It is rare for a nova to remain at maximum brightness for any length of time; usually they start to fade almost immediately, although at a much slower rate than the rise to maximum.

The rate of fading usually decreases after a time; thus a typical nova might fade to a tenth of its maximum brightness in two weeks but not reach its former (minimum) magnitude for perhaps two years.

A generalized form of light curve for a typical nova is shown in Fig. 93. The magnitude and time-scales are approximate and would of course vary in particular cases. The figure shows the rapid rise and slower fall in brightness shared by all novae, and some additional features displayed by some but not all of them, e.g. the pre-maximum halt a magnitude or two before the peak.

Most novae seem to behave very erratically for a time during the fade from maximum; after the early, fairly rapid decline they display short-term fluctuations in brightness with an amplitude of about one magnitude, superimposed on the pattern of steady fading—which process begins at this point to slow down (i.e. the light curve appears to 'flatten out'). In a few cases, however, this fluctuation has been replaced by a plunge to a deep minimum, the nova then

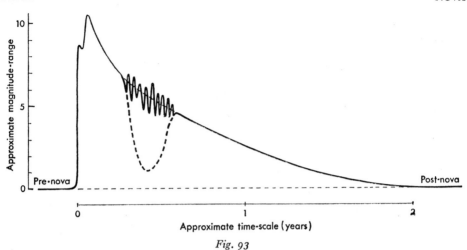

Fig. 93

brightening again until it reaches the normal light curve once more and continues its normal fading; this variant of the light curve is shown as a dashed line in Fig. 93. Nova Herculis (1934) was an example of this type.

Prior to its outburst the star is termed a *pre-nova*; it is usually impossible to recognize a nova in advance, however, so that almost all observations of pre-novae are made retrospectively, by examination of plates kept in observatory archives, etc.

Once a nova has returned to its former minimum brightness it is termed a *post-nova*. Known post-novae are regularly observed in order to detect any evidence of further fluctuation; occasionally novae are known to recur, e.g. RS Oph which suffered outbursts in 1898 and 1933, and T CrB which did so in 1866 and 1946.

About 100 post-novae are known; it has been estimated that more than 25 nova outbreaks occur each year, but only one or two per annum are actually observed. Some of the brightest novae recorded are listed in Table 25. [See also Plate 23(a).]

In cases where the distance of a nova can be determined it is possible to calculate the actual change in luminosity represented by the increase in apparent magnitude. For most typical novae the luminosity at maximum is of the order of 50,000 times that of the Sun. In a few cases the actual luminosity is very much greater—up to a hundred million times that of the Sun. These are the *supernovae*; they are very rare, only three supernova outbreaks have ever been recorded within the Galaxy.

In 1885 a bright nova was observed in the great spiral galaxy in Andromeda, M 31. Since that time a number of nova outbursts have been detected in other galactic systems, notably M 31 and those satellites of our own Galaxy, the Magellanic Clouds. A number of the extra-galactic novae are of such high luminosity that they are clearly supernovae, including the 1885 discovery, now known as S And.

The spectra of novae are extremely difficult to classify, and undergo major changes at the time of an outburst; it is therefore usual for novae to be allocated to a special spectral class, Q. The study of the changes in a nova spectrum is an important aspect of any attempt to determine the physical processes underlying a nova outburst.

Little is known of the spectral types of pre-novae; it appears that they are most likely to be of types A or F. A few hours before reaching maximum strong emission lines due to highly ionized elements

Table 25.   The brightest novae

Nova		Apparent magnitude	
date	designation	(maximum)	(minimum)
1843	η Car	−1	8
1918	V 603 Aql	−1·4	10·8
1901	GK Per	0·0	14·0
1942	CP Pup	0·0	
1925	RR Pic	1·0	12·7
1934	DQ Her*	1·3	15
1920	V 476 Cyg	1·5	<16
1866, 1946	T CrB*†	2·0	10·6
1936	CP Lac	2·2	15
1600	P Cyg	3	< 6
1912	DN Gem	3·7	14·5
1898, 1933	RS Oph†	4·3	11·8

* binary system; † recurrent.

appear, similar to those in the spectrum of the solar corona. The absorption lines are displaced towards the violet, by amounts proportional to the wavelengths of the lines concerned. At maximum the spectrum undergoes a transition to a broad-band emission spectrum, with absorption lines bordering the violet edges of the emission bands.

The spectrum often shows complexities at this phase which can be interpreted as the spectra of two or more layers of material, in differing states of ionization, superimposed. As the nova fades the spectrum usually settles as type O, often closely resembling the W spectrum of the Wolf–Rayet stars.

A number of the well-observed brighter novae have been seen to be surrounded by an expanding shell of nebular matter following the outbreak, e.g. Nova Persei (1901) and Nova Aquilae (1918). The close resemblance between such post-novae and the planetary nebula suggests that some, at least, of the latter may be the remnants of nova outbursts of long ago. The beautiful filamentary nebula in Cygnus (N.G.C. 6960) is probably the result of a supernova outburst some 90,000 years ago. [Plate 23(b).]

Another recent nova which threw off a shell of nebulosity was Nova Herculis (1934), which was discovered by a leading amateur meteor observer, J. P. M. Prentice; it was later found to be a binary system, with the shortest known period of any binary (4 hr 39 min).

It is possible that a nova outburst is part of the normal evolutionary pattern for many stars; if so, the spectral resemblance between post-novae and the Wolf–Rayet stars may prove to be a significant factor in unravelling the life history of the stars.

(See also **Supernova; Variable stars.**)

NOX Martian surface feature, approximate position Ω 105°, Φ − 10°. Prominent canal connecting Tithonius Lacus and Phoenicis Lacus; forms the north-west boundary of Thaumasia.

NUBECULA MAJOR The Large Magellanic Cloud, situated in the southern circumpolar constellation Mensa; a satellite nebula of our own Galaxy.

(See **Magellanic clouds.**)

NUBECULA MINOR The Small Magellanic Cloud, situated in the southern

circumpolar constellation Tucana; also a satellite nebula of our own Galaxy.
(See **Magellanic clouds.**)

NUCLEUS, COMET'S A bright, star-like point usually observed in comets bright enough for their structure to be studied. One or more nuclei may be seen within the central condensation but not always centrally placed within it. (See **Comets—structure of.**)

NUFFIELD RADIO ASTRONOMY LABORATORIES The radio-astronomy observatory of the University of Manchester at Jodrell Bank, Cheshire, directed since its inception by Sir Bernard Lovell.

The principal instruments are the 'Mark I' 250-ft steerable paraboloid erected between 1953 and 1957, and the 'Mark II' 125 × 83 ft elliptical paraboloid completed in 1964. [Plate 32(a, c).]

NUTATION It was shown by **Bradley** that the observed variations in the positions of stars were not fully explained by the effects of precession, aberration and proper motion; he showed in 1748 that super-imposed upon the precessional motion of the Earth's pole, which had a period of 25,800 years, was a further cyclic motion having a period of about 19 years. From this period Bradley deduced that it was connected with the Moon, whose nodes complete one revolution of the Ecliptic in that time. The effect may be regarded as a 'nodding' movement of the Earth's axis, and was therefore termed 'nutation' which means 'nodding'.

Nutation is now known to consist of a number of perturbations affecting the Earth. It is known that precession is due to the gravitational attraction of the Sun and Moon upon the spheroidal Earth; the actual combined effect is constantly varying, however, as their relative positions vary. The part played by each in the total perturbative effect depends upon their distances and directions at the instant. The variations introduced by their changing positions are the *Lunar nutation*, which can displace the pole from its mean position by $\pm 9''$ and has a period of 18·6 years, the *Solar nutation*, having a displacement of up to $1''2$ and a period of 0·5 tropical years, and the *Fortnightly nutation* having a displacement of up to $0''1$ and a period of 15 days.

(See also **Precession.**)

O

O STARS Stars of spectral class O; they are bluish-white stars having surface temperatures of approximately 35,000 °K.

OBERON Satellite IV of Uranus, *q.v.*

OBJECT-GLASS Term used to indicate the principal lens of a refracting telescope. The function of the object-glass is to gather the light and bring it to a focus. The object-glass (usually abbreviated 'O.G.') is normally a **doublet**, so as to minimize **chromatic aberration**. (See also **Telescope, astronomical; Telescope, refracting.**)

OBJECTIVE The principal light-gathering and image-forming element of a telescope. The term is more usually applied to the object-glass of a refracting telescope, the objective of a reflector being usually referred to as 'the mirror'.

OBJECTIVE PRISM A large prism placed before the objective of a refracting telescope. Widely used for the spectral classification of large numbers of stars, as in the Draper Catalogue. The prism used is usually one made from crown glass and having a rather small angle, of the order of 15°; wider-angle objective prisms (about 30°) are, however, used for special tasks such as the spectral analysis of meteors.

The technique seems to have been first devised by Josef Fraunhofer early in the nineteenth century. Fraunhofer observed a shaft of sunlight formed by a vertical slit in his window shutter with a flint-glass prism positioned in front of the objective of a small theodolite telescope. With this apparatus Fraunhofer discovered the principal absorption lines in the solar spectrum which bear his name; he continued to study the spectra of the Sun, Moon, planets and stars with a larger objective prism attached to his $4\frac{1}{2}$-in. refractor.

OBLIQUE ASCENSION The geocentric longitude of a body, measured along the Ecliptic from the Vernal Equinox, as the Right Ascension is measured along the Equator; the name derives from the 'obliquity'—the inclination between the planes of the Equator and the Ecliptic. It is not frequently encountered.

OBLIQUITY OF THE ECLIPTIC The inclination between the **Ecliptic** and the Celestial Equator; it is approximately 23° 27′. This value therefore represents the greatest angular distance the Sun can have from the Equator; i.e. the Sun's declination varies between 23° 27′ N and 23° 27′ S. (See **Celestial sphere.**)

OBSERVATORIES There are a great many observatories throughout the world; the current *Astronomical Ephemeris* lists 311, plus a further 64 radio observatories. These include the national observatories and the major research establishments and university observatories. There are many more which are privately owned or run by small institutions, amateur societies, etc., all contributing useful observationa work.

Some of the more important observatories are described in this book under their own names, as follows:

Armagh Observatory;
Boyden Observatory;
Crimean Astrophysical Observatory;
Dunsink Observatory;
High-Altitude Observatory, Climax;
Leiden Observatory;

Lick Observatory;
McDonald Observatory;
McMath–Hulbert Observatory;
Meudon Observatory;
Mount Palomar Observatory;
Mount Stromlo Observatory;
Mount Wilson Observatory;
National Radio Astronomy Observatory (Green Bank);
Nuffield Radio Astronomy Laboratories (Jodrell Bank);
Pic-du-Midi Observatory;
Pulkowa Observatory;
Royal Greenwich Observatory;
Royal Observatory, Cape of Good Hope;
Royal Observatory, Edinburgh;
U.S. Naval Observatory;
Yerkes Observatory.

OBSERVATORY, NATIONAL One of the leading observatories in each country, normally one run by the state, is usually considered to be the national observatory and assumes certain functions in addition to the lines of astronomical or astrophysical research in which it may specialize. The earliest example was the Royal Observatory at Greenwich; among other notable national observatories are the U.S. Naval Observatory in Washington and the Paris Observatory.

The routine observations undertaken by a national observatory are vital to the social, scientific and commercial life of our times. One of the most important functions is the maintenance of a national time service, for which purpose the national observatory usually includes a department specializing in meridian astronomy, which often contributes positional observations of the Sun, Moon and Planets for the improvement of their ephemerides, in addition to the routine observations of fundamental stars necessary for the time service.

OCCULTATION The phenomenon of one heavenly body interposing itself between another body and the observer, thus causing the more distant body to disappear from view, is termed an occultation. The term is also loosely used to describe the phenomenon properly known as a lunar occultation, but occultations of planetary satellites by the planet and by other satellites, and of radio sources by the Sun, can also be observed.

OCCULTATION, LUNAR As the Moon travels across the sky, it naturally passes in front of background stars from time to time, thus temporarily preventing the star from being observed; the star is then said to be 'occulted' by the Moon. Often the star to be occulted is sufficiently bright to be observed with quite a modest telescope, and as the Moon has no atmosphere to 'dim' the star's light slowly, the disappearance and reappearance of the star take place instantaneously; they can therefore be timed with considerable accuracy. From these observations the Moon's apparent position at the time of occultation can be very accurately determined, making use of the precisely known position of the occulted star. Other more usual methods of determining the Moon's position (e.g. **transit-circle observations**) are subject to certain observational errors which do not affect occultation observations, and the latter are therefore a very valuable supplement to the usual measurements. Occultation observations have assisted in the past in the detection of changes in the rate of rotation of the Earth.

As the Moon's apparent motion against the background stars is eastward, stars are always seen to disappear at the eastern limb of the Moon and to reappear at the western. From New Moon, through First Quarter to Full Moon, the disappearance takes place at the dark limb of the Moon; from Full Moon through Last Quarter to New Moon the reappearance takes place at the dark limb.

The occurrence and circumstances of an occultation can be predicted by means of a formula devised by Bessel; a number of astronomical almanacs—notably the annual *Handbook of the British Astronomical Association*—tabulate the circumstances of occultations of stars within the light-grasp of moderate telescopes.

Timings of occultations must be made against a clock or watch or known rate (which must be compared with a standard time signal, preferably both before and after the observation), and must be accompanied by the precise latitude and longitude of the observing station. Provided that this is done and observations of occultations are made with sufficient care, they will be accepted and analysed by H.M. Nautical Almanac Office. (See also: **Phases of the Moon**.)

OCCULTATION, SATELLITE The occultation of a planetary satellite by the parent planet or by another satellite. (See **Satellite phenomena**.)

OCCULTING BAR A bar placed in the focal plane of a telescope eyepiece as a means of obscuring an object in the field of view. It has numerous uses, notably to occult a bright object in order to enable a nearby faint object to be observed—such as a faint planetary satellite.

OCCULTING DISK An alternative form of **occulting bar**, in which a small obscuring disk of metal is placed in the focal plane of the eyepiece.

OCEANUS PROCELLARUM The largest of the lunar maria, which with the adjoining Mare Imbrium practically covers the north-eastern quadrant of the Moon's face. It is also extended to the south by the Mare Nubium and Mare Humorum.

There is a considerable amount of detail on this vast grey plain, notably Copernicus, Kepler and Aristarchus; all three are the origins of great ray systems, which combine to cover much of the plain at Full Moon.

OCTANS (The Octant. *Genitive* Octantis, *I.A.U. abbreviation* Oct.) A southern circumpolar constellation, including the celestial south pole itself. The brightest stars are four of the fourth magnitude.

OCULAR Alternative term for a telescope **eyepiece**, *q.v.*

OGYGIS REGIO Martian surface feature, approximate position $\Omega\,65°$, $\Phi-45°$. Dusky area along the Southern edge of Phrixi Regio.

OLBERS, H. (1758–1840) A German amateur astronomer who was a prolific observer and one of the foremost interpretative theorists of his day. He discovered two of the four first and largest minor planets—Pallas in 1802 and Vesta in 1807. He was the originator of the theory that the asteroids were the fragments of a disrupted planet.

Olbers also discovered, in 1815, a comet having a period of 74 years which now bears his name; in 1812 he propounded the theory that the tails of comets were highly rarified material being expelled from the head of the comet by some form of electrical pressure emanating from the Sun. He was also the first person to postulate a long period for meteor streams, suggesting that the Leonids had a period of 33 years.

OLBERS Lunar surface feature, coordinates $\xi-962$, $\eta+124$. A crater ring 40 miles in diameter, lying in the libratory region at the Moon's east limb and consequently very difficult to observe.

OLBERS' PARADOX A cursory examination of the night sky reveals that there are many more faint stars than there are bright ones; it is reasonable to suppose that, on average, the fainter stars appear so because they are farther away than the brighter ones. On this assumption the greater number of fainter (i.e. more distant) stars is predictable, for the volume of space enclosed increases rapidly with increasing distance from the Earth. (This also assumes a uniform distribution of stars, on average, throughout all observed space.) The early-nineteenth-century German astronomer Olbers made the further assumptions that the known laws of physics applied throughout the whole of space, and that the universe was static, in both time and space; Olbers then proceeded to calculate that the cumulative effect of the radiation from all the stars in the universe would be so great that the night-sky should be some 50,000 times as bright as a tropical noon. The fact that this was demonstrably not the case became known as 'Olbers' paradox'.

Olbers' reasoning has been beautifully described in simple terms by Bondi, upon whose description the following summary is based. We imagine a huge spherical shell of space centred on the Earth, having a thickness h very small compared with its radius r, which contains a vast number of stars. The volume of the thin spherical shell can be taken to be $4\pi r^2 h$. If the number of stars per unit volume is n, the total number of stars contained in the shell will thus be $4\pi r^2 hn$; if the average radiative power of each star is l, the total radiative output of the stars in the shell will be $4\pi r^2 hnl$. Not all this radiation will reach the Earth, however, for each star is radiating in all directions; that is to say the radiation from each star is distributed over a sphere of surface $4\pi r^2$. Therefore the total radiation from all the stars in the shell *which reaches the Earth*, L, must be

$$L = \frac{^2 hnl}{4\pi r^2} = hnl.$$

This calculation can be repeated for shells of any radius, and it will be noted from the expression $L = hnl$ that the total radiation received from any shell of thickness h will be the same whatever the radius of the shell, i.e. the total radiation falling upon the Earth will be the sum of the L's for an infinite number of concentric shells, which may be expressed as

$$\sum_{0}^{\infty} hnl.$$

There is a further factor to be considered—the fact that the light from a proportion of the more distant stars would be prevented from reaching the Earth by the presence of a nearer star in the same line of sight. Nevertheless, Olbers cal-

culated that the radiation which would reach the Earth would result in a surface temperature on Earth exceeding 5,000° C.

The explanation of Olbers' paradox must lie, of course, in the assumptions he made, at least one of which must have been incorrect. It is now accepted that he erred in assuming that the universe was static, both in time and space. We know that light travels with a finite velocity, and hence we see the very distant stars not as they are, but as they were when the light now reaching us started its journey millions of years ago. Further, we now know that almost all of the bodies we can observe are receding from us, from which we conclude that the universe is expanding. It is a known fact that light emitted by a receding object is reduced in observed intensity, and consequently the light from the most distant stars will be so diminished in intensity as to be undetectable. Thus Olbers' paradox was in fact an early demonstration of the expansion of the universe, which was not to be discovered by direct observation until more than a century later.

OLYMPIA Martian surface feature, approximate position Ω 200°, $\Phi + 80°$. A prominent bright marking running around the 80th parallel of latitude from Ω 170° to Ω 230°. There is a very dark break at Ω 170°, but beyond this a similar bright feature extends to Ω 115°, which may be regarded as a part of Olympia.

OORT, Jan Hendrik One of the foremost contemporary astronomers, particularly well known for his research into the structure of the Galaxy; in recent years a leading radio-astronomer, he has pioneered the study of the all-important 21-cm. wavelength radiation transmitted by interstellar hydrogen. Oort is Professor of Astronomy and Director of the Observatory at Leiden, Holland, and was General Secretary of the International Astronomical Union from 1935–1948. In 1946 he was awarded the Gold Medal of the Royal Astronomical Society.

OPHIR Martian surface feature, approximate position Ω 65°, Φ – 10°. Light area north-west of Auroræ Sinus, between the canali Bætis and Agathodæmon.

OPHIUCHUS (The Serpent-bearer. *Genitive* Ophiuchi, *I.A.U. abbreviation* Oph.) A large equatorial constellation, but situated mainly south of the celestial equator, between Hercules and Libra. There is also a southern extension, between Sagittarius and Scorpius, through which the Ecliptic passes; Ophiuchus is thus a zodiacal constellation. There are three second-magnitude stars and seven of the third magnitude. There is a fine globular cluster, M19, some 5' in diameter.

OPPOSITION That point in the orbit of a superior planet, or of the Moon, where its elongation is 180°. (See **Moon, motion of; Planetary motion.**)

OPTICAL AXIS The central axis of a telescope or other optical instrument, along which the optical elements are placed; not to be confused with the light-path, which may be inclined to the optical axis. (See **Telescope,** *et seq.*)

OPTICAL DOUBLE A double star whose component stars are not part of a single system but are at different distances from the Earth, appearing close together solely for the fortuitous reason that they lie on adjacent lines of sight. (See **Binary system; Double star.**)

OPTICAL GLASS A term used to denote the many forms of glass developed specifically for the manufacture of components for optical instruments of all kinds. For astronomical purposes we are mainly interested in three types of glass: prisms and lenses (notably refracting telescope objectives) are made from the traditional crown glass and flint glass; the mirrors used in reflectors are nowadays usually made of a low-expansion glass such as Pyrex.

A typical crown glass might be composed of SiO_2 70%, K_2O 20%, CaO 10%, and have a refractive index of 1·516. Flint glass is much denser, having a substantial lead content, and contains much less silica: SiO_2 45%, K_2O 9%, PbO 46%. This mixture would produce a glass of refractive index 1·618.

These are, of course, only typical compositions; crown and flint glasses can be, and are, made in a wide range of slightly different compositions, each having different properties—notably the refractive index. By combining crown and flint glasses it is possible to reduce undesirable optical effects. (See, e.g., **doublet**.)

Pyrex typifies a range of low-expansion, borosilicate glasses which have found a wide application in optical instruments, particularly in the reflecting telescope where their low coefficient of expansion and consequently small reaction to temperature changes have proved ideal for the purpose. A typical formula for such a glass would be SiO_2 78%, Na_2O 5%, Al_2O_3 5%, B_2O_3 12%.

Great advances have been made in the techniques of glass manufacture in the last few decades, and it is now possible for glass to be made to an optimum specification for the job for which it is intended.

(See also **Reflection; Refraction; Telescope.**)

OPTICAL WINDOW Most of the radiation incident upon the Earth is absorbed by its atmosphere. The only radiation able to penetrate the atmosphere and reach the Earth's surface is found in two bands of the electromagnetic spectrum. One of these, termed the 'optical window', comprises visible light, extending from deep violet light (wavelength approximately 4×10^{-5} cm) to deep red (wavelength approximately $7\cdot2 \times 10^{-5}$ cm).

(See also **Electromagnetic spectrum; Radio window.**)

OPTICS The study of light and its behaviour. Particularly important to the astronomer as so many of his instruments are optical systems. The behaviour of light rays from an astronomical object must be fully determined, both before they reach the instrument and during their passage through it, before any value can be obtained from the observation.

(See also **Telescope.**)

ORBIT The path of a planet or other heavenly body, usually a closed path relative to the focus of the system to which the body belongs; e.g. planetary orbits around the Sun, the orbits of the components of a binary system around their common centre of gravity, etc. (See **Binary system; Comets, motion of; Planetary motion.**)

ORBIT OF A PLANET The plane of the Ecliptic is taken as the fundamental reference plane when considering the orbits of all planets, minor planets, etc., in the solar system. Most of the planes of such orbits are inclined to the plane of the Ecliptic. Each planetary orbit is an ellipse, the Sun being situated at one of the foci; the actual path followed by any planet is a highly complex one, owing to the perturbing effect of the gravitational pull exerted by each of the other bodies in the system.

Seven elements are necessary to determine the orbit of a planet and the position of the planet in its orbit. These are the semi-major axis of the orbit, a; the eccentricity of the orbit, e; the inclination between the planes of the orbit and of the Ecliptic, i; the longitude of the ascending node, Ω; the longitude of perihelion, ϖ; the epoch, T; the period, P (or, alternatively, the mean motion, n)

(See **Planetary motion; Solar system.**)

ORBIT OF A PLANETARY SATELLITE The orbits of the satellites of the planets are found to be elliptical, with the planet at one focus. Broadly speaking, they are subject to the same considerations as the orbits of the planets, save that

their inclinations are usually referred to the equatorial plane of the primary planet, rather than to the plane of the Ecliptic. The orbits of satellites Jupiter VIII, IX, XI and XII, Saturn IX and Neptune I are retrograde.

(See also **Planetary motion; Orbit of a planet; Solar system.**)

ORBITER Name given to circumlunar probe vehicles of the American project **Lunar Orbiter,** *q.v.*

ORCUS Martian surface feature, approximate position Ω 185°, $\Phi + 15$°. A prominent, fairly broad canal radiating south-eastwards from the Trivium Charontis.

ORION (The Hunter. *Genitive* Orionis, *I.A.U. abbreviation* Ori.) An equatorial constellation, one of the best known—no doubt because of its easily recognizable pattern which dominates the winter sky. Of all the constellations it is perhaps the one whose figure, as depicted by the ancients, best fits its actual configuration of stars; it is easy to envisage the mighty huntsman, with shield and club upraised and his dogs at his heels, as depicted in Flamsteed's *Atlas Cœlestis* of 1729.

Not only is Orion itself easy to identify, but it provides 'pointers' which assist in the identification of many of the stars of the winter sky. The constellation reaches midnight culmination in mid-December.

The principal stars are the great quadrilateral of first- and second-magnitude stars (*Betelgeuse, Rigel, Bellatrix* and *Saiph*), and the trio of second-magnitude stars forming 'Orion's Belt' (δ, ϵ and ζ Ori).

Orion contains a great deal of gaseous nebulosity; long exposure photographs show that much of the area of the constellation is nebulous [Plate 21(d)]. There appear, to the naked eye, to be three rather faint stars in a north–south line, south of ϵ Ori, which represent the hunter's sword (42, θ and ι Ori). Of these, θ Ori is in fact a fine multiple star, consisting of the famous 'Trapezium' of four close stars of magnitudes 6·0, 7·0, 7·5 and 8·0. There are also two fainter components. This multiple is situated at the heart of M42, the famous 'Great Nebula'. One of the best-known absorption nebulae, the so-called 'Horsehead', lies just to the south of ζ Ori. [Plate 21(c).]

Orion contains several interesting double stars, notably *Rigel* and δ, ζ, η, ι and λ Ori.

σ Orionis is another fine multiple; there are four components brighter than tenth magnitude, and eight are visible with a 4-in. refractor.

α Orionis (*Betelgeuse*) is an irregular variable of spectral type *M1*—one of the reddest stars in the heavens and one of the largest known.

There is a beautiful open cluster just to the north of 42 Ori; this is well shown in Plate 21(d).

ORION, GASEOUS NEBULOSITY IN
Situated as it is, adjoining the southern edge of the Milky Way, it is not surprising that Orion is one of the constellations most notable for the presence of gaseous (or 'galactic') nebulosity. Almost the entire area of the constellation proves, in a long-exposure photograph, to be covered by bright, diffuse nebulosity [Plate 21(d)]. The most prominent concentration of this is, of course, M42—the 'Great Nebula'; smaller, but equally beautiful and complex in structure, is the nebulosity surrounding 42 Ori, the star just to the north of M42. [See Plate 21(b).]

Orion also contains several examples of the dark, obscuring (or 'absorption') nebulae; prominent among these is the famous 'Horsehead' [Plate 21(c)]. This is in fact a projection at the boundary of a dark nebula with the bright nebulosity in the region south of ζ Ori. The extra bright appearance of the boundary is probably due to the additional energy released by the collision of particles from both nebulae.

ORION, GREAT NEBULA IN Probably the best known of the galactic, or bright gaseous, nebulae. Numbered M42 in

Messier's Catalogue, it is visible to the naked eye as a faint, rather greenish, misty patch, the centre of three objects forming Orion's sword [Plate 21(d)]. It is centred upon the multiple star θ Ori, the famous 'Trapezium'—so called from the appearance of its four principal stars.

The nebula is in fact part of the vast cloud of interstellar dust and gas situated in this part of the sky, which has been rendered highly luminescent by the radiation from the component stars of the Trapezium. It can be determined from the emission lines in the spectrum of the nebula that the atoms of its constituent material are in a highly ionized state, due to the energy released by the ultra-violet radiation from these intensely hot *O*- and *B*-type stars.

Plate 21(d) is of the entire constellation, taken in blue light, and shows the vast clouds of nebulosity; similar photographs taken in red light show only the central part of the nebula; they do reveal, however, the principal stars of the Trapezium, given a suitable exposure.

(See also **Galactic nebulae**.)

ORION-TYPE STARS Name frequently used to denote stars of spectral class *B*, several of the major stars of Orion being in this class, e.g. β Ori, *B8*; γ Ori, *B2*; ε Ori, *Bo*. (See **Stars—spectral classification of**.)

ORIONIDS One of the major meteor showers, from a radiant near the 'head' of Orion. The shower normally lasts a week or more, centred on October 22; the maximum hourly rate is usually about 20. The shower is caused by the Earth's passing close to the orbit of Halley's Comet, and encountering débris from it. The Orionids are the second meteor shower associated with this comet, the other being the **Eta Aquarids**.

ORTYGIA Martian surface feature, approximate position Ω 0°, Φ + 60°. Lighter area in north temperate belt, north-east of the Mare Acidalium.

OUTER PLANET An arbitrary term used to denote the group of distant planets of which the closest to the Sun is Jupiter—i.e. Jupiter, Saturn, Uranus, Neptune and Pluto.

OWL NEBULA Large planetary nebula, M 97 in the **Messier catalogue,** also numbered N.G.C. 3587. Situated in Ursa Major, at R.A. 11 hr 12 min, Dec. +55° 17′, almost one-third of the distance between β and γ UMa.

The name derives from its unique appearance; it has two large, circular, darker areas in an otherwise opaque spherical shell, bearing a strong resemblance to an owl's face. There is a bright star at the centre of the nebula, no doubt a former supernova from which the shell of nebular matter has been expelled. The shell has a diameter of 3 minutes of arc. The nebula is, however, very faint, and a good view can be obtained only with a large aperture and a low power on a clear, moonless night. [Plate 23(d).]

OXIA PALUS Martian surface feature, approximate position Ω 18°, Φ + 8°. Dusky condensation at the northern end of the Margaritifer Sinus; the feature is continued in its north-eastern direction by the canal Oxus.

OXUS Martian surface feature, approximate position Ω 10°, Φ + 20°. Faint canal, running north-east from Oxia Palus, so that it appears as a continuation of the Margaritifer Sinus.

OXYGEN One of the principal constituents of the Earth's atmosphere, of which it forms approximately one-fifth, and (with carbon and hydrogen) one of the main constituents of all organic matter. Oxygen is gaseous at normal temperatures, liquefying at −183° C under normal pressure. It has an atomic weight of 16.

Spectroscopic analysis of the planetary atmospheres suggests that free oxygen is not present in great quantities; it may, however, be present in the form of oxides and other compounds. The presence of oxygen in the Sun and many stars has been confirmed spectroscopically.

OZONE An allotropic form of oxygen. A molecule of ozone contains three atoms of oxygen and is chemically symbolized as O_3. It is formed from normal oxygen in the presence of an electrical discharge or ultra-violet radiation. In the stratosphere it exists in some quantity, no doubt due to the high incidence in the stratosphere of ultra-violet radiation from the Sun.

P

P CYGNI STARS A group of explosive variables of spectral type *B*, characterized by broad emission lines and strong absorption in the violet spectrum. Some twenty-five stars similar in behaviour to P Cyg, to a greater or lesser extent, have been studied.

P Cyg is a nova, albeit one of unusually small amplitude; it underwent two explosive maxima, in 1600 and 1657–1659, and several minor fluctuations. It reached third magnitude at both maxima, and its post-nova brightness has been in the fifth and sixth magnitudes. It is believed to be a **shell-star**.

P.Z.T. The **photographic zenith tube**, *q.v.*

PALITZSCH Lunar surface formation, co-ordinates $\xi + 801$, $\eta - 457$. An interesting formation close to the south-west limb, adjoining the western wall of Petavius. It is a great valley 60 miles long and some 20 miles wide, which appears to have been formed by the breakdown of the dividing walls in a chain of crater formations.

PALLAS Minor planet number 2, discovered by Olbers in 1802; has a diameter of about 304 miles and an apparent magnitude of about $+8\cdot5$. Pallas is notable for the very high inclination of its orbit to the plane of the Ecliptic—nearly $35°$.

(See also **Minor planets**.)

PALOMAR SKY ATLAS The most modern of the large-scale photographic star charts; it comprises some 2,000 plates covering the entire sky visible from the Mount Palomar Observatory. Each region was photographed twice, in red and blue light with the 48×72-in. Schmidt tele-scope, and all objects are recorded down to about magnitude 20.

This colossal and invaluable project was sponsored and financed by the National Geographic Society, Washington.

PALUS SOMNII (Marsh of Sleep) A dusky area in the north-west quadrant of the Moon, adjoining the western side of the much darker Mare Tranquillitatis. A little to the west lies the Mare Crisium.

PAMBOTIS LACUS Martian surface feature, approximate position $\Omega\,223°$, $\Phi + 5°$. Dusky 'oasis' in the equatorial zone, at the southern boundary of Elysium. The focal point for a number of important radial canali, notably Eunostos, Cyclopia, Antæus and Cerberus.

PAN Proposed name of satellite XI of Jupiter, *q.v.*

PANCHAÏA Martian surface feature, approximate position $\Omega\,200°$, $\Phi + 60°$. That part of the dusky north temperate belt east of Utopia and due north of Trivium Charontis.

PANDORÆ FRETUM Martian surface feature, approximate position $\Omega\,340°$, $\Phi - 25°$. An important dark feature in the south tropical region; a dusky streak some $40°$ in longitude, connecting the Mare Serpentis and the Mare Erythræum. It is to the south of, and parallel to, the Sinus Sabæus, from which it is separated by the Deucalionis Regio.

The Pandoræ Fretum is a particularly important feature to observers of the Martian surface, as it has long been known to be subject to seasonal changes: faint or even invisible during the Martian winter, it darkens during spring to become prominent during the summer.

(See also **Mars—observed features and notable phenomena.**)

PARABOLA An open form of conic section, being the curve whose eccentricity is exactly 1. It may be described as the locus of a point which moves in such a way that it remains equidistant from a fixed point called the *focus* (*F*) and from a fixed straight line called the *directrix* (*D'D''*). This is shown in Fig. 94, where

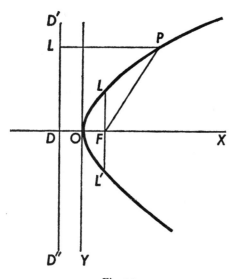

Fig. 94

$PF = PL$ for any position of P on the curve, $OF = OD$, O being termed the *vertex*; if $OF = a$, we derive the equation

$$(x - a)^2 + y^2 = (x + a)^2,$$

from which the standard form of the equation of a parabola,

$$S \equiv y^2 - 4ax = 0$$

may be reduced.

The chord through the focus, LFL', is termed the *latus rectum* and OX is termed the *axis of symmetry*; note that this need not be synonymous with the abscissa, or '*x*-axis', as it has been drawn in Fig. 94.

PARABOLIC COMET Approximately 52 per cent of all comets observed have parabolic or near-parabolic orbital elements, i.e. they have an orbital eccentricity approximating to 1·0. The implication that these comets arrive from outside the solar system (the parabola being an open curve) is almost certainly erroneous, at least in most cases; the comets are only observable over a short arc of their orbits around perihelion, and it is almost impossible to deduce their orbital elements with sufficient accuracy to distinguish between parabolic orbits of eccentricity exactly 1·0 and very elongated elliptical orbits of eccentricity slightly less than 1, especially as the comets are subject to considerable perturbations by the major planets on their journey towards aphelion.

(See also **Comets—orbits of.**)

PARALLACTIC ANGLE Also known as the 'angle of situation'; it is the angle formed at a celestial body between the great circles passing through the body and the celestial pole and the zenith respectively.

PARALLACTIC DISPLACEMENT The apparent changes in the observed position of a star due to the motion of the Earth in its orbit. (See **Parallactic ellipse.**)

PARALLACTIC ELLIPSE The changing position in space of the observer, due to the Earth's motion in its orbit around the Sun, will be reflected in a parallactic displacement of the observed star relative to the background (infinitely distant) stars.

A star situated at the pole of the Ecliptic will appear to move in a circular orbit of radius equal to the annual parallax of the star. A star situated on the Ecliptic will appear to have a back and forth motion along a straight line of length equal to its parallax. Stars in intermediate positions will appear to move in elliptical orbits of semi-major axes equal to their parallaxes—their 'parallactic ellipses'.

(See also **Parallax, stellar.**)

PARALLACTIC INEQUALITY An inequality in the motion of the Moon, arising from the fact that the perturbing effect of the Sun on the Moon is greater in that half of the Moon's apparent orbit around the Earth from quadrature through conjunction (New Moon) to quadrature, than at corresponding points in the other half of the orbit, due to the Sun's being slightly closer.

(See also **Moon—motion of.**)

PARALLACTIC SHIFT The **parallactic displacement**, *q.v.*

PARALLAX The angle subtended at a heavenly body by a baseline of known length, usually designated P or π. It is of course directly related to the distance of the body, and provides the only direct means of measuring the distance; the word has therefore come to be used by astronomers as synonymous with distance.

The baseline used for nearer objects, such as the members of the solar system, is the equatorial radius of the Earth; parallaxes determined on this basis are termed *geocentric parallaxes*. The observations may be made in a number of ways: from positional observations made simultaneously from two widely separated stations on the Earth's surface; from observations made twelve hours apart from the same station; and by variations of these methods, appropriate adjustments being made in the mathematical reduction of the observations.

For more distant objects, the baseline used is the semi-major axis of the Earth's orbit; these are termed *heliocentric parallaxes*. The usual method of determining heliocentric parallaxes is from a comparison of positional observations made at intervals of six months.

(See also **Parallax, solar; Parallax, stellar; Parallax, stellar—determination of.**)

PARALLAX, ANNUAL The angle subtended at a star by the semi-major axis of the Earth's orbit—i.e. by 1 A.U. (See **Parallax, stellar.**)

PARALLAX CATALOGUE See **General Catalogue of Trigonometrical Stellar Parallaxes.**

PARALLAX, CHROMATIC A form of optical parallax arising in optical instruments which are not fully colour-corrected and in which optical parallax is present; it arises from the fact that the position of the focal plane depends upon the wavelength of the light being observed. (See **Parallax, optical.**)

PARALLAX, DYNAMICAL It can be deduced from Newtonian gravitational theory that, for a binary system,

$$(m_1 + m_2) = \frac{a^3}{\pi^3 P^2}$$

where m_1, m_2 are the masses of the component stars (expressed in terms of the Sun's mass), a is the semi-major axis of the relative orbit in seconds of arc, π is the parallax in seconds of arc and P the period in years. It is found to be a reasonable assumption that the combined mass of the system is twice the Sun's mass, and by substitution the expression then becomes

$$\pi = \sqrt[3]{\left(\frac{a^3}{2\,P^2}\right)};$$

thus the parallax can be determined from normal double-star observations. That the assumption $(m_1 + m_2) = 2$ is a reasonable one can be seen from the fact that even if the true value of $(m_1 + m_2)$ is 16, the parallax deduced is only in error by a factor of two.

Parallaxes of binary systems determined in this way are termed 'dynamical' or 'hypothetical' parallaxes.

PARALLAX, EQUATORIAL HORIZONTAL The geocentric parallax of a body when on the observer's horizon, measured with the Earth's equatorial radius as baseline. (See **Parallax, solar; Parallax, stellar.**)

PARALLAX, GEOCENTRIC The parallax of an object, usually a member of the solar system, determined from simultaneous positional observations made at two stations on the Earth's surface a known distance apart—the maximum baseline by this method approximating to the Earth's diameter. An alternative method is to make positional observations from one station several hours apart, the baseline being the distance travelled by the observatory during the interval due to the diurnal rotation of the Earth.

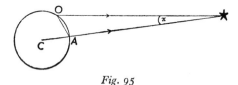

Fig. 95

The geocentric parallax (π) is defined as the angle subtended at a body by the baseline on the Earth's surface (OA) formed by its directions from the observing station (O) and the centre of the Earth (C)—see Fig. 95.

PARALLAX, HELIOCENTRIC The parallax of a star obtained from positional observations made six months apart, i.e. with the diameter of the Earth's orbit as baseline. (See **Parallax, stellar.**)

PARALLAX, HORIZONTAL The geocentric parallax of a body observed when on the horizon; that is, the angle between the direction of the body when on the observer's horizon and the direction it would have if viewed from the centre of the Earth. (See **Parallax, stellar.**)

PARALLAX, HYPOTHETICAL Term often used formerly for the dynamical parallax of a binary system. (See **Parallax, dynamical.**)

PARALLAX, OPTICAL A fault in optical measuring instruments arising when the image being observed is not formed exactly in the plane containing the fiducial wires or graticule with reference to which the measurement is being made; in this condition any movement of the observer's eye will introduce a displacement of the image relative to the wires or graticule.

PARALLAX, PHOTOMETRIC The parallax of a star too distant for its parallax to be measured directly. The apparent magnitude of the star (m) is observed, and its absolute magnitude (M) inferred from its spectral type; its parallax (π) may then be calculated from the formula:

$$M = m + 5 + 5 \log \pi.$$

PARALLAX, SECULAR The apparent angular movement of a star due to the motion through space of the Sun.

PARALLAX, SOLAR Strictly, the Sun's mean equatorial horizontal parallax, i.e. the angle subtended by the Earth's equatorial radius at the mean distance of the Sun. This is one of the most important constants in astronomy, since it determines the value adopted for the mean distance of the Earth from the Sun—the **Astronomical Unit**. A great deal of effort has therefore been expended on the observational determination of the solar parallax to the highest possible degree of accuracy. Unfortunately it is not easily measured, and is still not known to the precision that is desirable.

Paradoxically, the most effective way of determining the mean distance between the Earth and the Sun is to determine the mean distance of another body from the Sun. This arises from the fact that the mean distances of all the planets, *relative to each other*, can be determined from observations of their periods of orbital revolution, by applying Kepler's laws of planetary motion; thus, if the mean distance of any one of them can be precisely determined, the scale of the whole system becomes known and the mean distance of any other body can be accurately evaluated.

The closer a body is to the Earth, the greater the **parallactic displacement**;

it is therefore desirable to measure the distance of a body passing close to the Earth. The two planets which are closest to the Earth are Mars and Venus; unfortunately when Venus is at perigee it is between the Earth and the Sun and cannot be observed, save on the rare occasions when it is in transit across the Sun's disk. This was realized by Halley, who proposed that the transits of Venus in 1761 and 1769 should be carefully observed in order to deduce the solar parallax; this was done, a value of 8″57 being obtained by Encke from an analysis of all the observations made. This exceeds the true value by about $2\frac{1}{2}$ per cent, but was by far the most accurate determination then obtained, and was accepted as the standard value for many years.

Careful preparations were made by astronomers of many countries for the next two transits, in 1874 and 1882; numerous expeditions were sent out and careful measurements were made of both transits. Unfortunately the uncertainties arising from the difficulties of timing the commencement and finish of the transit, no doubt due to the effects of the deep atmosphere of Venus, exceeded the precision required, and it was not possible to obtain a more accurate value of the solar parallax than that already in use.

It thus became necessary to find an alternative means; even the development of astronomical photography did not provide a ready solution, as it did in the case of stellar parallaxes; it was not possible to measure the parallactic shift of the Sun relative to background stars, as any stars photographed close to the Sun were lost in its glare. Sir David Gill, H.M. Astronomer at the Cape of Good Hope, therefore decided to attempt to determine the solar parallax from observations of Mars at a perihelic opposition. He travelled to Ascension Island and set up a **heliometer** in readiness for the 1877 opposition. He made a series of measures of the position of the planet relative to the background stars, in pairs, the first position being obtained early in the night and the second

several hours later. The diurnal rotation of the Earth during the night thus provided the baseline for a trigonometrical parallax, the parallactic displacement being the apparent shift in the planet's position, corrected of course for the orbital motion of both Mars and the Earth during the period between the observations.

Gill was a very skilled observer with the heliometer—one of the most difficult instruments with which to observe—and obtained values of the solar parallax of much improved accuracy, the mean value being 8″78.

Gill decided to enlist the aid of other observatories, so as to improve the accuracy of his determinations by making simultaneous measures of the position of the planet from widely separated stations, thus obtaining his baseline without the unfortunate time-lag and the possibility of errors being introduced in the more complicated reductions. He was joined by observers at Leipzig, Göttingen and New Haven, and with their help obtained a large series of observations, in 1888–1889, of the minor planets Victoria, Iris and Sappho; these all have very eccentric orbits and therefore approach quite close to the Earth.

Gill again improved the accuracy of his determination, his new value of 8″80 being adopted for some years. In 1898, however, a new minor planet—Eros—was discovered whose orbit was such that it would pass in 1901 within only 30 million miles of the Earth. It was therefore ideally suited to a redetermination of the solar parallax, and a worldwide programme of observation was prepared. Photographic positions of the asteroid were obtained at no less than 58 observatories, and were analysed by A. R. Hinks who obtained a result of 8″806. It began to appear that this fundamental but elusive quantity had now been reliably determined. Eros was due to make a much closer approach in 1931, however, when it would pass within 16 million miles of the Earth. The International Astronomical Union decided that this opportunity should be seized, and appointed a special commission under the Presidency of Sir Harold Spencer Jones, then H.M. Astronomer at the Cape, to conduct the investigation.

In a meticulously planned programme, 2,847 plates were obtained with 30 different telescopes at observatories throughout the world; these were all measured and reduced under Spencer Jones' personal supervision, largely at Greenwich—Spencer Jones having been appointed Astronomer Royal in 1933. This monumental labour occupied ten years; in 1943 Spencer Jones announced a result of 8″790, with a probable error of only ±0″001. In terms of its internal probable error, this was a far more accurate determination than any of the previous ones; the entire venture, and Spencer Jones' scholarly control of it, will long rank as an outstanding example of international cooperation in scientific research. The actual value obtained, however, was rather puzzling; it differed from the previous result by nearly five times their combined probable error. It appeared that either one or both of these determinations had been subject to an undetected systematic error, and that they were not so accurate as their internal consistency suggested. A new attempt was made by Rabe in 1950, using a new method in which he analysed the perturbations due to the Earth in the orbit of an asteroid making a close approach; he obtained a value almost midway between that of Hinks and Spencer Jones.

It would appear safest, therefore, to accept a value expressed to a lower degree of accuracy, say 8″79, and to await opportunities for further investigation of the problem. The figure of 8″79 is equivalent to a value for 1A.U. of 93,009,000 miles.

PARALLAX, SPECTROSCOPIC

The parallax of a distant star, deduced from a study of the relative intensities of certain spectral lines compared with those in the spectra of closer stars whose parallaxes have been determined by trigonometric methods.

PARALLAX, STELLAR

The parallax of a star which may be observed by direct means (*trigonometric parallax*) or deduced from an examination of the star's spectrum (*spectroscopic parallax*). This is one of the most important measurable quantities relating to a star, providing as it does the only direct means of determining the star's distance. Stellar parallaxes are extremely small angles, that of the nearest star being only about three-quarters of a second of arc, and all others are, of course, smaller than this. Stellar parallaxes are therefore determined in the form of 'heliocentric parallaxes', with the radius of the Earth's orbit as baseline.

The first determinations of stellar parallax were made in 1838; the acceptance of the Copernican heliocentric concept of the solar system, which followed Bradley's discovery of the aberration of light in 1725, recognized that stellar parallaxes must exist, only their smallness and the lack of sufficiently accurate instruments preventing their detection. It is interesting to note in passing that Bradley's discovery of aberration arose from his unsuccessful attempts to detect and measure the parallax of γ Dra.

The first parallax determinations were not of great accuracy; using Fraunhofer's 6¼-in. heliometer at Königsberg in 1838 Bessel obtained a parallax for 61 Cyg of 0″314, compared with the currently accepted figure of 0″292; a redetermination by Bessel in 1840 yielded a less accurate result (0″348). Bessel's 1838 result for 61 Cyg was the first published stellar parallax, but a parallax for α Cen by T. Henderson was in fact based on earlier observations. Henderson, Director of the Cape Observatory, used the meridian circle there to obtain values of the zenith distance of α Cen at different seasons of the year, from which he was able to deduce the parallactic shift and hence the parallax. He obtained a value of 1″0 compared with the currently accepted figure of 0″752. The third parallax measured in 1838 was that of *Vega*, measured by F. G. W. Struve with a ring micrometer attached to the famous 9·6-in. refractor at the Dorpat Observatory, Estonia. Struve obtained a parallax of 0″.262, greatly in excess of the correct value of 0″.123. The brightness of *Vega* and the consequent glare surrounding its telescopic image no doubt contributed towards the inaccuracy of this first determination of its parallax. The heliometer was found to provide the most accurate visual means of measuring stellar parallaxes; it was very difficult to use, however, and progress in extending the records of known stellar parallaxes was extremely slow in the days prior to the development of astronomical photography.

The distances (*r*) corresponding to the observed parallaxes (*π*) are indicated in Table 26; it will be appreciated that the difficulties of making accurate parallax measurements are such that the derived distances are necessarily approximate. Even with the most refined techniques parallaxes of stars at distances greater than 100 parsecs are almost impossible to measure, the parallax being of the same order as the possible errors of the observation.

The major catalogue of stellar parallaxes is the *General Catalogue of Trigonometric Stellar Parallaxes* compiled at Yale University Observatory in continuation of the great programme started there by

Table 26. Equivalent parallaxes and stellar distances

π (″)	r (light years)	r (parsecs)
1·00	3·26	1·0
0·50	6·52	2·0
0·33	9·78	3·0
0·25	13·04	4·0
0·20	16·30	5·0
0·15	21·84	6·7
0·10	32·6	10·0
0·05	65·2	20·0
0·04	81·5	25·0
0·02	163·0	50·0
0·01	326·0	100·0

Table 27. Distribution of stars of known parallax

Distance from Earth (parsecs)	Parallax (″)	Number of Stars
0–5	> 0·20	35
5–10	> 0·10	130
10–20	> 0·05	586
20–50	> 0·02	2017
50–100	> 0·01	1255
> 100	< 0·01	1799

Schlesinger at the beginning of the century, and published in 1952. It contains details of parallax observations of 5,822 stars, made at fourteen observatories between 1910 and 1950 and reduced to a uniform system.

Table 27 shows the numbers of stars found within radii from the Earth of up to 100 parsecs and included in this catalogue.

PARALLAX, STELLAR—DETERMINATION OF

Owing to the great distances involved, stellar parallaxes are so small that they can only be measured from a very large baseline; they are therefore determined as heliocentric parallaxes, on a baseline equal to the semi-major axis of the Earth's orbit.

Formerly obtained by visual methods—notably the **heliometer**—parallaxes are now determined solely by photographic methods, which are more practicable and reliable as well as yielding more accurate results.

Parallax programmes have been carried out for some sixty years at a number of major observatories; particularly notable are the great series of parallax determinations made at the Johannesburg station of the Yale University Observatory, the Allegheny and Leander–McCormick Observatories in the U.S.A., the Cape Observatory and the Royal Observatory, Greenwich.

The principle followed in a parallax programme is to obtain a series of plates of a given field at six-monthly intervals; it is usual to obtain three or more plates of the field at each epoch. A long-focus telescope of great stability is required, and observing skill of a high standard. The work has mainly been carried out with photographic refractors with apertures of 24 inches or more. It is important to make the exposures when the field concerned is close to the meridian, so as to reduce the possibilities of atmospheric disturbance and instrumental error.

The position of the star whose parallax is to be determined is measured very carefully relative to a number of fainter and more distant 'comparison stars'. The star's position is measured relative to the same comparison stars on the plates exposed six months later, enabling the parallactic displacement to be determined; it will, however, be inextricable from the star's proper motion. During the next six months, however, the star's proper motion will continue in the same direction, whereas the parallactic displacement will change its sign. From the three sets of plates it is therefore possible to determine both quantities. It is usual to continue the series for at least five epochs, and preferably more, so that the parallax obtained can be as accurate as possible.

The limitations of present techniques render it extremely difficult to measure the parallaxes of stars at distances much in excess of 100 parsecs; for more distant stars it is necessary to extrapolate the known scale of parallaxes and to deduce their parallaxes from a study of the characteristics of their spectra or from a comparison of their observed apparent magnitudes and the absolute magnitudes inferred from their spectral type. (See **Parallax, spectroscopic; Parallax, photometric.**)

PARALLAX, TRIGONOMETRIC The parallax of an object obtained by a direct observational method, utilizing the principle of triangulation and a measured baseline. (See **Parallax, stellar—determination of.**)

PARALLEL-SLIT INTERFEROMETER A type of stellar interferometer, consisting of a diaphragm containing two narrow parallel slits whose separation is adjustable. The diaphragm is normally placed over the O.G. of the telescope with which it is used (see **Interferometer, stellar**).

PARHELION A diffuse spot of light, sometimes showing the colours of the spectrum, being an image of the Sun caused by the refraction of sunlight by minute ice crystals suspended in the atmosphere. They are usually seen at an angular distance of 22° from the Sun. Parhelia are not commonly seen outside the polar regions.

(See also **Coronae; Halo; Parselena.**)

PARKES RADIO OBSERVATORY The Parkes Field Station of the Government Observatory, Sydney, New South Wales, Australia; one of the major radio-astronomical observatories of the world.

PARSEC One of the fundamental units of distance used in astronomy, especially for very large distances. It is the distance at which an object would have a parallax of one second of arc, taking the mean Earth–Sun distance (1 Astronomical Unit) as baseline. (The name is derived from PARallax of one SEC-ond.)

Multiple units are used for the large distances often encountered in astrophysics, the *kiloparsec* (1,000 parsecs) and even the *megaparsec* (1,000,000 parsecs). One parsec is equal to 3·26 **light years**, or a little over 19 billion miles.

The usual abbreviations are pc, kpc, Mpc, etc.

PARSELENA A diffuse image of the Moon, sometimes coloured, caused by refraction of the Moon's light due to the presence of tiny ice crystals in the atmosphere. Not commonly observed outside the polar regions. They are usually seen at an angular distance of 22° from the Moon.

(See also **Coronae; Halo; Parhelion.**)

PARTIAL ECLIPSE An eclipse in which, as seen from a given observing site, the eclipsed body is never totally immersed in the umbra of the eclipsing body.

PAVO (The Peacock. *Genitive* Pavonis, *I.A.U. abbreviation* Pav.) A southern circumpolar constellation containing one second- and three third-magnitude stars; there are a number of the fourth magnitude and fainter, but on the whole the constellation is rather an 'empty' one.

κ Pav is a **Cepheid variable**, with a magnitude range of 4·0–5·5 and a period of 9·1 days.

There is a large globular cluster, N.G.C. 6752, a couple of degrees east of ω Pav.

PEGASUS (Mythological character. *Genitive* Pegasi, *I.A.U. abbreviation* Peg.) A vast northern constellation reaching from Cygnus, Lacerta and Andromeda almost to the equator. There are several second- and third-magnitude stars, of which the most prominent are β, α and γ Peg, which form with α And the 'Great Square of Pegasus'. This formation dominates the summer skies, reaching midnight culmination in August and September.

There are few double or variable stars of note, and few nebulae or clusters.

PENCIL In optics, the term used to denote a beam of light, either parallel-sided or a cone of light rays of very small angle, so that the spread of the light is minimal.

PENDULUM CLOCK A form of clock which measures intervals of time by relating them to the period of swing of a pendulum. This period is governed by the length of the pendulum and the extent of the arc through which it swings; it is therefore essential to control these factors precisely if accurate time-determination is required.

The length of the pendulum can be kept constant by a simple temperature-compensating device, but the amplitude of swing can be maintained only by regularly imparting a force to the pendulum in one of its directions of travel. This was formerly achieved by mechanical means, but in some more recent designs the force is imposed electromagnetically; the friction due to the use of a mechanical escapement is also avoided nowadays by the use of photo-electronic apparatus to 'count' the oscillations of the pendulum; the pendulum being freed from mechanical contact of any kind.

A form of pendulum clock capable of high accuracy, and which provided the national time services from observatories all over the world for many years, was the free-pendulum clock produced by the Shortt–Synchronome company, usually known as the **'Shortt clock'**.

Although superseded for work of the highest accuracy by the **quartz clock** and, more recently, the so-called **atomic clock**, Shortt clocks are still giving superb service in many observatories. Under carefully controlled conditions they are capable of a rate of about ± 0·003 sec/day. (See also **Time—determination of**.)

PENUMBRA The outer parts of the shadow cast by an object obstructing the passage of light from an extended source, where light from *part* of the source is not obstructed, e.g. the region enclosing the shadow-cone of the Moon during a solar eclipse, from any part of which the eclipse appears partial.

The term is also used to denote the lighter, peripheral region of a sunspot.

(See also **Eclipse, lunar; Eclipse, solar; Sunspot; Umbra**.)

PERIASTRON Closest approach in orbit of one component of a binary system to the other star.

(See also **Apastron**.)

PERIGEE The point of closest approach to the Earth by another body.

(See also **Apogee**.)

PERIHELION That point in the orbit of a planet or comet which is closest to the Sun.

(See also **Aphelion**.)

PERIJOVE The point of closest approach to Jupiter by another body; usually applied to the satellites of Jupiter.

(See also **Apojove.**)

PERIOD–LUMINOSITY LAW A relationship between the period and absolute magnitude of Cepheid variables, discovered by Miss Henrietta Leavitt of the Harvard College Observatory in 1912. Miss Leavitt was studying the Cepheid variables in the Magellanic Clouds, and showed that the greater the luminosity of a Cepheid the longer its period (see Fig. 96).

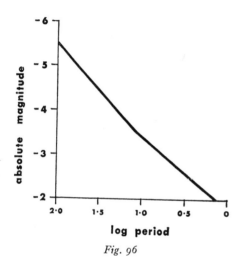

Fig. 96

This relationship is of great importance, since the period of light-fluctuation of Cepheids too distant for their parallax to be measured can be observed, and thus their absolute magnitude can be deduced, and their distances (*r*) can be calculated from the known relationship

$$M = m + 5 - 5 \log r,$$

where *M* is the absolute and *m* the apparent magnitude. (This relationship is often expressed in the slightly different form

$$M = m + 5 + 5 \log \pi,$$

where π is the parallax of the star.)

As Cepheid variables have been dis-

covered in many distant galaxies, this valuable relationship has provided a means of determining the distances of those galaxies with some precision.

PERIODIC COMET Colloquial term used to denote a short-period comet; i.e. one for which it is (or will be) possible to inter-relate observations made at two or more apparitions. The usual criterion is taken to be a calculated period of less than 200 years.

(See also **Short-period comet.**)

PERISATURNIUM The point of closest approach to Saturn by another body; usually applied to the satellites of Saturn.

(See also **Aposaturnium.**)

PERRINE, C. D. (1867–1951) Notable observer who, in 1904 and 1905, discovered satellites VI and VII of Jupiter with the 36-in. Crossley reflector of the Lick Observatory. Later became Director of the National Observatory of the Republic of Argentina at Cordoba.

Perrine was a leading comet observer; his name is associated with the discoveries of Comets 1895 IV, 1896 I, 1896 VII, 1897 I, 1897 III, 1898 I, 1898 VI, 1898 IX, 1902 III, 1909 III, 1916 III.

PERSEIDS One of the most prolific meteor showers, and one of the most persistent; usually observed between July 27 and August 17 each year, and reaching a maximum between August 10 and 13. There are records of observations of the August Perseids throughout the past 1,200 years. These days the shower usually reaches a zenithal hourly rate of 50–70. The radiant is on the border between Perseus and Cassiopeia, about 4° north of γ Per.

The shower is believed to be associated with the debris of Comet P/Swift–Tuttle, 1862 III.

PERSEUS (Mythological character. *Genitive* Persei, *I.A.U. abbreviation* Per.) A large northern constellation situated between Andromeda and Auriga, which reaches midnight culmination in November. There are quite a number of stars brighter than the fourth magnitude, and almost the whole of the constellation is situated in the Milky Way.

One of the most interesting objects is *Algol* (β Per), the best known of a type of eclipsing variable, having two minima in its period of 69 hours.

One of the most spectacular cluster-fields is to be found near the northern tip of Perseus, about 4° west of η Per and slightly to the north; here are two superb clusters (N.G.C. 869 and 884), each about three-quarters of a degree in diameter and with their centres only three-quarters of a degree apart. On a clear night the great 'Double Cluster' can be seen with the unaided eye; with a small telescope it is a splendid sight. There is a beautiful ruby-red star at the centre of the easternmost cluster. [Plate 22(e).]

Another large, and rather loose, cluster is M34 (N.G.C. 1039), about 4° west of Algol.

(See also **Algol.**)

PERSEUS—DOUBLE CLUSTER IN A superb pair of globular clusters, just visible to the unaided eye, marking Perseus' upraised Sword-handle in the ancient constellation figure. They are situated close to the northern boundary of the constellation, approximately midway between γ Per and δ Cas. The centres of the clusters are only three-quarters of a degree of arc apart. Numbered 869 and 884 in the N.G.C., the clusters were not catalogued by Messier; they were listed by Herschel in his class VI (Very compressed and rich clusters of stars) and are therefore sometimes referred to by their Herschel catalogue numbers H VI 33 and H VI 34. [Plate 22(e).]

The clusters are physically close, not an optical pair, and are a superb sight with quite modest apertures.

PERSISTENCE OF VISION If the eye is stimulated by an exposure to light of finite duration, the 'seeing' sensation persists for a brief interval after the exposure has ended. This is known as persistence of vision. As a result, if the eye is subjected to brief exposures in rapid succession, provided their frequency exceeds a certain minimum value the longer seeing sensations produced will overlap, and no 'flicker' will be experienced.

It is this physiological phenomenon, of course, which permits cinematograph films and television broadcasts to be viewed satisfactorily; it also has important applications in astronomy—notably in the use of the **spectrohelioscope** and the **blink microscope,** *q.v.*

PERSONAL EQUATION It is known that when making observations of a measuring nature or otherwise involving the visual 'setting' of instrument—e.g. a micrometer wire—each individual observer's accuracy of observation is subject to systematic errors. These lead to a result which is spurious by an amount which varies for each observer—known as that observer's 'personal equation'.

It is not possible to measure personal equations directly, but the corrections to be allowed for them are obtained statistically; it is assumed that the mean of the results obtained by all the observers participating in a programme is closest to the correct result, and the personal equations of all the observers are calculated relative to the 'mean observer'. The observations are then corrected so that all were apparently made by the mean observer. This may still result in the observations containing a residual systematic error, but in practice the consistency of personal equations of experienced observers indicate that such residual error is minimal.

PERTURBATIONS If a number of bodies are in orbit about a primary body, as the planets are in orbit around the Sun, the motion of any one of them is affected by the changing gravitational attractions of all the others as they too move around their orbits; the effect of another body upon the motion of a body is termed a 'perturbation'. The calculation and prediction of the movements of a planetary body involve, firstly, the solution of a two-body problem involving only the Sun and the planet and assuming that there are no other perturbing bodies in the system, and then the calculation of the changes to this basic orbit due to the perturbations of the other bodies.

In the case of a system of planets with near-circular orbits the process can be repeated, using the corrected motion, a sufficient number of times for an orbit of great accuracy to be determined. This is termed the *General method of perturbations*.

In the case of bodies having highly eccentric orbits, such as the long-period comets, the orbit can only be obtained by a series of successive approximations, and it is not possible to attain similar accuracy; this method is known as the *Special method of perturbations*.

PETAVIUS Lunar surface feature, coordinates $\xi + 785$, $\eta - 430$. One of the largest formations in the south-western quadrant, this 100-mile diameter walled plain is a superb sight under low illumination; it becomes invisible around Full Moon. The broad and rugged walls rise to 7,000 ft. in the west and, double, to 11,000 ft. in the east. The great valley-formation Palitzsch adjoins the western rampart. The floor of Petavius is convex, and there is a great central mountain mass with a peak rising to 5,600 ft. This mountain is connected to the south-east wall by a great cleft which can easily be seen with quite modest apertures. Part of the great meridional chain that includes Furnerius, Vendelinus, Langrenus, Cleomedes and Endymion.

PHÆTHONTIS Martian surface feature, approximate position Ω 155°, $\Phi - 50°$. Dusky area in the south temperate zone, just south of the eastern end of the Mare Sirenum.

PHASE The phase of a planet or of the Moon is a measure of the amount of the illuminated hemisphere of the body visible from Earth at a given instant, and hence is an indication of the apparent shape of the body at the time. The diagrams in the succeeding entries show the reason for the observed phases of various types of body; if any reader finds it difficult to understand them, he should imagine himself stood on the Earth at the position indicated and looking towards the other body in each of its positions in turn, noting the amount of the sunlit portion that will be visible to him in each case. It will then be easy to comprehend that the apparent outline of the body will be as indicated in the sketches adjacent to each position. It may also be found helpful to experiment in a darkened room, using a torch as the Sun and a tennis ball to represent the Moon or planet.

PHASE OF INFERIOR PLANET In the case of the inferior planets the entire orbit of the planet is seen from the Earth from an 'outside' viewpoint, and the full range of phases, as displayed by the Moon, can be seen. There is one important difference, however; the Moon being apparently in orbit around the Earth, its diameter remains approximately constant through all its phases. The inferior planets, being in orbit around the Sun, are at different distances from Earth at each phase and consequently their apparent diameters differ from phase to phase.

Fig. 97 (which is not, of course, to scale) shows the appearance of the inferior planet at a number of positions in its orbit. At superior conjunction (1) the entire illuminated hemisphere is visible, but the planet is at its greatest distance from the Earth; its outline will therefore be a full, but very small, circle. As it moves on in its orbit, towards (2), its distance from the Earth decreases and it increases in apparent diameter; the illuminated portion is beginning to turn away from the Earth, however, resulting in a gibbous phase. At Greatest Elongation

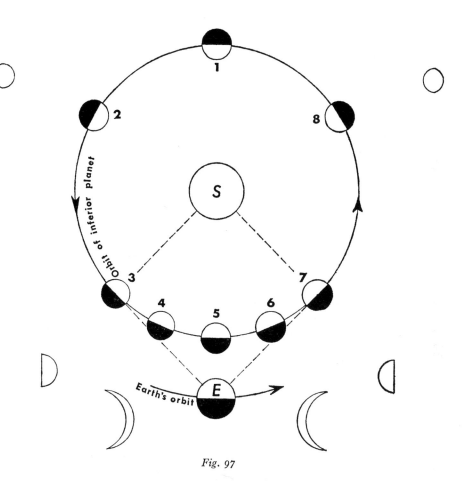

Fig. 97

East (3) the planet is at the half-moon phase ('dichotomy') but larger still. As it passes through the crescent phase (4) it continues to grow, until at inferior conjunction (5) the greatest diameter is reached, but the illuminated hemisphere is turned completely away from the Earth and the planet becomes invisible. After a few days it will reappear as a thin crescent (6), which gradually widens (with the apparent diameter now decreasing) until dichotomy is again reached at Greatest Elongation West (7); the planet then passes through gibbous phases again (8) until it reaches the next superior conjunction.

315

Owing to their proximity to the Sun, neither Mercury nor Venus are observable at all parts of their orbit—see **Mercury— visibility from Earth; Venus—visibility from Earth.**

The phase of an inferior planet is normally tabulated in the astronomical almanacs as the percentage of the area of the full disk of the planet which is illuminated as seen from the Earth. It will be appreciated that the **visual magnitude**

depends on the phase as well as the distance of the planet from both the Sun and Earth, and its **albedo**; the planet Venus appears brightest, in fact, about 35 days before and after inferior conjunction, when its phase is a fairly thin crescent. (See also **Apparition, planetary; Planetary motion.**)

PHASE OF SUPERIOR PLANET The superior planets are always observed

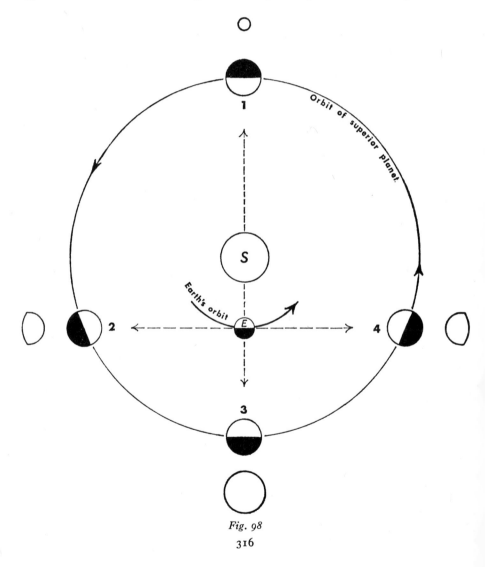

Fig. 98

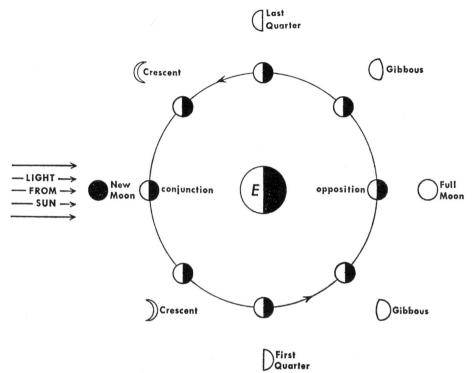

Fig. 99

'from within', as the Earth has a smaller orbit, and thus they are never seen to pass between the Earth and the Sun, through inferior conjunction, as do the inferior planets.

It will be seen from Fig. 98 that the 'full' phase is seen at both conjunction (1) and opposition (3), the planet appearing rather larger at (3) owing to its smaller distance from the Earth; between these phases, however, there is a slightly gibbous phase effect; this is at a maximum at the quadrature positions (2, 4). Owing to the small radius of the Earth's orbit compared with the radii of the orbits of the superior planets, the effect is very slight; it is undetectable for Saturn and the more distant planets, and even for Mars, the nearest of the outer planets, only about 12% of the total hemisphere is obscured at maximum phase. (See also **Planetary motion.**)

PHASE OF THE MOON Fig. 99 depicts the Moon in eight positions in its apparent orbit around the Earth; adjacent to each position is a representation of the appearance of the Moon in that position, as seen from the Earth.

The interval between successive New Moons—the synodic period—can vary by some hours owing to the orbital eccentricities of both Earth and Moon; its mean value is 29d 12hr 44min 2·9sec.

The phase of the Moon is usually tabulated in ephemerides in the form of a figure for the Age of the Moon; this is the time in days that has elapsed since the previous New Moon. Hence the age at New Moon would be 0 days, at Full Moon 14·8 days, etc.

Phase is an important consideration for observers of the lunar surface, as surface features are best defined when they cast long shadows—i.e. when they are near the terminator and the angle of illumination is low. (See also: **Lunation; Metonic Cycle.**)

PHILLIPS, Rev. Dr. T. E. R. (1868–1942) One of the most successful amateur astronomers of all time, and (with E. M. Antoniadi) one of the two leading planetary observers of his generation. A graduate of Oxford University, Theodore Phillips commenced systematic observation of the planetary surfaces in 1896, when a curate in Somerset. He used a 9¼-in. reflector on an altazimuth mounting, but remounted it as an equatorial when he moved to Croydon. Later, at Ashtead, Surrey, he substituted a 12¼-in. Calver reflector in the same mounting. In 1911 he added an 8-in. Cooke refractor to his equipment. In 1916 he became Rector of Headley, Surrey, and there, on the northern slopes of Box Hill, established a superb observatory, the principal equipment being an 18-in. reflector by With and the 8-in. refractor. Some of his most valuable observations were made during the 26 years life of the Headley Observatory.

Phillips was a notable observer of double-stars, but his greatest contributions were in the study of the surface features of the planets, especially Mars, Jupiter and Saturn. His series of observations of Jupiter, which span his entire observing career—almost half a century—are unparalleled in the history of planetary observation; their contribution to our knowledge of the planet is immeasurable.

In addition to being an observer of the highest ability, Phillips was also a splendid organizer of amateur observers; he was Director of the Jupiter Section of the British Astronomical Association for no less than thirty-four years (1901–1934), and retired from that arduous post only to become Director of the Saturn Section (1934–1939). He was President of the Association (1914–1916) and the first recipient of its Walter Goodacre Medal and Gift, in 1930. He was accepted among professional astronomers as few amateurs have been before or since, and was twice

honoured by the Royal Astronomical Society—in 1918 when he was awarded the Jackson–Gwilt Medal and Gift, and by being elected President of the Society (1927–1929). He was also President of Commission 16 of the International Astronomical Union from shortly after its foundation in 1922 until 1935.

His final honour came, unfortunately, less than three months before his death, when his alma mater paid him a rare compliment: on 1942 February 28 the University of Oxford conferred upon him the degree of Doctor of Science, *honoris causa*, in recognition of his great contributions to the science of astronomy.

PHILOLAUS Lunar surface feature, co-ordinates $\xi - 165$, $\eta + 949$. A well-defined formation in the north polar region, very close to the limb; 46 miles in diameter, it has terraced walls rising to 12,000 ft. in places and a floor broken up with many minor features stretching from Furnerius to Endymion in the far north.

PHISON Martian surface feature, approximate position Ω 320°, $\Phi + 20°$. Faint canal running north-east from the Portus Sigeus, through some 40° of latitude to join the eastern end of Protonilus; separates Æria and Arabia.

PHLEGRA Martian surface feature, approximate position Ω 190°, $\Phi + 35°$. Slightly dusky area to the north of Trivium Charontis, between Hades and Styx.

PHOBOS Satellite I of Mars, *q.v.*

PHOEBE Satellite IX of Saturn, *q.v.*

PHŒNICIS LACUS Martian surface feature, approximate position Ω 110°, $\Phi - 12°$. Condensation in north-western boundary of Thaumasia, connected to Tithonius Lacus by Nox and to the eastern end of the Mare Sirenum by Araxes.

PHOENIX (The Phoenix. *Genitive* Phoenicis, *I.A.U. abbreviation* Phe.) A southern constellation containing one second-magnitude star, two of the third magnitude and a number of fainter ones; it is not, however, an over-populated constellation.

β Phe is a nice close binary (magnitudes 4·1 and 4·2, separation 1″·3).

PHONIC MOTOR A small synchronous motor driven by an oscillating current of constant frequency, usually produced by a valve oscillator or 'electronic tuning-fork'. The frequency of the oscillations governs the speed of the motor, which is thus kept constant to a high degree of accuracy. A common frequency of signal used for this purpose is 1,000 c/s.

The phonic motor is used in a variety of astronomical instruments of modern and sophisticated design, especially instruments of precision where a driving speed of great accuracy is required, such as the **photographic zenith tube**. The **quartz clock** is essentially a phonic motor controlled by a crystal oscillator.

PHOTO-ELECTRIC CELL A device utilizing the **photo-electric effect** to provide a means of measuring the intensity of a beam of radiation incident upon it. It contains two electrodes, a cathode of a metal such as selenium which emits electrons when subjected to radiation, the other an anode which collects the freed electrons. The potential difference between the electrodes is proportional to the intensity of the incident radiation and is measured by a potentiometer in circuit with the photo-electric cell (often termed a 'photo-cell' or 'p.e.c.').

PHOTO-ELECTRIC EFFECT It was discovered by Hallwachs in 1888 that when a beam of light or other form of electromagnetic radiation was allowed to impinge on the surface of certain metals, electrons were emitted by the metal. Thus a *photo-electric cell* can be constructed, in which electrons emitted by a 'target' cathode of suitable metal (often selenium) are collected by an anode, the two electrodes

being connected by a circuit containing a potentiometer. The voltage recorded is directly proportional to the intensity of illumination falling upon the cell.

This principle is utilized in astronomy in the **photo-electric photometer.**

PHOTO-ELECTRIC PHOTOMETER A form of photometer in which the measurement of the intensity of the incident radiation is effected by means of a **photo-electric cell** in circuit with a recording potentiometer.

This instrument has found wide applications in astronomy, especially for comparative determinations of photo-electric magnitudes of large numbers of stars, and for recording the activity of variable stars.

PHOTOGRAPHIC ZENITH TUBE A newly developed fundamental instrument of great importance, based upon a principle first used by Airy in his reflex zenith tube at Greenwich. The modern, photographic version was first developed by F. E. Ross for the U.S. Naval Observatory in Washington. The prototype was used at Gaithersburg, Maryland, from 1911 to 1914 before being installed in Washington in 1915. A much more highly developed version, with many novel and ingenious refinements, was designed by the late D. S. Perfect of the Royal Greenwich Observatory. It is used to determine the time of transit of fundamental stars which culminate very close to the zenith, from which observations the clock error is determined, and to measure the Zenith Distance of these stars at transit. Both of these measurements are made to a high degree of precision, transit times with a probable error of the order of ±0·005 sec and Zenith Distances with a probable error of about ±0″·05. The clock errors are used in the control of the time service and the Zenith Distances in the determination of latitude variation. The instrument designed by Dr Perfect was constructed for the Royal Greenwich Observatory by Grubb, Parsons & Company and erected at Herstmonceux in 1955. 'P.Z.T.s' are installed in ten observatories [Plate 29(e)].

The P.Z.T. is essentially a photographic refractor permanently directed towards the zenith, as its name suggests. The tube length is halved by the expedient of introducing a bath of mercury (as a horizontal reflecting surface) in the light path, bringing the focal plane of the objective just below the objective itself. The objective is an achromatic doublet of 10-in. aperture. It is mounted horizontally in a sturdily built rotating platform (the 'rotary') which is set on the upper end of the sturdy tube. The general layout of the instrument is shown schematically in Fig. 100. The plate is held in a carriage which

can traverse a short distance in the east–west direction in the focal plane of the O.G., driven by a phonic motor through a simple clutch. The rotary can be rotated about the optical axis of the instrument through exactly 180°, the clutch being disengaged; when the rotary has come to rest on the other stop the clutch engages a second phonic motor which drives the plate carriage back again towards its starting position. The times at which the plate carriage passes certain points in its traverse are recorded electrically. The speed at which the plate is traversed by the phonic motors is electronically controlled and can be varied. A rotating shutter is provided which controls the exposure.

The operating sequence for a single traverse is as follows:

1. Rotary in 'clutch East' position (say);
2. Clutch engages, drives plate from West to East;
3. Shutter opens;
4. Shutter closes;
5. Clutch disengages;
6. Rotary turns through 180° to 'clutch West' position.

The shutter remains open for a period of approximately 20 seconds. The speed of the phonic motors is pre-set so as to drive the plate across the field of the O.G. at exactly the same rate as the image of the star being observed traverses the field due to the diurnal rotation of the Earth—this speed factor is a function of the star's Declination; by this means the star is recorded on the plate as a point image. There are four traverses in a complete observation, made alternately from the 'clutch West' and 'clutch East' positions; it will be noted that the effect of the rotation between traverses is to restrict the motion of the plate carriage always to the same direction. The complete cycle produces four images of the star, on opposite sides of the zenith alternately (see Fig. 101). The cycle is commenced from the 'clutch West' position for stars north of the zenith, and from the 'clutch East' position for stars south of the zenith. In the latter case the

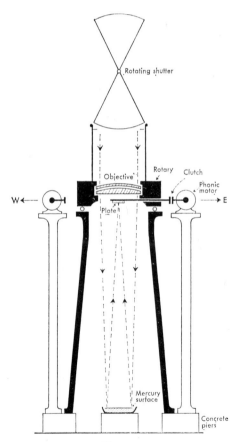

Fig. 100

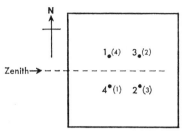

Fig. 101

images are produced in the order shown by the numerals in parentheses on Fig. 101.

The entire sequence is controlled electronically; it is related to the time shown by the quartz crystal clock (whose error is required) only by the instant at which the cycle commences—a known interval before the calculated time of transit. If the clock error is nil the observed time of transit will agree exactly with the calculated time—the effect of this will be to produce the four images in a rectangle ($ACBD$ on Fig. 102); if the clock has an error, however, the effect of starting the cycle at an incorrect moment will be to displace the first and third images to one side of the predicted position and the second and fourth images to the other, thus forming the parallelogram $WYXZ$ on Fig. 102. The extent of the clock error, Δt, is given by the total displacement of either the first and fourth ($\Delta t = WA + DZ$) or the second and third images ($\Delta t = YC + BX$). The electrically recorded times at which the plate carriage passes known points in

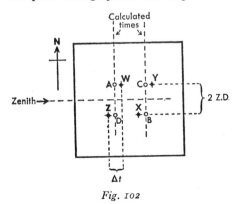

Fig. 102

the field are used only to discover any slight deviations from the planned movement so that they can be allowed for when reducing the observations.

It will readily be seen from Fig. 101 that the distance apart of the first and fourth (or second and third) images depends upon the star's Zenith Distance; the measured separation of these images gives twice the required Z.D. of the star (Fig. 102).

The P.Z.T. is housed in a building whose roof can be driven off completely in two sections, so that the instrument is reduced, as far as possible, to the temperature of the surrounding air during operation: this is to prevent thermal air-currents disturbing the light rays falling on the O.G. and thus blurring the images on the plate.

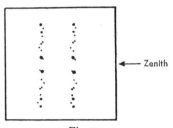

Fig. 103

The instrument is completely remote-controlled from a console in a separate building some way off, so that the observer needs to visit the instrument pavilion only every hour or so to change the plate, read the thermometers, etc. It is usual to photograph 10–15 stars on one plate—their varying Z.D.s ensuring that their images are separated. When the plates are measured the presence of up to 60 images may seem confusing, but in fact the quadrilateral pattern for each star and the fact that their arrangement can be plotted in advance if necessary renders identification relatively simple (Fig. 103).

The accuracy of the P.Z.T. is significantly greater than that of the transit-circle; its inability to observe objects away from the zenith however restricts its rôle considerably, and it complements, rather than replaces, the transit circle. It is likely to become the major source of time-service observations and latitude-variation determinations, however, leaving the transit circle to provide the positional observations.

PHOTOGRAPHY Process by means of which an optical image can be permanently recorded. This is usually achieved with the aid of a plate (or film) coated with an emulsion of light-sensitive salts (usually silver halides); after exposure in a camera the plate is 'developed'—that is to say treated with a chemical reagent which causes silver to be precipitated as black grains in the emulsion, the amount of precipitation being dependent upon the amount of light that has fallen on the part of the plate concerned. After development the plate is 'fixed'—the remaining silver halide dissolved off—and dried. It is then available for measurement or examination in its negative form, or for the manufacture of 'contact' or enlarged prints.

The development of photography led to the greatest step forward in observational astronomy since the invention of the telescope; it has now virtually superseded visual observation in many branches of the subject, especially those involving the use of large telescopes. All studies of galaxies, nebulae and clusters are made with the aid of photographs, using long exposures which permit detail to be recorded which would be quite beyond the range of visual observers. In fields in which visual observation still plays a major part, e.g. observation of the surface features of the Sun, Moon and planets, photography is also used a great deal as well. Spectroscopic investigations are normally carried out by means of photographs of the spectra concerned.

Another important use of photography in astronomy is the recording of instrumental settings, as in the case of the circle-reading microscopes of a modern transit circle.

PHOTOHELIOGRAPH A refracting telescope specifically designed for photographing the Sun's disk. Sir John Herschel had long advocated that such an instrument be provided so that daily photographs of the solar surface could be obtained. Eventually funds for the purpose were provided by The Royal Society and the instrument was erected at Kew Observatory in 1858. It was designed by Warren De la Rue and constructed by Ross. De la Rue took it to Spain in 1860 and obtained the first collodion plate of a total solar eclipse. On his return to England De la Rue installed the instrument in his observatory at Cranford; it was re-erected at Kew in 1861. In 1873 it was removed to the newly founded Solar Department of the Royal Observatory at Greenwich, where it was used daily until replaced by a new instrument in 1875. It had an achromatic objective of $3\frac{1}{2}$-in. aperture, and an enlarging lens which produced an image of the solar disk 4 inches in diameter. It is now in the Science Museum, London.

The new Greenwich photoheliograph was also a remarkable instrument. Constructed by Dallmeyer it has an aperture of 4 inches; its original enlarging lens produced a solar image 4 inches in diameter but this was replaced in 1884 by one producing an 8-in. disk. The objective was replaced in 1910. In 1949 it was transferred to the Royal Observatory's new location at Herstmonceux, Sussex, where it is still in daily use. The Greenwich photoheliographic records are the longest series in existence. They are combined with the similar plates exposed at the Royal Observatory, Cape of Good Hope; any gaps in the combined series due to cloudy conditions at both stations are filled by plates obtained at the Kodaikanal or Mount Wilson Observatories.

PHOTOMETER An instrument for measuring the intensity of light falling upon it; the most accurate form is the **photo-electric photometer** which is widely used in astronomical observation.

PHOTON The smallest quantity of radiation; it is the energy realized by a single energy-transfer within an atom. The value of one photon is a variable, depending upon the wavelength of the radiation concerned.

PHOTOSPHERE, SOLAR One of the outermost layers of the Sun; it is a gaseous shell having a temperature of some 6,000° K, forming a comparatively stable upper 'skin' to the **convective zone**. As the layers above it are highly transparent, the photosphere is the 'surface' which we actually observe.

PHRIXI REGIO Martian surface feature, approximate position Ω 70°, $\Phi-40°$. Dark area forming south-eastern border of Thaumasia and connecting the Auroræ Sinus region to Chrysokeras.

PIAZZI, Giuseppe (1746–1826) Professor of Mathematics and Astronomy in the University of Palermo, Sicily, and Director of the observatory there.

Piazzi discovered the first minor planet (Ceres) on 1801 January 1.

With an excellent vertical circle, made by Ramsden and completed in 1789, Piazzi produced a superb catalogue of the positions and other data for some 8,000 stars.

PIC-DU-MIDI OBSERVATORY The observatory of the University of Toulouse, situated on the Pic-du-Midi at an altitude of nearly 9,400 ft. in the French Pyrénées. The first **coronagraph** was established there by Lyot, to take advantage of the superb observing conditions in the rarified atmosphere. Fot the same reason it has long been the source of some of the finest lunar and planetary observations also.

PICCOLOMINI Lunar surface feature, co-ordinates $\xi+463$, $\eta-496$. One of the most perfectly formed crater formations on the Moon, situated in the centre of the south-west quadrant. It is 56 miles in diameter and the terraced walls tower to 15,000 ft. in places. There is a fine central mountain divided by a great ravine.

PICKERING Lunar surface feature, co-ordinates $\xi+730$, $\eta-035$. Named after W. H. Pickering, the distinguished American selenographer. An elliptical crater with its major axis running north–south, approximately 10 miles in diameter. The companion of Messier, at the root of the double ray known as the 'Comet's Tail'.

PICKERING, Edward Charles (1846–1919) Famous American astronomer; born in Boston, Massachusetts, he became in 1865 Instructor of Mathematics at the Lawrence Scientific School, Harvard, at the age of only 19. In 1867 he was appointed Professor of Physics at the Massachusetts Institute of Technology, where he remained until 1876 when he was appointed Director of the Harvard College Observatory.

At Harvard Pickering controlled the development of the great Harvard photometry programme initiated by Draper; he published in 1884 a catalogue based upon nearly 100,000 observations made with a meridian photometer in the period 1879–1882. With the assistance of Mrs. Fleming and Miss Cannon, Pickering devised the Harvard–Draper sequence of spectral classification, first used in the original Draper catalogue of 1890. Before his death in 1919 Pickering supervised almost the entire production of the revised *Henry Draper Catalogue of Stellar Spectra* and the *Henry Draper Extension*, giving the spectral classifications of more than 350,000 stars.

In 1889 Pickering and Miss Maury made the first discovery of a spectroscopic binary, obtaining plates on which absorption lines in the spectrum of ζ UMa appeared double.

Pickering was a great director, under whose guidance pioneering work of the greatest importance was done; his contribution in this capacity was superseded only by his personal achievements as one of the most assiduous and able observers of his day. In his career he made a total of more than a million photometric measures.

That Harvard is one of the world

centres of astronomical thought today is in no small measure due to the foundation laid by E. C. Pickering. He was twice awarded the Gold Medal of the Royal Astronomical Society, in 1886 and 1901.

PICKERING, William Henry (1858–1938) Notable American observer who specialized in observations of the Moon and planets. In 1898, using a 24-in. refractor at the Harvard College Observatory's southern station at Arequipa, Peru, Pickering obtained a series of plates on August 16–18 on which he discovered a new satellite (IX) of Saturn—which he named Phoebe—and which was found to have retrograde motion, the first known example of a satellite having contrary motion to that of the other satellites of the same planet, and the first planetary satellite to be discovered photographically.

At the turn of the century Pickering was observing from an observatory in Jamaica, a Harvard sub-station, with a polar refractor of 12-in. aperture fed by an 18-in. equatorial coelostat. With this instrument Pickering photographed all parts of the Moon's surface under a representative series of conditions of illumination, and published the resulting photographic atlas of the lunar surface features in 1903.

Pickering spent many years in calculating the orbit and position of the hypothetical trans-Neptunian planet; in 1919 he instituted a photographic search programme which was carried out by M. L. Humason at Mount Wilson Observatory. Although images of Pluto were in fact obtained during this search, a series of unlucky events conspired to prevent its discovery at this time despite the accuracy of Pickering's calculations.

PICO Lunar surface feature, co-ordinates $\xi-106$, $\eta+717$. A beautiful and completely isolated conical mountain on the Mare Imbrium, about 60 miles due south of the southern wall of Plato. There are three summits, the highest reaching 8,000 ft.

There is another isolated mountain 36 miles south of Pico, 4,000 ft. high, which has a small summit crater.

PICTOR (The Painter: formerly Equuleus Pictoris, the Painter's Easel. *Genitive* Pictoris, *I.A.U. abbreviation* Pic.) A southern constellation, partly circumpolar, containing no bright stars—the brightest being one of the third and two of the fourth magnitude.

The constellation is most notable as the site of Nova Pictoris, 1925. A star of the twelfth magnitude—a couple of degrees from α Pic, close to the southernmost boundary of the constellation—brightened rapidly during the early months of 1925, reaching third magnitude by mid-April. The nova was discovered by a South African observer on 1925 May 25, its magnitude then being 2·3; by the following day it had reached 1·7, then dropped back to the third magnitude by the next, May 27. It brightened again in early June, and reached 1·1 on June 9, falling to fourth magnitude by the beginning of July. Its final maximum came on 1925 August 9, when it reached 1·9; thereafter it fell, with the usual minor fluctuations, reaching sixth magnitude by the end of 1925 and finally settling at ninth magnitude. Later photographic observation showed two nebulous filaments, separated by more than half a second of arc.

PIONEER Name given to the first series of space-probe vehicles launched from the U.S.A.; their principal function was the development of launching and guiding techniques for the later *Lunar Orbiter, Mariner, Ranger* and *Surveyor* projects. A late addition to the series was *Pioneer 6*, an experimental Sun-probe vehicle. Details of the series are given in Table 28.

PISCES (The Fishes. *Genitive* Piscium, *I.A.U. abbreviation* Psc.) A large and straggling zodiacal constellation in the northern skies, remarkably empty of bright stars; despite its area it contains only one third-magnitude star (η Psc).

Table 28. Pioneer space-probe vehicles

Vehicle	Date launched	Purpose	Achieved orbit	Result
Pioneer 1	1958 Oct. 11	Development	Geocentric	Reached height of app. 75,000 miles.
Pioneer 2	1958 Nov. 9	Development	—	Third-stage rocket failed.
Pioneer 3	1958 Dec. 6	Development	Geocentric	Reached height of app. 68,000 miles.
Pioneer 4	1959 Mar. 3	Lunar probe	Heliocentric	Passed app. 37,300 miles from Moon, 1959 Mar. 5.
Pioneer 5	1960 Mar. 11	Development	Heliocentric	
Pioneer 6	1965 Dec. 16	Solar probe	Heliocentric	

Its stars reach midnight culmination during September and October.

Apart from a few double-stars it contains little of note.

PISCIS AUSTRINUS (The Southern Fish. *Genitive* Piscis Austrini, *I.A.U. abbreviation* PsA.) A small southern constellation containing one brilliant white star (*Fomalhaut*—magnitude 1·2), the most southerly first-magnitude star visible from the British Isles, whence it can be seen hanging low in the south on clear, September evenings. There are also six fourth-magnitude stars in this small constellation.

PITATUS Lunar surface feature, co-ordinates $\xi-203$, $\eta-498$. A splendid walled plain, 50 miles in diameter, at the southern border of the Mare Nubium. The walls are very rugged and broken, especially the southern wall which borders the Mare. A valley runs through the eastern wall into the adjoining ring formation Hesiodus. Pitatus has a low hill slightly south-east of centre.

PITON Lunar surface feature, co-ordinates $\xi-012$, $\eta+652$. This is an isolated mountain peak on the western part of the Mare Imbrium, about 100 miles north of Aristillus. The peak is 7,000 ft. high and appears double, due to the presence of a summit craterlet. About 120 miles to the north-east is another splendid isolated mountain peak, Pico.

PLAGE, SOLAR A large area of calcium vapour surrounding a sunspot, seen as a large bright patch on a calcium-light spectroheliogram. Plages are sometimes referred to as *calcium flocculi*.

PLANET Term used to indicate a body in orbital motion around a star, but which is non-stellar itself; that is to say it shines only by reflecting the light of the primary star and has no luminosity of its own.

It is of course generally applied to the planets of the solar system, although spectroscopic studies of some binary systems have suggested that one of the components has a planetary companion. Examples of these planets discovered in recent years outside the solar system are the planetary companions of 61 Cyg and 70 Oph.

For comparative studies the planets of the solar system are usually considered in groups of similar characteristics; thus, see **Inferior planet; Inner planet; Major planet; Minor planet; Outer planet; Superior planet; Terrestrial planet.**

PLANETARIUM A specially designed and constructed building in which, by means of a **planetarium projector**, an accurate representation of the heavens is produced on the white-painted inside surface of a hemispherical dome which forms the roof of an auditorium.

The positions and motions of all the heavenly bodies, both north and south hemispheres, can be reproduced; the motions can be accelerated very considerably, enabling long-term phenomena to be quickly demonstrated, and provision is made for additional information to be projected (such as co-ordinate grids, outlines of constellation figures, etc.), thus rendering the planetarium potentially one of the most powerful tools for instruction in astronomy and allied subjects. Unfortunately the high cost of the equipment necessitates most existing planetaria being operated on a commercial basis, and their programmes have therefore to be devised more for popular appeal than for purely educational value; for this reason the full educational potential of the planetarium is far from being realized, despite the great efforts of planetarium directors to achieve the greatest possible educational value from their popular programmes.

There are now more than forty large planetaria throughout the world, and numerous smaller ones. The United Kingdom lagged behind the U.S.A. and most European countries for many years in lacking a major planetarium; this was rectified, early in 1958, of The London Planetarium, which is equipped with one of the latest and most versatile Zeiss projectors and which has presented many enjoyable and valuable programmes.

Of particular importance in the field of astronomical education are two other planetaria in the British Isles: a small planetarium has recently been installed in one of the old buildings of the former Royal Observatory at Greenwich, now an astronomical annexe to the National Maritime Museum. This will largely be used for the instruction of cadets from the nearby Royal Naval College in navigational astronomy, etc., thus continuing the historical link between Greenwich

Observatory and the Admiralty.

There is also a new planetarium in the grounds of Armagh Observatory in Northern Ireland, recently completed; this planetarium is equipped with a Japanese projector of considerable versatility, and will be run entirely as a non-profit-making educational establishment. There will be an adjoining observatory specially equipped for public demonstrations, and the programmes will be integrated with demonstrations at the telescope whenever possible, and will be aimed solely at helping members of the public to develop an interest in the heavens. This approach must be regarded as one of the most important developments in the history of the planetarium.

PLANETARIUM PROJECTOR The extent and complexity of a planetarium programme depend upon the complexity of the projector used. The first optical planetarium projector was designed and built by Walther Bauersfeld of the Carl Zeiss company in 1923; in 1925 it was erected in the Deutsches Museum in Munich. A second projector was built in 1926, and used in Düsseldorf and Liegnitz before being finally erected at The Hague in 1934. The Zeiss company then produced a more versatile projector which is the basis of the range of superbly versatile instruments they have built and supplied to almost all the world's large planetaria, including The London Planetarium and several in the U.S.A. [Plate 24(c).]

The Zeiss instrument is of a characteristic 'dumb-bell' form, having two large spheres connected by a cylindrical 'cage' of open girderwork. Each sphere contains a powerful tungsten-lamp at its centre, and has sixteen optical projectors on its surface; each of these projectors has a positive slide of a star field, and between them project a mosaic of star-fields covering the entire sky, one sphere for each hemisphere. There are automatic shutters which cut off the light of stars which are below the planetarium horizon.

There are between 40 and 50 special

projectors for the brightest stars and for certain variable stars.

The 'dumb-bell' is mounted in such a way that it can be driven, at various speeds, about three separate axes of rotation; its long axis is inclined to a polar axis (contained in a vertical plane) by $23\frac{1}{2}°$. Rotation about this 'ecliptical' axis reproduces the **precession of the equinoxes**; rotation about the polar axis reproduces the diurnal east–west motion of the stars and other heavenly bodies. The instrument may also be rotated around a horizontal 'east–west' axis, which permits the aspect of the heavens from any latitude on the Earth to be shown. Either one setting may be selected, to show the view of the sky from a particular place, or the instrument may be slowly rotated about this axis to show the changing appearance of the sky during a long imaginary journey across the Earth's surface.

In the latticed cage between the spheres there is a series of special projectors, one for each of the planets; these are driven through gear-trains which faithfully reproduce their motions relative to the background stars. There are also a number of special effects projectors for showing such phenomena as comets, the aurorae, a meteor shower, etc. The operation of the instrument is effected through a large and complex electronic installation and controlled by a narrator seated at an elaborate control console.

A number of other companies manufacture planetarium projectors. Particularly notable are the instruments made by the Spitz Laboratories, who offer a graded range of instruments for all sizes of planetarium and schoolroom, and the 'Goto' instruments manufactured in Japan [Plate 24(d)].

PLANETARY ATMOSPHERES It may be presumed that the material from which the planets were formed originally comprised a mixture of elements similar to those obtaining throughout the universe, containing hydrogen and helium in quantities far exceeding those of the other elements. Subsequently the gases would slowly escape, the lightest molecules more readily than those of the heavier elements: ultimately a position will be reached in which an extremely tenuous gaseous mixture will pervade the whole of interplanetary space but no planet will have a separate atmosphere of its own. The rate at which a planet will lose its atmosphere will also depend upon its size and mass and upon its average temperature.

At the present time the planets of the solar system are at an intermediate stage, all of them being known to possess atmospheres, with the exception of Pluto and possibly Mercury.

The main evidence is summarized for each planet below.

Inner Planets

Mercury. The velocity of escape for gases is so low in the case of this planet that it would not be expected to have retained any of the lighter gases. In 1963, however, Kozyrev found spectroscopic evidence of a very tenuous atmosphere of hydrogen, and suggested that it might have survived by being constantly replenished by hydrogen nuclei emitted by the Sun. If this atmosphere does, in fact, exist it is not very extensive—Kozyrev gives its density as approximately one-thousandth of that of the Earth. Observations of the planet in transit across the disk of the Sun confirm the lack of any extensive atmosphere.

Venus. This planet has a very deep, dense atmosphere; its surface is permanently obscured by dense cloud. It has been confirmed spectroscopically that the atmosphere contains large quantities of carbon dioxide (CO_2). It is considered likely that water vapour is present at lower levels, also nitrogen (N_2), argon (A) and carbon monoxide (CO).

Earth. The atmosphere of the Earth has, of course, been studied in considerable detail (see **Atmosphere, terrestrial**); it extends to a height of several hundred miles, but is extremely tenuous at all but the lowest levels—approximately 99·9 per cent is below a height of 30 miles, and about 90 per cent below 10 miles.

The three gases nitrogen, oxygen and argon account for 99·97 per cent of dry air at the surface—N, 78·09%; O, 20·95%; A, 0·93%. The remainder consists of very small amounts of carbon dioxide (CO_2), neon (Ne), helium (He), methane (CH_4), krypton (Kr), hydrogen (H_2), nitrous oxide (N_2O), carbon monoxide (CO), xenon (Xe), ozone (O_3) and radon (Rn). Air at the surface of the Earth normally contains about 1·2 per cent of water vapour.

Mars. This planet has an extensive atmosphere, although it is a much less dense one than that of the Earth. The fall-off in pressure with height is also different; the atmospheric pressure at a height of 20 miles is approximately the same for both planets, although at the surface of Mars it is only $8\frac{1}{2}\%$ that at the surface of the Earth. Above 20 miles, however, the Martian atmospheric pressure exceeds that of the Earth at corresponding heights.

The principal constituent detected spectroscopically in the Martian atmosphere is carbon dioxide (CO_2); it is believed however that the most abundant constituent is molecular nitrogen (N_2). The calculated composition of the Martian atmosphere is N, 93·8%; A, 3·9%; CO_2, 2·2%.

Outer planets

An 'atmosphere' is a rather different concept in the case of the major planets, for it is believed that they have no solid surface *per se*, but consist of a homogeneous mixture of gases, increasing in density with depth below the surface (see **Planets, major—constitution of**). Only the surface layers can be studied, visually and spectroscopically, however, and for the present purpose of comparison with the other members of the solar system this outer mantle may be regarded as the 'atmosphere'. [Plate 13(f).]

Jupiter. The surface of Jupiter has been observed in great detail for many years, and the turbulent motions of its gaseous

outer layers well established. The parallel belts and zones are indicative of currents parallel to the equator, induced by the rapid axial rotation. The velocities of the various currents have been established from observations of individual spots and other markings. The principal constituents of the upper 'atmosphere' are methane (CH_4) and ammonia (NH_3), which produce prominent absorption bands in the visible and infra-red spectrum. The hydrogen content at this level is probably less than 10 per cent, although it is believed to constitute between 76 and 84 per cent of the mass of the planet as a whole.

Saturn. Although less readily observable, due to the much greater distance involved, the surface of Saturn bears a strong resemblance to that of Jupiter. The spectrum shows absorption bands due to methane even more prominently than that of Jupiter; ammonia is also present, but is much less prominent. This is probably due to its being far less abundant near the surface, being 'frozen out' by the intense cold at the distance of Saturn. Hydrogen is again believed to be the major constituent of the planet as a whole.

Uranus. Methane is the only constituent whose presence has been confirmed spectroscopically; parallel belts and zones similar to those of Jupiter and Saturn can be observed, albeit with difficulty, suggesting that the 'atmospheric' movements are similar.

Neptune. Methane is the only confirmed constituent in this case also; dusky belts flanking a bright equatorial zone have been recorded, suggesting that Neptune too has 'atmospheric' motions similar to those of Jupiter.

Pluto. There is no evidence indicative of the presence of an atmosphere on Pluto. The diameter of the planet is extremely difficult to measure and is not known with any certainty; this renders it impossible to arrive at a reliable value for the mean density, so that there is not even a sufficiently strong basis to enable a possible composition of an atmosphere to be estimated.

Planetary satellites

The Moon is, of course, the only satellite in the solar system that can be observed in great detail: it is probable that the Moon has no atmosphere at all and certain that if there is one it must be an extremely tenuous one. Some observations of transient phenomena in recent years have suggested the presence of gases released from the surface rocks, but these would soon escape into space.

Of the planetary satellites, Titan—the largest satellite of Saturn—was shown spectroscopically by Kuiper in 1944 to have an atmosphere containing methane; at the same time Kuiper found possible evidence of a similar atmosphere surrounding Triton, the principal satellite of Neptune.

There is no evidence of an atmosphere surrounding any of the Galilean satellites of Jupiter; this is probably due to the velocity of escape being lower, in consequence of the higher temperature, than in the case of Titan.

PLANETARY CO-ORDINATES Tables of the heliocentric co-ordinates of the planets, used to calculate ephemerides of the planets themselves and when computing ephemerides for comets, asteroids, etc. They are published under the title *Planetary Co-ordinates* by H.M. Stationery Office on behalf of H.M. Nautical Almanac Office. Three volumes have been published, covering the periods 1900–1940, 1940–1960 and 1960–1980.

PLANETARY MOTION The motion of a planet in its orbit around the parent star (the Sun in the case of the planets in the solar system), and also that of a satellite around its primary, etc., are governed by Newton's law of gravitation and Kepler's laws of planetary motion.

Newton's law of gravitation states that any body in the universe attracts every other body, with a force proportional to their masses and inversely proportional to the square of their distance apart.

Kepler's laws state: (1) that a planet's orbit is an ellipse, with the Sun at one of the foci; (2) that a planet moves in its orbit with a varying velocity such that its radius vector sweeps out equal areas in equal intervals of time; (3) that the square of the period of revolution of a planet is proportional to the cube of its mean distance from the parent star.

The actual motion of a planet, relative to the background sky as seen from the Earth, is extremely complex, as each body in the solar system is affected by the gravitational pull of each of the others; these effects are constantly changing as the planet's positions relative to each other are varying. The *mean* motion of the planet will be the orbit as defined by the laws quoted above, but its *actual* motion must be calculated taking into account the changing gravitational attractions of each other significant body in the system—the *perturbations*.

The orbit of a planet is defined by seven *elements*: a, the semi-major axis; e, the eccentricity; i, the inclination between the orbital plane and the plane of the Ecliptic; Ω, the longitude of the ascending node; ϖ, Σ the longitude of perihelion; T, the epoch; n, the mean motion.

PLANETARY NEBULAE These were so-called because they show measurable disks in quite small telescopes; they have nothing whatsoever to do with planets and are not really true nebulae in the same sense as the other galactic nebulae, in that they are each closely related to a specific star.

These objects, of which about 150 are known, were first classified separately by Sir William Herschel.

They appear as well-defined circular or elliptical disks, often of an apparently annular form, and have a star at the centre; they are usually of a greenish hue. Perhaps the best known example of the type is the Ring Nebula in Lyra, M57 (N.G.C. 6720).

The nebulosity is, in fact, a gaseous shell thrown off by a nova-like explosion thousands of years previously; some planetaries appear to have a double shell, implying more than one such explosion. The diameter is usually of the order of 20,000 A.U.

Possibly the oldest and largest 'planetary' nebula is the huge network of filamentary nebulae in Cygnus. [Plate 23(b).]

The spectra of planetary nebulae show numerous bright emission lines, notably of hydrogen and helium; the 'forbidden lines' of ionized oxygen, nitrogen, etc. are usually very prominent. The spectra are similar to those of the Wolf–Rayet stars.

Planetary nebulae obtain their energy from the central star, which is usually a very luminous dwarf; they are believed to be close to the white dwarfs in the pattern of stellar evolution. They must have surface temperatures in the range $50,000°–100,000°$ K in order to provide the radiation required to stimulate the observed emission in the 'shell'.

Being very faint, many of the central stars are difficult to observe and their spectra are not fully known in consequence.

Planetary nebulae have been observed in external galaxies, notably in the satellite galaxy (M52) of the Great Galaxy in Andromeda, and in the satellites of our own Galaxy, the *Magellanic Clouds*. [Plate 23(c, d).]

PLANETARY PRECESSION

The secondary component of the precession of the equinoxes, due to the gravitational effects of the other planets upon the oblate geoid. (See **Precession**.)

PLANETOCENTRIC CO-ORDINATES

A system of co-ordinates referred to the centre of a planet. The planetocentric latitude and longitude are the fundamental co-ordinates normally used in theoretical work; if the figure of the planet departs significantly from a true spheroid the observed positions of surface markings will be in planetographic co-ordinates. If the figure of the planet is known planetographic co-ordinates can be simply converted to planetocentric co-ordinates for analytical purposes, if so desired.

(See also **Co-ordinate systems; Planetographic co-ordinates**.)

PLANETOGRAPHIC CO-ORDINATES

A system of co-ordinates referred to the actual mean surface of a planet. If the surface of the planet departs significantly from a true spheroid (most of them are oblate) the planetographic co-ordinates of a point on the surface will differ from the planetocentric co-ordinates. Observed measurements of the position of a surface marking will, of course, be in planetographic co-ordinates; these can, however, be converted to planetocentric co-ordinates if the figure of the planet is known.

In practice, since most of the planets are oblate spheroids symmetrical about their axes of rotation, the differences between planetocentric and planetographic longitude are negligible, but there may be significant differences between planetocentric and planetographic latitudes (in the case of Jupiter, for instance, the maximum difference is nearly $4°$).

(See also **Co-ordinate systems; Planetocentric co-ordinates**.)

PLANETOID A small planetary body; the term is usually employed when describing a **minor planet**, although 'asteroid' is more common.

PLANETS—DENSITY OF The mean densities (ρ) of the planets are listed in Table 29, in gram/cm^3; on this scale the density of water would be 1·0. The densities of the Sun and Moon are shown for comparative purposes.

It will be noted that the terrestrial planets all have densities similar to that of the Earth, save Mars, which seems to have a surprisingly low density. The density quoted for Pluto is an assumed value, as there is an unresolved anomaly between the measured diameter of this planet and the mass derived dynamically, which imply an impossibly high density.

The major planets have very low densities—that of Saturn being less than

Table 29. Planetary densities

Body	Density (g/cm^3)
Sun	1·41
Moon	3·34
Mercury	5·41
Venus	4·99
Earth	5·52
Mars	3·96
Jupiter	1·33
Saturn	0·71
Uranus	1·70
Neptune	2·26
Pluto	5·5

that of water; this is an important factor in considerations of their internal constitution.

(See also **Planets, major—constitution of; Planets, terrestrial—constitution of.**)

PLANETS, MAJOR—CONSTITUTION OF

A great deal of effort has been devoted to the development of theories of the internal constitution of the major planets. They are believed to be basically very similar, and hence may conveniently be considered together.

There is a considerable amount of observational evidence in the case of Jupiter, the nearest of the major planets, but much less for Saturn and very little indeed for Uranus and Neptune. Visual and (with very large telescopes) photographic observations of the surface markings, especially of Jupiter, provide a great deal of evidence about the surface currents, and possibly of activity in subsurface layers also (see **Jupiter—observed features and notable phenomena**).

The spectrum of the major planets is basically that of reflected sunlight, with some additional absorption bands.

The observations of radio noise

associated with Jupiter in recent years may prove to be of value in studies of the constitution of the planet in years to come; at present, however, the study of the radio bursts and their origin is still too highly speculative for them to be utilized in this way.

The only source of additional information is dynamical analysis, both of the planet's satellite system and of the motion of the planet in the solar system as a whole. One of the most important facts obtained in this way is the mean density of each planet. The deduced values of their mean densities reveal immediately that the major planets must have a constitution very different from that of the terrestrial planets, for they are very much less dense. The mean densities, on the scale water $= 1$, are Jupiter, 1·33; Saturn, 0·71; Uranus, 1·70; Neptune 2·26. In contrast, the values for the terrestrial planets range from 3·96 (Mars) to 5·52 (Earth).

In the light of these very low densities it is clear that the constitution of the major planets must include a great deal of gaseous material. The foundations for the erection of theories of the constitution of the planets were laid by Sir Harold Jeffreys in the early years of this century. In the 1930s proposed models for the outer planets were published by R. Wildt, which were based upon the known mass, volume and mean densities of the planets. Wildt suggested that each planet consisted of a solid core of highly metalliferous rock, surrounded by a deep layer of frozen vapours which, in turn, was surrounded by a deep gaseous 'atmosphere'. The dimensions of the three parts of Wildt's proposed models are summarized in Table 30.

The dark absorption bands in the visible spectrum become progressively broader and more prominent for planets farther from the Sun [Plate 13(f)]; by a superb piece of deductive reasoning Wildt suggested that these were due to the presence of methane (CH_4), and that less prominent bands in the spectrum of Jupiter, also faintly visible in that of Saturn,

Table 30. Dimensions of models for major planets proposed by Wildt

Planet	of core	Approximate radii (miles) of frozen layer	of gaseous layer
Jupiter:	18,500	17,000	8,000
Saturn:	14,000	6,000	16,000
Uranus:	7,000	6,000	2,000
Neptune:	6,000	6,000	6,000

were due to ammonia (NH_3). These suggestions were subsequently confirmed by laboratory experiment and by means of the high-quality infra-red spectra obtained by Dunham at the Mount Wilson Observatory. Wildt calculated that both ammonia and methane should be present in equal amounts, but pointed out that because of its lower vapour pressure ammonia would condense at lower levels and would therefore appear less abundant than methane at the surface level observed. This would also account for the lower incidence of ammonia in the outer layers of Saturn and its apparent absence from Uranus and Neptune.

Even more surprising was the low hydrogen content—determined by Wildt as less than 10 per cent for Jupiter; for planets as massive as Jupiter and Saturn the velocity of escape for gases is very high indeed, and one would expect them to have retained the original mixture of material from which they were formed. This would be the usual mixture of elements in their 'cosmic abundance', i.e. similar to the material comprising the Sun—which consists of more than 90 per cent hydrogen.

Notwithstanding these difficulties Wildt's theories were generally accepted for many years; only in the early 1950s were new approaches made to the problem, notably by W. H. Ramsey. Ramsey showed that the accepted densities for the core and frozen layer were too low, and the deduced amounts of heavy elements too large; his approach was a radical one, he suggested that there were no definite boundaries

separating layers in different states as Wildt had supposed, but that each planet was composed of a homogeneous mixture. The density would, of course, increase steadily towards the centre, due to the gravitational compression. Although the mixture would remain homogeneous, the elements included in it might undergo important changes deep inside the planets. From studies of the effects of high pressures upon the molecular structure of a number of substances it was known that some non-metals underwent a change of phase under very high pressures and became very dense and assumed metallic properties. Ramsey pointed out that the pressure at the centre of Jupiter, for instance, is about 40 times the critical pressure for the transition of hydrogen into an alkali metal.

On the basis of this hypothesis Ramsey calculated that the hydrogen content of Jupiter would be between 76 and 84 per cent by mass, and that of Saturn between 62 and 69 per cent, values which are far more compatible with the concept that the planets were formed from a quasi-solar mixture. Ramsey also calculated that his estimated hydrogen content for Jupiter and Saturn would not be significantly altered if the planets were not entirely homogeneous, but had a central condensation of heavy elements.

Uranus and Neptune, denser and much less massive than Jupiter and Saturn, must have lost a far greater amount of their original hydrogen and other light elements; they are believed to contain a higher proportion of the heavier elements and of simple compounds such as methane, ammonia and water.

PLANETS, TERRESTRIAL—CONSTITUTION OF

The constitution of the Earth can be studied directly, using the techniques of geology, geophysics, seismology, etc.; the constitutions of the other terrestrial planets—Mercury, Venus and Mars—can only be deduced by analogy and by theoretical studies.

Earth. The Earth consists of an inner core some 1,520 miles in diameter, probably composed largely of iron and nickel and therefore very dense. The inner core is surrounded by an outer core approximately 1,400 miles in thickness; this is believed by some also to consist of iron and nickel, and by others to be high-pressure phases of iron oxides, silica, etc. Surrounding the outer core is the upper mantle, some 1,800 miles thick. The upper mantle is composed principally of basic rocks such as olivine; in its lower layers it probably includes a considerable quantity of silica, iron oxides and magnesium oxide. The Earth's mean density is 5·52 times that of water; it is thus the densest body in the solar system.

Mercury. The mean density of Mercury is 5·41 times that of water—almost as high as that of the Earth; this is very high for such a small body and suggests the presence of large quantities of free iron in the planet's structure. This may be due to much of the material in its upper mantle having been volatized by the great heat of the Sun.

Venus. The internal structure of Venus must be very similar to that of the Earth; almost identical in size, Venus has a mean density slightly lower than that of the Earth (4·99 times that of water). The core of Venus is probably only half as massive as that of the Earth.

Mars. The general structure of Mars is also probably very similar to that of the Earth, but the rocky core must be very much smaller in order to account for the lower mean density (3·96 times that of water).

PLANISPHERE A simple but effective device which can be used to discover which constellations are visible at a given time, and as an aid to star recognition. It consists of a map of the heavens on a polar projection, pivoted at the pole so that it can be rotated behind a mask. The mask has a specially shaped aperture which reveals the area of the heavens visible at any one time. The star disk has a scale of the days of the year around its perimeter, and the mask one showing the hours of the day. The appropriate date and hour of the day are made to coincide by rotating the star disk appropriately—the stars then visible will be shown in the aperture. The compass directions of the appropriate horizons are indicated at the edges of the aperture to facilitate use.

PLATE CENTRE In photographic astrometry the positions of the star images on the plate are measured in rectangular co-ordinates. The origin of these co-ordinates, the *plate centre*, is ideally the point on the plate which coincided with the optical axis of the telescope during the exposure. The axes are drawn on the plate perpendicular (the ξ-axis) and parallel (the η-axis) to the meridian.

(See also **Astrometry; Plate constants; Standard co-ordinates.**)

PLATE CONSTANTS In photographic astronomy the standard co-ordinates (ξ, η) of a star are derived from the measured co-ordinates (x, y) of the star's image on the plate by means of the equations:

$$\xi - x = a\xi + b\eta + c$$
$$\eta - y = d\xi + e\eta + f$$

where a, b, c, d, e and f are small quantities dependent upon errors in the adopted co-ordinates of the plate centre, the adopted value of the plate scale and the orientation of the plate in the measuring machine; they are termed the *plate constants*.

(See also **Astrometry; Plate centre; Plate scale; Standard co-ordinates.**)

PLATE SCALE In photographic astrometry, the ratio between the angular separation of two stars (measured in the tangential plane to the celestial sphere) and the linear distance between their images on the plate. Its value is a function of the focal length of the telescope objective.

(See also **Astrometry; Plate constants; Standard co-ordinates.**)

PLATEAU RING-STRUCTURE A lunar ring-structure in which the floor is significantly higher than the surrounding surface. The best-known example of the type is Wargentin. (See **Moon—surface features of.**)

PLATO Lunar surface feature, co-ordinates $\xi - 100$, $\eta + 782$. One of the most prominent objects in the northern hemisphere of the Moon, it is a splendid walled plain in the Jura Mountains, at the north-west corner of the Mare Imbrium, close to the southern border of the Mare Frigoris. It lies due north of Archimedes, to which it appears to form a twin. It is notable for its smooth dark floor, of a distinct dark grey; it remains a dark object even under the overhead illumination of Full Moon.

The walls are steep on the inside, rugged and extensive outside, with a sharp crest between 3,000 and 4,000 ft. above the interior; there are a number of peaks rising to 7,000 ft. and more, which cast superb shadows across the floor under low angles of illumination. The western half of the wall is almost continuous, but the eastern half is broken by several ravines and a great triangular valley apparently formed by a huge landslip into the interior; the latter feature is most prominent at the eastern end of the ring under low illumination from the east— i.e. at about Last Quarter.

Although apparently very smooth and featureless, the floor contains several small crater-cones, and a number of small bright spots have been recorded with the aid of very large instruments.

PLEIADES One of the best-known open clusters, visible to the naked eye as a tiny group of stars in Taurus, about $15°$ north-west of *Aldebaran*.

There are seven fairly bright stars, hence the name frequently applied to this cluster in the past, 'The Seven Sisters'. The principle star is *Alcyone* (η Tau), magnitude 3·0, spectral type $B5$.

There are five stars of the fourth magnitude and four of the fifth, and on a good night persons with moderately good eyesight should have no difficulty in seeing at least these ten stars with the unaided eye. Many can see more, there being another nine stars of the sixth magnitude, and it is not uncommon for observers to record twelve or more.

The cluster is a beautiful field to observe with binoculars or a low-power instrument such as a Predictor telescope. Long-exposure photographs reveal that the principal stars of this cluster are surrounded by bright nebulosity. [Plate 22(d).]

PLINIUS Lunar surface feature, co-ordinates $\xi + 387$, $\eta + 265$. A beautifully formed crater-ring, 30 miles in diameter, at the south-west corner of the Mare Serenitatis, where it runs into the Mare Tranquillitatis. The walls are practically circular. Observers have differed about the form of the central mountain, which presents very differing appearances under varying angles of illumination; this is probably due to the presence of a pair of craterlets at the summit.

PLOUGH The most frequently used pseudonym of the most prominent part of the constellation Ursa Major, formed by the seven stars α, β, γ, δ, ϵ, ζ and η UMa. Usually known in the United States as 'The Big Dipper'. An early name used in England was 'Charles' Wain'.

PLUTO The third discovered planet, and the outermost known planet of the solar system. It is also the planet about which we know least, owing to the difficulties of observing such a small and distant object.

The diameter of its apparent disk has been measured only with the world's most powerful telescope, the 200-in. reflector on Mount Palomar, and then with considerable difficulty and uncertainty. Its mass cannot be easily determined as it has no known satellite, and can only be deduced from a dynamical analysis of the solar system as a whole, which again leads to imprecision. Unfortunately the figures resulting from even the best of recent determinations of the mass and diameter are not compatible, which adds further to the mysteries of this remarkable planet. If the mass derived in this way is correct (approximately eight-tenths that of the Earth), the measured diameter of 3,700 miles implies a mean density greater than that of gold!

We know from environmental and other considerations, however, that Pluto is much more likely to have a rocky constitution similar to the terrestrial planets, and it is therefore assumed that the density is similar to that of the Earth and that the observed values for the diameter or the mass, or possibly both, are incorrect. This is quite possible; the apparent disk may be smaller than the true disk, due to optical effects arising from the nature of the planet's surface, and the mass is extremely difficult to determine accurately in any case. It can only be deduced from perturbative effects attributed to Pluto from studies of the motions of the other bodies in the solar system, and it is very difficult to apportion these effects with precision.

The mass of Pluto is in any case a paradoxical quantity, for although the planet was discovered by means of an analysis of its perturbative effects on other bodies, it is not, in fact, a sufficiently massive body to account for those effects in full! It has even been suggested that the discovery of a planet so close to the position predicted in this way must have been fortuitous. This seems an overstatement of the problem, however: there can be little doubt that the discovery genuinely arose from the predictions, for the planet's behaviour after discovery continued to follow the predicted pattern closely, and the discrepancies between the mass, size and perturbative effects must arise from errors in the determined values due to the extreme difficulties involved in making the necessary observations. For the present, however, Pluto may truly be dubbed 'the Mystery Planet'!

PLUTO—DIMENSIONS AND PHYSICAL DATA Owing to its small size and great distance, it has not been possible to make accurate determinations of the physical data of Pluto; the figures that follow are based upon the best recent determinations.

The apparent diameter, corrected to mean opposition distance, is only about $0''.21$, corresponding to an actual diameter of 3,700 miles—slightly less than half that of the Earth. This corresponds to a volume one-tenth that of the Earth. The value currently assumed for the density is 5.5 times that of water. This figure is highly conjectural, however, and does not agree with the mass as determined dynamically; the mass is difficult to determine accurately, owing to the absence of a Plutonian satellite system; it is also possible that the diameter derived from measurements of the apparent disk may be too low, due to optical diminution of the apparent disk arising from the reflecting properties of the planet's surface.

The acceleration due to gravity at the surface of Pluto is about half that at the surface of the Earth; the velocity of escape would therefore be about 3.2 miles per second.

Pluto is believed to have a low albedo (0.14), and to be a rocky body with little or no atmosphere. Apart from the lack of an atmosphere, and the probably higher density, it seems to be a very similar body to Mars.

PLUTO—DISCOVERY OF Even before the discovery of the planet Neptune in 1846 it had been suggested that the existence of a single extra planet would be insufficient to account for the observed anomalies in the orbital motion of Uranus.

The possibility of the presence of a trans-Neptunian planet were therefore recognized by many workers, and a number of systematic search programmes were carried out. These involved a careful telescopic search of parts of the sky where the planet was expected to be found as a result of an elaborate mathematical analysis of the orbits of Uranus and the other planets.

Probably the first search was that carried out in 1877 and 1878 at the U.S. Naval Observatory, Washington, by D. P. Todd, observing visually with the 26-in. refractor. He was expecting to find an object with a measurable disk, however, and deduced from his lack of success that the suspected planet did not exist.

A notable series of calculations were made by W. H. Pickering, who predicted the probable orbit and position of a trans-Neptunian planet by analysing its perturbative effect on the orbits of a number of comets. A search was carried out in 1919 by M. L. Humason with a 10-in. astrographic refractor at Mount Wilson Observatory, using Pickering's predictions; the planet was not detected in this search, although it was found to have been recorded on some of the plates when they were re-examined in 1930 following the actual discovery of the planet. This failure to detect the expected planet was particularly unfortunate for Pickering, whose calculations had, in fact, produced a correct position; unfortunately the image of the planet coincided with a flaw in the emulsion of one plate, and with the image of a background star on another. On such small factors depended the success or failure of years of patient effort! Another decade was to elapse before the elusive planet was finally detected.

Meanwhile, Percival Lowell, the central figure in the Martian canals controversy, had founded the Lowell Observatory at Flagstaff, Arizona, principally for the regular observation of Mars and the other planets. He had also been interested for many years in the possibility of a trans-Neptunian planet, and instituted photographic search programmes with various instruments as early as 1905; these were continued until his death in 1916, but without success.

Following the death of Lowell the search was temporarily abandoned, but a new 13-in. photographic refractor was built (largely at the expense of Percival Lowell's brother, A. Lawrence Lowell, then President of Harvard University) for the purpose of resuming Lowell's search programme. This instrument was completed and brought into operation in 1929, and Clyde Tombaugh was appointed to conduct the programme.

The method used was that developed by Lowell himself during the earlier searches; plates were exposed in sequence along a programmed path, and repeat exposures of the same areas were made after intervals of two and four days, subject of course to variations arising from inclement weather, etc. The plates of each area were then examined under a **blink comparator** in pairs, whereupon the motion during the interval between the two exposures would be revealed for any planetary body. The blink examination of the plates was in itself a Herculean task; each plate covered an area of sky of almost $12° \times 14°$, and contained an average of 400,000 star images in the region in Gemini where the planet was eventually detected; in Scorpius and Sagittarius as many as a million images per plate were obtained. Using a standard exposure time of one hour per plate, all stars down to the seventeenth magnitude were recorded. In the entire search programme—which was continued, after the discovery of Pluto, until 1945—Tombaugh estimates that he has checked about 20,000 'suspect planets' detected with the blink comparator.

The discovery field was photographed on 1930 January 21, in poor conditions, and again on January 23 and 29—the third exposure being delayed due to bad weather. The planet was discovered on 1930 February 18 when the plates were blink-compared; on February 19 Tombaugh was able to obtain a confirming plate. During the next three weeks the planet was observed, visually and photo-graphically, on all possible occasions, in the hope of determining its size and mass as well as accurate orbital elements. The absence of any satellites prevented any straightforward determination of the mass, however, and the faint object (magnitude 14·8) showed no detectable disk with either the 24-in. refractor or the 42-in. reflector. The discovery was announced to the world on 1930 March 13. The planet's position was within 5° of that predicted by the calculations of both Lowell and Pickering. From the many suggestions submitted, the name Pluto (originally suggested by H. H. Turner) was adopted for the new planet—obviously a suitable name for the planet forever doomed to dwell in the outer darkness, and doubly appropriate since it com-menced with the initials of Percival Lowell. This happy connection was reinforced by the symbol eventually adopted for the planet, ♇, formed by combining those initials. [Plate 15(a, b).]

Following the discovery of Pluto it was decided that the search should be extended, and by 1945 the entire sky north of Declination − 50° had been photographed, and the plates of from Dec. − 50° to a line at least 35° north of the Ecliptic at all points had been examined, but no more planets had been discovered. Tombaugh's work has proved that if any more trans-Neptunian planets exist they must be very small and insignificant, as well as distant. There were, however, many other valuable discoveries made during this gigantic survey, including a cluster of 1,800 galaxies, a new globular cluster and a number of galactic clusters, and more than 700 new minor planets, for 145 of which data have been measured and published.

PLUTO—ORBITAL DATA In order to establish the elements of a planetary orbit with high precision, it is necessary to obtain a considerable number of positional observations over a period of time, and it is desirable that these should include observations of the planet in all parts of its orbit, or at least in a substantial portion of it. Pluto is not an easy object to observe, and accurate observations of its position are only possible with powerful instru-ments, such as are normally engaged on other important programmes in the major observatories. Added to this, in the 38 years since its discovery Pluto has only traversed about 15 per cent of one revolu-tion of its orbit. For these reasons the orbital elements are less precisely deter-mined than for the other planets.

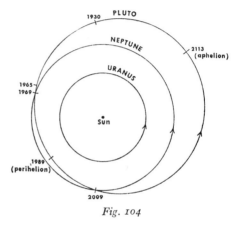

Fig. 104

The orbit has a semi-major axis of 39·44 A.U., corresponding to a mean distance from the Sun of 3,667 million miles. The eccentricity of the orbit is the highest of all the planets, 0·2494; the actual distance from the Sun therefore varies from almost 4,600 million miles at aphelion, to about 2,750 million miles at perihelion. This latter distance is rather less than the mean distance of Neptune, and for part of each orbit Pluto is closer to the Sun and ceases to be the outermost planet of the solar system (see Fig. 104). This will shortly be the case, from about 1970 to about 2010; Pluto will be at peri-helion (and, of course, at perigee) in 1989.

Pluto's orbit is much more highly inclined to the plane of the Ecliptic than that of any of the other planets, the actual inclination of 17° 10′ being nearly 2½ times that of Mercury, and five times that of Venus, the next highest.

Pluto moves with a mean orbital velocity of 2·9 miles per second, resulting in a sidereal period of 90,700 days, or about 248·4 years. It is rather awe-inspiring to think that this planet will not return to that part of its orbit in which it was discovered until the year 2178!

PLUTO—ORIGIN OF Pluto differs from the other planets in the solar system in so many ways that it has been suggested that it may have had a different origin. In particular, the eccentricity of its orbit and the inclination of the orbital plane to the plane of the Ecliptic are far greater than for any other planet; also the period of axial revolution, more than $6\frac{1}{3}$ days, is many times longer than that of any of the other outer planets.

These facts have led to the propounding of an interesting theory that Pluto was originally formed not as an independent planet, but as a satellite of Neptune. The eccentricity of Pluto's orbit is so great that it is closer to the Sun than Neptune for about a sixth of each revolution; this implies that at some epoch in the remote past Neptune and Pluto were very close together in space. The theory postulates that Neptune's principal satellite, Triton, once travelled in an orbit much closer to the parent planet than its present one, and in *direct* motion as opposed to its present *retrograde* motion; Pluto is postulated to have been a second Neptunian satellite, also in direct motion, in an orbit outside that of Triton.

The theory suggests that a particularly close approach of the two bodies resulted in Triton being torn out of its orbit and set in retrograde motion in a much larger one, and in Pluto being ejected entirely from the system, thereafter to follow its own independent orbit around the Sun (see Fig. 105).

It is usual, due to tidal forces, for planetary satellites to rotate on their axes in exactly the period of orbital revolution, thus presenting the same face to the

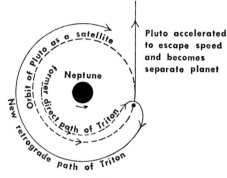

Fig. 105

primary; this would explain the extraordinarily long rotation period of Pluto, which may have been very similar when it was a satellite of Neptune orbiting in the same period.

There is, of course, no way of proving or disproving this theory in the present state of knowledge, but the argument fits the observed facts so well that it must be considered a very cogent one.

PLUTO—TELESCOPIC APPEARANCE Pluto has a mean visual magnitude of only 14·9; it can therefore be observed only with apertures of the order of 10 inches, and is even then very difficult to identify with certainty. Were Pluto near aphelion, instead of approaching perihelion as at present, it would require one of the world's few 'giant' telescopes to detect it at all.

It presents only a yellowish stellar image with most instruments—in order to determine the apparent diameter of the disk with any accuracy G. P. Kuiper had to use the 200-in. reflector on Mount Palomar.

Very slight but regular variations in brightness have been detected, from which it has been deduced that the period of axial rotation is 6·39 days.

PLUTONIC THEORY Theory that the surface features of the Moon were formed by plutonic (i.e. volcanic) activity. (See **Moon—origin of surface features.**)

POINTERS, THE Descriptive term given to the stars α and β UMa, which 'point' to the north celestial pole and *Polaris*.

POLAR CAPS The polar caps most frequently referred to in astronomy are those of the planet Mars. The term is sometimes used erroneously to describe the **cusp caps** of Venus, which may not be at the poles of rotation at all.

(See also **Mars—observed features and notable phenomena.**)

POLAR LIGHTS Name sometimes used, especially in former times, for the **Aurora**, *q.v.*

POLAR VARIATION A periodic movement of the poles of rotation of the Earth relative to the geoid; it has two components. One component is due to the asymmetry of the geoid and has an amplitude of 0".36 (*ca.* ±30 ft.) and a period of 432 days; the other component arises from seasonal shifts of air-masses and has an amplitude of 0".18 (*ca.* ±15 ft.) and a period of exactly one year. (See **Latitude variation.**)

POLARIS The star α UMi, which at the present time marks the north celestial pole, being in fact within a degree of the exact spot. It is a creamy supergiant of spectral type *F8*, magnitude 2·0. It has a ninth magnitude companion star at a separation of 18".3, position angle 217°.

(See also **Pole star.**)

POLARIZATION The electromagnetic radiation we call 'light' is normally vibrating in all planes; after reflection, refraction, absorption or scattering the vibrations may be confined to one plane, that is to say 'plane polarized'.

It has been found that the light reaching us from many astronomical bodies is polarized. With the aid of polarizing media such as 'polaroid' filters or Nicol polarizing prisms the degree and orientation of polarization can be studied; this has permitted useful advances in our knowledge of nebular structure, of the physics of the solar corona, etc.

POLE STAR The bright star closest to the position of a celestial pole. These vary from one epoch to another, due to the effect of **precession**. Thus the northern pole star is now *Polaris*, but some 4,600 years ago it was *Thuban* (α Dra) and about 2,000 years hence it will be *Alrai* (γ Cep).

There is no bright star within 10° of the southern celestial pole at the present time; the present south pole star is σ Oct, magnitude 5·5.

POLES, CELESTIAL All heavenly bodies may be regarded, for practical purposes, as being infinitely distant; that is to say, they may be regarded as being situated in the surface of a transparent sphere centred on the Earth (the 'celestial sphere'). Due to the axial rotation of the Earth the celestial sphere appears to rotate in the contrary direction; the celestial poles are the ends of the diameter of the sphere about which it is apparently rotating— the poles of rotation, in fact, of the celestial sphere. They are termed the *north celestial pole* and the *south celestial pole*, and are situated exactly in the zenith for observers situated at the north and south poles of the Earth respectively. A star situated at either pole would have no detectable diurnal motion. In fact there are no stars exactly at the celestial poles at the present time, although the 'Pole Star'—*Polaris* (α UMi)—is within a degree of the north celestial pole. There is a faint star within a degree of the south celestial pole also (σ Oct, magnitude 5·5), but as it is barely visible to the naked eye it is almost impossible to identify without accurate instruments.

(See also **Celestial sphere; Precession.**)

POLES OF ROTATION The ends of the **axis of rotation** of a rotating body such as a planet.

POLLUX The star β Gem, one of the well-known twins. It is an orange-yellow giant of spectral class *K0* and apparent magnitude 1·2. There is an optical companion of the fourteenth magnitude.

Pollux is the closest giant star to the solar system, being at a distance of 10·7 parsecs from the Sun (a little less than 35 light years).

POLYGONAL RING-STRUCTURES
Lunar ring-structures having walls approximating to a polygon in shape. Many are in the form of a regular hexagon—e.g. Albategnius. (See **Moon—surface features of.**)

POND, JOHN (1767–1836) The sixth Astronomer Royal, holding the office from 1811–1835. Prior to his appointment at Greenwich, Pond observed with a superb 30-in. altazimuth circle by Troughton at his own private observatory at Westbury. This was one of Troughton's finest instruments, and in the hands of so accurate an observer as Pond contributed a great deal to positional astronomy. From his observations of the declinations of a number of reference stars Pond was able to show that Bradley's 8-ft. quadrant, made by Bird and installed at Greenwich in 1750, was no longer producing accurate results. As a result of this Troughton was commissioned to produce an instrument to replace it; he produced a 6-ft. mural circle, which was installed in 1812. Maskelyne had died in the previous year, and Pond had been appointed in his place. So as to make Right Ascension determinations comparable in accuracy with the Declinations measured with the mural circle, Pond ordered from Troughton a 5-in. transit instrument which was erected in 1816. [Plate 27(a, c).]

Aided by these instruments Pond was able to make positional observations of hitherto unsurpassed accuracy, and in 1833 he published a catalogue giving the positions of 1,112 stars which remained for many years one of the most reliable pieces of fundamental observation.

Unfortunately Pond's enthusiasm for observational astronomy did not extend to routine computation, and the work of the Nautical Almanac Office began to suffer accordingly, and the high reputation for accuracy built up for the *Almanac* by Maskelyne began to be tarnished. The post of Superintendent of the Nautical Almanac Office was created, and Thomas Young appointed to fill it, in 1818. Young restored the lost accuracy in some measure, but was unable to realize fully the needs of astronomers and was in any case unwilling to countenance any change in the format of the *Almanac*. When Young died in 1829 Pond took over again temporarily, and this time made a number of improvements. It was decided with the appointment in 1831 of Lieutenant Stratford, a retired naval officer who was Secretary of the Royal Astronomical Society, as the second Superintendent, to separate the Nautical Almanac Office entirely from the Royal Observatory, which remained the case for more than a century.

It was during Pond's tenure of office, in 1821, that the charge of the chronometers used by the Royal Navy passed to a department of the Royal Observatory, and in 1833 the famous Greenwich **Time-ball** was also introduced.

Pond was a great observer and contributed much to the great series of Greenwich observations, and it is unfortunate that his time at Greenwich ended under a cloud; dogged by ill-health Pond was forced to be absent from the Observatory more and more towards the end of his career, and his First Assistant was not of sufficient calibre to be able to replace him. The Observatory became disorganized and inefficient, and Pond was forced to resign in 1835. He died within a year at the comparatively young age of 69, a broken man, his once-high reputation lost, largely through no fault of his own. In the early years, however, he had been a worthy addition to the select list of incumbents of his high office.

POPULATION I STARS The intensely luminous, bluish, stars found in the spiral arms of the galaxies. (See **Stellar populations.**)

POPULATION II STARS The pre-dominantly red stars of low luminosity found in the cores of the spiral galaxies, in elliptical galaxies and the globular clusters. (See **Stellar populations**.)

PORE Tiny dark spot on the Sun, formed by the parting of adjacent **flocculi**; may be the first stage in the development of a new **sunspot**, but pores frequently have a separate, and usually short-lived, existence.

PORTUS SIGEUS Martian surface fea-ture, approximate position Ω 335°, $\Phi - 5$°. A dusky 'promontory' sometimes observed mid-way along the northern edge of the Sinus Sabæus. The canali Phison and Euphrates radiate northwards from it.

POSEIDON Proposed name of satellite VIII of Jupiter, *q.v.*

POSIDONIUS Lunar surface feature, co-ordinates $\xi + 419$, $\eta + 526$. A most interesting formation at the north-western corner of the Mare Serenitatis. 62 miles in diameter, Posidonius has a narrow wall rising to 6,000 ft. in the west, with a break at the easternmost point. The remains of an inner wall can be traced around the north, west and south parts of the floor. There is a prominent crater (Posidonius A) almost in the centre of the floor, from which several prominent clefts radiate. The wall is broken with several craters, including a particularly prominent one on the southern wall (Posidonius J).

POSITION ANGLE A means of recording the position of a body, or part of a body, relative to another body or a reference point; usually abbreviated to P.A. It is normally encountered in two forms:

1. To record the position of a marking or other feature on the observed disk of a planet, the Sun, etc. In this case the position angle is the angular distance east of a line joining the centre of the disk (C) to the north point (N); i.e., in Fig. 106, the position angle of the point P is $\angle NCP$.

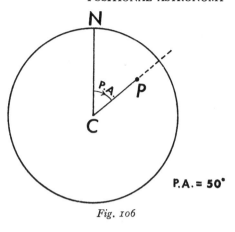

Fig. 106

2. To record the relative positions of the components of a visual double star. In this case the position angle is the angular distance of the fainter companion star (S_2) east of a line from the primary

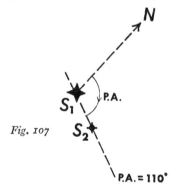

Fig. 107

star (S_1) pointing in the direction of the north celestial pole (S_1N); thus in Fig. 107 the position angle of S_2 relative to S_1 is $\angle NS_1S_2$.

POSITIONAL ASTRONOMY That branch of astronomy concerned with the determination of the positions of celestial bodies; as the latter are not stationary but constantly moving relative to each other it is necessarily concerned with motions also.

Observationally, positional astronomy involves the precise determination of the apparent place of a body; this can later be corrected to derive the true place or the mean place, whichever is required (see **Star places**). The observation may be needed for a number of reasons: it may be part of a programme for improving the known positions of a selected list of stars; it may be intended for comparison with positions observed many years previously in order to determine the proper motions of a group of stars; it may be an observation of the position of a planet or other body in the solar system, to be analysed with many other such observations in order to improve the ephemeris for the body concerned.

Observations of position are normally made in one of two ways, either by direct measurement, as in meridian astronomy, or by photographic astrometry.

The instruments used in meridian astronomy (notably the **transit circle**, *q.v.*) are designed to permit the sidereal time of meridian transit of a body to be accurately determined, from which its Right Ascension at that moment can be calculated; its Declination can be calculated directly from the setting of the telescope.

In the case of photographic astrometry a plate is exposed on the region of the sky concerned; the positions of the star images can then be measured. These measures may be used to obtain *differential positions*, by comparing them with a plate of the same field taken with the same instrument some years previously; alternatively, if some fundamental stars are included on the plate, the *absolute positions* of other stars may be determined by measuring their positions relative to the fundamental stars whose places may be assumed.

POST-NOVA Name given to a nova when the slow fade from the maximum has been completed and the star has reached its former magnitude; post-novae usually remain steady at this minimum magnitude. (See **Nova**.)

PRÆSEPE One of the best known open clusters, visible to the unaided eye as a hazy patch in Cancer, in the centre of the triangle formed by γ, δ and η Can. Known to the ancients as 'The Beehive', it is listed in Messier's Catalogue as M44, and by Dreyer as N.G.C. 2632. This large cluster is a splendid sight with binoculars or low-power telescope.

PRECEDING LIMB The axial rotation of the Earth (from west to east) gives the heavenly bodies an apparent motion across the sky from east to west—the 'diurnal motion'; therefore if a telescope is trained on a particular object it will appear to move across the field of the telescope, unless the latter is equatorially mounted and clock-driven in the opposing direction at sufficient rate to counteract it.

If the body concerned has an appreciable disk, the 'leading' limb due to this apparent motion across the field is termed the *preceding* limb and the opposite one is termed the *following* limb; these terms are very useful in the description of observational results.

In the case of planets having rapid axial rotation, such as Jupiter, the motion due to the axial rotation of the planet is in the same direction as its apparent diurnal motion, and the surface features therefore traverse the disk from the following limb towards the preceding limb.

PRECESSION Properly termed the *precession of the equinoxes*. It is a westward motion of the equinoxes (the nodes of the Ecliptic) relative to the background stars, arising mainly from the gravitational attraction of the Sun and Moon on the non-spherical Earth. It was first discovered by Hipparchus in about 125 B.C., and amounts to 50″.2 per annum; a complete revolution of the nodes of the Ecliptic therefore occupies 25,800 years. The pole of the heavens for terrestrial observers thus appears to trace out a small circle in the heavens, of radius equal to the inclination of the Earth's axis ($23\frac{1}{2}°$) and centred upon the pole of the Ecliptic, in a period of 25,800 years. Since positional observations are made relative to the celestial poles at the epoch of observation, due allowance has to be made when reducing series of positional observations to a

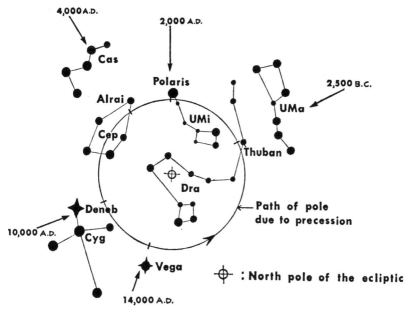

4,000 A.D.

2,000 A.D.

Cas

Polaris

2,500 B.C.

Alrai

UMa

UMi

Cep

Thuban

Dra

Deneb

← Path of pole
due to precession

10,000 A.D.

Cyg

Vega   ⊕ : North pole of the ecliptic

14,000 A.D.

Fig. 108

common epoch for comparative purposes.

It is therefore evident that the proximity of *Polaris* to the north celestial pole at the present time is a purely temporary circumstance; when precession was discovered by Hipparchus a little over 2,000 years ago *Polaris* was 12° from the north celestial pole of that time. About 2,500 B.C. the 'pole star' was *Thuban* (α Dra); in A.D. 4,000 it will be *Alrai* (γ Cep) and in A.D. 14,000 the closest star to the pole will be *Vega*. The precessional track of the north celestial pole among the stars is shown in Fig. 108.

The main component of precession, that due to the combined effects of the Sun and Moon, is termed the *luni-solar precession*. There is a smaller component which arises from changes in the inclination of the Earth's orbit caused by the gravitational effects of the other planets; this is known as *planetary precession*. The total effect, combining the luni-solar and planetary precessions, is termed *general precession*.

(See also **Nutation.**)

PRE-NOVA Name given to a star destined to become a nova, before the outburst takes place. Novae cannot be discovered until the rapid rise in luminosity has commenced, and hence observations of pre-novae as such are retrospective—on existing photographs of the region concerned, etc. (See **Nova.**)

PRIME FOCUS The position at the open end of the tube of a reflecting telescope, on the central axis of the primary mirror, at which the primary image is formed. In the case of instruments of small aperture it is impracticable to use the prime focus, and the **Newtonian focus** is normally preferred. In the case of moderate apertures a camera, and in the case of large apertures a 'cage' to carry an observer and his ancillary equipment, can be mounted at the prime focus without significant loss of usable aperture.

PRIME MERIDIAN The zero of longitude of a planet. (See **Meridian, prime.**)

343

PRIME VERTICAL That vertical circle which passes through the east and west points on the horizon, and is therefore perpendicular to the meridian.

PRINCIPIA The publication in which Sir Isaac Newton propounded his theory of gravitation, the full title being *Principia mathematica philosophiæ naturalis*. It was published in 1687 by The Royal Society, although the cost was largely borne by Halley owing to the Society's lack of the necessary funds. The *Principia* owed even more to Halley, but for whose encouragement and insistence Newton—then almost a recluse—might never have completed it.

PRISM An optical element consisting of a block of glass or other translucent material; it functions by refraction and, in some cases, by internal reflection at one or more of its surfaces. Its principal uses in optical equipment are to deviate and/or to disperse beams of light. There are numerous forms.

In astronomy prisms are mainly used as secondary equipment; they are usually replaced by diffraction gratings in astronomical spectroscopes, and optical flats are preferred for deviating functions in astronomical instruments where the loss of illumination due to transmission through the prism would be a disadvantage.

Perhaps their most important use in astronomy has been in the form of the **objective prism**, which has permitted tremendous advances to be made in the study of stellar spectra.

PRISMATIC ASTROLABE Instrument designed to make fundamental observations of stars, at a fixed altitude of 60°. It is based upon a simple principle, shown diagrammatically in Fig. 109. A 60° prism is mounted with its emergent face vertical, in front of the O.G. of a fixed, horizontal, refracting telescope. Immediately in front of the prism is a bath of mercury, forming a horizontal reflecting surface. The whole instrument is mounted so that it can be rotated about a vertical axis. In use, it is set in the azimuth of a star that is about to cross the almucantar of 30° radius (i.e. a small circle of 30° radius, centred on the zenith). When the star is close to the almucantar (when its altitude will be exactly 60°), part of the light beam from it will enter the prism through its upper face and be reflected off the interior of the lower face, and part will be reflected by the mercury surface, enter the prism through its lower face and be reflected off the interior of the upper face. These two beams will emerge parallel and enter the O.G., to form separate images in the focal plane. As one beam has been subjected to

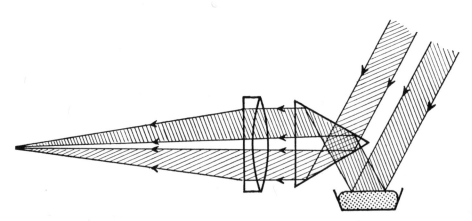

Fig. 109

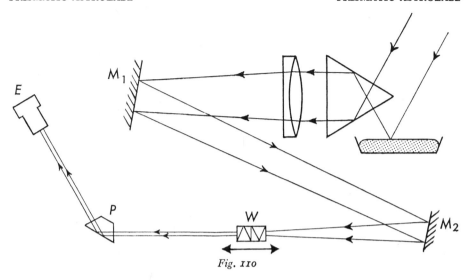

Fig. 110

an extra reflection, the motions of these images due to the star's apparent motion will be in opposing directions; the images will be coincident when the star is exactly on the almucantar. If the star's place and the clock error are assumed, and also the current position of the pole (due to latitude variation), the observer's latitude and longitude may be determined: the prismatic astrolabe is used in this way as a field instrument by surveyors, etc. If the observer's latitude and longitude are accurately known, however, and stars of known place are observed (i.e. fundamental stars), the astrolabe can be used to determine clock errors (and hence to control a time service) and to record latitude variation. The basic form of the prismatic astrolabe is subject to considerable errors of adjustment and errors arising from the observer's 'personal equation', and is not therefore sufficiently accurate to be used for the latter purposes. However, a modified version was developed a decade or so ago by A. Danjon, Director of the Paris Observatory, which removes the deficiencies present in the basic instrument. These largely arise from the fact that the focusing is so critical—the slightest deviation from .exact focusing

results in gross errors. The principal feature of the *Danjon impersonal prismatic astrolabe*, outlined in Fig. 110, is the introduction of a Wollaston birefringent prism, W, just inside the focus. The effect of this is to convert the two converging beams into two parallel beams and two diverging beams. The latter are screened off, and the parallel beams are fed into the eyepiece (*E*); since they are now parallel slight inaccuracies in focusing will not affect the accuracy of the timing of their coincidence. The Wollaston prism can be traversed at a preselected speed so as to keep the two images coincident (or, as is normal observing practice, in close juxtaposition); the times at which the prism reaches certain positions are automatically recorded, enabling the exact time of the star's crossing the almucantar to be determined.

Further refinements in the Danjon instrument are the introduction of two plane mirrors, M_1 and M_2, to 'fold' the optical path in the interests of compactness, and an additional prism (*P*) to direct the beam to a convenient eyepiece position. The O.G. has an aperture of 10 cm and a focal length of 100 cm; stars down to magnitude 6·3 can be observed. The instrument gives results of high accuracy; although its use is limited to those stars which cross the 30° almucantar, by combining its results with those obtained with Photographic Zenith Tubes from zenithal stars, it is possible to obtain time and latitude determinations of unsurpassed precision. It is also hoped to establish a chain of prismatic astrolabes at latitude intervals of about 15°, from about 60° N to about 60° S; their zones of observable stars will overlap to cover virtually the whole sky.

PROBABLE ERROR When a series of observations is statistically analysed, the arithmetic mean of a number of determinations is adopted as the measured result, and a figure indicating the probable range of error of this result is appended, calculated from the internal consistency of the individual determinations. This is termed the *probable error*.

The result is quoted in the form, for example,

$$\pi = 0''105 \pm 0''008;$$

this means that the parallax being determined almost certainly lies between 0''097 and 0''113, according to the measurements being analysed, the most likely figure being 0''105.

PROCLUS Lunar surface feature, co-ordinates $\xi + 702$, $\eta + 277$. A brilliant crater, 18 miles in diameter, approximately 50 miles east of the border of the Mare Crisium. The walls are very steep, and rise to 8,000 ft. Proclus is the centre of a bright ray system, the most prominent rays spreading south, north-east and westwards (across the Mare Crisium).

PROCYON The eighth brightest star in the heavens—*a* CMi. It is a creamy sub-giant or dwarf star of spectral class *F5* and magnitude 0·3. It is a binary with a white dwarf companion of the eleventh magnitude 4''4 distant, position angle 81° (1960); the period is 41 years.

PROMETHEI SINUS Martian surface feature, approximate position Ω 280° $\Phi - 65°$. A prominent dark streak in the far south of the planet's surface, extending from Ω 250° along the southern boundaries of Ausonia and Hellas to Ω 310°.

PROMINENCES, SOLAR Eruptions of incandescent gas, mainly hydrogen, from the surface of the Sun; they may attain a height of many thousands of miles, and may last only a few hours; major prominences tend to last for two or three days at least, although undergoing many changes of structure, and on occasion last for many weeks. They are seen as bright extensions to the solar limb when the Sun is viewed in monochromatic light with suitable equipment, and during total solar eclipses or when the disk is artificially occulted with a **coronagraph**. They are somewhat cooler than the photospheric surface, and therefore appear as dark 'filaments' when viewed on the disk. [Plates 1(b); 2(d, f).]

They usually occur in one of a number of well-known forms. (See **Solar activity; Sun—physical constitution of.**)

PROPER MOTION The observed motion of a star, over a period of time, relative to the other 'fixed' stars. It is determined from comparisons of the star's position measured on plates exposed at widely separated epochs—often half a century or more apart. Stars having large proper motions will show up if two such plates are compared in a **blink microscope**; as all stars have proper motions, most of them being small ones, precise measurement and extensive analysis is necessary for accurate determinations. This observed angular displacement is corrected for geodetic factors such as precession, nutation, etc., to produce what is termed the *restricted proper motion*; if this is converted to a velocity (in km/sec) for stars of known distance it is termed the *reduced proper motion*.

The largest known proper motion is that of **Barnard's star**, 10''25 per annum. Most stars have proper motions of only about 0″1 per annum; fewer than 350 are known to have proper motions greater than 1″ per annum.

PROPONTIS Martian surface feature, approximate position Ω 180°, Φ+45°. Dusky area south-east of Trivium Charontis, to which it is connected by Hades; continues westward as Phlegra, to join Cebrenia.

PROTEI REGIO Martian surface feature, approximate position Ω 50°, Φ−23°. Dark condensation south of Auroræ Sinus, at north-eastern end of Bosporus Gemmatus.

PROTON One of the heavy particles of an atom, which bears a positive electrical charge and is situated inside the atomic nucleus. (See **Atom**.)

PROTON–PROTON REACTION One of the processes by which hydrogen atoms in the Sun and the other stars combine to form helium atoms, with a release of energy in consequence.

The full reaction may be simply expressed as follows:

proton + proton → hydrogen atom + electron;
hydrogen atom + proton → helium atom + radiant energy.

The proton–proton reaction is believed to be the principal source of stellar energy at temperatures below about 15,000,000° K. (See also **Stars—energy of**.)

PROTONILUS Martian surface feature, approximate position Ω 315°, Φ+42°. Prominent canal in the north temperate region, extending eastwards from Ismenius Lacus, along the southern edge of Dioscuria and merging into Nilosyrtis; forms part of the northern boundary of Arabia.

PROTO-STAR An embryonic star. It is believed that the **globules** (small, dense absorption nebulae, approximately spherical in shape) found at the edges of emission nebulae may be new stars in the

process of being formed; they are dense concentrations of interstellar matter and may be condensing into stellar form.
(See also **Evolution, stellar; Nebulae, dark**.)

PROXIMA CENTAURI The closest star to the solar system; it is a component of the α Cen system of magnitude 10·7 and spectral class $M5$; it has a trigonometrical parallax of 0″762, corresponding to a distance of 4·3 light years (approximately 1·3 parsecs.).

PTOLEMÆIC SYSTEM The geocentric system of planetary motion, in which the planets move in epicycles and deferents, devised by **Ptolemy**, *q.v.*

PTOLEMÆUS Lunar surface feature, co-ordinates ξ−048, η−158. A vast walled plain, 90 miles in diameter, situated just a little south of the centre of the Moon's visible disk. It is the northernmost member of a great trio with Alphonsus and Arzachel, and is the largest of the three. Unlike the other two it has no central mountain; the floor is comparatively smooth save for the prominent crater Lyot, 4 miles in diameter, in the north-western part of the floor. Closer inspection with fairly powerful instruments reveals that there are a number of shallow, rimless, saucer-like depressions on the floor, the largest and most prominent of which lies immediately north of Lyot. There are also a number of well-defined but tiny craterlets, particularly in the north-east.

The outline is more hexagonal than circular, and the walls are complex and broken. The southern wall, which is common to Alphonsus, is particularly rugged. The outer slopes of the ramparts, especially to the north, show many parallel ridges and valleys running SSW–NNE, an important and recurring feature in this region. [Plate 5(a).]

PTOLEMY (Claudius Ptolemæus, *fl.* A.D. **130)** The last of the great Greek astronomers and natural philosophers. Ptolemy spent most of his active life as an observer in Alexandria.

Ptolemy believed in the geocentric theory of the universe, and that the Earth was by far the largest of the bodies in the firmament. He believed that the planets moved around the Earth at a uniform speed but in a rather complicated orbit: this may be described as a circle (the *epicycle*) whose centre is itself in uniform motion around a large circle (the *deferent*) which is *eccentric* (i.e. not centred on the Earth). By carefully selecting the dimensions of this rather clumsy system it is possible to reproduce approximately the apparent motions of the planets. This is known as the 'Ptolemæic system'.

Ptolemy produced a catalogue giving the positions of 1,028 stars, and measured the distance of the Moon by a parallax method, using observations of its position made from two stations some distance apart.

His main work was published in a volume originally entitled *The Mathematical Collection* but which came to be known as *The Almagest*—an Arabian corruption of the Greek for 'The Greatest'.

The value of Ptolemy's observational work has been questioned, but there can be no doubt of the standard of his theoretical work; despite the erroneous premise upon which they were based his tables of planetary motion were used until the sixteenth century.

PULKOWA OBSERVATORY The leading observatory for fundamental astronomy in the U.S.S.R., situated near Leningrad. Pulkowa has a long and distinguished history. Fraunhofer's famous 9½-in. equatorial refractor was transferred there from Dorpat, and later supplemented by a 15-in. refractor made by Merz in 1845. In 1885 a giant 30-in. refractor was installed, with objective by Alvan Clark and mounting by Repsold. For a short time this was the world's largest refractor; it was equalled by the 30-in. refractor built for the private observatory at Nice

of R. Bischoffsheim in 1886, now the observatory of the University of Paris, and was superseded by the Lick 36-in. in 1888, the Meudon 33-in. in 1889 and the Yerkes 40-in. in 1897.

The observatory was almost totally destroyed during the siege of Leningrad in World War II, but has been rebuilt and restored as the principal observatory of the Soviet Union.

PULSAR In 1967 a new radio telescope was erected at the Mullard Radio Astronomy Observatory, Cambridge, designed to investigate the scintillation of compact radio sources. When systematic observation commenced in November 1967, a radio source was discovered from the early records which was emitting a pulsed signal, the pulses each lasting about one-third of a second and occurring with great regularity at intervals of 1⅓ sec. Three more similar sources were discovered within a short time. These 'pulsating radio sources' soon became popularly known as *pulsars*.

By the end of 1968 some twenty or so pulsars had been discovered. Their nature is still the subject of much speculation; it seems to be generally accepted that they must be some form of superdense body, such as a neutron star. Gold has suggested that their pulsation may be due to the rotation of a jet of radiation from the surface of such a star; this theory is compatible with the recent discovery that their pulsation is gradually slowing down.

Early in 1969 the light from a star visible in the Crab nebula was discovered to be flashing in pulses exactly matching those of the radio pulsar in the nebula. This first optical identification of a pulsar may be of great importance in understanding their nature and origin, for the star concerned is suspected to be the post-nova phase of the great supernova of 1054 A.D. which gave birth to the nebula.

PULSATING STARS Regular variables whose fluctuating brightness appears to arise from a regular pulsation of the star. The changing size of the star is not by itself sufficient to account for the observed variation in luminosity; it is believed that this arises from a periodical conversion of radiant energy to gravitational energy and back again. This theory also accounts for the observed lag between maxima of luminosity and maxima of size.

The most important group of pulsating stars are the **Cepheid variables**, *q.v.* It is also believed that many of the long-period variables owe their fluctuations to their being pulsating stars.

PULSATING VARIABLES See **Pulsating stars.**

PUPPIS (The Poop. *Genitive* Puppis, *I.A.U. abbreviation* Pup.) A large southern constellation, one of three which once formed **Argo Navis**; shares a single sequence of **Bayer Letters** with the others, **Carina** and **Vela**. Contains three second-magnitude stars and many fainter ones; the Galactic Equator crosses the constellation, which therefore embraces part of the Milky Way and is rich in nebulae and clusters. There are a few double and variable stars of some interest.

Near the northern tip of the constellation lies M46 (N.G.C. 2437), a beautiful cluster with an irregular planetary nebula (N.G.C. 2438) on its northern edge. Three or four degrees to the south lies N.G.C. 2440, a bright, bluish planetary nebula well seen with moderate powers.

PURBACH Lunar surface feature, co-ordinates $\xi - 029$, $\eta - 428$. A rugged walled plain in the very mountainous region south-west of the Mare Nubium. Hexagonal in form, it intrudes in the south into Regiomontanus. The walls are very complex, and rise to 8,000 ft. in the west; the northern wall is broken by a large crater, Purbach G, with a very pitted floor. The remains of a former crater ring occupy the centre of the floor, which is broken by a number of craterlets and crater-pits. Purbach is 75 miles in diameter.

PYRRHÆ REGIO Martian surface feature, approximate position Ω 30°, $\Phi - 15°$. Dusky region in northern part of Mare Erythræum, adjoining the southern end of the Margaritifer Sinus.

PYTHAGORAS Lunar surface feature, co-ordinates $\xi - 397$, $\eta + 894$. A superb crater ring, 75 miles in diameter, close to the north-north-eastern limb. Photographs taken under favourable angles of illumination reveal vast terraced walls rising to 17,000 ft. in places, and a superb central mountain of 5,000 ft.

PYXIS (The Compass; formerly Pyxis Nautica, The Mariner's Compass. *Genitive* Pyxidis, *I.A.U. abbreviation* Pyx.) A small and rather empty southern constellation containing only one third- and two fourth-magnitude stars.

Q

QSO Abbreviation for **quasi-stellar object,** *q.v.*

QUADRANS An old constellation name, now no longer used, its stars forming part of **Boötes.** Mainly remembered through the name of the **Quadrantid** meteor shower.

QUADRANT One of the oldest instruments for making precise determinations of the positions of heavenly bodies. The principle of the quadrant was proposed by Ptolemy about 150 B.C.; it was to comprise a quadrant in stone, wood or metal, subdivided to small fractions of a degree, and a sighting bar pivoted from its centre (Fig. 111). The upright bar was made exactly vertical with the aid of a plumb-line, the sight aligned on the star and the zenith distance of the star read off on the scale. [Plate 25(d).]

With refinements the large mural quadrant was used by all the great fundamental observers for nearly 1,800 years; towards the end of the seventeenth century the sighting bar was replaced by a refracting telescope. Such instruments were the principal means of determining the declinations of planets and stars until almost the end of the eighteenth century when it was replaced by the mural circle.

Among the more notable mural quadrants were those erected at the Royal Observatory, Greenwich: the 8-ft iron quadrant constructed by Graham for Halley in 1725, and the 8-ft brass quadrant made by Reid for Bradley in 1750.

(See also **Sextant.**)

QUADRANTIDS One of the principal meteor showers, occurring in early January; the radiant is situated in that part of the

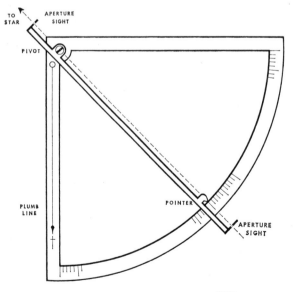

Fig. 111

constellation Boötes formerly known as Quadrans.

QUADRATURE The positions of the Moon or a superior planet when the angle Sun–Earth–Moon (or planet) is a right-angle; that is to say when its elongation is 90° or 270°.
(See also **Planetary motion**.)

QUARTZ CLOCK If a plate of quartz crystal is given a positive charge on one face and a negative charge on the other, it will expand or contract; it is therefore possible to keep the crystal in a state of oscillation by means of an alternating electrical current. If the frequency of the oscillation is chosen so as to be as nearly as possible the natural resonance frequency of the quartz plate, this frequency will dominate and the crystal will maintain this frequency of oscillation to a high degree of accuracy.

This principle has been utilized to provide a highly accurate means of time measurement; the selected frequency of oscillation is usually 100,000 cycles per second, and is reduced electronically to 1,000 c/sec. The 1,000 c/sec signal is used to drive a synchronous motor (this combination is termed a *phonic motor*) which can be used to drive a clock-dial or (more usually) a contact-wheel giving an electrical signal every second.

The quartz-crystal oscillator (or 'quartz clock') is capable of keeping time with errors less than 1 millisecond (0·001 sec) per day; this accuracy has proved sufficient to detect minute variations in the length of the day due to discontinuities in the rotation of the Earth.

QUASAR Popular alternative name for **quasi-stellar object**, *q.v.*

QUASI-STELLAR OBJECT With the steady increase in the precision of position determinations of radio sources it became possible to identify many of them positively with optical objects discovered on plates obtained with large telescopes.

Most of the well-determined radio sources proved to be identified with visible galaxies (thus proving incidentally the unsuitability of the early description of radio sources as 'radio stars').

The angular diameters of most radio sources can be determined by the use of a radio interferometer; the majority of them were found to have diameters of the order of one minute of arc. A few were found to be unresolvable even with the largest interferometers, however, indicating angular diameters of less than 3 seconds of arc. Three of these were found to coincide with blue star-like objects. The optical spectrum of one of these, numbered 3C 48 in the 3rd Cambridge catalogue of radio sources, proved to be quite peculiar, very strong in the ultra-violet and with extremely bright emission lines. The others were found to have similar spectral characteristics, but the emission lines could not be identified. In 1963 the radio source 3C 273 was identified with a brighter blue 'star' which also has a wisp of nebulosity associated with it. The emission lines of 3C 273 were finally identified by Marten Schmidt as being the Balmer lines of hydrogen, but affected by an enormous red shift of $z = 0.158$. The other objects were then found to follow the same pattern, with differing but very large red shifts.

These remarkable objects have been termed, perhaps most accurately, *quasi-stellar objects*; the shorter term *quasar* is more convenient in everyday use and has proved a popular alternative.

The distinguished American observer Sandage has led the effort to obtain optical identifications of quasars, and has found more than 100 positive identifications, amounting to approximately 30 per cent of the radio sources examined; it is considered likely that the same percentage may be found to apply to the 10,000 catalogued radio sources. Their angular size can now be determined with greater precision—most of them are only 0″.1–0″.2 in diameter.

If the enormous observed red shifts are

interpreted as **Doppler shifts**, distances derived by means of the **Hubble constant** indicate that the quasars are enormously distant, on average much the most distant objects known. The radio source 3C 295 has been identified with a normal optical galaxy whose red shift ($z = 0.461$) was the largest known; the quasar 3C 147, one of the first to be discovered, has a red shift of $z = 0.545$ and many of those discovered more recently are much more distant than this.

From the distances indicated by their red shifts the absolute magnitudes of the quasars can be determined; these indicate that they are also the most luminous bodies yet discovered in the universe, many of them being more than a hundred times as luminous as known galaxies. Despite this they are all faint objects, most of them detectable only by means of long-exposure photographs using very large telescopes. An exception is 3C 273, which has a visual apparent magnitude of 12·7 and can thus be detected visually with a fairly large aperture and a suitable identification chart; the distance of this object, however, (more than 1,500,000,000 light years), belies its true brightness; it is in fact one of the most luminous bodies known, with an absolute magnitude of −26.

The brightness of the quasars is particularly remarkable in view of their very small diameters. Their unprecedented distance and brightness, determined from their red shifts, have led astrophysicists to question the validity of interpreting their large red shifts in terms of the Hubble effect in the usual way; no satisfactory alternative explanation has been forthcoming, however, and it seems likely that the observed red shifts must largely be due to great distance.

If we accept this we must then endeavour to conceive a process capable of generating the incredible amount of energy radiated by the quasars, in such a relatively small compass—for the typical quasar would appear to have a diameter only a fraction of that of our Galaxy. If the energy arises from the breakdown of hydrogen nuclei, as does normal stellar radiation, the quasar must be equivalent to more than one thousand million Suns— which in its relatively small volume implies a density of material unknown elsewhere in the universe. It would seem that only a catastrophic process of energy release could account for the extraordinary luminosity of these bodies—a kind of supernova on a galactic scale. The concept of the **gravitational collapse** of a massive body, postulated by Hoyle and Fowler shortly before the quasars were discovered in 1963, may provide the required mechanism.

The tremendous efforts being made to obtain and correlate optical and radio data to further our knowledge of these enigmatic objects are matched only by the efforts of leading theoretical astrophysicists to solve the problems posed by the observational results. New features are constantly being discovered to complicate the issues: the quasars are found to be variable in luminosity; many are found to be associated with double radio sources; they are not apparently connected with optical galaxies, yet one of them is situated at the centre of the radio galaxy 3C 47; and so on. Surely the quasars are the most important celestial discovery since the nature of the spiral galaxies was determined, and it seems quite possible that they may be found in time to be cosmologically the most significant celestial objects ever discovered; it may be that the collaboration of the optical and radio astronomers of the 1960s has produced a vital piece of evidence in the quest for the true nature of the universe.

R

R.A. Usual abbreviation for **Right ascension,** *q.v.*

R CORONÆ BOREALIS STARS A class of irregular variable stars, named after the best known star of the type. They are characterized by long periods of maximum brightness, of unpredictable duration, followed by a sudden diminution of several magnitudes and a slower, often erratic, brightening until the former magnitude is reached. The cause of their variation has not been established.
(See **Variable stars.**)

R STARS Stars of spectral class *R*; they are red stars similar to class *M* stars but containing less oxygen and more carbon. They have surface temperatures around $2,200°K$.

RGU SYSTEM The system of three-colour determinations of photographic magnitudes devised by W. Becker of Basle.
(See also **Stellar magnitude—determination of.**)

RR LYRAE STARS A class of pulsating variable stars, named after the first of the type to be thoroughly studied. They are sometimes known as *cluster-type variables*, owing to their high incidence in the globular clusters, but as other types of variable are also found in fairly large numbers in the clusters the use of this name is not to be encouraged. RR Lyrae stars have very short periods, few of them exceeding a few hours.
(See **Variable stars.**)

RV TAURI STARS A class of long-period pulsating variables, occurring in both the Galaxy and the globular clusters. Their periods range from about 50 to 150 days, but in other ways they resemble the shorter-period W Virginis stars.
(See **Variable stars.**)

RW AURIGAE STARS A class of variable stars whose light variations are both irregular and very rapid. (See **Variable stars.**)

RADAR ASTRONOMY That branch of radio astronomy based upon 'radar' (or 'radio-echo') techniques, wherein a transmitter is used to generate a signal which is then directed towards a selected object and reflected from it, the returning signal being collected by the same aerial and fed to a receiver. As the speed of radio waves through space is known, the time taken for the return journey enables the distance of the object to be deduced.
Echoes have been obtained from the surfaces of the Moon, Venus and Mars; the technique is also widely used to determine the heights of the various ionized layers of the upper atmosphere. The principle is also used to plot the tracks of meteors by both day and night.
(See also **Radio astronomy.**)

RADIAL VELOCITY The velocity of an object in the line of sight, i.e. directly towards or away from the observer. In most cases, of course, the actual motion of the body being observed is not exactly in the line of sight, and the radial velocity is only that component of the true motion which is.
Radial velocities are determined spectrographically, by measurement of the shift of lines in the spectrum of the body caused by the **Doppler effect.**
Measurements of the radial velocities of stars (usually abbreviated to 'R.V.s')

are a most valuable aid in determining the structure of the Galaxy—and, indeed, of the whole universe. All galaxies have a radial velocity away from the Earth, determined from the 'red shift' of their spectral lines; it was upon this discovery that the concept of the expanding universe was based.

RADIAL VELOCITY CATALOGUE See `General Catalogue of Stellar Radial Velocities.

RADIAN A unit of angular measure; it is the angle subtended by an arc of a circle equal in length to the radius of that circle. It is convenient to measure angles in radians rather than degrees for certain types of calculation.

There are 2π radians in a full circle, 1 radian being equivalent to $180/\pi$ degrees (57·2958 degrees—approximately 57° 17′ 45″).

RADIANT The point in the sky from which the trails of **shower meteors** appear to meet if produced back, due to their approaching the Earth from practically the same direction in space.

RADIATION The process in which energy is propagated and transmitted from its source through the surrounding medium; also used to denote the transmitted energy itself.

Radiation has electrical and magnetic properties, and is properly termed *electromagnetic radiation*. It is propagated in a wave-form.

The wavelength determines the type of radiation, thus a typical example of X-radiation might have a wavelength of 50 Ångströms; or a ray of red light a wavelength of about 6,500 Ångströms, whilst the wavelengths used for long-wave broadcasting are about 750 metres. (See **Electromagnetic spectrum.**)

RADIATION PRESSURE It is known that the various forms of electromagnetic radiation exert a small but determinable pressure upon objects upon which they impinge; if these are very small particles (or molecules of gas) having very little mass, they can be moved by this pressure. Thus the pressure of the solar radiation forces out material from the nuclei of comets as they approach perihelion, forming the characteristic tails.

RADIATION ZONES Areas of high-intensity radiation surrounding the Earth. (See **Van Allen belts.**)

RADIO ASTRONOMY In 1931 Jansky discovered that radiation having a wave-length of about 15 metres was subject to a diurnal variation with a period of 23 hr 56 min—one sidereal day—indicating that it emanated from a source fixed in space. Further investigation showed that it was received from all directions in the galactic plane, the greatest intensity being in the direction of the galactic centre; thus the source of the radiation must be our Galaxy itself.

This was the first discovery of observable radiation arriving at the Earth's surface through the **radio window,** and signified the birth of the new science of radio astronomy. In the last three decades many new sources of radio emission have been discovered and studied, among them the Sun, Moon, Venus, Jupiter and Saturn in the solar system, discrete radio sources ('radio stars') and interstellar gas in the Galaxy, and even extragalactic sources.

Radio-echo techniques are used to plot the paths of meteors (the transmitted signal being reflected by the trail of ionization left along the meteor's path through the atmosphere) and also to study the physics of the upper atmosphere (see **Radar astronomy**).

Observations of the background radio 'noise' emitted by interstellar hydrogen at a wavelength of 21 cm have been used to extend considerably our knowledge of the structure of the Galaxy. Other strong radio sources within the Galaxy are emission nebulae (such as M42, the Great Nebula in Orion) and the remnants of

Table 31. Some important radio sources

I.A.U. designation	Popular name	Position R.A. hr min	Dec. ° ′	Optical object with which identified
00N4A	Andromeda	00 40	41 00 N	M31 (The Great Nebula in Andromeda)
03N4A	Perseus	03 16	41 19 N	N.G.C. 1275 (a peculiar galaxy)
05N2A	Taurus A	05 31	21 59 N	M1 (The Crab nebula), Plate 23(e)
08S4A	Puppis A	08 20	42 48 S	A peculiar nebulosity
12N1A	Virgo A	12 28	12 40 N	M87 (a peculiar galaxy), Plate 23(f)
13S4A	Centaurus A	13 22	42 46 S	N.G.C. 5128 (a peculiar galaxy), Plate 24(b)
19N4A	Cygnus A	19 58	40 36 N	(2 colliding spiral galaxies), Plate 24(a)
23N5A	Cassiopeia A	23 21	58 32 N	A peculiar nebulosity

supernovae (such as the Crab nebula).

Radio emission received from the Sun consists of both a continuous radiation generated in the solar atmosphere and sporadic outbursts associated with flares and other types of specific activity. Much has been learnt about the structure of the solar corona from observations of occultations of radio sources by the Sun.

Thermal radiation from the Moon has been detected by short-wave radio observation, and radio emissions from Venus and Saturn are also believed to have a thermal origin. Much the most interesting planet from the point of view of radio observation, however, is Jupiter, which has been shown to emit radiation from specific locations on the planet.

Few of the discrete radio sources correspond with bright optical objects, and mutual identification has therefore been a long and difficult process. Some of the most interesting identifications of discrete radio sources have been with extragalactic objects observable at optical wavelengths only with the largest telescopes. The strongest radio source (Cygnus A), for instance, has been identified with the pair of colliding galaxies shown on a photograph taken with the 200-in. reflector at Mount Palomar [Plate 24(a)]. Other strong extragalactic sources have been shown to be galaxies with jets,

multiple galaxies, galaxies of peculiar structure, etc.

Nomenclature. Radio sources are identified by a code adopted by the International Astronomical Union, in the form: hours of Right Ascension, tens of degrees of North (N) or South (S) Declination, and a serial letter; thus 19N4A—the source usually known by its more popular name Cygnus A. Some of the most important sources are listed in Table 31.

(See also **Jupiter—radio observations of; Radio telescope.**)

RADIO INTERFEROMETER A type of radio telescope using separated receiving aerials on the same principle as the optical interferometer. (See **Radio telescope.**)

RADIO SOURCE A discrete source of radio waves of higher intensity than the background radiation. (See **Radio astronomy.**)

RADIO STAR Popular but incorrect term for a discrete **radio source.**

RADIO TELESCOPE Name usually given to a radiometer specially constructed to detect, collect and record radio emissions received from sources in space.

Radio telescopes are constructed in a number of forms; they may be steerable or fixed; the latter are of restricted value,

355

of course, being able to observe only a fixed area of the heavens, but are much less expensive to construct than the former.

Many radio telescopes consist of a parabolic reflector to gather the radiation and focus it onto an aerial mounted centrally in it; the largest steerable instrument of this type yet constructed is the 250-ft diameter instrument at the Nuffield Radio Astronomy Laboratories at Jodrell Bank, Cheshire. [Plate 32(a).]

Other types of radio telescope consist of arrays of static aerials, the direction of the incoming radiation being derived from an analysis of the differential intensities recorded with the various aerials.

The aerials may be arranged in two parallel rows and used as an interferometer, or in two rows at right angles, either as an + or an L, etc. The various arrays are devised to give maximum resolution and suitability for the type of work to be carried out. [Plate 32(b–d).]

RADIO TIME SIGNALS Commonly used term for **wireless time signals,** *q.v.*

RADIO WINDOW Most of the radiation incident upon the Earth is absorbed by the atmosphere, save for that found in two bands of the electromagnetic spectrum which are able to penetrate the atmosphere and reach the Earth's surface. One of these bands, the 'radio window', comprises radio wavelengths from approximately 0·25 cm to about 30 m.

(See also **Electromagnetic spectrum; Optical window.**)

RADIO-ECHO OBSERVATION An application of the principle of radar to astronomical research. A radio pulse, or brief transmission at a selected frequency, is transmitted by a directional aerial towards the body concerned, and is received via the same aerial after being reflected back again. As the velocity of radio waves through space is known, the distance of the body can be accurately determined from the journey time.

The technique is widely used to record meteors and ionized layers in the Earth's atmosphere, but has also been successfully applied to the Moon, the nearer planets and to artificial Earth satellites.

RADIOMETER A device for collecting, recording and measuring radiation; a telescope is thus a form of radiometer. The term is usually reserved for instruments operating at radio frequencies, however, (i.e. **radio telescope.**)

RADIUS VECTOR A hypothetical straight line connecting an orbiting body with a focus of the orbit; usually used in calculations of planetary motion, as a line connecting the planet concerned and the Sun.

RAMSDEN DISK The **exit pupil,** *q.v.*

RANGER Name given to a series of lunar-probe vehicles launched from the United States; details of the nine launchings of the series are given in Table 32. The outstandingly successful *Ranger 7* transmitted 4,316 photographs of the highest quality during the last 17 minutes of its approach to the lunar surface; this approach was almost vertical, so that the same features appeared on long series of exposures made from a rapidly decreasing height. The illumination was near-vertical, similar to that of the Full Moon. This success was followed by that of *Ranger 8*, which transmitted over 7,000 photographs during its descent; this time the approach was highly inclined, so that a much longer belt of the lunar surface was photographed, and the illumination was tangential, the point of impact being close to the terminator.

The last of the series, *Ranger 9*, was another outstanding success; its 5,814 photographs were relayed live over television networks throughout the U.S.A. at the same time as they were being recorded for subsequent analysis. The first was transmitted from a height of 1,405 miles, the last from only a few hundred feet, 0·2 sec before impact.

Table 32.   Ranger lunar-probe vehicles

Vehicle	Date launched	Orbit achieved	Result	(date)
Ranger 1	1961 Aug. 23		Failure	
Ranger 2	1961 Nov. 18		Failure	
Ranger 3	1962 Jan. 26	Heliocentric	Passed approx. 23,000 miles from Moon, no successful photographs.	1962 Jan. 28
Ranger 4	1962 Apr. 23	Selenocentric	Hard landing, no data transmitted.	1962 Apr. 26
Ranger 5	1962 Oct. 18	Heliocentric	Passed approx. 456 miles from Moon, but con-contact lost.	1962 Oct. 21
Ranger 6	1964 Jan. 30	Selenocentric	Hard landing, no photographs obtained.	1964 Feb. 2
Ranger 7	1964 Jul. 28	Selenocentric	Hard landing; 4,316 photographs obtained.	1964 Jul. 31
Ranger 8	1965 Feb. 17	Selenocentric	Hard landing; over 7,000 photographs obtained.	1965 Feb. 20
Ranger 9	1965 Mar. 21	Selenocentric	Hard landing; 5,814 photographs obtained.	1965 Mar. 24

RARE EARTH Name given to a group of very rare substances occurring naturally; they mainly comprise the basic oxides of a series of chemically and physically similar elements.

RARE-EARTH ELEMENTS Name given to a number of elements whose physical and chemical properties are remarkably similar; they occur naturally in the form of their basic oxides (the 'rare earths'). They comprise those elements having atomic numbers 21, 39, 57–71 and 89–102. (See **Chemical elements**.)

RATE (OF CLOCK, ETC.) The rate at which a timepiece is gaining or losing; the rate of timepieces used in precise astronomical observations must be accurately determined at intervals throughout the observing period, so that corrections for the **clock errors** (errors due to the cumulative effect of the rate and to changes in the rate) may be applied to the observed times before their astronomical significance is deduced.

RAYLEIGH LIMIT The theoretical limit to the resolving power of a telescope or other optical system. (See **Resolution, optical.**)

READING MICROSCOPES Microscopes, usually four or six in number, used for the precise determination of the angle of inclination of the tube of a transit-circle, by readings of the division circle. They are usually spaced at equal intervals around the circle, so that a straight mean of their readings can be taken.

In modern instruments they are fitted with circle-reading cameras to obviate time-consuming measurements by the observer on duty.

(See **Transit circle.**)

RECTANGULAR CO-ORDINATES Any system of co-ordinates based upon axes perpendicular to each other. (See **Cartesian co-ordinates; Co-ordinate systems.**)

RECTILINEAR PROPAGATION OF LIGHT In simple terms, the concept that 'light travels in straight lines'. In fact, light (in common with the other forms of electromagnetic radiation) is known to have a wave-form; this is of extremely short wavelength, however, and light may be regarded as having a linear path in practice. The linear path is diverted only when the light passes into a medium of different density (**refraction**) or by **reflection.**

(See **Light.**)

RED SHIFT The phenomenon in which the absorption lines in the spectra of distant galaxies are shifted towards the red end of the spectrum, owing to the wave-lengthening due to the **Doppler effect.**

The amount of shift is dependent upon the velocity of recession in the line of sight, which may therefore be calculated from it.

The shift (z) is usually expressed by the relation

$$z = \Delta\lambda/\lambda,$$

where λ is the normal wavelength of the line and $\Delta\lambda$ the observed difference in wavelength from this figure.

Hubble's work on the recession of the galaxies, and the resulting concept of the expanding universe, were based upon observations of the red shift.

RED SPOT The longest-known and often one of the most prominent surface features of the planet Jupiter.

(See **Jupiter—observed features and notable phenomena.**)

REDUCED PROPER MOTION The **restricted proper motion** of a star converted to a linear velocity; it can only be calculated, of course, for stars of known distance. (See **Proper motion.**)

REDUCTION OF OBSERVATIONS The mathematical analysis of an astronomical observation, carried out so as to obtain the required astronomical information from the observed data. For instance, the basic observed data of a transit-circle observation of a culminating star are the apparent time of transit and apparent zenith distance of the star. This observation is then 'reduced' by incorporating corrections for instrumental errors, clock errors, proper motion of the star since the epoch to be used, atmospheric refraction, etc.

The reduction of many kinds of astronomical observation is, to an ever-increasing extent, being carried out immediately by electronic computers connected directly to the telescope.

REDUCTION OF STAR PLACES The process of transforming the **apparent place** of a star, given by the observation, to the **mean place** for a given epoch. It consists of computing a series of corrections to the apparent right ascension and declination, in respect of precession, nutation, aberration, annual parallax and proper motion, the size of these corrections depending upon the length of time between the date of the observation and the chosen epoch.

REFERENCE STARS Stars whose positions and proper motions have been determined with great accuracy, and whose places can therefore be assumed as a basis for differential positional observations of other bodies. (See **Fundamental stars.**)

REFLECTION One of the basic properties of light, of considerable importance

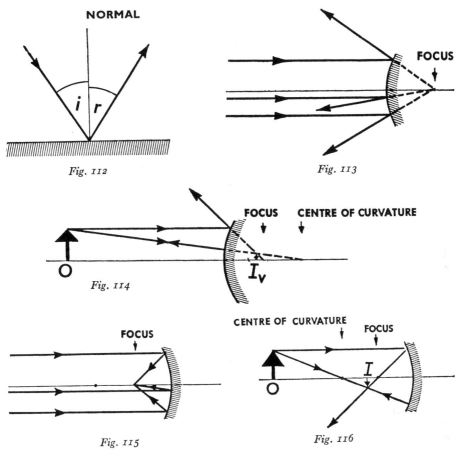

Fig. 112

Fig. 113

Fig. 114

Fig. 115

Fig. 116

in optical systems and the principle upon which the reflecting telescope is based.

Reflection by a plane surface. If a ray of light is incident upon a plane surface, at a certain angle of incidence (measured from the normal to the surface), it will be reflected in such a direction that the angles of incidence and reflection are equal. Thus in Fig. 112, $\angle i = \angle r$.

Reflection by a curved surface. If a beam of light is incident upon a curved reflecting surface, it will be diverged in the case of a convex mirror (Fig. 113) and will therefore form a virtual image I_v, behind the mirror, of the object O (Fig. 114), but in the case of a concave mirror it will be converged (Fig. 115) and will form a real

image I, located in front of the mirror (Fig. 116).

Concave mirrors are widely used as telescope objectives; their surface is then usually paraboloidal rather than spherical, in order to minimize **spherical aberration.**

(See also **Optics; Telescope,** etc.)

REFLECTOR A telescope having a form of mirror as its objective element.

(See **Telescope, reflecting.**)

REFRACTION One of the basic properties of light, and an important principle upon which the refracting telescope is based. If a ray of light passes from one

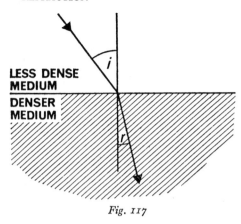

Fig. 117

of the medium. This law of refraction may be expressed in the form:

$$\frac{\sin i}{\sin r} = \mu$$

where i is the angle of incidence, r is the angle of refraction and μ is the refractive index of the substance concerned. If the light ray passes from a less dense to a denser medium it will be refracted towards the normal (Fig. 117); if it passes from a denser to a less dense medium it will be refracted away from the normal.

Refraction by a prism. If the above principles are applied to glass prisms, it can be shown that the paths of a ray of light through a rectangular prism, an equilateral triangular prism and a right-angled triangular prism are as shown in Figs. 118, 119 and 120 respectively.

Refraction by a lens. If a beam of light

medium to another of different density its direction will be changed in such a way that the ratio of the sines of the angles of incidence and refraction is constant. This constant varies for different media, and is termed the *refractive index*

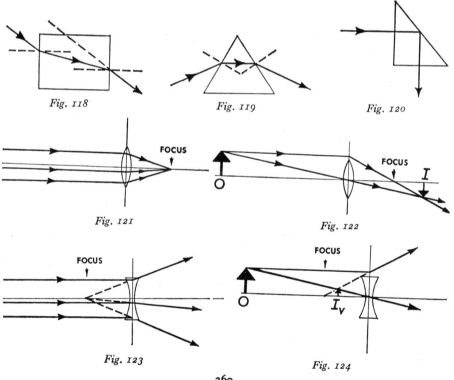

Fig. 118

Fig. 119

Fig. 120

Fig. 121

Fig. 122

Fig. 123

Fig. 124

is passed through a lens it will either be converged in the case of a convex lens (Fig. 121), producing (usually) a real image I of the object O (Fig. 122), or it will be diverged in the case of a concave lens (Fig. 123), producing a virtual image I_r of the object O (Fig. 124). The size of the image relative to the object depends upon the position of the latter in relation to the focal plane of the lens; also, the convex lens will produce an enlarged virtual image of an object situated within its focal length.

The positions of object and image for a lens are *conjugate foci*, that is to say, they are completely interchangeable. If the distance of the object from the lens is u, that of the image from the lens is v and the focal length of the lens is f, then the following expression holds:

$$\frac{1}{f} = \frac{1}{u} + \frac{1}{v}$$

(See also **Optics; Telescope,** etc.)

REFRACTION, ATMOSPHERIC The density of the Earth's atmosphere depends upon the 'packing' of its constituent molecules by the Earth's gravitational force; as the strength of the latter depends in its turn upon distance from the Earth's centre, the density is found to decrease progressively with increasing height above the Earth's surface.

The effect of this density gradient is to refract rays of light passing through the atmosphere (Fig. 125), causing stars to appear to have an altitude greater than the correct value. The effect is maximal for objects near the horizon, and decreases to nil for objects in the zenith. All positional observations of stars and other bodies must therefore be corrected for this effect by an amount dependent upon their zenith distance. This may be approximately calculated from the formula:

$$\xi = (\mu - 1) \tan Z$$

where μ is the refractive index of the atmosphere and Z is the zenith distance.

REFRACTIVE INDEX In optics, the ratio between the angles of incidence and refraction of a ray of light on its passing from one medium to another. Used as an indication of the refractive power of a substance, especially the various types of glass used in optical systems.

(See **Refraction.**)

REFRACTOR A telescope having a form of lens as its objective element.

(See **Telescope, refracting.**)

REGIOMONTANUS Lunar surface feature, co-ordinates $\xi - 020$, $\eta - 475$. A large but very broken oval ring plain, 80 miles east–west and some 65 miles north–south. Its northern wall is common to the newer crater Purbach. There is a large mountain mass to the west of centre.

REGULAR VARIABLES Those types of variable star whose light fluctuates in a regular, cyclic manner. (See **Variable stars.**)

REGULUS The star α Leo, magnitude $+1\cdot3$; situated in the handle of 'the Sickle' which comprises the forepart of the constellation of Leo. A white star of spectral type $B7$.

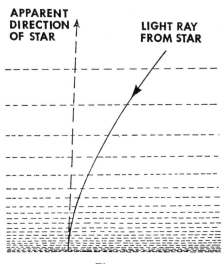

APPARENT DIRECTION OF STAR

LIGHT RAY FROM STAR

Fig. 125

RELATIVE ORBIT The apparent orbit of the fainter component of a binary star, relative to the brighter component. (See **Binary system**.)

RELATIVITY Concept of major importance in cosmological theory, but equally important as a background to all aspects of physical research as it applies to the whole of space and time. The theories of relativity were formulated by the late Albert Einstein, regarded by many as the greatest theoretical scientist of all time. The theories of relativity postulate the concept of space–time as a four-dimensional continuum, in which absolute motion cannot be determined.

In 1905 Einstein published his Special Theory of Relativity which develops the physical laws governing events as seen by observers in a state of uniform motion relative to each other. Two major assumptions are made, that the laws governing physical phenomena are the same for all observers, and that the velocity of light is a constant having the same value for all observers. Two major consequences follow from this theory:

(i) that the mass (m) of a body is related to its velocity (v), by the formula

$$m = \frac{m_0}{\sqrt{(1 - v^2/c^2)}}$$

where m_0 is the mass of the body at rest and c is the velocity of light;

(ii) that energy and mass are interchangeable, being related by the now famous formula.

$$e = mc^2$$

where e is the energy in ergs released when a mass of m grams is transmuted into energy.

Einstein also showed that the **Lorentz–Fitzgerald contraction** was a natural consequence of Special Relativity.

In 1916 Einstein published his General Theory of Relativity, extending the physical laws to phenomena seen by observers not in uniform motion relative to one another.

Einstein's theories of relativity are the foundation upon which much of the development of modern gravitational and cosmological theory has been built.

RESIDUAL The reduction and analysis of astronomical observations is often carried out by the derivation of the differences between a predicted quantity and the observed quantity, known as the residuals. They are usually expressed in the sense 'observed minus computed' and termed 'O − C'. If O − C residuals for a given phenomenon (e.g. the time of meridian transit of a body) are obtained and tabulated over a long period of time they can be analysed statistically in order to determine any long-term trends or variations.

RESOLUTION, OPTICAL The resolution of an optical system, such as a telescope, is its ability to produce separate observable images of close but separate sources—e.g. the two components of a close double star. The maximum resolution of a system (known as the *Rayleigh Limit*) can be calculated, taking into account the optics of the system and the nature of the source being observed.

RESTRICTED PROPER MOTION The angular movement of a star, relative to the surrounding stars, over a given period of time (usually a year). It is the observed proper motion after corrections for precession, nutation, etc.

(See **Proper motion**.)

RETICULUM (The Net; originally Reticulum Rhomboidalis, the Rhomboidal Net. *Genitive* Reticuli, *I.A.U. abbreviation* Ret.) A small, southern circumpolar constellation, adjoining Dorado. Contains one third-magnitude star (α Ret, mag. 3·4) and four stars of the fourth magnitude.

RETROGRADE MOTION All the planets in the solar system share, with most of the satellites and comets, a direction of motion around the Sun which is, in fact, that of the Sun's apparent annual motion relative to the background stars, and which is termed 'direct motion'.

Certain comets and planetary satellites revolve in the contrary direction, and are said to have 'retrograde motion'.

The planetary satellites having retrograde motions are Jupiter VIII, IX, XI and XII; Saturn IX; Neptune I. The five satellites of Uranus are also sometimes said to have retrograde motion; this is true only in the sense that they lie in the equatorial plane of Uranus, which is inclined to the plane of the Ecliptic by more than 90°: the satellites therefore have an *apparently* retrograde motion relative to the plane of the Ecliptic.

Retrograde motion should not be confused with **Retrogression, apparent,** *q.v.*

(See also **Jupiter—Satellites of; Neptune—Satellites of; Planetary motion; Saturn—satellites of; Uranus—satellites of.**)

RETROGRESSION, APPARENT Any other planet, if observed from the Earth over a long enough period of time, undergoes an apparent change of direction; if its apparent motion against the background stars was direct before the stationary point was reached, it will be retrograde after it. After a period of retrograde motion it will pass through another stationary point before reverting to direct motion.

The effect is due to the faster orbital speed of an inferior planet, relative to that of the Earth, and the relatively slower orbital speed of a superior planet.

(See **Planetary motion.**)

RETROGRESSION, LOOP OF The 'loop' in the apparent orbit of a planet, relative to the background stars, as observed from the Earth during the period when it retrogresses.

(See **Planetary motion; Retrogression, apparent.**)

REVERSING LAYER The lower layer of the solar chromosphere, at which the radiation from lower levels is absorbed and re-emitted by the atoms present; this is the level at which the Fraunhofer absorption lines are formed.

(See also **Flash spectrum; Sun—physical constitution of.**)

REVISED HARVARD PHOTOMETRY The extended version of the Harvard Photometry compiled by E. C. Pickering. (See **Harvard Photometry.**)

REVOLUTION The term usually used to denote *orbital* revolution, i.e. the motion of a planet or other body around its orbit, as opposed to axial *rotation*.

RHEA Satellite V of Saturn, *q.v.*

RHEITA Lunar surface feature, co-ordinates $\xi + 590$, $\eta - 605$. A beautifully defined crater 42 miles in diameter, situated fairly close to the Moon's southwestern limb. It has sharply delineated walls, terraced on its eastern side and rising to more than 14,000 ft in places. It lies at the head of the western wall of the greatest valley on the known surface of the Moon.

RHEITA VALLEY Lunar surface feature, co-ordinates (northern end) $\xi + 576$, $\eta - 594$; (southern end) $\xi + 595$, $\eta - 682$. A great valley, the largest known on the Moon's surface. It is a huge gash across the rugged south-west quadrant, between 10 and 15 miles wide over most of its length.

It commences at the north-eastern rampart of Rheita, and stretches south-westwards for nearly 120 miles, to the wall of the crater Mallet, broken only by a small crater (Young) which straddles the valley about halfway along its length. Beyond Mallet there is a slight gap, then another section of valley, a small crater and then a cleft formed by the running together of three small craters. The appearance of these suggest very strongly that they are an extension of the Rheita Valley; if so they would extend its southern end to the position $\xi + 595$, $\eta - 753$, and its overall length to almost 200 miles.

RICCIOLI Lunar surface feature, co-ordinates $\xi - 961$, $\eta - 053$. A large walled plain, with much-broken walls, situated in the libratory region at the Moon's east limb. Like its larger neighbour, Grimaldi, it has a dark floor which aids identification, but detail inside this 900-mile diameter plain is only detectable at a favourable libration and with powerful instruments.

RIGEL The star β Ori, magnitude $+0.08$. A star of very high luminosity with a spectrum of type *B8*. Situated at the left foot of the hunter in the ancient constellation figure.

Rigel is a multiple star of some interest; it is in fact a spectroscopic binary with a period of 22 days. There is a visual companion of the eighth magnitude, *Rigel B*, at a separation of $9''5$; this companion is itself a visual binary, the separation being about $0''2$.

RIGHT ASCENSION One of the two co-ordinates commonly used to define the position of a celestial object (the other being **Declination**). It is the angular distance, measured along the celestial equator, between the declination circle containing the object and the First Point of Aries (Υ). It is always reckoned eastwards from Υ, and is normally related to the diurnal rotation of the Earth and expressed in units of time—hours, minutes and seconds.

(See also **Celestial sphere; Co-ordinate systems.**)

RIGIL KENT The star α Cen; in fact a splendid binary. The combined magnitude is -0.27, making it the third brightest star in the heavens. The components are a *G2* star, magnitude 0.0, and a *K1* star of magnitude 1.4. The separation is at present about $2''5$ and the period 80 years.

Although the nearby *Proxima Centauri* is usually cited as the nearest star, the latest determinations give the parallax of the components of *Rigil Kent* as $0''751$, and of *Proxima* $0''762$, so it appears that this binary is, by a small margin, the nearest star. The distance is equivalent to 4.3 light years.

RILLE Name now adopted for the broad trench-like clefts in the surface of the Moon, such as that associated with Hyginus. They are often formed, at least in part, by chains of contiguous craters, and may be straight, curved (arcuate) or sinuous. They are sometimes found as extensions of wrinkle ridges, and probably had with them a common origin in the cooling and faulting of the lunar crust. (See **Moon—surface features of.**)

RILLE-CRATER Term used to denote a lunar crater forming part of a rille. (See **Moon—surface features of.**)

RING NEBULA The planetary nebula M57 in Lyra (N.G.C. 6720), a notable example of a 'shell' of nebulosity ejected by a nova of millions of years ago. The present diameter of the shell is approaching 1 light year. [Plate 23(c).]

RING-STRUCTURE The general term now preferred for the circular formations of all sizes found on the lunar surface, the earlier term *crater* now being reserved for the smaller rings 10–40 miles in diameter. (See **Moon—surface features of.**)

RINGWALL CRATER A lunar ring-structure situated with its centre exactly on the wall (or line of the wall) of a larger ring-structure. The ringwall crater may be a small craterlet superimposed on the rampart of a large structure or may be a somewhat larger feature completely breaking the wall of the large ring. (See **Moon—surface features of.**)

ROCHE'S LIMIT If a small body is revolving about a larger one in an orbit which is gradually decreasing in size, there is a critical value of the radius of its orbit, depending upon the relative densities of the two bodies and the size of the primary body. If the radius of the orbit of the secondary body is reduced below this critical value, the tidal forces exerted by the gravitational attraction of the primary will disrupt the secondary into fragments—unless, perhaps, it consists of unbroken and highly cohesive rock. This effect was studied by E. Roche of Montpellier, and the limiting distance is named after him.

Roche's limit (R) may be calculated from an expression of the form:

$$R = 2 \cdot 45 \; (\lambda r),$$

where r is the radius of the primary body and λ is a factor involving the relative densities of the two bodies. If both bodies have the same density the expression simplifies to the form:

$$R = 2 \cdot 45 \; r,$$

i.e. no satellite may safely approach within a distance of $2 \cdot 45$ times the primary's radius from the centre of the primary—or rather less than $1\frac{1}{2}$ times the primary's radius from its surface.

It has been suggested that the rings of Saturn were formed from the disintegration of one or more former satellites; it is notable that the ring-system lies well within Roche's Limit if suitable densities are estimated, whereas Mimas, the innermost satellite, lies well outside it.

RÖMER, Ole (1644–1710) A Danish astronomer remembered for his discovery of the finite velocity of light. In 1675, whilst working at the Paris Observatory, Römer found that eclipses of the satellites of Jupiter seldom occurred exactly at the times predicted from theories of their motion. After a lengthy analysis of many observations, Römer found that the eclipses occurred exactly at the predicted times only when Jupiter happened to be equidistant from the Sun and the Earth. Near opposition, when Jupiter was closer to the Earth, the eclipses took place earlier than predicted; near conjunction, when Jupiter was farthest from the Earth, they occurred later than the predicted times. From his analysis Römer was able to make the first calculation of the velocity of light.

(See also **Jupiter—satellite phenomena; Velocity of light.**)

ROSSE OF PARSONSTOWN, LORD (1800–1867) William Parsons was born at York and educated at Dublin and Oxford. He succeeded to the title in 1841, becoming the third Earl of Rosse and inheriting the family seat, Birr Castle at Parsonstown in County Offaly, southern Ireland. He devoted his time, engineering knowledge and considerable means to the development and manufacture of large reflecting telescopes.

After a great deal of experimental and development work he constructed a series of mirrors culminating in 1840 in a very successful 36-in. mirror cast in speculum metal and mounted in a 26-ft tube supported by a huge altazimuth mounting at Birr. This famous instrument proved very successful, and was used by a number of observers, notably Dr. T. R. Robinson.

In about 1875, some years after Rosse's death, the 3-ft instrument was remounted in a more modern (fork-type) equatorial mounting, and continued to perform very successfully. From the point of view of the volume of useful observation achieved with it, this was easily Rosse's most successful instrument.

Parsons himself (as he then was) was not content to use the telescope he had constructed, but immediately proceeded to plan a successor which would have double the aperture—a 6-ft mirror. (The largest reflector then in existence was Herschel's 48-in.)

Altogether five speculum disks were cast for the 6-ft telescope, two of which (the second and fifth) were figured and polished for use in the telescope. The erection of the 6-ft telescope was completed in 1845; its wood and metal tube, 56 feet long, was supported between two parallel masonry walls, each 72 feet long and

56 feet high [Plate 26(a, b)]. The telscope, popularly known as 'The Leviathan of Parsonstown', had taken over three years to construct and had cost £12,000. It was principally used for the study of nebulae; after many hours' observation with it, Lord Rosse produced a drawing two feet square of the Great Nebula in Orion, which was the most detailed and accurate representation of a complex, nebulous object executed by visual observation, and was superseded only much later by long-exposure photographs.

The most notable observation made with the 6-ft telescope was Rosse's observation, in 1845, of the spiral nature of M51 in Canes Venatici—the first discovery of a spiral galaxy. In 1846 M99 in Virgo was also discovered to be a spiral, and in time a number more were discovered. Many of the nebulae catalogued by Herschel were also shown to be resolvable into individual stars.

Rosse himself was not a very assiduous observer, and his great telescope, destined to remain the world's largest aperture reflector until the completion of the Mount Wilson 100-in. in 1917, was used principally by other observers, notably his son Lord Oxmantown (later the fourth Earl of Rosse), Dr. Robinson, Dr. G. J. Stoney, Sir Robert Ball, etc. Their work was not aided by the cumbersome mounting of the instrument or the very limited area of the sky to which it could be directed (the prevailing weather at Parsonstown was also very unfavourable), but Rosse's 6-ft. nevertheless must rank as a great milestone in the development of the giant reflecting telescope.

ROTATION The term usually used to denote axial rotation, i.e. the *spinning* of a planet or other body on its axis, as opposed to orbital **revolution.**

ROTATION OF THE EARTH The Earth rotates as a solid body, about an axis which is inclined to the perpendicular to the plane of the Ecliptic by 23° 27'. The period of axial rotation is, expressed in sidereal time, 23 hr 56 min 4 sec.

The rotation of the Earth is subject to small variations, detectable only by precise astronomical observations or by the use of clocks of the highest accuracy, such as the **atomic clock.** Apart from these slight variations which tend on the whole to average out, there have been major discontinuities observed on occasion. There is also a seasonal variation, due to the effects of winds and tides, which tend to slow the Earth's rotation in spring and speed it up in the autumn.

ROTATION OF THE MOON The period of axial rotation of the Moon, expressed in sidereal time, is 27 d 7 hr 40 min 48 sec.

ROTATION OF THE PLANETS The periods of axial rotation for the other planets are, expressed in sidereal time, as follows:

Table 33. Planetary rotation periods

Mercury:	87 d 23 hr 16 min 48 sec
Venus:	unknown
Mars:	24 hr 37 min 23 sec
Jupiter:	09 hr 50 min 30 sec
Saturn:	10 hr 14 min
Uranus:	10 hr 49 min
Neptune:	15 hr 08 min
Pluto:	6 d 09 hr 21 min 36 sec (estimated)

ROTATION OF THE SUN See **Solar rotation.**

ROYAL ASTRONOMER FOR IRELAND In 1783 a Chair of Astronomy was endowed in Trinity College, Dublin, out of funds bequeathed by Francis Andrews, Provost of Trinity College. Also largely financed by this bequest, the Dunsink Observatory was erected at Castleknock, some five miles north-west of Dublin.

The first Andrews Professor of Astronomy and first Director of the Dunsink Observatory was the Rev. Henry Ussher; in 1791 he was succeeded by the Rev.

Table 34. Royal Astronomers for Ireland

Royal Astronomer	lived	served
1. Rev. John Brinkley	1763–1835	1791–1827
2. Sir William Rowan Hamilton	1805–1865	1827–1865
3. Franz Friedrich Ernst Brünnow	1821–1891	1865–1874
4. Sir Robert Stawell Ball	1840–1913	1874–1892
5. Arthur Alcock Rambaut	1859–1923	1892–1897
6. J. H. Joly	–	1897–1906
7. Sir Edmund Taylor Whittaker	1873–1956	1906–1912
8. Henry Crozier Plummer	1875–1946	1912–1921

John Brinkley. Although the post remained entirely within the jurisdiction of Trinity College it was decreed by Royal Letters Patent that Brinkley and his successors as Andrews Professor should be designated Royal Astronomer for Ireland. There were eight bearers of this title before it became defunct, following the establishment of the Republic of Ireland in 1919, on the resignation of Plummer in 1921; they were:
(See also **Dunsink Observatory**.)

ROYAL ASTRONOMICAL SOCIETY

The premier astronomical society of the world, founded in 1820. Meetings are held regularly in the Society's apartments in Burlington House, Piccadilly, London, which also house a magnificent library of astronomical works for the benefit of the Fellows of the Society. The *Monthly Notices* of the R.A.S. have long been one of the principal media for the publication of astronomical research, and other publications of the Society include the *Memoirs,* the *Quarterly Journal* and the *Geophysical Journal.*

The Society's crest and seal depicts the 40-foot telescope of its first President, Sir William Herschel, encircled by the motto *Quicquid nitet notandum*—'Observe whatsoever shines'.

ROYAL GREENWICH OBSERVATORY

The national observatory of Great Britain, situated at Herstmonceux Castle, Sussex, the successor of the original Royal Observatory in Greenwich Park, London, whose longitude was adopted as the zero of longitude in 1884.

The original castle at Herstmonceux was built in 1440; it fell into disrepair during the eighteenth century, and much of the interior was gutted in 1777. It was repaired and rebuilt during the first half of the twentieth century, and purchased by the Board of Admiralty in 1946, together with about 380 acres of the surrounding estate, as the new home of the Royal Observatory.

The castle itself is now used for several purposes; it houses the Observatory's extensive library, provides canteen and dormitory facilities for staff and visitors, a private residence for the Astronomer Royal, and offices for the administration and several of the departments of the Observatory.

There is also a large modern building some distance away (the 'West Building') which houses the H.M. Nautical Almanac Office (whose extensive equipment includes an electronic computer), the Time Department with its numerous quartz-crystal clocks and electronic apparatus, the Chronometer (testing and repair) Departments, and the electronic and general engineering workshops. There are also offices housing more of the astronomical departments.

The telescopes are located in three

groups of buildings in different parts of the estate—the Solar Observatory, the Meridian Group and the Equatorial Group. A further building houses the **Isaac Newton Telescope**. [Plate 31(b).]

The Solar Observatory houses a general-purpose equatorial telescope whose mounting is shared by the photoheliograph formerly at Greenwich, used every clear day to obtain a whole-disk photograph of the Sun's surface, and a Lyot birefringent monochromator. There are also two spectrohelioscopes and an air-conditioned subterranean laboratory, 100 ft in length, in which images of the Sun, fed in by a 16-in. cœlostat, are examined in a high-dispersion spectroheliograph.

The Meridian Group houses those instruments used for fundamental positional observations. The 7-in. Cooke Reversible Transit Circle, originally erected in Greenwich Park in 1936, is still used for the traditional purposes of the transit circle, but has been considerably adapted and brought up to date. Among the refinements introduced in recent years are the provision of semi-automatic recording cameras on the circle-reading microscopes, and the automatic and immediate transcription of observed meridian-transit timings into punched-card form for reduction by computer. [Plate 27(e).]

The principal instrument used for accurate time determination and latitude-variation observations is the Photographic Zenith Tube, supplemented by a Danjon Prismatic Astrolabe. [Plate 29(e).]

The Equatorial Group is a splendid collection of buildings housing the six principal equatorial instruments, an optical laboratory, darkrooms, an installation for aluminizing the mirrors of the reflecting telescopes, etc. Its six domes are designated by the letters A–F.

Dome A contains the 30-in. reflector formerly at Greenwich; given by Sir Henry Thompson, a distinguished surgeon, it is the instrument with which Melotte discovered Satellite VIII of Jupiter. Formerly sharing a mounting with the Thompson 26-in. refractor, it has now

been provided with a separate mounting. Its mirrors were refigured to modern standards before it was re-erected, and it is now used for photo-electric photometry and spectrography. [Plate 28(a).]

Dome B houses the 36-in. reflector donated by William Johnston Yapp in 1931 to mark the retirement of Sir Frank Dyson from the post of Astronomer Royal. It is used for stellar spectrography, notably the determination of radial velocities. [Plate 28(d).]

Dome C will eventually house a Schmidt Camera; for a time it temporarily housed the Isaac Roberts 20-in. reflector borrowed from the Science Museum to supplement the 30-in. reflector.

A small, but nonetheless important, instrument is to be found in Dome D—the Greenwich 13-in. astrographic refractor, one of the original Carte-du-Ciel instruments. It is now used principally to rephotograph areas photographed in that programme, for the determination of proper motions.

Domes E and F house the great twin equatorial refractors from Greenwich, the 26-in. photographic and 28-in. visual, respectively. The 26-in. was a gift to the Observatory from Sir Henry Thompson, and at Greenwich shared a mounting with the other Thompson telescope, the 30-in. reflector; it has now been mounted separately so as to permit more flexible use of the two instruments. It is used principally to obtain plates for the determination of stellar parallaxes. [Plate 28(b, c).]

The 28-in. refractor was constructed in 1894, and erected in the mounting of the former 'Great Equatorial' at Greenwich—a 12¾-in. now used as the guiding telescope for the 26-in. refractor. To permit this rather makeshift arrangement, the 28-in. was provided with a most unusual flat-sided tube. It is mainly used for double-star observations.

(See also **Astronomer Royal; Royal Observatory;** and also under instruments referred to, notably **Lyot birefringent filter; Photographic zenith tube; Prismatic astrolabe.**)

ROYAL OBSERVATORY, CAPE OF GOOD HOPE

The southern-hemisphere observing station founded by the British Admiralty to complement the observational work of the Royal Observatory at Greenwich (later Herstmonceux). Many important programmes of observation have been carried out under the direction, as H.M. Astronomer at the Cape, of such distinguished astronomers as Gill, Spencer Jones, Jackson and Stoy.

ROYAL OBSERVATORY, EDINBURGH

The first major observatory in Edinburgh was that of the University Department of Astronomy, on Calton Hill, which became the Royal Observatory for Scotland with the appointment of Thomas Henderson as the first **Astronomer Royal for Scotland** in 1834. In 1895 new observatory premises were opened on Blackford Hill.

Under the direction of such men as Piazzi Smyth, Dyson, Sampson and Greaves this small observatory has made notable contributions to astronomical and astrophysical observation.

ROYAL OBSERVATORY, GREENWICH

The original national observatory of Great Britain, founded in 1675 by Royal Warrant of Charles II 'in order to the finding out of the longitude of places for perfecting navigation and astronomy'. A further Royal Warrant appointed the **Rev. John Flamsteed** 'our astronomical observator' at a salary of £100 per annum; Flamsteed thus became the first incumbent of the office of H.M. Astronomer Royal.

A fine building was designed by Sir Christopher Wren and erected on the high ground in Greenwich Park, where it may be seen today overlooking the Royal Naval College on the bank of the River Thames.

The story of this great observatory, and of the work of the ten Astronomers Royal who directed it during its 280 years of active life on the original site, is one of the most eventful, interesting and important in the history of astronomy; it would be impossible to do justice to it in this brief summary, however, and only a few of its more notable aspects can be mentioned here.

Flamsteed held office for 44 years, until his death in 1719, and carried out a programme of positional observations of unparalleled extent and accuracy; this resulted in the publication of his great catalogue of star places, the *Historia Cœlestis* in 1725.

Flamsteed's successor, Halley, concentrated, during his term at Greenwich, mainly on positional observations of the Moon and the improvement of our knowledge of the Moon's motion. Halley died aged 86 in 1742, after 23 years in office.

The third Astronomer Royal, **Bradley,** was noted for his discovery of the aberration of light; at Greenwich he overhauled the equipment and added to it his own 24-ft zenith sector. His continuing use of this instrument enabled him to announce in 1748 the discovery of nutation. He also determined the effects of atmospheric refraction, and demonstrated the importance of careful determination of instrumental errors.

Maskelyne's most notable feat at Greenwich was the foundation of the Nautical Almanac; he also extended the positional observations, making important improvements to the tables of the motion of the Moon. He also ordered a 6-ft mural circle by Troughton, to which his successor, Pond, added a Troughton 5-in. transit instrument; these instruments enabled Pond to publish in 1833 a star catalogue of great accuracy and lasting value. In Pond's time also, the responsibility for the testing of chronometers for the Royal Navy was transferred to the Royal Observatory in 1821, and in 1833 the famous Time-Ball was erected.

Pond was succeeded as Astronomer Royal by **Sir George Airy,** whose long tenure of the office proved to be the turning point in the history of the Royal Observatory, and the beginning of its expansion and development to its present-day eminence. Under Airy's supervision the instrumental equipment was modernized and increased; the existing observing programmes replanned and expanded; observations of the Sun's surface, of the Earth's magnetism, for the determination of time and of meteorological phenomena were commenced; thanks to Airy's revitalization of the fundamental observations, including the establishment of the famous **Airy Transit Circle**, the way was prepared for the adoption (in 1880) of Greenwich Mean Time as the legal time of Great Britain and (in 1884) of the longitude of Greenwich as the Prime Meridian of longitude, and the baseline of the zone-time system, for the whole world. [Plate 27(b).]

Airy retired in 1881 after 45 years as Astronomer Royal, but his influence has persisted, and the expansion of the Royal Observatory has continued, to the present day. Under the direction of **Christie** and **Dyson** many major programmes were introduced; the Greenwich zone of the Carte-du-Ciel project, double-star observations, photography of comets, minor planets and planetary satellites, stellar parallaxes, colour–temperatures, latitude variation, etc., etc. During this period many of the instruments still in service now were introduced.

When many of the instruments had to be dismantled during the Second World War, it was obvious that the history of the Royal Observatory at Greenwich was drawing to a close, and that many of them would not be used there again. The growth of industrial London had engulfed the Observatory's once-rural location and the deterioration of observing conditions over the years necessitated a complete removal to a new site.

The Board of Admiralty therefore purchased in 1946 Herstmonceux Castle in Sussex, and during the 1950's the equipment and staff of the Royal Observatory were transferred stage-by-stage, to their new home, now one of the largest and most modern observatories in the world.

The old buildings at Greenwich are now used, most appropriately, to house a Museum of Astronomy and Navigation, and the Airy Transit Circle remains in its old position, defining the Prime Meridian. The Greenwich tradition will be preserved, however, His Late Majesty King George VI having graciously consented to the adoption of the name Royal Greenwich Observatory for the new establishment at Herstmonceux.

(Further details of the work of the Royal Observatory will be found under the names of the various Astronomers Royal. See also **Airy Transit Circle; Astronomer Royal; Royal Greenwich Observatory.**)

RUSSELL, Henry Norris (1877–1957) A notable American astronomer and one of the world's leading astrophysicists. Apart from three years' postgraduate work at the University of Cambridge he spent almost the whole of his career at Princeton; he was Director of the Princeton University Observatory from 1912–1947, and Director Emeritus from 1947 to his death.

From the great number of his important contributions to the development of astrophysics, one must single out his work on the relationship between the absolute magnitudes and spectral types of stars, which together with the work of Ejnar Hertzsprung, led to the development of the **Hertzsprung–Russell diagram** that has figured so largely in astrophysical research.

Internationally honoured, Russell was awarded the Gold Medal of the Royal Astronomical Society in 1921 and was elected a Foreign Member of the Royal Society in 1937.

RUSSELL DIAGRAM Name sometimes used for the **Hertzsprung–Russell diagram**, *q.v.*

RUSSELL MIXTURE A concept used in theoretical astrophysics to denote a mixture of elements in the same relative proportions as those found to obtain in the Sun and other stars—i.e. comprising about 80 per cent hydrogen.

S

S STARS Stars of spectral class *S*; they are red stars having a surface temperature of about 2,200° K. They resemble the *M* stars but differ slightly in constitution; zirconium oxide (ZrO) is prominent in the spectra of *S* stars.

SS CYGNI STARS Alternative name for the **U Geminorum stars**, *q.v.*

SAGITTA (The Arrow. *Genitive* Sagittae, *I.A.U. abbreviation* Sge.) A tiny northern constellation along the northern boundary of Aquila, reaching midnight culmination in mid-July. It has one third- and three fourth-magnitude stars. S Sge is a Cepheid variable (magnitude range 5·4–6·1, period 8·38 days).

About 2½° south-east of γ Sge is the site of Nova Sagittae, 1913.

SAGITTARIUS (The Archer. *Genitive* Sagittarii, *I.A.U. abbreviation* Sgr.) A large and rather scattered zodiacal constellation in the southern hemisphere, containing three second-magnitude stars and eight of the third magnitude. The Galactic Equator passes through one end of the constellation; part of one branch of the Milky Way crosses its western half which also has a number of nebulae and clusters.

W and Y Sgr are both Cepheid variables; W Sgr has a magnitude range of 4·8–5·8 and a period of 7·59 days, and Y Sgr a magnitude range of 5·4–6·5 and a period of 5·77 days.

About one third of the distance between λ and ξ Sgr there is a fine, bright globular cluster of reddish stars, M22 (N.G.C. 6656).

Some 5° west of λ Sgr, in a field rich in star clouds and nebulosity, lies the Lagoon Nebula (M8, N.G.C. 6523), a ragged oval

patch of bright nebulosity streaked with dark absorption clouds; it is faintly visible to the unaided eye. Close by is the Tryfid nebula.

Close to the northern boundary of the constellation, about 3° south-west of γ Scu, lies M17 (N.G.C. 6618)—the so-called Horseshoe Nebula.

The constellation contains the sites of three important novae—Nova Sagittarii 1898 (about 5° north-west of ν Sgr, on the border of Scutum), Nova Sagittarii 1910, about 3° east of X Sgr, and Nova Sagittarii 1936, 3° west of ε Sgr.

SAGITTARIUS A. A discrete radio source, numbered 17S2A in the I.A.U. Catalogue of Radio Sources; it is situated at the south-eastern end of the great rift in the southern Milky Way, approximately midway between γ and θ Sgr. The source is a double one, apparently comprising a small dense core surrounded by a gaseous envelope. It is one of the 'brightest' radio sources known, and is of particular importance as the best determinations of its position place it within 0°·1 of the galactic centre as determined by all other methods, at R.A. 17 hr 42·4 min, Dec. −28° 55′ (Epoch 1950·0).

SAHA, Meghnad N. (1893–1956) Indian physicist, one of the pioneers of theoretical astrophysics.

SAIPH The star κ Ori, marking Orion's right foot. It is a blue-white star of spectral type *B*0 and magnitude 2·2.

SAMPSON, R. A. (1866–1939) Ralph Allen Sampson was a native of County Cork; he was however educated in England, at school in Liverpool and then

371

at St John's College, Cambridge, where he graduated as 3rd Wrangler in 1888. From 1889–91 he was lecturer in Mathematics at King's College, London; in 1890 he was awarded the Smith's Prize at Cambridge where he returned in 1891 to study astrophysics as the first incumbent of the Isaac Newton Studentship endowed by Mr Frank McClean. From 1893–96 he was Professor of Mathematics at the Durham College of Science, and from 1896–1910 Professor of Mathematics and Astronomy in the University of Durham, in which post he also had charge of the University Observatory.

Whilst at Durham he made a lengthy investigation of the motions of the Galilean satellites of Jupiter; his *Tables of the Four Great Satellites of Jupiter*, published in 1910, is still used today for the computation of their ephemerides. He published his mathematical theory of the motions of the satellites in 1921. In 1928 he was awarded the Gold Medal of the Royal Astronomical Society for this work.

In 1911 January he succeeded F. W. Dyson as Astronomer Royal for Scotland and Professor of Astronomy in the University of Edinburgh. In his early days at the Royal Observatory, Edinburgh, he made an invaluable study of observatory time-keeping, and pioneered the use of the Shortt free-pendulum clock for this purpose which was later adopted by major observatories throughout the world.

In 1923 he published the first of a series of papers on the colour-temperatures of stars, a field in which Edinburgh became pre-eminent under the direction of Sampson and his successor, W. M. H. Greaves. He realized the need for the Observatory to be re-equipped in order to take an effective part in astrophysical programmes of this kind, and was responsible in particular for the installation of the 36-in. reflector with slit spectrograph, with which Greaves was to make most valuable contributions.

Sampson retired in 1937 and died at Bath only two years later at the age of 73. He served as President of the Royal Astronomical Society 1915–17.

SANDAGE, Allan R. Contemporary American astronomer; outstanding both as an optical observer and as a theoretical astrophysicist. Allan Sandage is on the research staff of the Mount Wilson and Palomar Observatories; he was elected an Associate of the Royal Astronomical Society in 1966 and awarded its Gold Medal in 1967.

SAROS The mean daily motion of the Sun is $59'\ 8''.33$, and the daily (retrograde) motion of the node is $3'\ 10''.64$; hence the daily motion of the node relative to the Sun is $62'\ 19''$. The period of revolution of the node relative to the Sun is therefore 346·62 days. Nineteen such revolutions occupy 6,585·78 days. This happens to be almost exactly the time occupied by 223 lunations (6,585·32 days); thus after this period the Sun, Moon and the nodes return to the same relative positions. This period was discovered by observation by the Chaldeans more than 2,500 years ago, and named by them the Saros; it amounts to 18yr 11⅓d (or 18yr 10⅓d if five, rather than four, Leap Years are included). One of the most valuable uses of the Saros is its use to facilitate the prediction of eclipses; if an eclipse of the Sun or Moon is observed, the return of the Sun, Moon and nodes to almost the same relative positions after a complete Saros makes it almost certain that a similar eclipse will occur. This rough means of prediction is still used today as a useful and rapid approximation; when an eclipse has been predicted by this means its exact circumstances are predicted by more precise methods.

That the ancients were able to make good use of their discoveries is suggested by a study of the records of their observations—which were usually inscribed on bricks, or clay tablets, and baked. It seems that Thales, of Miletus, often referred to as the Founder of Greek Astronomy, had visited Mesopotamia in the course of business and while there had studied such records, and in particular details of the Saros, and that he used it successfully to predict that an eclipse of the Sun would take place on 585 B.C. May 28.

(See also **Eclipse, lunar; Eclipse, solar; Metonic cycle.**)

SATELLITE PHENOMENA The satellites of both Jupiter and Saturn can be seen undergoing some interesting phenomena—being both eclipsed and occulted by the primary, and in transit across its disk. These phenomena can be seen continually in the case of the satellites of Jupiter; owing to the inclination between the orbital plane of the Earth and the equatorial plane (the 'ring-plane') of Saturn, they are less frequently observable in the case of the satellites of Saturn—they can be seen during five consecutive apparitions of the planet around each passage of the Earth through the ring-plane, which occur at intervals of slightly less than 15 years.

Sometimes, when the Earth passes through the orbital plane of the satellites of either planet, mutual phenomena occur, in which the satellites eclipse or occult each other. These are quite rare phenomena.

(See also **Jupiter—satellites, phenomena of; Saturn—satellites, phenomena of.**)

SATELLITES, ARTIFICIAL Bodies placed in orbit around the Earth by the hand of man; they are normally launched by means of a multi-stage rocket.

The first artificial satellite was launched by the U.S.S.R. on 1957 October 4; it was approximately spherical, nearly 23 inches in diameter and weighed 184 pounds. By the end of 1965 some four hundred satellites had been launched by the U.S.S.R., U.S.A. and France, some of them weighing many tons. These include a wide range of objects with diverse functions, from the highly sophisticated manned 'spaceflight' vehicles to simple aluminized balloons used as reflectors for long-range radio and television communication.

SATELLITES, PLANETARY There are 32 known natural satellites of the planets in the solar system; physical and other data for these is given in Table 35.

The four principal satellites of Jupiter were among the first telescopic discoveries (by Galileo in 1610); three of the most recent discoveries were the triumphant results of brilliantly planned and executed searches with two of the world's most powerful telescopes. A tenth satellite of Saturn has been discovered very recently, by Dr Audouin Dollfus of the Meudon Observatory, on plates obtained at the Pic-du-Midi Observatory.

The satellites range in size from Ganymede, whose diameter of 3,100 miles is greater than that of the planet Mercury, to Deimos, a mere five miles in diameter.

On closer inspection the satellites appear to fall into three distinct groups, in terms of their size: the Moon, the four Galilean satellites of Jupiter, Titan and Triton are all of the order 2–3,000 miles in diameter; all the remaining satellites of Saturn and Neptune, all those of Uranus and two more of Jupiter's are between 60 miles and 800 miles in diameter; the remaining Jovian satellites and those of Mars are all less than 20 miles in diameter.

There is good reason to exclude the Moon from the list of satellites, and to regard it, with the Earth, as a 'binary-planet' system; although the Moon is only the fifth largest satellite, the ratio of its mass to that of the Earth is 1:81, whilst the next highest ratios of satellite's mass to that of the primary are Triton (1:750) and Titan (1:4150). The approximate ratios of the diameters are perhaps even more impressive: Moon 1:4, Triton 1:12, Titan 1:25, Ganymede 1:28.

The existence of satellite systems whose motions around the primary can be accurately determined has enabled the masses of those planets having them to be calculated with great accuracy. The absence of any known satellite has been a great nuisance in this respect, in the case of Pluto especially.

Observation of the satellites is both interesting and rewarding; unfortunately

SATELLITES, PLANETARY

Table 35. Satellite data

Planet, satellite	Discoverer	Year of discovery	Diameter (miles)	Mean distance from primary (miles)	Inclination of orbit plane to equatorial plane of primary °	Mean synodic revolution period d	hr	min	sec	Apparent magnitude at opposition
EARTH										
I Moon			2,160	238,853	23·4	29	12	44	02·9	−12·7
MARS										
I Phobos	Hall	1877	8	5,810	1·1	00	07	39	26·6	11·6
II Deimos	Hall	1877	5	14,594	1·8	01	06	21	15·7	12·8
JUPITER										
V Amalthea*	Barnard	1892	100	112,468	0·4	00	11	57	27·6	13·0
I Io	Galileo	1610	2,000	262,074	0·0	01	18	28	35·9	4·8
II Europa	Galileo	1610	1,800	416,977	0·5	03	13	17	53·7	5·2
III Ganymede	Galileo	1610	3,100	665,126	0·2	07	03	59	35·9	4·5
IV Callisto	Galileo	1610	2,800	1,169,820	0·2	16	18	05	06·9	5·5
VI Hestia*	Perrine	1904	60	7,131,940	28	265	22	43		13·7
X Demeter*	Nicholson	1938	10	7,282,620	29	275	17	09		18·6
VII Hera*	Perrine	1905	20	7,292,940	28	276	04	56		16·0
XII Adastrae*	Nicholson	1951	10	13,199,900	147	551†				18·8
XI Pan*	Nicholson	1938	10	14,036,500	163	597†				18·1
VIII Poseidon*	Melotte	1908	10	14,594,250	148	635†				18·8
IX Hades*	Nicholson	1914	10	14,687,200	157	645†				18·3

Table 35. Satellite data (continued)

Planet, satellite	Discoverer	Year of discovery	Diameter (miles)	Mean distance from primary (miles)	Inclination of orbit plane to equatorial plane of primary °	Mean synodic revolution period d hr min sec	Apparent magnitude at opposition
SATURN							
X Janus*	Dollfus	1966	?	98,267	0	00 17 58 30	14
I Mimas	W. Herschel	1789	300	115,322	1·5	00 22 37 12·4	12·1
II Enceladus	W. Herschel	1789	400	147,950	0·0	01 08 53 21·9	11·8
III Tethys	J.-D. Cassini	1684	600	183,153	1·1	01 21 18 54·8	10·3
IV Dione	J.-D. Cassini	1684	600	234,577	0·0	02 17 42 09·7	10·4
V Rhea	J.-D. Cassini	1672	800	327,590	0·3	04 12 27 56·2	9·8
VI Titan	Huyghens	1655	3,000	759,087	0·3	15 23 15 31·5	8·4
VII Hyperion	Bond	1848	300	921,343	0·6	21 07 39 05·7	14·2
VIII Iapetus	J.-D. Cassini	1671	700	2,212,190	14·7	79 22 04 59	11·0
IX Phoebe	W. H. Pickering	1898	100	8,047,750	150	523 13†	16·5
URANUS							
V Miranda	Kuiper	1948	200	81,058	0·0	01 09 55 31‡	16·5
I Ariel	Lassell	1851	500	119,171	0·0	02 12 29 39·0‡	14·4
II Umbriel	Lassell	1851	400	166,021	0·0	04 03 28 25·8‡	15·3
III Titania	W. Herschel	1787	700	272,392	0·0	08 17 00 01·2‡	14·0
IV Oberon	W. Herschel	1787	600	364,271	0·0	13 11 15 36·5‡	14·2
NEPTUNE							
I Triton	Lassell	1846	2,300	220,745	159·9	05 21 03 29·8†	13·5
II Nereid	Kuiper	1949	200	3,456,112	27·7	362 01	18·7

* Proposed name, not yet adopted by the International Astronomical Union.
† Retrograde motion.
‡ Apparent motion retrograde, as inclination between equatorial plane of planet and its orbital plane exceeds 90°.

the majority of them are so faint that they are observable only with very powerful instruments.

Some of the smaller satellites with high orbital inclinations may well be bodies that have been captured by the gravitational attraction of the primary, and may therefore be relatively recent acquistions.

(See also entries under individual planets.)

SATURN The sixth planet in order of distance from the Sun, and the outermost of the bright, naked-eye planets known to the ancients.

Saturn provided a great puzzle to Galileo and the other early observers, their primitive telescopes being unable to resolve the peculiar appendages which the planet appeared to possess at times but which appeared to alter in shape and to disappear altogether for a time every fifteen years or so. Galileo took them to be two smaller globes; Riccioli and others recorded them as arc-shaped 'handles'. It was Huyghens who deduced their true nature; in the manner of the time he recorded his discovery in the form of a Latin anagram: when solved this read 'Annulo cingitur tenui, plano, nusquam cohaerente, ad eclipticam inclinato'—'it is surrounded by a thin flat ring, nowhere touching, and inclined to the ecliptic'. Huyghens also made a good estimate of the ratio of the diameters of the ring-system and the globe, 9:4.

The existence of the ring-system makes Saturn unique among known astronomical bodies, and also renders it one of the most beautiful and awe-inspiring sights, even with quite modest telescopes.

The globe of the planet is the second largest in the solar system, is the most oblate and the least dense; it has the second largest family of satellites. Saturn is frequently a bright naked-eye object, and is a rewarding object of study for the serious observer. [Plate 13(a, b, d).]

SATURN—DIMENSIONS AND PHYSICAL DATA The apparent equatorial diameter of Saturn at mean opposition distance is 19″27, corresponding to an actual equatorial diameter of 74,160 miles (rather more than nine times that of the Earth). The planet is an oblate spheroid with a polar compression of approximately 20:23, the polar diameter being only 66,890 miles.

The density is the lowest of all the bodies in the solar system (0·706), and the only one less than that of water; this underlines the fact that whilst the volume is 744 times that of the Earth, the mass is only 95 times that of the Earth.

The force of gravity at the surface of Saturn is 1·16 times that at the Earth's surface; the resulting velocity of escape is therefore about 22·5 miles per second.

The albedo is very high (0·76), almost identical to that of Jupiter and Venus. The high albedo observed for this and the other major planets supports the theory that they have a very high gaseous content.

SATURN—OBSERVATION OF Owing to its great distance there are few types of observation of Saturn that can be carried out other than with telescopes of fairly large aperture; the observing programme of the Saturn Section of the British Astronomical Association has, however, been drawn up so as to extract the maximum value from the work of observers working with small apertures.

All observers should record as accurately as possible width and position on the globe of any longitudinal belts that may be visible and of any bright or dark spots or other markings; the outline and position of the shadows of the globe on the rings and of the rings on the globe; the width and appearance of the Crêpe ring and any appearance of a faint ring outside ring A; the position and darkness of any minor divisions in the ring system. Positional observations of such features should ideally be made by micrometer, but where this is not available the positions should be estimated as accurately as possible.

Drawings of the complete planet are

useful in clarifying the identification of the features observed; they should be made to a scale of about 4 inches to the diameter of the ring system, using blank outlines preconstructed to the correct shape. Sets of templates for this purpose can be fairly simply constructed using data available in *The Astronomical Ephemeris* or the *Handbook of the British Astronomical Association.*

One of the most important routine observations is the estimation of the relative intensities of all parts of the surface of the globe and the ring system. For this purpose a fixed scale of reference has been adopted, ranging from 1 for the brightness of the outer part of ring B to 10 for 'black' shadows and a very dark sky background. Estimates of 0 and the fractions between 0 and 1 are reserved for any exceptionally bright features; it is rare, however, for any feature to appear brighter than ring B.

Observers should also record any detectable colour in the various features. The longitudes of any detectable spots on the globe should be determined by timing their central-meridian transits.

The apparent magnitudes of the five brightest satellites should be estimated regularly; this is usually done by estimating their brightness relative to each other and assuming a magnitude of 8·3 for Titan. When the Earth is in or close to the ring-plane a number of interesting satellite phenomena take place; the satellites may be seen to transit the planet and are eclipsed and occulted by it, and sometimes by each other. When the Earth is in the ring-plane and the rings are seen edge-on satellites may be seen apparently impaled on the needle-like side-view of the rings. All such phenomena should be carefully recorded.

Occultations of stars by Saturn are very rare, and of great importance, as observations of them allow the translucency of the various parts of the ring-system to be determined.

Most occultations will be predicted in the almanacs, but an observer with a large aperture may be fortunate enough to see a faint star about to undergo an unpredicted occultation; in such a case he should make every effort to alert other observers before the occultation begins.

Some important observations can be made at the times when the Earth passes through the ring-plane. At such times the rings may disappear briefly, due to a number of causes: (i) the rings being exactly edge-on to the Earth; (ii) the rings being exactly edge-on to the Sun, so that neither face is illuminated; (iii) the Sun and Earth being on opposite sides of the ring-plane so that the unilluminated face is presented to the Earth. On these occasions the times of disappearance and reappearance of the rings should be recorded, and their 'needle of light' appearance carefully examined for variations in thickness, brightness, etc. [Plate 13(e).]

SATURN—OBSERVED FEATURES AND NOTABLE PHENOMENA The regular Saturn observer has his rewards in interesting phenomena, but they are far less frequent and spectacular than those of Jupiter; for much of the time the globe is well-nigh featureless, there being perhaps only an ill-defined equatorial belt to record. The planet appears to be subject to occasional outbreaks of spots and streaks in the equatorial region similar to those observed on Jupiter, but they are often faint and difficult to observe.

The first really reliable determination of the rotation period of the planet was made by Asaph Hall from observations of a bright equatorial spot in 1876; Hall deduced a rotation period of 10 hr 14 min 23·8 sec, ±2·5 sec. This value was confirmed by observations of other equatorial spots made by A. Stanley Williams and others during the next two decades.

In 1903 a series of white spots in higher latitudes (*ca.* 36° N) were observed by Barnard, Denning and others; these proved to have much longer rotation periods, averaging about 10 hr 38 min. Later observations of high-latitude spots produced rotation periods longer than 11 hr in latitudes between 50° and 60° N.

The most spectacular spot observed on Saturn was discovered on 1933 August 3 by W. T. ('Will') Hay, an amateur astronomer of note as well as a leading figure in the entertainment world. This spot was to prove one of the largest and most persistent features ever recorded, and appeared to undergo some small movements in longitude; its mean rotation period was about 10 hr 15 min. Twenty years were to elapse before another major equatorial spot appeared. [Plate 13(c).]

The outline of the shadow of the globe on the rings sometimes assumes unusual forms; observations of these are important as they provide a clue to the cross-section of the rings. Bright spots and dark radial streaks are sometimes seen in the rings, and irregularities in the ring edges can sometimes be detected.

Bright spots appearing to project from the limb of the globe, due to irradiation, are also seen from time to time.

SATURN—ORBITAL DATA The orbit of Saturn has a semi-major axis of 9·538844 A.U., corresponding to a mean distance from the Sun of 886·7 million miles; owing to the orbital eccentricity (0·0557) the actual distance varies between about 836 and 936 million miles.

The orbit is inclined to the plane of the Ecliptic by 2° 29′ 22″·6; the mean orbital velocity is 5·99 miles per second, giving a sidereal period of 10,759·20 days—about 29·46 years.

SATURN—RINGS OF The ring system of this strikingly beautiful planet is quite unique, and has long provided problems for both observers and theorists.

There are three distinct rings, known as ring A (the outermost), ring B (the outer portion of which is usually brighter than the brightest part of the globe of the planet) and ring C (the innermost, also known as the 'Crêpe ring', due to its faint, misty appearance). The gap between rings A and B was first detected by J.-D. Cassini, and is known as 'Cassini's Division'. A prominent 'division' was discovered in ring A by Encke in 1837; it is now known as 'Encke's Division'.

The dimensions of the ring system are determined from micrometrical measures; the apparent angular diameters of the various components of the system are shown in Table 36. From these data it can be seen that the overall diameter of the system is 169,200 miles; the width of ring A is 10,150 miles; of Cassini's Division 1,700 miles; of ring B, 16,500 miles and of ring C, 9,850 miles. There is a gap some 9,320 miles wide between the globe and ring C. There is a division only a few hundred miles wide between rings B and C.

The most remarkable feature of the ring system is its extreme thinness. The

Table 36. Ring System of Saturn

	Angular diameter at mean opposition distance	Actual diameter
	″	miles
Ring A outer edge	43·96	169,200
inner edge	38·69	148,900
Ring B outer edge	37·80	145,500
inner edge	29·24	112,500
Ring C inner edge	24·12	92,800
Globe (equatorial)	19·27	74,160

precise measurement of this dimension has exercised the ability of observers ever since the true nature of the rings was deduced by Huyghens in 1659. As observational techniques have improved so estimates of the thickness of the rings have resulted in smaller and smaller values; in 1790 Sir William Herschel estimated the thickness as about 850 miles, by comparing the thickness of the rings seen edgewise on with the diameters of the satellites; using modern determinations of the diameters of the satellites these measurements would in fact have given a maximum thickness for the ring system of 220 miles. Other determinations were made by Schröter in 1808, 540 miles; Sir John Herschel (1833), less than 250 miles; G. P. Bond (1848), less than 42 miles; Barnard (1891), less than 50 miles; Russell (1908), less than 13 miles, and Bell (1919), less than 10 miles. The ring-system is in fact much thinner, in relation to its surface area, than a foolscap-sized sheet of ordinary typing paper. Small wonder that when the Earth passes through the plane of the rings they are frequently invisible.

It was suggested by Jacques Cassini (the son of J.-D. Cassini) and Thomas Wright, of Durham, that the rings were in fact not solid but consisted of myriads of tiny satellites in a common orbital plane. This hypothesis gained little credence for many years, but the discovery of the transparent Crêpe ring, independently by Bond and Dawes in 1850 (it had been drawn by earlier observers who did not recognize its nature), raised further doubts as to the solidity of the rings. The discovery of further divisions in rings A and B also suggested that the rings were not solid. Finally it was proved mathematically by J. Clerk Maxwell in 1857 that the ring could not be solid; he stated that 'the only system of rings which can exist is one composed of an indefinite number of particles, revolving round the planet with different velocities according to their respective distances'. In 1895 Keeler provided experimental proof of this by setting the slit of a spectrograph along the

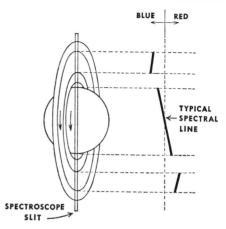

Fig. 126

major axis of the rings. The lines of the spectra of both the globe and the rings were displaced, half towards the red (indicating recession) and half towards the violet (indicating approach); hence both globe and rings were rotating. Further, the amounts of the shift were such (Fig. 126) as to demonstrate that the outer parts of ring A were rotating more slowly than the inner parts of ring B, in accordance with Kepler's third law of planetary motion: the particulate nature of the rings was confirmed. It has been deduced mathematically that the individual 'satellites' must be extremely small.

In 1914 Hepburn detected the globe visible through ring A on photographs of the planet taken at the Mount Wilson and Lowell Observatories. This evidence of the translucency of the rings was confirmed in 1917 when a star was observed passing behind ring A by two British Astronomical Association observers independently, M. A. Ainslie and J. Knight. The star was dimmed, but remained visible throughout the crossing. They were also able to observe the star as it passed some distance behind the limb of the planet, thus demonstrating the gaseous nature of the latter.

It is widely believed that the ring particles are the debris of a former satellite, disrupted by tidal forces due to its approaching the globe closer than **Roche's limit** (*q.v.*).

In 1867 it was suggested by an American astronomer, Daniel Kirkwood, that gaps in the ring system may be due to the perturbative effects of the satellites, their positions being resonance positions at which the orbital period of the ring particles would be a simple fraction of the period(s) of one or more of the satellites. Kirkwood computed that a ring particle at the position of Cassini's Division would have a period of 11·3 hours—which is about half that of Mimas, a third that of Enceladus, a quarter that of Tethys and one sixth that of Dione. This would account for the lack of particles in the

Table 37.   *Divisions in the ring system of Saturn*

LYOT'S MARKINGS	Position in rings	KIRKWOOD'S GAPS	Position in rings	OTHER CORRELATIONS	Position in rings
RING A					
(Outer edge of ring)	(0)		(0)		(0)
		$\frac{9}{7}$ E	10	Ainslie's star brightened	5
Outer division	20			Ainslie's star brightened	18
Inner division:					
outer edge	36				
minima	{40, 62}	$\frac{3}{5}$ M, $\frac{2}{3}$ E	39, 57	} Encke's division	40
inner edge	80				
(Inner edge of ring)	(100)		(100)		(100)
CASSINI'S DIVISION		$\frac{1}{2}$ M, $\frac{1}{3}$ E		$\frac{1}{4}$ T, $\frac{1}{6}$ D	
RING B					
(Outer edge of ring)	(0)		(0)		(0)
Outer division:					
outer edge	11				
minimum	17				
		$\frac{5}{11}$ M	24	Division observed	
		$\frac{4}{9}$ M	31		
inner edge	39				
Middle division	42	$\frac{9}{22}$ M	41		
		$\frac{2}{5}$ M	57		
Inner division:					
outer edge	70	$\frac{3}{8}$ M	76	} Division observed	
minima	{80, 89}	$\frac{1}{4}$ E	89		
inner edge	96				
(Inner edge of ring)	(100)		(100)		(100)
DIVISION BETWEEN RINGS B & C		$\frac{1}{3}$ M		Division observed	

M: period of Mimas; E: period of Enceladus; T: period of Tethys; D: period of Dione.

Division and the superfluity of them in the adjoining outer portion of ring B.

In 1871 Kirkwood also pointed out that particles at the position of Encke's Division in Ring A would have periods equal to three-fifths that of Mimas and two-fifths that of Enceladus. As a result of his work the gaps in the ring system became known as 'Kirkwood's gaps'.

Several astronomers (notably Lowell) extended Kirkwood's work to other resonance positions and attempted to correlate them with observed ring divisions. This work was collated by A. F. O'D. Alexander in 1953 in a paper in which he correlated the most precise measurements of the positions of the ring divisions, made by Lyot in 1943, with theoretical resonance points with the satellites Mimas and Enceladus and with divisions recorded by other observers.

Table 37 is based upon Alexander's work, and shows Lyot's observed positions of ring markings and the calculated resonance positions of Kirkwood's gaps. The last column shows the positions at which Ainslie saw his star brighten momentarily as it passed behind the ring, and the positions in which divisions have been reliably observed by American workers. It is notable that Encke's Division has been observed double under unusually good observing conditions—by Tombaugh on three separate occasions.

It should be emphasized that most of the 'divisions' observed are dusky streaks in the ring, rather than true gaps. Apart from Cassini's Division possibly the only true gap is that between rings B and C. If Kirkwood's hypothesis is correct, the number of particles orbiting at the resonance distances might be expected to decrease progressively over a long period of time.

SATURN—SATELLITES OF Saturn has ten known satellites, a total surpassed only by Jupiter. Satellite VI, Titan, is the second largest satellite in the solar system, being slightly smaller than Ganymede. Although Saturn's next largest satellite,

Rhea, is only 800 miles in diameter, all the satellites have diameters of at least 300 miles except Phoebe (100 miles), in contrast to the seven outermost satellites of Jupiter which are all very much less than 100 miles in diameter. This difference in size, and hence in magnitude, is reflected in the discovery dates of the satellites: thus, whilst no Jovian moons other than the four Galilean satellites were discovered until the twentieth century, five of Saturn's moons were discovered in the seventeenth century, two in the eighteenth, two in the nineteenth and one in the twentieth century. Data for all the satellites are given in Table 38.

Titan was discovered by Christiaan Huyghens on 1655 March 25, using a refractor of $10\frac{1}{2}$-ft. focal length which he had newly constructed with the assistance of his brother Constantyn.

Four satellites were discovered by Jean-Dominique Cassini, the first Director of the Paris Observatory: Iapetus in 1671, Rhea in 1672 and Dione and Tethys in 1684. Cassini had also discovered the major division in the ring system, now named after him (in 1675) and thus made a remarkable number of the early discoveries in the study of Saturn.

The satellites are assumed to present the same face permanently towards the primary, as do the Galilean satellites of Jupiter, but no observations have been made which confirm this absolutely. A remarkable series of observations of faint dusky markings on the surface of Titan was obtained by Lyot and his colleagues, using the 24-in. refractor at the Pic-du-Midi Observatory in the 1940s.

In 1944 Kuiper, using a spectrograph attached to the 82-in. reflector of the McDonald Observatory, showed that Titan has an atmosphere which includes methane. Thus the markings observed by Lyot and his colleagues may in fact be atmospheric features.

Iapetus was found by Cassini to vary considerably in brightness, being easily visible to him when at western elongation but invisible in his comparatively primi-

Table 38. Satellites of Saturn

	Satellite	Discoverer	Year of discovery	Mean distance from primary (miles)	Synodic period				Orbital inclination °	Diameter (miles)	Mean apparent magnitude
					d	hr	min	sec			
X	Janus	Dollfus	1966	98,590	00	17	58	30	0	<200	14
I	Mimas	W. Herschel	1789	115,322	00	22	37	12·4	1·5	300	12·1
II	Enceladus	W. Herschel	1789	147,950	01	08	53	21·9	0·0	400	11·8
III	Tethys	J.-D. Cassini	1684	183,153	01	21	18	54·8	1·1	600	10·3
IV	Dione	J.-D. Cassini	1684	234,577	02	17	42	09·7	0·0	600	10·4
V	Rhea	J.-D. Cassini	1672	327,590	04	12	27	56·2	0·3	800	9·8
VI	Titan	Huyghens	1655	759,087	15	23	15	31·5	0·3	3,000	8·4
VII	Hyperion	Bond	1848	921,343	21	07	39	05·7	0·6	300	14·2
VIII	Iapetus	J.-D. Cassini	1671	2,212,190	79	22	04	59	14·7	700	11·0
IX	Phoebe	W. H. Pickering	1898	8,047,750	523	13			150	100	16·5

tive telescope when at eastern elongation. This implies that the satellite's periods of revolution and axial rotation are equal, so that it permanently presents the same face towards Saturn. The range of light variation is two whole magnitudes, i.e. the luminosity at maximum is approximately six times that at minimum. The magnitudes of most of the other satellites are subject to slight variations.

There is an interesting commensurability between the mean motions of the four innermost satellites: if n_i is the mean daily motion of the satellite i, then:

$$5n_I - 10n_{II} + n_{III} + 4n_{IV} = 0.$$

Shortly after discovering Phoebe in 1898 W. H. Pickering announced the discovery of a tenth satellite which became known as Themis. Its orbital data were derived from thirteen photographic plates, but the object has never been subsequently recovered; it has been suggested that it may in fact have been a minor planet that chanced to be in the same field as Saturn and appeared to share its motion. The mean distance of Themis from the primary was given as 908,000 miles, and its period 20·85 days; its orbit was alleged to have an eccentricity of 0·23, and to be inclined to the plane of the Ecliptic by 39°.

A tenth satellite was discovered by A. Dollfus of the Meudon Observatory on 1966 December 15. It was subsequently located on plates exposed in 1966 October. Preliminary studies of these first few observations indicate that the satellite is in a near-circular orbit in the equatorial plane of Saturn, at a mean distance of 98,590 miles; the period of orbital revolution is slightly less than 18 hours. The name 'Janus' has been proposed for the newly discovered satellite.

There would appear to be good reason to suspect that Iapetus and Phoebe had a different origin from the other satellites. The seven innermost satellites all have mean distances within a million miles of the primary and orbital planes inclined to the ring-plane (equatorial plane) of the planet by $1\frac{1}{2}°$ or less; by contrast Iapetus

is at a mean distance of more than two million miles and has an inclination of $14\frac{3}{4}°$, whilst the diminutive Phoebe is nearly four times this mean distance from Saturn and its orbit is inclined to the ring-plane by 150°—the apparent motion of this satellite being, therefore, retrograde. These facts suggest that these two satellites may not date from the origin of the Saturnian system, but may have been captured by the planet at a later epoch.

SATURN — SATELLITES, PHENOMENA OF

Since the seven innermost satellites lie in or very close to the ring-plane of the planet, there are two periods during each sidereal revolution of the planet, during which the Earth passes through the ring-plane, when satellite phenomena similar to those of the Galilean satellites of Jupiter occur. These periods last for five successive apparitions around each passage of the Earth through the ring-plane, which occur every $14\frac{3}{4}$ years.

For a very short period around the actual passage of the Earth through the ring-plane it is possible for mutual eclipses and occultations of the satellites to occur. These are rare phenomena and fairly powerful instruments are necessary to observe them satisfactorily.

Another phenomenon that can often be observed when the Earth is close to the ring-plane is the apparent impaling of a satellite by the edgewise-on rings, looking like a bead threaded on a needle.

(See also **Jupiter—satellites, phenomena of**.)

SATURN—STRUCTURE AND CONSTITUTION

Saturn is of especial interest in studies of the internal constitution of the planets, having the lowest density of any of them. It is also the only planet whose mean density (0·706) is less than that of water.

As in the case of the other major planets the early work on the constitution of Saturn was carried out by Jeffreys and Wildt; the latter, in 1938, proposed a three-state model for the planet very similar to those he proposed for Jupiter, Uranus and Neptune, the major difference lying in the much greater depth of 'atmosphere' necessary to account for the very low mean density. Wildt postulated a solid core 28,000 miles in diameter, surrounded by a mantle of frozen material 6,000 miles thick and a gaseous 'atmosphere' no less than 16,000 miles deep.

Wildt deduced from theoretical calculations that the prominent absorption hands in the spectrum of Saturn must be attributable to the presence, in the gaseous mantle, of methane; this was later confirmed by the analysis of infra-red spectrograms obtained by Dunham at Mount Wilson. [Plate 13(f).]

In 1951 Ramsey pointed out a number of difficulties in the way of acceptance of Wildt's theoretical models for the major planets: notably in the case of Saturn, the fact that Wildt's proposed structure implied the presence of far too large a proportion of free hydrogen. Ramsey postulated a chemically homogeneous planet comprised largely of hydrogen together with helium and other light elements and simple compounds. He explained the high density towards the centre of the planet as being due not to the presence of heavier elements, but by phase-transitions, principally of hydrogen, to a metallic state due to the gravitational compression.

(See also **Planets, major—constitution of.**)

SATURN — TELESCOPIC APPEARANCE

The apparent equatorial diameter of Saturn at mean opposition distance is only 19$''$.27, less than half that of Jupiter, and at unfavourable apparitions may be as little as 14$''$; it is therefore a far inferior telescopic object to Jupiter, and substantially larger apertures are required for useful observation. The ring system can be clearly seen with a good 3-in. refractor, and with somewhat larger instruments, such as a 6-in. reflector, the planet is an awe-inspiring sight; even this aperture would normally be found insufficient for serious work, however, instruments of 8–10 inches aperture or more being necessary for most observing programmes.

The most striking feature is, of course, the ring system; on studying the globe of the planet itself it is readily apparent that there are great similarities to Jupiter. The planet is more obviously flattened at the poles than Jupiter, its polar compression being the greatest of any of the planets. The dark longitudinal belts, interspersed with light zones, are present as on Jupiter. The Equatorial Zone is very bright and both Equatorial Belts may be fairly prominent; on the whole, however, the belts are much fainter and more difficult to detect than those of Jupiter. To facilitate reference to the various areas of the disk a standard nomenclature similar to that used for Jupiter was adopted many years ago; the locations of the principal belts and zones are shown in Fig. 127, together with their conventional abbreviations. The full descriptions of the belts and zones depicted are as follows:

SPR: South Polar Region
SSTB: South South Temperate Belt
STB: South Temperate Belt
SEB_S: South Equatorial Belt (South Component)
SEB_N: South Equatorial Belt (North component)
EB: Equatorial Band
NEB_S: North Equatorial Belt (South component)
NEB_N: North Equatorial Belt (North component)
NTB: North Temperate Belt
NNTB: North North Temperate Belt
NPR: North Polar Region

SSTZ: South South Temperate Zone
STZ: South Temperate Zone
STrZ: South Tropical Zone
EZ_S: Equatorial Zone (South)
EZ_N: Equatorial Zone (North)
NTrZ: North Tropical Zone
NTZ: North Temperate Zone
NNTZ: North North Temperate Zone

It will be noted that both the Equatorial

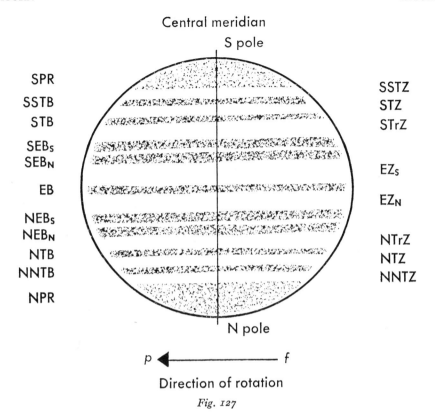

Central meridian

S pole

SPR	SSTZ
SSTB	STZ
STB	STrZ
SEB$_S$	
SEB$_N$	EZ$_S$
EB	EZ$_N$
NEB$_S$	
NEB$_N$	NTrZ
NTB	NTZ
NNTB	NNTZ
NPR	

N pole

p ◄——————— f

Direction of rotation

Fig. 127

Belts are sometimes seen to be double; any belt, including the prominent Equatorial Belts, may fade to the point of insignificance or even disappear altogether for a time. The belts generally appear to be a dusky grey, the zones creamy; sometimes blue, green and brown colorations have been reported in the belts, and pink or orange tints in the zones. [Plate 13(a, b).]

Fine structure is rarely seen in most of the belts, although the Equatorial Belts seem prone to structural complexity at their edges. Differential rotation is observed, as in the case of Jupiter, but the various currents are difficult to separate owing to the rarity of spots or other markings sufficiently prominent for their rotation periods to be determined. For this reason there is no standard system of longitudes as for Jupiter. [Plate 13(d).]

One significant difference from Jupiter arises from the fact that the pole of rotation of Saturn is highly inclined to the plane of its orbit (26° 44′, compared with 3° 04′ for Jupiter). Saturn is thus frequently observed to have one hemisphere tilted towards the Earth, giving an excellent view of one of the polar regions and (apparently) highly curved belts.

SATURN—VISIBILITY FROM EARTH
The opposition distance of Saturn from the Earth varies between about 744 million miles at perihelic oppositions and about 1,028 million miles at aphelic oppositions. The mean synodic period is 378·09 days, and hence oppositions occur about a fortnight later each succeeding year. The planet is observable, on average, for about ten months each apparition; the

observing conditions vary tremendously, however, owing to the fact that the planet's declination ranges between 26° N and 26° S. During one sidereal period of 29½ years it is therefore usual for observers at a particular station to experience comparatively favourable apparitions for some fourteen years, followed by unfavourable apparitions for a similar period. Winter oppositions are the most favourable for observers in the northern hemisphere.

SATURNICENTRIC CO-ORDINATES

A system of co-ordinates referred to the centre of the spheroid of Saturn; the co-ordinate usually encountered is the saturnicentric latitude, there being no significant difference between saturnicentric and saturnigraphic longitude. The saturnicentric latitude is the angle between a line joining the point being observed to the centre of Saturn and the equatorial plane of the planet.

Latitude observations of surface markings are usually expressed in the saturnicentric system; any observations recorded as saturnigraphic latitudes can readily be converted to saturnicentric latitudes, however, for comparison.

(See also **Co-ordinate systems; Saturnigraphic co-ordinates.**)

SATURNIGRAPHIC CO-ORDINATES

A system of co-ordinates referred to the mean surface of Saturn. As Saturn is an oblate spheroid, with a polar compression of approximately 1/10, these differ from saturnicentric co-ordinates. The difference between saturnicentric and saturnigraphic longitudes is not significant for practical purposes, but the maximum possible difference between saturnicentric and saturnigraphic latitude is almost 6°. Saturnigraphic latitudes are obtained by direct observation, but are rarely used for analytical purposes, however, the saturnicentric latitude being a more fundamental and appropriate quantity, and as the figure of the planet is known with some accuracy

it is a simple matter to convert from one system to the other.

(See also **Co-ordinate systems; Saturnicentric co-ordinates.**)

SAUCER CRATER A very shallow form of lunar **bowl crater.** Some typical examples are found in the floor of Ptolemæus. (See **Moon—surface features of.**)

SCANDIA Martian surface feature, approximate position Ω 150°, Φ + 60°. That part of the dusky north temperate belt north-east of Propontis and north-west of Arcadia.

SCATTERING, ATMOSPHERIC See **Dispersion, atmospheric.**

SCHEINER Lunar surface feature, co-ordinates ξ − 230, η − 870. A well-defined crater ring, 70 miles in diameter, close to the south-south-eastern limb. The walls include peaks rising to 18,000 ft., and are broken by several craters. There are several craters on the floor, including a prominent central one (Scheiner A).

SCHIAPARELLI, Giovanni V. (1835–1910) Celebrated Italian astronomer who was one of the pioneers of the observation of the planetary surfaces. Working at the Brera Observatory, Milan, with refractors of 8·7 and 19·3-in. aperture, he studied Mars at the opposition of 1877 and recorded detail—including the 'canali' that were to prove the cause of so much controversy—far finer than any that had been recorded previously. He extended his mapping of the Martian surface at the following apparitions, but it was not until 1885 that other experienced observers began to confirm Schiaparelli's discoveries. His nomenclature for the surface features has been used ever since.

Schiaparelli was also an assiduous observer of Mercury, the most difficult of all but the outermost planets to observe. He began observing it in 1882, and was the first to discover permanent surface markings and to determine the period of axial rotation—which is, in fact, equal to the period of orbital revolution, nearly 88 days. Schiaparelli observed the planet until 1889, when he published a book summarizing his findings and including a map of the surface detail which has remained a standard reference until the present day, supplemented by Antoniadi's map, with which it agrees in all essentials and which was not published until 1936.

Schiaparelli also observed Venus, and derived a rotation period of 225 days, equal to the period of orbital revolution as in the case of Mercury; this was supported by a number of observers at the time, including Lowell, but has never been substantiated.

In 1866 Schiaparelli discovered the identity of the orbits of the Perseid meteors and Comet 1862 III P/Swift–Tuttle, the first indication that the great meteor swarms may be cometary debris.

Schiaparelli's numerous accomplishments seem all the more remarkable when it is recalled that they were all achieved during a period of little more than two decades. In 1872 he was awarded the Gold Medal of the Royal Astronomical Society. He was forced to give up observing in 1890 owing to failing eyesight; during his last years he became, alas, totally blind.

SCHICKARD Lunar surface feature, co-ordinates $\xi - 590$, $\eta - 700$. A vast walled plain close to the south-eastern limb, 135 miles in diameter. The walls are mostly rather low, between 4,000 and 5,000 ft., but there are peaks rising to 9,000 ft. on the south and west. There is a large, sharply defined, triangular shaded patch on the north-western part of the floor, and two smaller ones in the north and east. The floor is broken with a number of craterlets and clefts. [Plate 6(b).]

SCHILLER Lunar surface feature, co-ordinates $\xi - 396$, $\eta - 783$. A prominent, elongated plain close to the south-east limb, about 110 miles in length and 50–60 miles wide; it appears to have

been formed by the coalescence of two ring-formations. [Plate 6(b).]

SCHMIDT, Bernhard (1879–1935) Estonian astronomer and instrument-maker, inventor of the 'Schmidt camera' which has revolutionized the techniques and the scope of astronomical photography. Schmidt spent the latter part of his life as a voluntary assistant at the Bergedorf Observatory near Hamburg; he produced the prototype Schmidt camera in 1930.

(See also **Telescope, Schmidt.**)

SCHMIDT, Julius (1825–1884) Perhaps the greatest selenographer of the nineteenth century; Schmidt was born in Germany and worked at a number of German observatories before being appointed Director of the Athens Observatory in 1858. He remained in Greece for the remainder of his life.

For a quarter of a century Schmidt kept going the systematic study of the Moon's surface practically single-handed; it was his announcement of the 'disappearance' of the formerly conspicuous crater Linné that reawakened interest in the subject and put an end to this situation. Schmidt continued his own studies, however, and in 1878 published his map of the lunar surface, to a scale of nearly 74 inches to the Moon's diameter. This map was the most important and accurate to be produced since that of Beer and Mädler published forty-one years earlier, and compares well with modern charts.

SCHMIDT, Maarten Contemporary Dutch–American astronomer, on staff of Mount Wilson and Palomar Observatories and Professor at the California Institute of Technology. Has made important contributions to observational and theoretical astrophysics, notably in connection with quasars. Elected an Associate of the Royal Astronomical Society in 1967 February.

SCHMIDT CAMERA Colloquial term; see **Telescope, Schmidt.**

SCHMIDT LENS Term sometimes used for the aspherical correcting plate of a Schmidt telescope.

SCHWABE, Heinrich (1789–1875) An apothecary of Dessau, Germany, who studied the Sun with a small telescope and compiled records of sunspot activity for over forty years. In 1843 he announced his discovery of a periodic fluctuation in the incidence of sunspots, quoting the period as about ten years. No one took his announcement very seriously, and it was not until he was able to publish an extensive tabulation of his results, in 1851, that he began to receive the recognition he deserved. In 1857 he was awarded the Gold Medal of the Royal Astronomical Society for his important discovery.

SCHWARZSCHILD, Martin Contemporary American astrophsyicist, a leading expert in the theory of stellar constitution and evolution. Schwarzschild is Professor of Astronomy in the University of Princeton; he was elected an Associate of the Royal Astronomical Society in 1962 and awarded its Gold Medal in 1969.

SCINTILLATION, STELLAR The 'twinkling' of the stars, due to local variations in the refracting power of the Earth's atmosphere arising from inhomogeneities and turbulence. These may cause fluctuations in the apparent brightness of a star, changes in its apparent colour and 'wanderings' in its apparent position.

Scintillation is one of the major contributory causes of bad **seeing**. It is believed to be caused relatively low down in the atmosphere, at altitudes below about 30,000 ft. Its effects can therefore be reduced by siting observatories in high mountain ranges, and can be virtually avoided by the use of balloon-, rocket- or artificial satellite-borne telescopes.

SCORPIUS (The Scorpion. *Genitive* Scorpii, *I.A.U. abbreviation* Sco.) Magnificent zodiacal constellation in the southern sky, containing some of the richest star fields in the heavens. Dominated by the first-magnitude supergiant *Antares*, a splendid red star that unfortunately never rises high enough in the sky to be seen to advantage from the United Kingdom, the constellation also has five second- and eight third-magnitude stars.

Antares (α Sco) has a magnitude of 1·2, and has a green companion of magnitude 6·8 at a separation of 3″·0.

RR Sco is a long-period variable, its magnitude varying between 5·6 and 11·3 in a period of 279 days.

Among the beautiful clusters that this constellation has to offer are M7 (N.G.C. 6475), to the north of G Sco and close to the border of Sagittarius; this open cluster of bright stars is faintly visible to the unaided eye. Another beautiful open cluster is M6 (N.G.C. 6405), about 4° north-west of M7. A cluster of faint stars, but easily resolved, is M4 (N.G.C. 6121) about 1° west of *Antares*. A very condensed globular cluster is M80 (N.G.C. 6093), nearly mid-way between σ and ν Sco and about 4° north-west of *Antares*.

SCOTT Lunar surface feature, co-ordinates ξ + 080, η − 990. A large ring-formation close to the lunar south pole, 66 miles in diameter. It is named, of course, after the English polar explorer. The walls are fairly well defined, and almost rectangular in form. The floor contains a number of craterlets and ridges.

SCULPTOR (The Sculptor. *Genitive* Sculptoris, *I.A.U. abbreviation* Scl; formerly Apparatus Sculptoris, the Sculptor's Workshop.) A southern constellation containing no bright stars, the brightest being four of the fourth magnitude.

The South Galactic Pole is located in the northern part of this constellation, close to α Scl.

There is a long-period variable, R Scl, having a magnitude range of 6·2–8·8 and a period of 376 days.

SCUTUM (The Shield. *Genitive* Scuti, *I.A.U. abbreviation* Sct. Formerly Scutum

Sobieskii, Sobieski's Shield.) A very small constellation just south of the equator, at the south-west corner of Aquila. It contains three fourth-magnitude stars and a number of nebulous objects; the Galactic Equator crosses one corner of it and much of it lies in the Milky Way.

There is an interesting irregular variable, R Sct, whose magnitude varies between 4·7 and 7·8.

About mid-way between α Sct and λ Aql there is a beautiful fan-shaped cluster, with a bright star at its tip—M11 (N.G.C. 6705).

SEASONS The phenomenon of the seasons arises from two causes—the ellipticity of the Earth's orbit and the inclination of its axis of rotation to the orbital plane.

The first of these effects can be understood by reference to Fig. 128, which shows the Earth's path as it orbits the Sun (*S*) in the direction $\Upsilon MP \simeq NA$. $S\Upsilon$ is the direction from the Sun to the First Point of Aries; Υ is the point the Sun appears to occupy at the vernal equinox, hence the Earth's position at that time must be $\simeq$. Similarly N is the position of the Earth at the summer solstice, Υ its position at the autumnal equinox and M its position at the winter solstice. The seasons in the Earth's northern hemisphere are defined as the periods during which the

Table 39. Duration of the seasons

Season in northern hemisphere	Season in southern hemisphere	Approximate duration	
Spring	Autumn	92 d	19 hr
Summer	Winter	93 d	15 hr
Autumn	Spring	89 d	19 hr
Winter	Summer	89 d	1 hr

Earth traverses the following arcs of its orbit: spring, $\simeq N$; summer, $N\Upsilon$; autumn, ΥM; winter, $M\simeq$. The corresponding seasons in the southern hemisphere are indicated in Table 39. The Earth's orbital velocity varies, in accordance with Kepler's second law of planetary motion (the 'law of equal areas'), and hence the durations of the four seasons differ. The approximate durations are listed in Table 39.

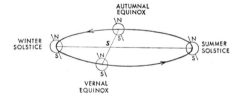

Fig. 129

The second effect is shown in Fig. 129. The Earth's axis of rotation is inclined to the perpendicular to the plane of its orbit by $23\frac{1}{2}°$; its direction in space is constant, save for very minor variations, and is perpendicular to the line of the nodes of the orbit (i.e. the line $\Upsilon \simeq$ in Fig. 128). As can be seen the result of this is that at the winter solstice the southern hemisphere, and at the summer solstice the northern hemisphere, is tilted towards the Sun; at the equinoxes this preferential tilt is reduced to zero. It will be noted that the Earth is close to aphelion at the summer solstice, when the northern hemisphere is experiencing summer, whereas during summer in the southern hemisphere it is close to perihelion and

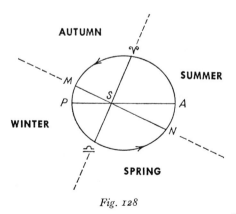

Fig. 128

the effect of the Sun's radiation is much greater; the average summer temperatures are therefore higher in the southern hemisphere, but conversely the average winter temperatures in the southern hemisphere are lower.

SECCHI, Angelo (1818–1878) Father Secchi was an Italian Jesuit priest and a distinguished astronomer of his time. He worked at the Vatican observatory.

Secchi may be described as one of the first astrophysicists, and devised the first practicable system of classification for stellar spectra. He is also reputed to have been the first to recognize the true nature of the dark absorption nebulae.

SECCHI SPECTRAL CLASSIFICATION The first practicable system of classification of the stellar spectra, devised by Secchi between 1863 and 1867. Secchi classified the stars into four groups according to colour; his class I comprised blue and white stars with strong hydrogen lines (e.g. *Sirius, Vega*); class II comprised yellow stars with strong metallic lines (e.g. the Sun, *Capella*); classes III and IV were the red stars with different types of strong absorption bands (e.g. *Antares, Betelgeuse*). In 1867 Wolf and Rayet of Paris added a further class, V, comprising the white stars whose spectra show strong enhancements as well as absorption, now often known as the Wolf–Rayet stars.

Secchi's pioneering work paved the way for the sophisticated systems of spectral classification used today, and his simple system remained, with minor modifications, the basis of research in this field for a quarter of a century, and undoubtedly contributed a great deal to the growth of the new science of astrophysics.

(See also **Stars—spectral classification of.**)

SECOND (OF ARC) A unit of angular measure, being one sixtieth part of a minute of arc (i.e. 1/3600 of a degree and 1/1,296,000 of a full circle).

SECOND (OF TIME) A unit of time measurement, being one sixtieth part of a minute of time, or 1/3600 of an hour.

SECONDARY A term used in celestial mechanics; the *secondaries* to a circle on the celestial sphere are great circles passing through its poles. (See **Celestial sphere.**)

SECULAR ACCELERATION OF THE MOON A progressive acceleration in the Moon's motion in geocentric longitude, equivalent to approximately $11°$ per century. It arises partly from the reduction in the eccentricity of the Earth's orbit due to the perturbative effects of the other planets, and partly from the gradual lengthening in the period of axial rotation of the Earth.

(See also **Moon—motion of.**)

SECULAR VARIATION A small periodic variation in the motion of the Moon, arising from variations in the gravitational attraction of the Sun on the Earth–Moon system during the synodic month. It amounts to $\pm 19''5$ and has a period of $14·76$ days (half the synodic month).

SEEING The quality of the images produced by a given telescope is variable, depending upon the state of the atmosphere at the time. The 'seeing' is an assessment by the observer of the average quality of the images at the time of observation, and is an invaluable aid to the comparative study of observations made at different times.

The seeing cannot be measured, and may in any case vary from minute to minute and from one part of the sky to another. It is usually assessed on a comparative basis, therefore, the observer relying on his own experience to provide a standard of reference and using simple descriptive phrases such as 'seeing poor', 'images diffuse and unsteady', etc., or using the **Antoniadi scale** (*q.v.*). This will ensure that when the observations are analysed undue weight will not be given to observations made with difficulty in unsatisfactory conditions.

Seeing is usually a combination of two different effects—distortion of the image and apparent motion of the image. Under good seeing conditions the image of a star (for example) should show the normal diffraction pattern for the telescope. In poor conditions, however, this may be lost and the star may appear to be a large, diffuse blob of light. Apparent movement of the image is not easy to detect, save in a telescope fitted with reference wires, as the movements are very small (of the order of one second of arc); it is probably due to currents of air in the tube of the telescope itself, or in the observing aperture in the observatory dome, etc.

Certain types of seeing trouble are associated with observation of particular bodies, such as the well-known 'boiling' appearance of the limbs of the Sun.

SELECTED AREAS See **Kapteyn selected areas.**

SELECTIVE ABSORPTION The absorption of the light from distant stars by interstellar gas and dust clouds varies with the wavelength of the light, since particles below a certain critical size scatter light of short-wavelength (blue) more than long-wavelength (red) light; this is termed selective absorption, and gives rise to the phenomenon of space reddening.

SELENOFAULT Fault observed in the surface of the Moon. (See **Moon—surface features of.**)

SELENOGRAPHIC CO-ORDINATES A system of co-ordinates for determining the positions of features of the lunar surface, referred to the centre of the mean sphere of the Moon. They may be in the form of selenographic latitude and longitude, but are more usually used in the form of Cartesian rectangular co-ordinates.

(See also **Lunar surface features—co-ordinates of.**)

SELENOGRAPHY The observational study of the surface of the Moon.

SELENOLOGY The deductive and theoretical study of the crustal rocks of the Moon, and of the nature and origin of the lunar surface features. The term is preferred to the alternative sometimes used, *lunar geology*—clearly a contradiction in terms.

SEMI-MAJOR AXIS The half-length of the major axis of an ellipse; the same quantity with reference to the (elliptical) orbit of a planet. It is therefore a measure of the planet's mean distance from the Sun.

(See also **Ellipse; Planetary motion.**)

SEMI-REGULAR VARIABLES A type of variable star whose light variations are roughly periodic but inconsistent, both in period and in the form of the light-wave, from one cycle to another. (See **Variable stars.**)

SERPENS (The Serpent. *Genitive* Serpentis, *I.A.U. abbreviation* Ser.) This most peculiar constellation is in fact two quite separate constellations; they represent the snake held by **Ophiuchus**, the serpent-bearer, and are sometimes termed *Serpens Caput* (the Head of the Serpent) and *Serpens Cauda* (the Tail of the Serpent). There is one set of Bayer Letters common to the stars of both parts.

Serpens Caput lies north-west of Ophiuchus, between Boötes and Hercules, and reaches midnight culmination in mid-May. It contains one second-, three third- and five fourth-magnitude stars.

Serpens Cauda is a very straggling constellation running eastwards from a point close to η Oph, almost to γ Sct, then northwards until it reaches the north-east corner of Ophiuchus when it runs north-eastwards again in a great rift of the Milky Way. In this very scattered, ribbon-like portion of the constellation there are few stars of note, the brightest being two of the third and four of the fourth magnitude.

There is a long-period variable, R Ser, in Serpens Caput between β and γ Ser and slightly to the south. Close to the southern boundary of Serpens Caput, about 7° south-west of α Ser, lies M5 (N.G.C. 5904), a fine globular cluster with a highly condensed centre.

SEXTANS (The Sextant. *Genitive* Sextantis, *I.A.U. abbreviation* Sex. Formerly Sextans Uraniæ, Urania's Sextant.) A small and barren constellation on the equator, at the southern border of Leo. There are no bright stars, only one of the fourth magnitude and comparatively few fainter ones.

SEXTANT The sextant is an instrument designed for the measurement of the angular separation between two objects. The classical sextant consisted of a graduated scale covering an arc of 60°—i.e. the 'sextant', one sixth of a full circle. Its modern derivatives are the marine sextant and the bubble sextant, designed as aids to navigation at sea and in the air respectively.

The principal use of the sextant as a navigational aid is the determination of the altitude of celestial bodies. The altitude of the celestial pole from a given place of observation is equal to the latitude of that place, and hence an observer in the northern hemisphere may determine his latitude approximately by measuring the altitude of the pole star. If he has the appropriate tables available, however, he can obtain his latitude much more accurately from measurements of the altitude of any bright star or, by day, the Sun.

(See also **Octant; Quadrant; Sextant, bubble; Sextant, marine.**)

SEXTANT, BUBBLE This instrument was developed mainly for use in aircraft, and is sometimes known as the 'air sextant'. It operates on the same basic principle as the marine sextant, but cannot be levelled by reference to the horizon owing to the great heights at which aircraft operate. The use of the conventional **artificial horizon**, embodying a bath of mercury, is also obviously impracticable on board a moving aircraft. The instrument is therefore aligned vertically by means of a small bubble in a quantity of liquid contained beneath a spherical glass dome (*B* in Fig. 130) at the top of the instrument. The bubble will naturally

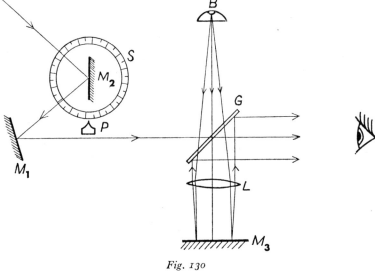

Fig. 130

seek the highest point, and the instrument is adjusted until the bubble coincides with the marked centre of the spherical glass; it is then vertical. The light rays from the bubble pass downwards, through a plane glass plate (G) inclined at $45°$ and thence through a collimating lens (L) to a horizontal plane mirror (M_3); they are reflected back through L, whence they emerge as a parallel beam, and are partly reflected out towards the observer's eye by the inclined plate G

The instrument contains two inclined mirrors (M_1, M_2) as in the marine sextant, M_1 being fixed and M_2 mounted on a rotatable disk which has a graduated scale (S) around its perimeter. The angle of M_2 is adjusted by rotating this disk until the image of the desired celestial object

appears in the eyepiece, after reflection in M_2 and M_1. The image is made to coincide with that of the bubble, and the altitude is then read off on the scale (S) by means of the pointer (P). This reading must then be corrected for atmospheric refraction (obtainable from tables) and for any significant instrumental errors.

(See also **Sextant, marine.**)

SEXTANT, MARINE The principle of the marine sextant is shown in Fig. 131. It consists of a rigid metal frame (not shown), usually constructed of brass with a sixty- or seventy-degree arc of a circle which carries a graduated scale (S). A movable index arm (A) is pivoted at (O) so as to ride over this arc, and has a pointer (P) to enable readings to be taken

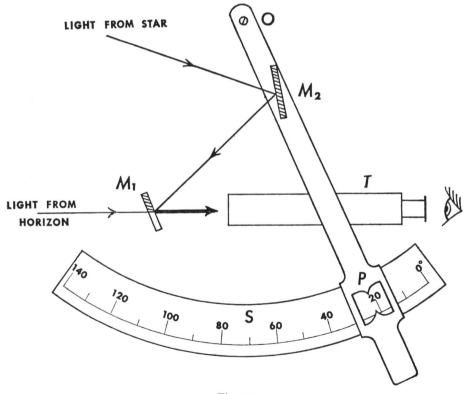

Fig. 131

on the scale. Also attached to the frame are a telescope (T) and a fixed inclined mirror (M_1). Only half of M_1 is silvered, enabling the horizon to be viewed through the unsilvered half with the telescope, so that the instrument may be accurately levelled. A second mirror (M_2) fully silvered, is mounted on the movable arm.

The inclination of the mirrors is adjusted so that when they are parallel the pointer P reads zero; it will be seen that in this position the horizon will be visible in the telescope both directly, through the unsilvered half of M_1, and by reflection in M_2 and the silvered half of M_1.

The frame is then held steady and the arm moved until the desired star or other celestial object is seen by reflection in M_2 and M_1, and adjusted until its image is coincident with that of the horizon seen direct through M_1; the apparent altitude of the star may then be read off at P. (Owing to the effect of the reflection at M_2, a change of $1°$ in altitude is equivalent to a movement of the arm of only $\frac{1}{2}°$; to compensate for this it is usual for S to be graduated in half-degree units, so that the altitude may be read off directly.)

The altitude obtained in this way must be corrected both for the dip of the horizon (due to the curvature of the Earth's surface) and for atmospheric refraction; both of these quantities can be determined from tables. It will also be necessary to correct for any systematic errors of the instrument used, should these be large enough to be significant.

Observations of the altitudes of stars may only be made with the sextant alone in twilight, while the horizon remains visible; during the hours of darkness they can be made with the aid of an **artificial horizon**. This consists, fundamentally, of a shallow basin of mercury; the sextant is used to measure the angle between a star and its image in the mercury-bath, half of this angle being the required altitude. This device also enables the sextant to be used on land where no true horizon is visible.

The marine sextant is normally pro-vided with a number of refinements, such as a vernier and scale-reading microscope, dark glasses to reduce the Sun's glare, etc.

(See also **Sextant, bubble.**)

SHACKLETON Lunar surface feature, co-ordinates $\xi+014$, $\eta+996$. Crater approximately 35 miles in diameter, close to the lunar north pole—hence its being named after the English polar explorer. The walls are massive, with some peaks rising to more than 8,000 ft.

SHAPLEY, Harlow Contemporary American astronomer, formerly Director and now Director Emeritus of the Harvard College Observatory. Shapley has made a special study of star clusters and of the structure of the Galaxy; he was the first to determine the Sun's true position in the Galaxy, from a study of the distribution of the globular clusters.

SHAULA The star λ Sco, a blue-white sub-giant of spectral class $B2$, magnitude $1·7$. It is a spectroscopic binary.

SHELL STAR A type of explosive variable, consisting of a relatively inert core surrounded by a gaseous 'shell' or envelope in which the release of energy due to the nuclear breakdown of hydrogen is still going on. They are usually main-sequence stars of spectral type B and have a bright-line emission spectrum. They are believed to represent a stage in the evolution of main-sequence stars.

SHORT-PERIOD COMET The so-called 'periodic comet'—one whose orbital period is sufficiently short as to enable observations made at two or more apparitions to be inter-related. The criteria usually adopted is that the period should not exceed 200 years.

The 1960 catalogue of cometary orbits gives elements of 566 comets; 210 of these have elliptical orbits, of which 94 (about 17 per cent of all comets) have periods of less than 200 years. Of these 94 short-period comets, 54 have been observed at more than one apparition.

SHORTT CLOCK A form of pendulum clock produced by the Shortt–Synchronome Company which is capable of very high accuracy.

The Shortt–Synchronome free-pendulum clock, usually known as the 'Shortt clock', consists of a master pendulum oscillating *in vacuo* in carefully controlled conditions of temperature and humidity; this master pendulum is given a small impulse every half-minute, to maintain its swing, but is otherwise completely free from mechanical contacts and has no work to perform. Its oscillations are used, however, to control by electrical means the oscillations of a slave clock; this clock drives the mechanism which enables the time to be indicated on dials, transmitted by wireless, etc. The control is so arranged that the oscillations of the slave pendulum are synchronized with those of the master pendulum, and therefore show the correct time despite the friction effects arising from the clock mechanism.

The Shortt clock is capable, under properly controlled conditions, of a rate of only ±0·003 sec/day. Their use was pioneered by Sampson at the Royal Observatory, Edinburgh; they were installed at the Royal Observatory, Greenwich, in 1924 and provided the basis for the national time-service for more than two decades before being superseded by the **quartz clock**. A large number of Shortt clocks are still in use at many observatories, supplying their day-to-day requirements in time measurement. Their accuracy has seldom been surpassed by other types of pendulum clock, and they remain unparalleled among pendulum clocks for accuracy combined with practicality.

SIDEREAL MONTH The sidereal period of the Moon; it is equal to 27·32 mean solar days.

SIDEREAL PERIOD The period of apparent revolution of a body, as seen from the Earth, relative to the background stars. It is therefore the actual period of revolution of the body around the Sun.

SIDEREAL TIME A system of time measurement based upon the actual rotation of the Earth. It is in fact determined by measurement of the diurnal motion of the fixed stars, one sidereal day being the interval between successive (upper) transits of any star across the observer's meridian (neglecting, of course, the effects of any proper motion, etc.).

It is usual for observatory clocks to show sidereal time, as this is related directly to the positions of the stars at the time.

SIDEREAL YEAR The interval between successive passages of the Earth through a point in its orbit fixed with reference to the stars; it is thus the interval between successive heliacal risings of any star. It is equal to about 365·2564 mean solar days—about 20 minutes longer than the tropical year, due to the retrograde motion of the First Point of Aries caused by the luni–solar precession.

SIDERITE A form of meteorite consisting almost entirely of metal, mainly iron and nickel. (See **Meteorite**.)

SIDEROLITE A form of meteorite containing mainly rocky material and some metal, principally iron and nickel. (See **Meteorite**.)

SIDEROSTAT A refined version of the heliostat; the latter is unsuitable for use on stellar objects, as its field has a non-uniform rotation. The siderostat has a modified mounting and with it the image of a star at the centre of the field can be kept stationary; the remainder of the field is, however, in (uniform) rotation around the centre.

(See also **Cœlostat; Heliostat**.)

SIMPLE LENS A lens composed of a single element.

SIMPLE RING A type of lunar surface feature, usually termed an elementary ring-structure. It comprises a simple wall of even cross-section enclosing a floor at the same level as the surrounding surface. (See **Moon—surface features of.**)

SINAÏ Martian surface feature, approximate position Ω 70°, Φ − 20°. Bright area in the north-eastern part of Thaumasia, between the Solis Lacus and Auroræ Sinus and bounded by the canali Nectar and Agathodæmon.

SINUS ÆSTUUM (Bay of Billows); a small dark extension of the Oceanus Procellarum, south-east of Eratosthenes and south of the lunar Appenines, in the north-east quadrant of the Moon.

SINUS ASTRONAUTARUM (Astronauts' Bay). Name adopted by the Academy of Sciences of the U.S.S.R. for the bay in the south side of the Mare Muscoviense, discovered on photographs of the far side of the Moon taken by the Soviet lunar probe vehicle *Lunik III.*
(See also **Moon—far side of.**)

SINUS IRIDUM (Bay of Rainbows); a large bay in the Jura Mountains which form the northern 'shore' of the Mare Imbrium in the north-east quadrant of the Moon. It is probably the remains of a vast walled plain whose southern wall has been overflowed by the surface material of the Mare; there are some very low ridges on the line of such a southern wall, visible for a very short time after sunrise. It is about 150 miles across, from the Promontarium Heraclides in the east to the Promontarium Laplace in the west.

SINUS MEDII (Central Bay); a small, rectangular dark area adjoining the south-western border of the Oceanus Procellarum, situated at the approximate mean centre of the Moon's visible disk.

SINUS MERIDIANI Martian surface feature, approximate position Ω 0°, Φ − 5°. The feature formerly known as 'Dawe's Forked Bay' or 'Furca', now used to define the prime meridian of areographic longitude. It is an extremely prominent and well-defined fork-like double promontory extending northwards from the western end of the Sinus Sabæus.

SINUS RORIS (Bay of Dew); a dark area close to the north-eastern limb of the Moon. It is a northern extension of the eastern part of the Oceanus Procellarum, and runs into the Mare Frigoris.

SINUS SABÆUS Martian surface feature, approximate position Ω 340°, Φ − 8°. One of the most prominent features on the planet, a long dark band stretching westwards from the Deltoton Sinus at the southern end of the Syrtis Major, and culminating in the Sinus Meridiani.

SIRENUM SINUS Martian surface feature, approximate position Ω 130°, Φ − 30°. A small dark extension at the eastern end of the Mare Sirenum. A number of important canali radiate from it, including Hyscus, Claritas, Araxes and Ulysses. The Sirenum Sinus is the most westerly point in the boundary of Thaumasia.

SIRIAN STARS Archaic name for stars of spectral class *A*, after the type star *Sirius* (class *A1*). (See **Stars—spectral classification of.**)

SIRIUS The star α CMa—the brightest, and one of the closest, in the firmament. Dominates the winter sky in the northern hemisphere. It is a dwarf of spectral class *A1*, and is also a binary; its companion, *Sirius B*, is a white dwarf, magnitude 8·4, at 9″ separation and a position angle of 90° (1960). The period is 49·9 years.
Sirius has a trigonometrical parallax of 0″.375, corresponding to a distance of 2·7 parsecs (8·7 light years).

SITHONIUS LACUS Martian surface feature, approximate position Ω 245°,

$\Phi + 45°$. Darkish condensation sometimes visible in north temperate region, between Utopia and Elysium.

SIXTY-ONE CYGNI The star 61 Cyg was the first to have its parallax successfully measured—by Bessel in 1837; using his newly constructed heliometer he obtained a parallax of 0″.314, equivalent to a distance of 10·2 light years. The accuracy of Bessel's work is evident from a comparison with the figures obtained by modern, photographic, methods — a parallax of 0″.292, equivalent to a distance of 11·0 light years.

61 Cyg is an interesting binary system; it comprises two components of almost similar magnitude—a $K5$ star of magnitude 5·2 and a $K7$ companion of 6·0 at a separation of 24″.6, position angle (1957) 140°. The period is 720 years.

Analysis of a long series of parallax plates of this star indicates that it has a third component, about sixteen times as massive as Jupiter, in orbit about one of the major stars. Russell analysed the system and deduced that the third object is non-luminous—is, in fact, a planet.

SKALNATÉ PLESO ATLAS The *Atlas Coeli Skalnaté Pleso*; a star atlas compiled by A. Bečvář of the Skalnaté Pleso observatory in Czechoslovakia, published in Prague in 1948. It contains all stars down to magnitude 7·75. There is an associated catalogue, published in 1951 and revised in 1959, giving the positions, proper motions, magnitudes, spectral types, parallaxes and radial velocities of all stars down to magnitude 6·25 and listing the double and variable stars, novae, clusters, nebulae and galaxies.

SKLODOWSKA-CURIE A prominent bright object on the far side of the Moon, discovered on the photographs obtained by *Lunik III*. It is believed to be a pair of craters surrounded by a bright nimbus. (See **Moon—far side of**.)

SKY—COLOUR OF The blue coloration of a cloudless sky is due to the differential scattering of different wavelengths of the Sun's light by molecules and particles in the Earth's atmosphere. At high altitudes the colour of the sky in the zenith is a deep blue, light of almost all other colours being scattered by oxygen molecules. At lower altitudes the scattering effect of dust particles, etc., result in a certain amount of white light being mixed with the blue, producing the characteristic 'sky-blue'.

SLIPHER, E. C. (1883–1964) One of the foremost American observers during more than half a century; Slipher spent his entire career at the Lowell Observatory, where he had originally worked with Lowell himself.

Throughout his long career E. C. Slipher specialized in the photography of the surfaces of the planets, and the standard of his work in this field remains unequalled. Both in integrated and monochromatic light his photographs, especially those of Mars, contain a wealth of detail scarcely ever achieved elsewhere. At the favourable oppositions of Mars of 1954 and 1956 he obtained very successful photographs of the planet in full colour.

Almost his last work was the preparation of collected editions of his best planetary photographs, which are now in the possession of the leading astronomical libraries of the world and are the best possible memorial to a truly great observer, whose selfless devotion to a field which does not bring the profession's highest awards has enriched it beyond measure.

SLIPHER, V. M. Leading American astronomer, Director of the Lowell Observatory since the death of Lowell himself, whom he had previously assisted. A brilliant spectroscopist, he obtained a classic series of spectra of the major planets in 1902–1909 in which there were a number of prominent absorption bands. Slipher was unable to identify these at the time, but in 1934, following Dunham's suggested identification of these lines as being due to methane and ammonia, he obtained with A. Adel a new series of spectra and in a masterpiece of observation and analysis proved the identification beyond all doubt.

V. M. Slipher is also a pioneer in the field of the spectroscopy of galactic systems; in 1914 he made the first determination of the radial velocity of a galaxy—that of the great galaxy in Andromeda; by 1925 he had obtained radial velocities for a further forty galaxies. He was the first President of Commission 28 (Extragalactic Nebulae) of the International Astronomical Union; for his great work in developing the techniques of planetary spectroscopy he was awarded the Gold Medal of the Royal Astronomical Society in 1933 and delivered the George Darwin Lecture to the Society in the same year.

SOLAR ACTIVITY There are a number of types of activity observable on the Sun; perhaps the best known, and one of the most extensively studied, is the sunspot, which is discussed in detail elsewhere in this book. The most important aspect of the study of sunspots is the **solar cycle**, first derived from an examination of the frequency and distribution of sunspots.

Regions of great intensity are often seen in photographs of the Sun obtained in integrated light; these, known as *faculae*, appear to be patches of incandescent gas raised above the surrounding surface, due to a high concentration of the hot convection currents in the convective zone. They are normally difficult to detect except when close to the limb, where contrast is heightened by **limb-darkening**; they are frequently seen close to large sunspots, but are usually much longer lived and tend to drift in longitude much more. They are, however, usually observed only in the latitude belt in which sunspots occur, viz. $35°$ N–$35°$ S.

From time to time sudden eruptions of incandescent hydrogen occur—these are termed *flares*. They reach maximum intensity very rapidly, often within a few minutes, but die down much more slowly.

They are usually associated with active sunspots and are believed to originate in the chromosphere: they are sometimes termed 'chromospheric eruptions'. Occasionally, major flares have been accompanied by bursts of cosmic radiation; a notable example occurred in 1956 February when the incidence of cosmic rays was the highest ever recorded. The observed amount of ultra-violet radiation increases when there is a solar flare; for a moderate flare the level of UV-radiation is about doubled.

Another form of eruptive activity which occurs very frequently is the solar *prominence*; these are giant eruptions of incandescent gas—principally hydrogen—which attain heights of many thousands of miles above the solar surface; they normally last for several hours, many of the larger ones lasting for several days. Occasionally they have been known to survive for several weeks. They are usually constantly changing in structural detail, although there are a number of basic forms which they usually take—rocket-like, tree-like, arcs, pyramids, arches, etc. They can be observed as bright protuberances from the limb in monochromatic light, by means of the **spectrohelioscope** or **Lyot filter**, and are also visible when the Sun's disk is occulted, as during a total eclipse or when using a **coronagraph.**

As prominences are slightly cooler than the photosphere they are seen, by contrast, as dark *filaments* when observed on the disk. [Plates 1(c, d); 2(d).]

A particularly eruptive type of prominence is termed a *surge*; this is a jet of material which suddenly erupts into the corona with tremendous velocity—of the order of 200 miles/sec—and reaches a height of perhaps 60,000 miles before falling back over much the same path. They are sometimes associated with major spot groups. [Plate 2(f).]

Prominences are not restricted to a particular zone of latitude as are the sunspots; they do, however, follow the 11-year cycle of solar activity, being more frequent, larger and more intense around sunspot maximum.

(See also **Solar cycle; Solar–terrestrial relationships; Sun—physical constitution of; Sunspots.**)

SOLAR CONSTANT A quantity used in determinations of the temperature of the Sun. It is defined as the quantity of heat which would fall on an area of one square centimetre at the surface of the Earth, if the Earth had no atmosphere and was at its mean distance from the Sun. It is determined from measurements of the actual solar radiation falling onto the surface of the Earth and estimates of the energy-absorption of the Earth's atmosphere.

The solar constant is a fluctuating quantity, not all of its variations having yet been explained. It is found to vary from day to day, and also with the solar cycle, and there are also some short-term fluctuations.

The mean value of the solar constant is $1 \cdot 93$ calories per minute.

SOLAR CYCLE The periodic fluctuation in the occurrence of sunspots was first recorded by Schwabe in 1843; the related variation in the latitude of the spots was discovered by Carrington and studied in detail by Spörer, to whom its discovery is often erroneously attributed. The phenomenon was beautifully demonstrated by Maunder in his classic 'butterfly' diagram (Fig. 144, p. 456). A useful guide to the level of sunspot activity is the **Wolf sunspot numbers** prepared in Zurich from observations made throughout the world. The annual mean Wolf numbers are plotted in Fig. 132, in which the periodic variation can be well seen.

The length of the cycle is usually taken as the interval between successive minima, and averages $11 \cdot 1$ years. The cycles are subject to considerable variation, however, both in duration and amplitude; the summary in Table 40 is based upon an investigation by Waldmeier of the records for the period 1750–1958.

Following his discovery that the mag-

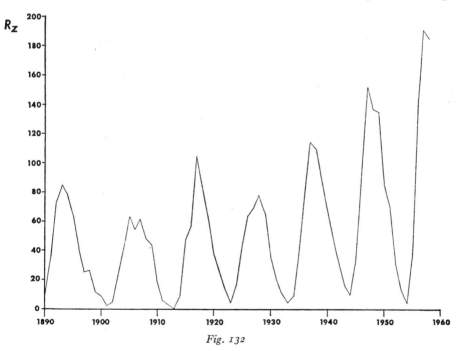

Fig. 132

Table 40.   Variations in the solar cycle

	Range	Mean value
Period between successive minima:	9·0–13·6 years	11·1 years
Time of rise to maximum:	2·9– 6·9 years	4·5 years
Time of fall to minimum:	4·0–10·2 years	6·5 years
Maximum sunspot number:	48·7–201·3	108·2
Minimum sunspot number:	0–11·2	5·1

netic polarity of sunspots in both the northern and southern hemispheres of the Sun is reversed each solar cycle, Hale suggested that the full cycle should be regarded as comprising two periods, i.e. 22·2 years on average.

Attempts have been made to derive a long-term effect which would account for the variations between individual cycles, but none of the attempts have produced data sufficiently reliable to be used as the basis for accurate predictions of sunspot activity.

The solar cycle has been found to apply to most forms of solar activity, as well as to sunspots; it is obviously of fundamental importance in solar physics and its ultimate explanation will only be achieved as part of a complete theory of solar magneto-hydrodynamics and of the Sun's internal constitution.

(See also **Solar activity; Sun— physical constitution of; Sunspots.**)

SOLAR MOTION If the observed positions of stars obtained many years apart are compared, it is found that the so-called 'fixed stars' have, in fact, a *proper motion*; this motion is the component (in a plane perpendicular to the line of sight) of the motion of the star during the interval. This motion is comprised of (i) any true motion of the star relative to the Sun, (ii) any motion the Sun itself may have and (iii) a periodic fluctuation due to the Earth's motion in its orbit. The latter component can be calculated and allowed for, but the first two can only be separated statistically.

If the proper motions of a large number of stars, distributed over the entire sky, are analysed, it is found that there is a well-defined trend for stars to diverge from a point in the constellation Hercules and to converge on the diametrically opposite point in Columba. From this we deduce that the Sun has a motion in the Galaxy, with a velocity of approximately 12 miles per second. The entire solar system, of course, shares this motion, which is usually known as the *solar motion*.

As a result of the solar motion the Sun appears to be travelling towards the above-mentioned point in Hercules, hence the apparent divergence of the stars from it; this point is termed the *solar apex* and is situated at approximately R.A. 18 hr, Dec. +30°. The diametrically opposite point in Columba is known as the *solar antapex* and is at R.A. 6 hr, Dec. −30°.

It should be emphasized that the solar motion represents a motion of the Sun relative to nearby stars only, and is more accurately described as the *local* solar motion; the Sun's motion due to the rotation of the Galaxy is very much more difficult to determine, owing to the difficulty of measuring the proper motions of stars in the more distant parts of the Galaxy.

It is found from a study of the radial velocities of the globular clusters, and of the high-velocity stars, that the Sun has a motion due to galactic rotation towards an apex in galactic longitude 96°, with a velocity of between 125 and 155 miles per second.

(See also **Sun—motion in space.**)

SOLAR PARALLAX The mean equatorial horizontal parallax of the Sun, measured to deduce the Sun's mean distance (the **astronomical unit**). (See **Parallax, solar.**)

SOLAR STARS Name sometimes used in the past to denote stars of spectral class G, of which the Sun is one. (See **Stars— spectral classification of.**)

SOLAR SYSTEM This is the general name given to the immediate neighbourhood of the Sun, and collectively to the Sun itself together with all bodies under the permanent or passing influence of its gravitational field. These comprise, in the main, the nine planets, their thirty-two natural satellites, and many thousands of minor planets, comets and meteors. Physical and statistical data for the planets are given in Table 41; satellite data are given in Table 35, pp. 374–5.

The Sun itself is a fairly typical dwarf, main-sequence, star of spectral type Go, with a surface temperature of approximately 6,000° K. The gaseous surface is in a state of constant turbulence, and there are many flares and other eruptive phenomena indicative of intense activity. Certain types of solar activity repeat after intervals of 11 or 22 years—the so-called 'solar cycle'. This causes variations in the solar radiation incident upon the surface of the Earth, and consequently the cycle is reflected in many terrestrial phenomena which are affected or stimulated by solar radiation, such as the aurorae, terrestrial magnetism, etc.

The inner planets. Both Mercury and Venus are alternately visible as 'morning' and 'evening' stars, being seen in the eastern sky before sunrise when near Western Elongation, and in the western sky after sunset when near Eastern Elongation. As both planets are situated inside the orbit of the Earth, they present a complete sequence of phases similar to those of the Moon—'full' at superior conjunction, 'half' at the quadratures and

'new' at inferior conjunction. Neither is known to have a satellite.

Apparitions of Mercury occur at intervals of 6 and 10 weeks alternately. As the periods of axial rotation and orbital revolution are equal, Mercury constantly presents the same face to the Sun; owing to its proximity to the Sun it must therefore have two hemispheres suffering extremes of heat and cold.

Very faint surface markings have been observed during favourable apparitions; they were first mapped accurately by Schiaparelli in Milan in 1889.

Venus, comparable in size with the Earth, has a much longer apparition than Mercury, due to its greater distance from the Sun; at a favourable Eastern Elongation it is visible for many weeks and is a very conspicuous object in the evening sky. Observation of its surface is impossible, owing to its deep, cloudy, atmosphere. Faint markings have been observed on occasion, but these are probably atmospheric features. This inability to see features of the solid surface has prevented the determination of the period of axial rotation and the inclination of the axis.

The Earth–Moon system. An examination of Table 35 will show that there is much dissimilarity between the Moon and the other planetary satellites, if their masses are compared in relation to the masses of their primaries; thus, whereas the Moon's mass is 1/81 that of the Earth, the next most massive in relation to its primary—Triton—is only 1/750 the mass of Neptune.

There are thus grounds for considering the Earth and the Moon as a double planet, rather than as planet and satellite.

The Moon's periods of axial rotation and (apparent) orbital revolution are equal, and hence it presents the same hemisphere permanently towards the Earth, although due to the effects of libration some 60 per cent of the total surface area is directly observable at one time or another. The remainder can only

Table 41. Planetary data

	Equatorial diameter (miles)	Mean distance from Sun (millions of miles)	Orbital velocity (miles/sec)	Sidereal revolution period (tropical years)	Sidereal period of axial rotation at Equator	Inclination of Equator to orbit plane	Mass (Earth = 1)	Density (water = 1)	Number of known natural satellites
MERCURY	3,010	35·98	29·75	0·24	87·97 days	?	0·05	5·41	0
VENUS	7,650	67·24	21·76	0·62	247 days	174°	0·82	4·99	0
EARTH	7,926	92·96	18·51	1·00	23 hr 56 min 04 sec	23° 27′	1·00	5·52	1
MARS	4,220	141·64	14·99	1·88	24 hr 37 min 23 sec	29° 59′	0·11	3·96	2
JUPITER	88,760	483·64	8·11	11·86	9 hr 50 min 30 sec	03° 04′	317·89	1·33	12
SATURN	74,160	886·70	5·99	29·46	10 hr 14 min	26° 44′	95·14	0·71	10
URANUS	29,300	1,783·1	4·23	84·01	10 hr 49 min	97° 53′	14·52	1·70	5
NEPTUNE	27,800	2,794·1	3·38	164·79	15 hr 48 min	28° 48′	17·46	2·26	2
PLUTO	3,700	3,666·2	2·94	248·4	6·39 days	?	0·10	5·5	0

be studied by means of photographs taken from 'lunar probes' or manned space vehicles.

The Moon has no detectable atmosphere and with the telescope is seen to have a very rugged surface. More than half of the observed surface consists of gigantic mountain ranges and crater formations, and the remainder of enormous plains ('maria') which some believe to have a surface covering of dust—although opinions are sharply divided as to the depth of this layer; the successful 'soft' landing of the *Luna 9* probe vehicle by the U.S.S.R. scientists seemed to confirm that it is very shallow indeed, if it exists at all, and the evidence obtained by the more recent American *Surveyor* probe vehicles supports this view.

Owing to its proximity and the comparative ease of making detailed observations, the Moon is an important object of study by both amateur and professional astronomers.

The outer planets. Although much smaller, Mars is more worthy of the description 'twin of the Earth' than is Venus. It has a fairly transparent atmosphere and much surface detail can be observed. There is an atmospheric block to ultra-violet radiation, thus enabling the upper atmosphere to be studied in detail also.

Jupiter is the largest planet, and offers a great deal of both interest and value to observers. It is of gaseous constitution and observation of its ever-changing surface detail is carried out extensively with a view to ascertaining the physical structure of its outer layers. In appearance it consists of a bright equatorial zone bounded by alternate, parallel dark 'belts' and other bright 'zones', all having a fine structure that is undergoing constant change.

In many ways Saturn may be regarded as a small replica of Jupiter, but it has a unique additional feature in its vast ring-system. This is believed to be the dèbris of a former satellite which has been disintegrated by tidal forces due to too close an approach to the primary.

Both Uranus and Neptune also appear to be of a similar nature, although the amount of detail visible is restricted by their considerable distance. Uranus is unique for its remarkable inclination to the plane of its orbit.

Although discovered by means of a prediction, based upon an extensive mathematical analysis of the motion of Uranus, Pluto appears not to have the size or mass to fulfil the requirements of that prediction, and consequently remains an object of mystery. Its extreme distance and small size render it impossible to make a useful telescopic examination of Pluto.

The Minor Planets are small planetary bodies in solar orbits lying mostly between the orbits of Mars and Jupiter. Many of them have very eccentric orbits which bring them inside the orbit of the Earth. The first minor planets were discovered early in the nineteenth century, and many thousands are now known. It has been suggested that they may have been formed by the breaking-up of a planet formerly orbiting between Mars and Jupiter.

Comets are usually small, diffuse objects moving in orbits of high eccentricity, and are only observable for a short time around perihelion. Many of them have elliptical orbits—albeit so eccentric that in some cases their aphelia lie beyond the orbit of Neptune—these return at predictable intervals and are known as 'periodic comets'. Others seem to have hyperbolic or parabolic orbits, suggesting an origin outside the solar system, but this may be simply due to the inadequacy of the orbit derived from too few positional observations.

Comets usually develop a 'tail', and often a very complex structure, when near the Sun.

Meteors are bodies which the Earth encounters as it travels in its orbit and which fall towards it under the influence of its gravitational attraction. They may weigh anything from a few ounces to many tons. They are usually burnt up by friction with the air molecules during their descent through the atmosphere, when they are briefly visible as 'shooting stars'. Some of the more massive ones are only partly burnt up, a portion remaining to reach the Earth's surface; these are the **meteorites**, invaluable in so far as they are the only material from outside the Earth available for laboratory examination.

(See also entries under **Comets; Earth; Jupiter; Mars; Mercury; Meteor; Minor planets; Moon; Neptune; Pluto; Satellites, planetary; Saturn; Sun; Uranus; Venus.**)

SOLAR–TERRESTRIAL RELATION-SHIPS The general term embracing all the observed effects, in the atmosphere and on the surface of the Earth, attributable to solar activity. These effects arise as a result of two types of solar emission reaching the Earth—ultra-violet radiation and corpuscular emission. Activity arising from the two types of emission can be separated by means of a study of the time-lag between events on the Sun and their terrestrial effects. Ultra-violet radiation travels, of course, with the velocity of light and therefore takes, on average, only 8·3 minutes to travel from the Sun to the Earth. The corpuscular emission consists of streams of charged particles whose journey-time is between 20 and 25 hours.

One effect of the Sun's ultra-violet radiation is to ionize air molecules in the upper atmosphere; this effect travels from the east to the west during the day, due to the Earth's rotation. The ionization affects the Earth's magnetism, and a diurnal variation in the magnetic field-strength can therefore be detected.

The Earth's magnetic field is also subject to a much more severe disturbance, termed a *crochet*, which is due to a sudden surge of solar UV-radiation. This usually arises from a solar flare, from which the level of UV-radiation is usually

comparable to the total emission from the whole of the Sun's disk.

We are fortunate in that the UV-radiation from the Sun ionizes oxygen atoms at a height of about 30 miles above the Earth's surface, forming a layer of ozone (O_3); this substance absorbs UV-radiation and therefore screens the Earth's surface from the greater part of this radiation, which in quantity would be fatal to all forms of life.

In addition to the diurnal effect on the Earth's magnetic field mentioned above, the field-strength of the Earth's magnetism varies with the intensity of solar UV-radiation; thus whenever the radiation is increased, due to the presence of sunspots, flares, etc., there is a corresponding increase in the field-strength, with the usual time-lag of some eight minutes. Variations in the strength of the UV-radiation also alter the characteristics of the various layers of the **ionosphere**, including their reflectivity to short-wave radio transmissions—hence the frequent association of 'fade-outs' in long-distance wireless communication with large sunspots and other solar events.

On arrival in the vicinity of the Earth after their 20–25 hour journey from the Sun, the particles comprising the corpuscular emission are attracted towards the Earth's magnetic poles; as these are close to the geographical poles the effects of the particle emission are rarely observable outside the polar regions. For this reason it is necessary to send expeditions to the Arctic and/or the Antarctic at times when special efforts are being made to make a thorough study of solar–terrestrial effects, as was done during the **International Geophysical Year**.

The most spectacular effect of the Sun's corpuscular emission is the **aurora**, or 'polar lights'; this is a form of electrical discharge due to the charged particles from the Sun impinging upon the charged layers of the ionosphere.

These are only a few of the more obvious of the many terrestrial phenomena which can be correlated with solar activity and which will be a most important field of study for many years to come.

SOLAR TIME A system of time measurement based upon the apparent diurnal movement of the Sun; as this is subject to such large variations, the system actually used is based upon the motion of a hypothetical 'mean Sun' moving around the celestial equator at a uniform rate, thus providing days of constant length whilst preserving an approximate relationship to the times of rising and setting of the Sun.
(See also **Time systems.**)

SOLAR TOWER A vertical instrument specially designed and constructed for research in solar physics. (See **Telescope, tower.**)

SOLAR WIND Name given to the ionized gaseous particles emitted by the Sun. (See **Storm, geomagnetic.**)

SOLIS LACUS Martian surface feature, approximate position Ω 90°, Φ −28°. A very prominent dark area centrally placed in the vast elliptical ochre area Thaumasia. A number of important canals radiate from it, connecting it to the features forming the borders of Thaumasia: Tithonius, Claritas, Bathys, Ambrosia and Nectar.

This whole region is frequently seen to undergo major changes of form, but there is no indication that these changes are seasonal. The border of Thaumasia is sometimes a smooth ellipse and at others polygonal, and both the border, the Solis Lacus condensation itself and the radiating canali are sometimes seen to be broken up into complex spots and streaks.

SOLSTICE Term given to both of the **solstitial points**, and also to the days on which the Sun occupies these points. On these two days the Sun rises at its farthest from the east and west points respectively, and there is the maximum disparity between the duration of night and day.
(See also **Celestial sphere; Summer solstice; Winter solstice.**)

SOLSTITIAL COLURE The declination circle which passes through the north and south celestial poles and also the solstitial points.
(See also **Celestial sphere.**)

SOLSTITIAL POINTS The positions of the Sun at the summer and winter solstices, at which times its north and south declination, respectively, are maximal.
(See also **Celestial sphere.**)

SOTHIC CYCLE A period of approximately 1,460 years in which the New Year of the calendar used by the ancient Egyptians retrogressed through a complete cycle of the seasons—i.e. became in error by a total of a year—due to the adopted year of 365 days being approximately a quarter of a day shorter than the mean solar year. (See **Calendar.**)

SOUTH POINT The point on the celestial sphere, due south of the observer, at which the meridian intersects the horizon.

SOUTH POLAR DISTANCE The angular distance, measured in the meridian, between an object and the south celestial pole. Usually abbreviated 'S.P.D.' it is equivalent to 90° minus the (southern) **Declination** of the object.
(See also **Celestial sphere; North polar distance.**)

SOUTH TROPICAL DISTURBANCE A long-lived and important feature observed in the South Tropical Zone of Jupiter between 1901 and 1940.
(See **Jupiter—observed features and notable phenomena.**)

SOUTHERN DOUBLE STAR CATALOGUE A catalogue of binary stars within 71° of the south pole, compiled by

R. T. A. Innes and published in 1926–1927. The stars are referred to in the abbreviated form 'S.D.S. 1250'.

(See also **Burnham catalogue; New General Catalogue of Double Stars; Star catalogues.**)

SOUTHERN MERIDIAN PHOTO-METRY The *Catalogue of 7,922 Stars observed with the Meridian Photometer, 1889–91*, compiled by S. I. Bailey and published in volume 34 of the *Harvard Annals*. It is the southern extension of the **Harvard Photometry**, *q.v.*

SOVIETSKI MOUNTAINS (Soviet Mountains) Name adopted by the Academy of Sciences of the U.S.S.R. for the range of lunar mountains discovered on photographs of the far side of the Moon taken by the Soviet lunar probe vehicle *Lunik III*. Their existence is now a matter of some doubt; the feature recorded on the photographs has been interpreted by E. A. Whitaker as part of a ray system of the crater Giordano Bruno. The Latinized version *Montes Sovietici* is now the preferred spelling.

(See also **Moon—far side of.**)

SPACE PROBE An unmanned spacecraft containing scientific apparatus, and/or photographic or television cameras, together with radio transmitters to 'telemeter' the information or pictures back to Earth; the probe vehicle is launched by rocket and manoeuvred into a trajectory carrying it close to (or onto), e.g., the Sun, Moon, Mars, Venus. (See **Luna; Lunar Orbiter; Mariner; Ranger; Surveyor; Zond.**)

SPACE REDDENING The light from distant stars is apparently reddened by an amount dependent upon their distance and galactic latitude, due to the selective absorption of their bluer light by the interstellar dust clouds concentrated in the galactic plane.

This factor must be allowed for in studies of the spectra of the distant stars, and in colour–temperature work; it is also an important factor in estimating the distances of remote stars in the Galaxy, as stars of a given spectral class will appear farther away than they really are if the amount of reddening is underestimated.

SPACE VELOCITY The true velocity of a star in space. From observations of the proper motion of a star its *tangential velocity* (T) can be calculated; if its *radial velocity* (V) is also known (by measurement of the Doppler shift in its spectrum) the space velocity v can be calculated from the relation

$$v = \sqrt{(V^2 + T^2)}.$$

SPECTRA The production of a spectrum arises from the optical phenomenon known as *dispersion*, first demonstrated by Sir Isaac Newton in 1666 in a classic experiment. Newton passed a beam of sunlight, from an aperture in his window blind, through a triangular prism. The emerging beam was allowed to fall onto a white screen. Newton found that the image consisted of a band of coloured light, red at one end and violet at the other—*the spectrum*. The spectrum is usually said to comprise seven distinct colours (red, orange, yellow, green, blue, indigo and violet), but the shades are infinitely variable and each merges into the next; there are no distinct boundaries between colours. The dispersion of a beam of light arises from the fact that light of different wavelengths is refracted by differing amounts when passing from one medium into another—light of short wavelength (i.e. violet light) being refracted through the greatest angle and long wavelength light (i.e. red light) being least refracted. This is the principle used in the **spectrograph**, one of the fundamental tools of the astrophysicist, in which the light is dispersed by a prism or diffraction grating.

The spectrum of a typical star (such as the Sun) is a continuous spectrum (or *continuum*) with an absorption spectrum superimposed upon it. The absorption spectrum is formed in the outer layers of the star which, although very hot, are cooler than the lower layers. The radiation from these hotter levels is absorbed by the relatively cool gases through which it passes; it was discovered by Kirchhoff that a substance will absorb radiation of the same wavelength as it emits itself: the dark lines of the absorption spectrum are therefore an indication of the substances present in the cooler outer layers of the star.

Emission spectra are formed by substances in an incandescent state under low pressure; they take the form of bright lines of the wavelengths appropriate to the substance. Emission lines occur in the spectra of some stars; it is believed that they originate in the outer layers of the gaseous envelope surrounding the star.

If a substance is raised to a very high temperature, its atoms may become ionized; the intensity of its emission spectrum will then increase. If such a substance is present in a star the emission lines will appear enhanced and additional lines may appear. The enhancement and the multiplicity of lines depend upon the degree of ionization. Spectral enhancements thus permit the detection not only of substances present in the star but also their ionization state.

(See also **Refraction; Spectroscope; Stars—spectral classification of; Stellar spectra.**)

SPECTRAL/LUMINOSITY CLASSIFICATION

A development from the Harvard–Draper system for the classification of stellar spectra, in which the spectral characteristics are related to the luminosity of the star concerned. The system was devised by W. M. Morgan, P. C. Kéenan and E. Kellman of the Yerkes Observatory, and is known variously as the 'MKK system', 'MK system' or 'Yerkes system'. (See **Stars—spectral classification of.**)

SPECTRAL TYPE

The abbreviation used to indicate the type of spectrum a star has. The form most commonly used is the **Harvard–Draper sequence**, but more refined systems of classification have been devised for research work. (See **Stars—spectral classification of.**)

SPECTROGRAM

A photographic record of the spectrum of an object, obtained with a spectrograph.

SPECTROGRAPH

A form of **spectroscope** in which the telescope is replaced by a camera, so that a permanent record of the spectrum may be secured for subsequent detailed examination. Photographs obtained in this way are termed *spectrograms*.

Astronomical spectrographs are usually designed for direct attachment to a specific telescope; they range from simple one-prism instruments to high-dispersion ones containing perhaps as many as five prisms in series. Others utilize **diffraction gratings**, or prisms of material other than glass (e.g. fused quartz), in order to achieve specific results. It is usual for large telescopes intended for spectrographic work to be provided with a range of ancillary spectroscopic equipment to fit it for a variety of observing programmes.

Sometimes use is made of the coudé focus to permit the use of large, static spectrographs; other important variations of the spectrographic principle are the **objective prism** and the **spectrohelio-graph**, *q.v.*

SPECTOGRAPH, SLIT

A type of astronomical spectrograph incorporating a narrow slit as in the simple **spectroscope**, *q.v.*

SPECTROGRAPH, SLITLESS

It is not vital to use a slit spectrograph to obtain stellar spectra, especially in programmes where the spectra of whole fields of stars are required for classification purposes, but where high-resolution spectra for detailed analysis are not needed. In such cases sufficient resolution is obtained from the fact that the image-size of an individual star is so small. The most common method of obtaining stellar spectra in this way is to use an **objective prism**, in which case the combination of prism and telescope may be regarded as a large slit-less spectrograph. It is not practicable to make prisms with sufficient accuracy larger than about 24 inches in diameter, however, and the technique cannot there-fore be used with very large instruments.

To overcome this difficulty a type of slitless spectrograph is used which is situated inside the telescope tube. It has a negative collimating lens, situated just inside the prime focus of the telescope, which is of sufficiently large aperture to accept the convergent beam in its entirety. This lens renders the beam parallel, and it is then fed into the spectrograph, dis-persed by a prism or grating, and focused onto the photographic plate. In this way the light-gathering power of the full aperture of the telescope objective is utilized, even though this may greatly exceed the aper-ture of the collimating lens of the spectro-graph. A further refinement is for the dispersed spectrum to be fed into a Schmidt-type camera rather than a con-ventional camera objective, which greatly reduces the exposure times required.

SPECTROHELIOCINEMATOGRAPHY

(Otherwise spelt spectroheliokinematog-raphy.) Term sometimes used for the recording of the development and struc-tural changes of prominences and other solar phenomena by means of time-lapse cinematography of the monochromatic image produced in a conventional spectro-heliograph.

This technique has been developed to a very high standard, mainly due to the efforts of Robert R. McMath and his colleagues at the McMath–Hulbert Ob-servatory. The films obtained there and at the High Altitude Observatory at Climax, Colorado, have been of immense value to solar physicists.

SPECTROHELIOGRAM A photograph

of the Sun's disk in monochromatic light, obtained by scanning the disk in a selected wavelength with a spectroheliograph. The

wavelengths most frequently selected for this purpose are the hydrogen-α and the calcium 'K' line. [Plate 1(c, d).]

SPECTROHELIOGRAPH An important discovery was made simultaneously in 1868 by Janssen, observing a total solar eclipse from India, and Sir Norman Lockyer in England. This was that if the slit of a spectroscope was set tangential to the Sun's limb at the site of a prominence, and the instrument adjusted so that the prominence was observed in one of its prominent emission lines (normally the hydrogen-α line), by opening the slit a little it was possible to observe the form of the prominence. For many years this remained the only means of observing prominences (except during a total eclipse): it had numerous disadvantages, notably the fact that its operation was limited to prominences extending beyond the limb. Good results could only be obtained with difficulty, but nevertheless in the hands of a number of skilled observers the technique was used to add substantially to our knowledge of solar activity. A more efficient method was badly needed, how-ever, and numerous workers devoted their time and energy to the search. Finally the breakthrough came, with the simultaneous development of the prin-ciple of the spectroheliograph by Hale and Deslandres, in 1890. Hale had just gradu-ated in engineering at the Massachusetts Institute of Technology, and with the financial backing of his father devoted the next six years to the development of the new instrument. He continued to design improved versions for many years, during his direction of the Yerkes and Mount Wilson Observatories.

The layout of a typical spectrohelio-graph is shown diagrammatically in Fig. 133. The high dispersion required necessitates a large and cumbersome lay-out, and the instrument is therefore a static installation—usually in an under-ground laboratory specially designed to provide a stable temperature and a dust-free atmosphere. The Sun's light is fed

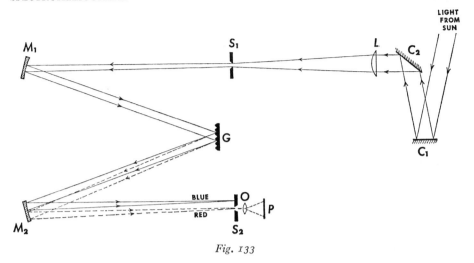

Fig. 133

into the instrument by means of a **helio-stat**: this sometimes comprises two plane mirrors (C_1, C_2) as shown, the sunlight then being focused onto the slit (S_1) by an objective lens (L); often, however, C_2 is replaced by a concave mirror which focuses the beam onto the slit and thus dispenses with the need for L.

The light passing through S_1 falls onto a concave mirror (M_1) of long focal length—of the order of $f/50$—which focuses an image of the slit on the diffraction grating (G); a similar mirror (M_2) focuses the dispersed spectrum onto a plate containing the second slit (S_2), which allows only one narrow strip of the spectrum to pass into the camera objective (O) and be recorded on the photographic plate (P). Specific strips of the spectrum may be selected by slightly rotating the grating, which is mounted on a turntable for this purpose.

If the clock-drive of the heliostat mirror C_1 is stopped, and the Sun's image thus allowed to drift across the slit S_1, the strip viewed in the selected wavelength at S_2 will appear to traverse the Sun's disk; the plate P is therefore driven slowly past the slit S_2 at a corresponding rate, so that a complete picture of the disk in the desired wavelength is built up.

Such a plate is termed a *spectroheliogram*, and is most commonly made in the wavelengths of the hydrogen-α and calcium 'K' lines.

A number of adaptations have been made to the basic layout to serve specific purposes.

(See also **Hale, G. E.; Spectroheliocinematography; Spectrohelioscope; Telescope, tower.**)

SPECTROHELIOSCOPE Greatly though it has contributed to the study of solar activity, the **spectroheliograph** was very soon found to have a number of limitations; one of the more serious was its inability to provide the visual observer with an immediate, overall picture of the state of the solar surface in the selected wavelength. By the time the plate had been exposed and developed the activity situation might have been changed considerably, and this was a real handicap to the observer in planning his work.

The first really practicable instrument for visual monochromatic observation of the entire solar disk was developed from the spectroheliograph by Hale in 1923. The general layout of Hale's instrument, known as the spectrohelioscope, is shown in Fig. 134, from which it will be seen that

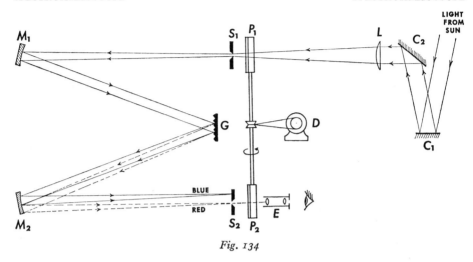

Fig. 134

it is basically the same as the spectrohelio-graph—the camera lens and plate being replaced by an eyepiece. The all-important difference was the introduction of a scanning mechanism by means of which the strip observed in the viewing slit should pass repeatedly across the Sun's disk, enabling the whole disk to be seen, thanks to the observer's **persistence of vision.** To achieve this Hale used a metal strip containing both the slits (S_1, S_2)—the instrument being so designed that they were located one above the other a few inches apart—and arranged for the strip to be rapidly oscillated about a central pivot. The complementary oscillation of the slits thus enabled S_1 to traverse the original solar image whilst S_2 followed the selected line in the spectrum.

Although this mechanism and refinements of it are still used in some instruments, an alternative method invented by J. A. Anderson (Hale's chief optician at Mount Wilson) has been widely adopted and is the method portrayed in Fig. 134. In this system the slits are fixed, the synchronized scanning being achieved by a pair of glass prisms of square cross-section (P_1, P_2), which are connected by an axle and rotated about it by means of a small electric drive motor (D). The varying effect of refraction by the rotating

prism (see Fig. 135) causes the image of the Sun to traverse the upper slit and the strip observed at S_2 to follow it exactly.

Typical dimensions of a Hale spectro-helioscope are as follows:

Objective	diameter:	4 in.
	focal length:	20 ft. (*f*/60)
Collimating mirror	diameter:	3 in.
	focal length:	13 ft. (*f*/52)
Grating	area:	4 in. × 3 in. approx.
	ruling:	15,000 lines per in.

Anderson prisms: 3 in. × $\frac{1}{2}$ in. × $\frac{1}{2}$ in. approx.

The diameter of the Sun's image in such an instrument is about two inches. It will be seen that the total length of the instrument is of the order of 40 ft.; modified spectrohelioscopes have been devised in which the optical axis has been 'folded' so as to reduce the space required.

A remarkable development was the combined spectrohelioscope–spectrohelio-graph developed by Ellison at Sherborne and later installed at the Royal Observatory, Edinburgh. This design owes more to the Littrow spectrograph than to Hale's instrument, and has a number of advantages over it, notably the fact that the five reflections inherent in Hale's design have

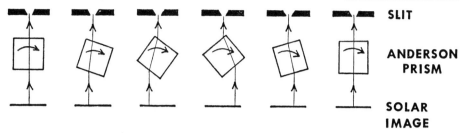

SLIT

ANDERSON
PRISM

SOLAR
IMAGE

Fig. 135

been reduced to two, with consequent reduction in light-loss.

The Ellison instrument is shown in schematic plan form in Fig. 136. The Sun's light is directed by a heliostat mirror (M) into the objective lens (L_1), which forms a 2-in. image of the Sun on the slit (S_1); the strip of light from S_1 is passed through the collimating lens (L_2) and onto the grating (G). The dispersed beam again passes through L_2 which focuses it on the viewing slit (S_2), behind which there is a low-power eyepiece (E). The slits (S_1, S_2) are connected and mutually oscillated by an ingenious motor-driven mechanism invented by F. J.

Sellers. A number of special design features, not shown in the diagram, were introduced to prevent unwanted internal reflections, etc.

The grating is mounted on a turntable and can be quickly rotated so that the spectrum is focused not on S_2 but on the photographic plate (P) when the instrument is required to be used as a spectroheliograph; this change can be made in about half a minute. This versatility is of tremendous value, as it permits a spectroheliogram to be obtained immediately a flare is seen to commence in the spectrohelioscope. The initial 'flash' of a solar flare lasts no more than 2–5 minutes, and

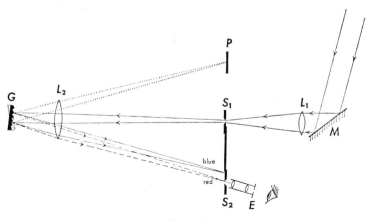

Fig. 136

when one is observed in a conventional spectrohelioscope it is not normally possible to adjust a separate spectrohelio-graph in time to obtain a plate during this important phase. This was the problem which stimulated Ellison to design the combined instrument, and he had the satisfaction on 1946 July 25 of obtaining the first plates of the continuous spectrum of a short-lived flare.

SPECTROMETER A type of **spectroscope** designed to measure the deviation of a given beam of light passed through it, or to identify the wavelength of a given line in the resulting spectrum; used principally in the laboratory rather than the observatory.

SPECTROPHOTOMETER Photometric studies of stellar spectra were until comparatively recently carried out by photographic means, in which high-dispersion spectrograms were obtained with conventional spectrographs and subsequently scanned with a recording microphotometer to produce a plot of the variation in intensity with wavelength. Recently, however, techniques have been devised whereby the spectrum produced by the dispersing element at the telescope, usually a grating, is scanned photo-electrically so as to produce an immediate trace of the intensity–wavelength graph for the object under observation. The equipment used is termed a spectrophotometer.

The photo-electronic technique produces results much more quickly than the photographic process and is much more productive; it is therefore becoming a major tool of the astrophysicist.

SPECTROPHOTOMETRY The study of the distribution of the radiation of a body among its component wavelengths, usually by the preparation of a plot of intensity versus wavelength; the shapes of the peaks and troughs in the resulting graph are termed *line profiles*.

SPECTROSCOPE Although the existence of the spectrum was first demonstrated in

Newton's classic experiment of 1666, in which he dispersed a shaft of sunlight with a triangular glass prism, it was not until the early nineteenth century that the spectra of the Sun and stars began to be studied in earnest; the spectroscope was originally developed as a laboratory tool, for both analytical and educational purposes. Many variations from the basic form were devised to meet special requirements, but these need not concern us here. Suffice it to say that the principle of the spectroscope has, in the past 150 years or so, been adapted to astronomical research so successfully that the spectroscope is probably the most important piece of ancillary equipment in observatory use; without it, the entire subject of astrophysics would probably never have been born.

The spectroscope occurs in three main forms: the straightforward spectroscope, in which the spectra are viewed by eye; the *spectrometer*, in which the deviation of a beam of light is measured, and the *spectrograph*, in which the spectrum is photographed in order to produce a permanent record.

The essentials of a simple prism spectroscope are shown in Fig. 137. The light from the source being observed is first passed through a narrow slit (*S*) and then through a collimating lens (*C*); the emergent, parallel, beam is then allowed to fall on one face of a triangular glass prism (*P*). The deviated beam emerges from the opposite face and a telescope (*T*) is used to produce a focused image of the slit. On passing through the prism, however, the beam of light will be dispersed, the light of shortest wavelength being refracted by the greatest amount and the longest wavelengths the least (see Fig. 25 on p. 99). Unless the source is monochromatic, the image produced will therefore be, in effect, a continuum formed of a series of images of the slit in each wavelength present; by rotating the prism slightly any part of this spectrum can be directed into the telescope for examination. To facilitate this it is usual for the prism

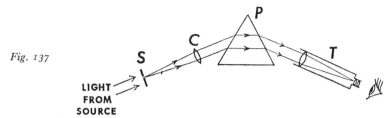

Fig. 137

LIGHT
FROM
SOURCE

to be mounted on a turntable.

The ultra-violet spectrum may be studied by substituting a prism manufactured from quartz. Where greater resolution is required it is usual to replace the prism with a **diffraction grating,** *q.v.*

(See also **Spectrograph; Spectroscope, direct-vision.**)

SPECTROSCOPE, DIRECT-VISION A small pocket spectroscope, designed for qualitative rather than quantitative use. Ideal for demonstrating the solar continuum, etc., to students. Its construction is shown in Fig. 138; the light from the object being examined is passed through a slit (*S*) and a lens (*L*) which produces a focused image in a position suitable for visual examination without an eyepiece.

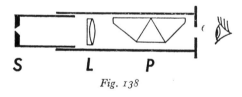

S   L   P

Fig. 138

The convergent beam from this lens is passed through an 'Amici' or similar type of prism (*P*). This consists of an odd number of triangular prisms, usually three, cemented together and arranged alternately as shown; the central prism is usually constructed of flint glass and the outside prisms of crown glass. This arrangement achieves high dispersion with the deviations cancelled out so as to give direct vision.

SPECTROSCOPIC BINARY A short-period binary system whose nature is

deduced from observations of the Doppler shift of the absorption lines in its spectrum, which varies due to the orbital motion of the component stars. (See **Binary system.**)

SPECTRUM If a beam of radiation is separated into its constituent radiations of different wavelengths, and these are observed in side-by-side presentation either directly or by projecting them onto a screen, this presentation is termed the *spectrum* of the radiation.

If visible light is so dispersed, by the use of a glass prism, the *visible spectrum* is formed, with its characteristic coloration of red, orange, yellow, green, blue and violet. With the aid of a spectrograph the spectrum can be photographed, the result being termed a *spectrogram*.

(See also **Spectra.**)

SPECULUM An alloy composed of copper 67 per cent, tin 33 per cent; it is hard but extremely brittle. It will take a very high polish and does not tarnish rapidly; it was therefore widely used for the manufacture of objective mirrors for reflecting telescopes, especially in the earlier years of their development. It became a common practice to use the term 'speculum' as a synonym for 'mirror' in this context, hence the observer's abbreviated description of his reflector, as, e.g. 'a 12-in. spec.'.

SPHERICAL ASTRONOMY The study of the positions and motions of the heavenly bodies, using the celestial sphere as a frame of reference. This being the case, all the problems requiring solution in this study are problems of spherical geometry. (See **Celestial sphere.**)

SPHERICAL TRIANGLE If any three points on the surface of a sphere are connected by three great-circle arcs, the figure enclosed is termed a spherical triangle. The study of the mathematical properties of this figure is termed *spherical trigonometry*.

As the mathematics of positional astronomy are based upon the concept of the celestial sphere, the properties of the spherical triangle are obviously of great importance to the astronomer.

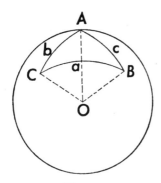

Fig. 139

In Fig. 139, *ABC* represents a spherical triangle, *AB*, *BC* and *CA* being arcs of great circles. It is conventional to refer to the angles $\angle CAB$, $\angle ABC$ and $\angle BCA$ as *A*, *B* and *C*, and the sides facing these angles—*BC*, *CA* and *AB*—as *a*, *b* and *c* respectively. The sides are measured in terms of the angles they subtend at the centre of the sphere (*O*); thus, *a* is measured as $\angle COB$, etc.

It can be shown that

$$\cos a = \cos b \cos c + \sin b \sin c \cos A;$$

this is the basic formula of spherical trigonometry, and is known as the *cosine-formula*. Similar formulae hold for the remaining sides of the triangle, thus:

$$\cos b = \cos c \cos a + \sin c \sin a \cos B;$$

$$\cos c = \cos a \cos b + \sin a \sin b \cos C.$$

It can also be shown that the following basic relations hold:

$$\frac{\sin A}{\sin a} = \frac{\sin B}{\sin b} = \frac{\sin C}{\sin c} \quad \text{(the \textit{sine-formula})};$$

$$\sin a \cos B = \cos b \sin c - \sin b \cos c \cos A;$$

$$\cos a \cos C = \sin a \cot b - \sin C \cot B.$$

These formulae are the basis of all the formulae used in celestial mechanics.

SPHERICAL TRIGONOMETRY The study of the mathematical properties of the **spherical triangle**; it is of fundamental importance in mathematical astronomy.

SPICA The star α Vir, a blue-white dwarf star of spectral class *B1*, magnitude 1·0. It is a spectroscopic eclipsing binary with a period of 4 days.

SPIRAL GALAXY Up to the early nineteenth century all observable objects outside our own galactic system tended to be classed as 'extragalactic nebulae'. As more powerful telescopes and more refined observing techniques were developed, it became apparent that many of them were not strictly speaking *nebulae* at all, the term implying a diffuse appearance and a predominantly gaseous or particulate constitution. It therefore became the practice to term these objects 'galaxies', to distinguish them from true nebulae.

In 1845 the third Earl of Rosse examined one of these galaxies—M51 in Canes Venatici—with his mammoth 72-in. reflector; to his astonishment he found that it had a spiral form, like a huge whirlpool. (This object has been popularly known as 'the Whirlpool nebula' ever since.)

Lord Rosse carefully drew the structure of the galaxy—his drawing accords perfectly with contemporary long-exposure photographs—and began to examine other 'nebulae' to see if there were any more examples of the spiral form. Within five years fourteen had been found, and they have continued to be discovered at a rapidly increasing rate as telescopes of ever-greater resolving power have been developed. Many thousands are now known.

The 'spiral galaxy' is now known to be the basic form of the great star systems; the solar system is situated in a typical one. There are a number of different forms of spiral galaxy, which were studied and classified by Hubble in the 1930s. There is also a parallel class of galaxies—the 'barred spirals'—which are also included in Hubble's classification.

(See also **Galactic evolution; Galactic structure.**)

SPIRAL RING-STRUCTURES A type of lunar surface feature, comprising some larger rings which have ridges spiralling inwards from the main wall onto the floor of the ring-structure, usually continuing as **rilles**. Well-defined examples can be seen in Gassendi and Posidonius. (See **Moon—surface features of.**)

SPÖRER, Gustav (1822–1896) German astronomer who studied the latitude-drift in the distribution of sunspots during the solar cycle, discovered by Carrington. This drift is frequently designated *Spörer's Law*.

SPÖRER'S LAW The relationship between the latitude of sunspots and the 11-year solar cycle. The variation was actually discovered by Carrington but has for many years been attributed to Spörer who analysed the latitude distribution of sunspots in detail. (See **Sunspots.**)

SPOT-GROUP A complex form of **sunspot**, having several umbrae; these are frequently contained by a common penumbra, although entirely separate spots having their own penumbra are sometimes observed which are nevertheless obviously members of the adjacent group.

SPUTNIK Name given to the first series of artificial earth satellites, launched from the Soviet Union 1957–63. The first earth satellite ever launched, *Sputnik 1*, was a spherical object 23 inches in diameter. It was launched on 1957 October 4. Ten

Sputniks had been successfully launched by 1961 March. The last recorded satellite in the series was *Sputnik 26*, launched on 1963 April 2.

STADIUS Lunar surface feature, co-ordinates $\xi - 236$, $\eta + 183$. The remains of an ancient ring formation, 40 miles in diameter; situated about 100 miles west of Copernicus (centre-to-centre) and about 85 miles south-east of Eratosthenes, to which it is connected by a rugged mountain mass. Except for the north-west boundary, where this mountain mass begins, the walls are almost entirely ruined, and are marked only by low ridges broken with a number of small crater pits. The floor is very pitted.

STAG'S-HORN MOUNTAIN Lunar surface feature, co-ordinates $\xi - 115$, $\eta - 412$. Peculiar-shaped mountain mass situated at the southern end of the Straight Wall, and reaching an altitude rather less than 2,000 ft. It appears to be the western rampart of a ruined ring-formation.

STANDARD CO-ORDINATES In photographic astrometry it is customary to compute the angular separation between a pair of stars from the linear separation between their images on the plate. The latter is obtained from the relative positions of the images on the plate, measured in rectangular co-ordinates. The plate scale must, of course, be known, and the Right Ascension and Declination of the point on the celestial sphere towards which the optical axis of the telescope was directed during the exposure.

Ideally the centre of the plate, used as the origin of the rectangular co-ordinates for the measurement of star positions, should lie on the optical axis of the telescope; any departure from this condition must be determined and corrected for.

From the plate centre rectangular axes are drawn on the plate, perpendicular and parallel to the meridian; these are termed the ξ-axis and η-axis respectively. The co-ordinates (ξ, η) of each star image (the *standard co-ordinates*) represent the differences in R.A. and Dec. between the position of each star and the assumed position of the plate centre. The measured co-ordinates of the images will differ from their true standard co-ordinates by a small amount, due to errors in the assumed position of the plate centre, the adopted plate scale and the orientation of the plate in the measuring machine. These errors are eliminated by small correction factors (the *plate constants*) introduced into the equations used to convert the measured co-ordinates into standard co-ordinates.

(See also **Astrometry; Plate centre; Plate constants; Plate scale.**)

STANDARD EPOCH If positional observations of stars are made on different occasions their positions will have changed between the observations, due to their proper motions and other factors; to simplify such comparisons it is customary for all positional observations made over a long period of time—of the order of half a century—to be reduced to one date, known as the Standard Epoch. The Standard Epoch in use at the present time is 1950·0; prior to 1925 it was 1900·0, and from 1975 onwards it is likely to be 2000·0.

STAR An entirely gaseous body held together by its own gravitation. The stars are radiant bodies which produce their energy by nuclear reactions—principally the breakdown of hydrogen nuclei to produce helium nuclei, plus radiant energy as a by-product.

The Sun is a fairly typical star, but the term 'star' is frequently used in astronomical work to designate the remaining 'background' stars, the Sun being treated separately by virtue of its proximity and the resulting opportunity to investigate its properties in much greater detail than those of the other stars.

STAR ATLASES These are charts of the heavens, usually in book form or a portfolio of separate charts, and drawn to a relatively small scale. They are therefore very convenient both for novice observers, making their first explorations of the heavens, and for observers of comets, minor planets, variable stars, etc., who do not require the accuracy of, or have not access to, the large-scale photographic charts.

Among the most useful atlases available are:

> **Norton's Star Atlas;**
> **Skalnaté Pleso Atlas;**
> **Webb's Atlas of the Stars.**

These are described as separate entries in this book. *Norton's Star Atlas* is the indispensible reference book of all amateur astronomers; Webb's Atlas is particularly useful to the experienced visual observer for both identification purposes and the estimation of rough positions of observed objects.

(See also **Star catalogues; Star charts.**)

STAR CATALOGUE DESIGNATIONS
The bright stars, including those which have proper names, are identified by **Bayer Letters** or **Flamsteed Numbers.** The fainter stars are known by a diversity of reference numbers from general catalogues, and may be seen designated by several different catalogue numbers in different works. Although the numbers from Argelander's *Bonner Durchmusterung* and more recent catalogues such as the Boss *General Catalogue* are principally used, some stars are traditionally known by their designations in older catalogues. The following list of prefixes commonly used in catalogue designations may therefore be of assistance in identifying their sources. Many of the modern general catalogues include tabulations of the older designations of their stars. The modern catalogues listed are described in this book under their titles, and also some of the older ones of particular interest.

ADS	Aitken's *New General Catalogue of Double Stars*, 1932.
AGK ⎫ AG ⎭	**Astronomisches Gesellschaft Catalogues**, *q.v.*
B	Bode's catalogue of 1801.
BAC	British Association Catalogue (Baily, 1845).
BD	Argelander's *Bonner Durchmusterung*, 1859–1862; also Schönfeld's extension of 1886.
BGC	Burnham's *General Catalogue of Double Stars within 121° of the North Pole*, published in 1906.
Br	Auwer's reduction of Bradley's observations.
CD	*Cordoba Durchmusterung*, 1892 + .
CGA	Gould's *Catalogo General Argentino*, 1886.
CPD	Gill and Kapteyn's *Cape Photographic Durchmusterung*, 1896–1903.
CZ	Cordoba Zone catalogues.
FK	Fundamentalkatalogs of the *Berliner Astronomischen Jahrbuch*.
G	Gould's *Uranometria Argentina*, 1879.
GC	Boss's *General Catalogue of 33342 Stars*, 1936.
GFH	**Geschichte des Fixstern-Himmels,** *q.v.*
Grb ⎫ Gr ⎭	Groombridge's *Catalogue of Circumpolar Stars*, 1838; also Dyson and Thackeray's *New Reduction of Groombridge's Circumpolar Catalogue, Epoch 1810·0*, published in 1905.
H	Hevelius' catalogue of 1660.
H	Sir William Herschel's catalogues of double stars, 1782-1822. Also, followed by volume numbers I–VI, his catalogues of nebulae and star clusters.
h	Sir John Herschel's catalogues of double stars and nebulae.
HD	The *Henry Draper Catalogue*, 1818–1824.
HP	The *Harvard Photometry*, 1884.
HR	The *Harvard Revised Photometry*, 1908.
IC	The *Index Catalogue* extensions to the N.G.C. (1904, 1908).
Lac	Lacaille's *Catalogue of Southern Stars*, *Epoch* 1750, published in 1847.
Lal ⎫ Ll ⎭	Lalande's catalogue of 1837.
M	The **Messier Catalogue,** *q.v.*
NGC	Dreyer's *New General Catalogue of Nebulae and Clusters of Stars* of 1888.

PGC	Boss's *Preliminary General Catalogue of 6188 Stars*, published in 1910.
Pi	Piazzi's catalogue of 1803–1814.
SDS	Innes' *Southern Double Star Catalogue* of 1926–1927.
SMP	The Harvard *Southern Meridian Photometry* of 1895.
UA	Gould's *Uranometria Argentina* of 1879.
UO	Pritchard's *Uranometria Nova Oxoniensis* of 1885.
Σ	F. G. W. Struve's **Dorpat Catalogue** of 1827, *q.v.*
OΣ	Otto Struve's *Revised Pulkowa Catalogue* of 1850.
OΣΣ	Part II of the *Revised Pulkowa Catalogue*.

(See also **Star nomenclature**.)

STAR CATALOGUES The compilation of star catalogues is one of the most important and fundamental activities of the astronomer; they are far from being simple lists, but contain comprehensive tabulations of observed data about the stars listed. They form the most concise summaries of the results achieved by decades of observational effort, and are invaluable works of reference. There are several basic types of catalogue, each compiled to meet a specific purpose. There are a number of *general catalogues*, mostly massive compilations of the basic data relating to a large number of stars; there are also a number of *fundamental catalogues*, which list a smaller number of stars but contain positions for them determined to a far greater degree of accuracy; these are used as the frame of reference for all positional observations. There are also specialist catalogues for observers of double stars, variable stars, stellar spectra, etc.

The following is a selected list of catalogues of various kinds; it is far from exhaustive, but includes some of the most important catalogues in each field and also some that are of particular value to amateurs. Further details about the catalogues listed here are given as separate entries in this book, under their respective titles.

General Catalogues
Astrographic Catalogue
Astronomisches Gesellschaft Catalogues
Bonner Durchmusterung
Cape Photographic Durchmusterung
Catalogue of Bright Stars
Cordoba Durchmusterung
General Catalogue
Skalnaté Pleso Atlas
Yale Catalogues

Fundamental Catalogues
FK3 Catalogue
FK4 Catalogue

Double Stars
General Catalogue of Double Stars
New General Catalogue of Double Stars
Southern Double Star Catalogue

Variable Stars
General Catalogue of Variable Stars

Circumpolar Stars
Groombridge Catalogue

Zodiacal Stars
Catalogue of Zodiacal Stars

Stellar Spectra
Draper Catalogue

Stellar Magnitudes
Harvard Photometry
Revised Harvard Photometry
Southern Meridian Photometry

Stellar Parallaxes
General Catalogue of Trigonometrical Stellar Parallaxes

Radial Velocities
General Catalogue of Stellar Radial Velocities

Radio Stars
Cambridge catalogues of radio sources
I.A.U. Catalogue of Radio Sources

(See also **Star atlases; Star catalogue designations; Star nomenclature.**)

STAR CHARTS Charts of the 'fixed stars' may be used by an observer for one of several purposes: to ascertain the precise position in which he must search in order to find the particular object he wishes to observe; to ascertain whether an object he has observed is a star (and if so to identify it); or to deduce the position (by reference to the nearby stars) of a non-stellar object he has observed, e.g. a comet or minor planet.

Most of the charts used by the professional astronomer, especially for the third of these purposes, are of course large-scale charts and have usually been produced photographically; hand-drawn charts were formerly used, but have now been largely superseded. For small-scale work, and for much of the work carried out by amateur observers, drawn charts are still used—usually in the form of a star atlas.

The following important photographic charts are described in separate entries in this book:

Carte du Ciel;
Franklin-Adams Charts;
Palomar Sky Atlas.

An important set of charts was prepared by the Belgian astronomer E. Delporte, showing the boundaries to the constellations adopted by the International Astronomical Union in 1928. These charts, with tables of the co-ordinates of the constellation boundaries, were published by the I.A.U. in 1930 as the *Atlas Céleste*; this also included a catalogue of all the stars down to magnitude 4·5, giving the positions, magnitudes and spectral types of these stars and listing the principal doubles, variables and nebulae. The charts were also published separately with the title *Délimitation Scientifique des Constellations* (*Tables et Cartes*).

(See also **Star atlases; Star catalogues.**)

STAR CLOUD Name given to vast concentrations of stars, in which the star density is significantly higher than the mean value for the galaxy concerned. There are numerous star clouds in our own Galaxy; they are situated mostly in the galactic plane and are visible to the naked eye as the brighter patches in the Milky Way. These are not to be confused with the Magellanic Clouds of similar appearance, which are quite separate 'satellites' to our Galaxy. [Plate 20(c, e).]

STAR CLUSTERS The term 'cluster' tends to be used for any apparent concentration of a number of stars in an area of a few square degrees of sky; strictly it should be reserved for those groupings which represent an actual spatial concentration of stars, i.e. whose distances are approximately equal and which share a common direction of motion.

Star clusters have been studied since the time of William Herschel; from a study of their morphology it was obvious that there were two main types which became known as *globular clusters* and *open clusters*. It is now known that these two types also differ in the kinds of star of which they are composed and in their distribution in the Galaxy.

The globular clusters are instantly recognizable from their characteristic shape: they consist of between 2,000 and 100,000 stars in a dense group of approximately spherical form. The stars are densely concentrated at the centre of the cluster and thin out towards the outside of it. Among the best known globular clusters are ω Centauri, M 3 and M 13. Globular clusters are found to consist of ageing, Population II stars; they are also remarkable for the very high incidence of very short-period variables. These are similar to Cepheid variables but have periods of less than a day in all cases: they were first discovered in globular clusters by E. C. Pickering in 1889 and are usually known as *cluster-type variables*. Similar variables were later discovered elsewhere in the Galaxy, these are usually termed *RR Lyræ stars* after the brightest example of the type.

Perhaps the most important feature of the globular clusters is their distribution within the Galaxy; they do not share the lenticular distribution of the other component stars, but are in an approximately spherical distribution centred on the galactic centre. More than 100 globular clusters have been recorded in our own Galaxy. Globular clusters have also been detected in other spiral galaxies (e.g. M 31, the great galaxy in Andromeda) where they are similarly distributed. [Plate 22(a).]

Where a number of stars appear to form an open cluster their proper motions must be studied, in order to confirm that they share a common direction of motion, and their radial velocities must be determined to confirm that they are all at approximately the same distance from the Earth. If both these criteria are satisfied the stars do indeed constitute a cluster. As the name suggests the open clusters are much less densely populated than the globular clusters; they also contain far fewer stars (usually between 100 and 2,000) which are quite irregularly distributed throughout the cluster. The 'diameters' of open clusters are between 1 and 50 parsecs.

Some of the nearer open clusters cover such large area of the sky that they do not form an obvious grouping, but their connexion is discovered from an examination of their proper motions which shows them to share a common motion, converging towards (or diverging from) a single point in the heavens. Such clusters are termed *moving clusters*.

The stars comprising the open clusters are the young, hot, Population I stars found in the spiral arms of galaxies; it is not therefore surprising to find that the open clusters are only found within about 200 parsecs of the galactic plane. For this reason they are often referred to as *galactic clusters*.

Two of the best-known open clusters are the *Hyades* and *Pleiades* clusters in Taurus; others are *Præsepe* in Cancer and (for southern-hemisphere observers) the 'Jewel Box' surrounding κ Crucis in the Southern Cross—both magnificent sights in a low-power telescope. [Plate 22(b, c, d).]

Another type of open cluster is the **stellar association** (*q.v.*); these are also groups of Population I stars but are very much larger, having diameters of the order of 100 parsecs.

STAR NOMENCLATURE Stars are identified for general purposes by a number or letter followed by the Latin genitive form of the name of the constellation in which they are situated.

For the brightest stars in a constellation the 'Bayer Letters' are used—the letters of the Greek alphabet as assigned by Bayer in his *Uranometria* of 1603—thus: δ Geminorum.

Rather less bright stars are known by the 'Flamsteed Numbers'—the numbers they were given in Flamsteed's *Historia Cœlestis Britannica*, the definitive edition of which was published in 1725; Flamsteed numbers have the form: 61 Cygni.

The fainter stars, which form a large proportion of the stars used for modern observational programmes, are identified by their designations in the catalogue most appropriate to the type of observation involved—i.e. general, fundamental, double-star, variable-star catalogues, etc.

(See also **Constellation names and abbreviations; Star catalogues; Star catalogue designations**.)

STAR PLACES The position of a star is normally measured in Right Ascension and Declination, which are referred to the equator and the equinox. Unfortunately these are slowly but constantly changing their position on the celestial sphere, due to the effects of precession. To record an accurate place for a star, therefore, its co-ordinates must be referred to the equator and equinox at a specified epoch.

Star places are normally encountered in one of three forms, the *true*, *apparent* and *mean places*.

The *true place* is the star's position on the true, heliocentric, celestial sphere at the moment of observation; that is to say, the actual position at the instant of observation, referred to the true equator and equinox at that instant, as it would be observed from the centre of the Sun.

The *apparent place* is the actual position of the star on a geocentric celestial sphere, referred to the true equator and equinox of date, as it is observed from the Earth. This is the place as determined by a meridian-circle observation, after correction for atmospheric refraction. The apparent place of a star is equal to the true place plus corrections for annual parallax and aberration.

The *mean place* of a star is its position on a heliocentric celestial sphere, referred to the mean equator and equinox for the beginning of the year of the observation.

For the statistical combination of several determinations of a star's place, made at different times, it is obviously necessary to reduce them all to a common basis. It is usual to reduce each observed apparent place to the mean place for the commencement of the year. To achieve this each apparent place must be corrected for the effect of precession, nutation, aberration, annual parallax and proper motion, during the interval between the beginning of the year and the moment of observation. For large-scale programmes of positional observations, extending over several years, it is usual to reduce all the observations to the fundamental epoch currently in use. At the present time this is 1950·0; epochs previously used were 1900·0 and 1925·0.

STAR STREAMING It was discovered by Kapteyn in 1904, from a study of the proper motions of the brighter stars, that these appeared to have two preferred directions of motion. Stars in all parts of the heavens shared these preferred directions, which were towards two points termed the *apparent vertices*. These points were situated in Lepus, at R.A. 6 hr, Dec. −15°, and in Pavo, at R.A. 19 hr, Dec. −64°.

The first stream, with its apparent vertex in Lepus, comprised about 60 per cent of the stars involved and became generally known as *Drift I*; the other stream, with the apparent vertex in Pavo, comprised about 40 per cent of the stars and is known as *Drift II*. The velocity of Drift I is approximately double that of Drift II.

If the apparent streaming is corrected so as to remove the effect of the local **solar motion**, the drifts are then found to be in exactly opposing directions; their *true vertices* are therefore in diametrically opposite positions in the heavens, in Orion (R.A. 6 hr 20 min, Dec. +12°) and Scutum (R.A. 18 hr 20 min, Dec. −12°). These true vertices are in the galactic plane, at galactic longitudes of 202° and 22°.

Not all stars take part in the streaming; the tendency of individual stars to do so varies with their spectral type. Type *A* stars are particularly prone to show the preferred directions of motion, but scarcely any type *B* stars do so. Stars in class *F* and later classes show a tendency to stream, but less strongly than class *A*.

As proper motion determinations extended to fainter stars the inequality in the number of stars in each Drift was found to disappear.

The phenomenon of star streaming is obviously of fundamental importance in studies of stellar motions and the structure and rotation of the Galaxy.

(See also **Galaxy, the; Solar motion; Stellar populations.**)

STAR TEST A means of testing the optics of a telescope, and its adjustment; it consists of setting the instrument onto a suitable star (usually of about the second magnitude) and examining the in-focus and extra-focal images. The existence and extent of aberrations and maladjustments can be detected from abnormalities in the diffraction pattern.

STARS, BACKGROUND Term used in general discussion to distinguish the stars proper from the Sun and the moving bodies of the solar system; i.e. the so-called 'fixed stars' of the ancients.

STARS, BINARY See **Binary system.**

STARS, BRIGHTEST The 25 brightest stars are listed in Table 42. They are the brightest stars, of course, only in terms of their apparent magnitude; many of them appear so bright only because they are relatively close to the Earth. Their absolute magnitudes are also listed as an indication of their true luminosity. The trigonometrical parallaxes, where known, the actual distances and the spectral classifications of the stars are also shown.

The position of *Betelgeuse* in Table 42 is somewhat arbitrary, as it is a variable with a magnitude range of 0·4–1·3.

(See also **Stars, nearest.**)

STARS—BRIGHTNESS OF The brightness of a star as we observe it from the Earth depends upon its distance from the Earth as well as its actual intrinsic luminosity. Thus the magnitude figure used to indicate the brightness a star appears to have is termed *apparent magnitude,* and for stars of known distance a second figure is calculated to indicate the brightness it would appear to have were it at a standard distance from the Earth—the *absolute magnitude.* The apparent brightness of a star also depends upon its spectral type and upon the effects of galactic absorption. (See **Magnitude, absolute; Magnitude, apparent; Stars, brightest; Stars—luminosity of; Stars, nearest; Stars—spectral classification of.**)

STARS—CHEMICAL COMPOSITION OF From analyses of stellar spectra it is found that the chemical composition of stars closely resembles that of the Sun. This applies not only to other yellow main-sequence stars similar to the Sun in spectral type, but to stars of all spectral classes.

Hydrogen is by far the most abundant element, accounting for more than 80 per cent of the stars by volume (more than 50 per cent by mass); the next most abundant element is helium (15–20 per cent by volume, 40–50 per cent by mass); all other elements comprise less than one per cent of the total volume.

Spectral analysis reveals only the com-

Table 42. *The brightest stars*

Star	Proper name	R.A. hr min	Dec. ° '	Apparent magnitude	Spectral type	Parallax "	Distance l.y.	Absolute magnitude
1 α CMa	Sirius	06 42·9	−16 39	−1·47	A1 v	0·375	8·7	+0·7
2 α Car	Canopus	06 22·8	−52 40	−0·71	F0 Ib	0·018	300	−5·5
3 α Cen	Rigil Kent	14 36·2	−60 38	−0·27	G2 v	0·751	4·0	+4·6
4 α Boo	Arcturus	14 13·4	+19 26	−0·06	K2 IIIp	0·090	36	−0·3
5 α Lyr	Vega	18 35·2	+38 44	+0·03	A0 v	0·123	26	+0·3
6 β Ori	Rigel	05 12·2	−08 15	0·08	B8 Ia	−0·003	850	−7·0
7 α Aur	Capella (binary)	05 13·0	+45 57	0·09	{G8 III} {G0 III}	0·073	45	{+0·12} {+0·37}
8 α CMi	Procyon	07 36·7	+05 21	0·34	F5 IV–v	0·288	11	+2·8
9 α Eri	Achernar	01 35·9	−57 29	0·49	B5 v	0·023	75	−1·3
10 β Cen	Hadar	14 00·3	−60 08	0·61	B1 III	0·016	300	−4·3
11 α Aql	Altair	19 48·3	+08 44	0·75	A7 IV–v	0·198	16	+2·1
12 α Tau	Aldebaran	04 33·0	+16 25	0·78	K5 III	0·048	65	−0·2
13 α Cru	Acrux	12 23·8	−62 49	0·80	B1 IV		270	−3·8
14 α Ori	Betelgeuse (var.)	05 52·5	+07 24	(mean) 0·85	M2 Ib	0·005	650	−5·5
15 α Sco	Antares	16 26·4	−26 19	0·92	M1 Ib	0·019	400	−4·5
16 α Vir	Spica	13 22·6	−10 54	0·98	B1 v	0·021	220	−3·2
17 β Gem	Pollux	07 42·3	+28 09	1·15	K0 III	0·093	35	+0·7
18 α PsA	Fomalhaut	22 54·9	−29 53	1·16	A3 v	0·144	23	+1·8
19 α Cyg	Deneb	20 39·7	+45 06	1·26	A2 Ia	−0·013	1,500	−7·0
20 β Cru	Mimosa	12 44·8	−59 25	1·28	B0 IV		370	−4·0
21 α Leo	Regulus	10 05·7	+12 14	1·33	B7 v	0·039	85	−1·0
22 ε CMa	Adhara	06 56·7	−28 54	1·42	B2 II		620	−5·0
23 γ Ori	Bellatrix	05 22·5	+06 18	1·61	B2 III	0·026	450	−4·1
24 λ Sco	Shaula	17 30·2	−37 04	1·61	B2 IV		300	−3·3
25 β Tau	El Nath	05 23·1	+28 34	1·64	B7 III	0·018	270	−3·0

position of the outer, 'atmospheric' layers of the star, of course, but it is believed that stars are a homogeneous mixture throughout their volume, and that the compositions determined in this way are valid.

STARS, CLOSE CIRCUMPOLAR Close circumpolar stars are of particular value to observers, as their diurnal motion is very slow; they are therefore in the field of a transit-circle, for example, for many minutes compared with the minute or less for which stars of lower latitude remain in the field. They can thus be re-observed several times during the same transit, and are valuable for the precise determination of azimuth error.

They are also of value in making adjustments to telescope mountings, e.g. when setting up a new equatorial instrument.

The principal naked-eye circumpolars within 10° of each pole are listed in Table 43.

The catalogue abbreviations used in the Table are: Br, Auwer's reduction of Bradley's observations; Grb, Groombridge's *Catalogue of Circumpolar Stars*; H, Hevelius' catalogue; G, Gould's *Uranometria Argentina*.

Table 43. Close circumpolar stars

Star	R.A. hr min	Dec. °	Apparent magnitude	Spectral type
NORTH				
43 H Cep	01 02	+85 59	4·52	*Ko*
Polaris	01 49	+89 02	2·12	*F8*
Br 402 Cep	03 20	+84 44	5·78	*Ko*
51 H Cep	07 19	+87 08	5·26	*Mo*
ɪ H Dra	09 30	+81 33	4·58	*K2*
30 H Cam	10 25	+82 49	5·34	*F2*
Grb 2196 UMi	14 54	+82 43	5·73	*Go*
ε UMi	16 51	+82 07	4·40	*G5*
δ UMi	17 48	+86 37	4·44	*Ao*
76 Dra	20 46	+82 21	5·69	*Ao*
32 H Cep	22 18	+85 51	5·38	*Ao*
36 H Cep	22 55	+84 05	4·96	*K5*
SOUTH				
4 G Oct	01 40	−84 57	5·63	*Ko*
ξ Men	05 05	−82 31	5·85	*Ko*
ζ Oct	09 04	−85 31	5·38	*Fo*
ι Oct	12 49	−84 56	5·38	*Ko*
κ Oct	13 32	−85 36	5·65	*A2*
ρ Oct	15 31	−84 21	5·66	*A2*
χ Oct	18 24	−87 39	5·22	*Ko*
σ Oct	20 15	−89 06	5·48	*Fo*
υ Oct	22 23	−86 11	5·74	*Ko*
β Oct	22 41	−81 34	4·34	*Fo*
τ Oct	23 21	−87 42	5·56	*Ko*

Position column heading: **Position (1950·0)**

STARS—COLOUR OF To the unaided eye, in favourable observing conditions, many of the stars are seen to have a recognizable colour. In fact any star has a specific colour, which is a function of its radiation and related to its effective temperature.

The light received from a star is, of course, an integration of light of many wavelengths; the apparent colour is therefore directly related to the spectral type, and a star's mean colour can be used to determine its spectral type with reasonable accuracy. This is usually done by deter-mining the **colour index** of the star, *q.v.*

(See also **Stars—spectral classification of.**)

STARS—DIAMETERS OF If the angular diameter of a star is measurable, and its parallax is known, its true diameter can be calculated by means of the relationship

$$D = \frac{214\,d}{\pi}$$

where D is the true diameter of the star expressed in terms of the Sun's diameter, d is the angular diameter of the star and π its trigonometrical parallax. (The factor

Table 44. Some stellar diameters

Star	Spectral/luminosity classification	Parallax "	Angular diameter "	Linear diameter (on scale Sun = 1)	(miles)
Betelgeuse	M2 I	0·005	0·047	1000	865,000,000
Mira Ceti	M6e II	0·023	0·056	480	415,000,000
Antares	M1 Ib	0·019	0·040	450	390,000,000
Aldebaran	K5 III	0·048	0·021	94	81,000,000
Arcturus	K1 III	0·091	0·020	47	40,500,000
Capella	G8 III	0·073	0·004	13	11,250,000
Sirius A	A1 V	0·375	0·006	1·85	1,605,000
SUN	G2 V	—	—	1·00	864,950
Sirius B	wA5 VI	0·375	0·000077	0·044	38,000
o² Eri B	wA0 VI	0·201	0·000034	0·036	31,000
van Maanen's star	wF5 VI	0·235	0·000019	0·009	8,000

214 derives from 2 × 107, the Sun's radius being $\frac{1}{107}$ A.U.

As can be seen from Table 44, the diameters of stars in different spectral/luminosity classes vary very considerably. The first five stars listed are red and orange giants and are very much larger than the Sun. It will be noted that the three red giants listed are so large that if they were placed in the position of the Sun the orbit of Mars would be entirely contained within them.

The next star listed—*Capella*—is a yellow giant and much smaller, although it is still substantially larger than the Sun which is a main-sequence star of the same spectral type. *Sirius*, a white main-sequence star, is less than twice the Sun's diameter; only its proximity to the solar system (8·7 light years) renders it the brightest star in the heavens. By contrast, *Sirius* has a faint white dwarf companion, *Sirius B*, which is less than one twentieth of the Sun's diameter. Two further white dwarfs are listed, the smaller (van Maanen's

Star) being less than one hundredth of the Sun's diameter.

(See also **Stars—density of; Stars—masses of.**)

STARS—DISTANCES OF The determination of stellar distances is of fundamental importance in astrophysics, being essential to studies of the structure of the Galaxy.

The most straightforward method of determining the distance of a star is from measurements of its trigonometrical parallax, but this method is not capable of producing reliable results for stars much more than a few hundred light years from the Sun.

The distance of the member stars of a moving cluster can be determined, from the radial velocities of the cluster stars—obtained from the **Doppler shift** of the spectral lines—and the observed diminution in the angular diameter of the cluster over a considerable period of time.

The distance of a star can also be calculated if its absolute magnitude can be inferred from observed data, by means of the well known relationship between a star's absolute magnitude (M), apparent magnitude (m) and distance (r):

$$M = m + 5 - 5 \log r.$$

There are four methods of determining a star's absolute magnitude; the most common is to deduce it from the spectral/luminosity classification of the star by means of the **Hertzsprung–Russell diagram.**

The absolute magnitude of the cooler stars (classes G, K and M) may be determined by measuring the widths of the **calcium reversal lines.** In the case of binary systems, whose masses can be determined from their observed orbital motions, the absolute magnitude can be determined from the **mass–luminosity relationship.** Finally, the absolute magnitude of Cepheid variables can be obtained from their observed period by means of the **period–luminosity law.**

The distances of the 25 nearest stars are tabulated under **Stars—nearest;** they range from 1·3 parsecs (4·3 light years) to 3·6 parsecs (11·9 light years). Only 27 stars are known with parallaxes exceeding 0˝.25, i.e. within 4 parsecs of the Sun; they comprise one triple system (a and *Proxima Centauri*), four binary systems and sixteen single stars. Only the triple system in Centaurus (1·3 parsecs) and Barnard's Star (1·8 parsecs) have parallaxes exceeding 0˝.5, i.e. are within 2 parsecs of the Sun.

The diameter of the Galaxy is believed to be 25,000 parsecs; as the Sun is situated approximately 8,000 parsecs from the galactic centre the outermost stars of the Galaxy lie between 17,000 and 33,000 parsecs from the Sun.

(See also **Galaxy, the; Parallax, stellar—determination of; Star clusters; Stars—spectral classification of.**)

STARS, DOUBLE See **Double stars.**

STARS, DWARF Stars whose spectral/luminosity classification places them low down in the **Hertzsprung–Russell dia-**

gram. They are comparatively few, and comprise the white dwarfs and the class M red-dwarf extension at the lower end of the main sequence.

The term is sometimes used erroneously to describe all main-sequence stars.

(See also **Stars—spectral classification of.**)

STARS, DWARF VARIABLE Most of the well-known types of intrinsic variable have spectral–luminosity classifications which place them in the upper part of the main sequence, or above it, in the **Hertzsprung–Russell diagram.** There are a number of the smaller groups of intrinsic variables, however, which appear to be dwarf stars, and these are of particular interest to the astrophysicist.

The principal types of dwarf variables are the **flare stars,** the **U Geminorum stars** and the **pre-novae** and **post-novae,** *q.v.*

STARS, EARLY-TYPE Term used to describe stars whose spectral types fall near the 'beginning' of the Harvard–Draper sequence, e.g. spectral classes O and B. (See **Stars—spectral classification of.**)

STARS—ENERGY OF The principal source of stellar energy is believed to be the energy produced when hydrogen atoms join together to form atoms of helium. The hydrogen nucleus contains one proton and the helium nucleus four; the hydrogen atom has an atomic weight of 1·008, and thus four would have a combined weight of 4·032, but a helium atom has a weight of only 4·004. The difference is due to the loss of mass in the form of energy released by the transformation process.

There are two principal mechanisms by which the transformation is believed to take place—the **carbon–nitrogen cycle** and the **proton–proton reaction.** The former is believed to be the predominant mechanism at temperatures above, say, 15,000,000° K, and the latter at lower temperatures.

Table 45.   Galactic concentration of stars

Limiting magnitude: Galactic latitude	6	10	14	16	18	20	
0°	0·128	7·71	371	2,140	10,200	40,100	Number of stars
20°	0·080	4·43	176	873	3,620	12,400	per square degree
40°	0·050	2·84	94	396	1,310	3,400	
60°	0·042	2·23	61	236	733	1,820	
90°	0·037	1·81	44	163	482	1,160	
Galactic concentration:	3·4	4·3	8·4	13·2	21·1	34·4	

STARS, FIXED Term adopted in former times to distinguish the stars proper from the bodies of the solar system; derived from the fact that the stars have no motions detectable in day-to-day observation. The term *background stars* is now preferred in general discussion, as the stars are now known not to be fixed but to have measurable, albeit small, *proper motions.*

STARS—GALACTIC CONCENTRATION OF The stars of the Galaxy are symmetrically distributed about the galactic plane; they are also concentrated towards it: that is to say, the star density decreases progressively with increasing galactic latitude.

The *galactic concentration* is a convenient index of this effect; it may be defined as the ratio between the star density in the galactic plane and that at the galactic pole. It is found to vary with the magnitude of the stars concerned: the density of naked-eye stars in the plane is almost $3\frac{1}{2}$ times that at the pole, but the

ratio increases rapidly for fainter stars indicating that the fainter stars are much more strongly concentrated towards the galactic plane.

Table 45 shows the average number of stars per square degree at selected galactic latitudes, down to various limiting magnitudes, and the galactic concentration index for all stars down to each of these limiting magnitudes.

(See also **Galactic structure.**)

STARS, GIANT Stars whose spectral/ luminosity classification places them in the giant sequence of the **Hertzsprung–Russell diagram**; they constitute classes II (bright giants) and III (normal giants) of the Yerkes luminosity classification.

There are very few giant stars of spectral classes *A* and *F* (termed the *Hertzsprung gap* in the H–R diagram), but there are many in classes *G, K* and *M*.

The mean absolute magnitudes of class II and class III giants are shown in Table 46.

Table 46. *Mean absolute magnitudes of giant stars*

Spectral class	Mean absolute magnitude	
	Class II	Class III
B	−4·5	−3·5
A	−2·5	−0·5
F	−2·0	+1·0
G	−2·0	+0·5
K	−2·3	0·0
M	−2·5	−0·5

Giant stars are found in both Populations I and II.

(See also **Stars—spectral classification of.**)

STARS, HIGH–VELOCITY Stars whose space velocities are abnormally high— exceeding 60 miles/sec., and in many cases 100 miles/sec.; they are Population II stars situated close to the centre of the Galaxy. Their motions suggest that their orbits around the galactic centre are both very eccentric and highly inclined to the galactic plane.

They are particularly important in studies of the Sun's motion in space and the rotation of the Galaxy.

STARS, LATE–TYPE Term used to describe stars whose spectral types are near the 'end' of the Harvard–Draper sequence, e.g. spectral classes *K* and *M*. (See **Stars—spectral classification of.**)

STARS, LOW–VELOCITY Stars of Population I situated in the spiral arms of the Galaxy, whose space velocities are abnormally low.

STARS—LUMINOSITY OF The luminosity of a star may be defined as the total flux, or amount of energy radiated, from its entire surface area every second. It is usually sufficient to consider the flux over a specific range of wavelengths, in which case the **absolute magnitude** can be used as a direct indication of the luminosity. If the distance of a star is known, the absolute magnitude, and hence its luminosity, can be obtained from its apparent magnitude.

It was noticed by Miss Maury of the Harvard College Observatory that the sharpness of the spectral lines varied between stars of otherwise identical spectral type; Adams and Kohlschütter, at Mount Wilson, found that these variations in the characteristics of the spectral lines could be used to determine the luminosity of the star, and hence to establish its position in the **Hertzsprung–**

Table 47. *Yerkes luminosity classification*

Class	Type of star	Example		Spectral class
Ia	brightest supergiants	*Rigel*	(β Ori)	*B8* Ia
Ib	supergiants	*Polaris*	(α UMi)	*F8* Ib
II	bright giants	*Gacrux*	(γ Cru)	*M3* II
III	giants	*Aldebaran*	(α Tau)	*K5* III
IV	sub-giants	*Achernar*	(α Eri)	*B5* IV
V	main-sequence and dwarf stars	*Sirius*	(α CMa)	*A1* V
VI	sub-dwarfs and white dwarfs		τ Cet	sd *G8* (VI)
		van Maanen's star		w*F5* (VI)

Russell diagram. Thus was developed the *Harvard–Mount Wilson system* of luminosity classification, in which the spectral type was prefixed with *d*, *g* or *c* to indicate that the star concerned was a dwarf, giant or supergiant, respectively. For example, the white supergiant *Rigel* was classified as *cB8*, the red giant *Aldebaran* as *gK5* and the Sun—a yellow dwarf—as *dG2*.

This system has now been largely superseded, at least for professional astrophysicists, by that devised by Morgan, Keénan and Kellman of the Yerkes Observatory, and hence known as the *MKK* or *Yerkes system*; it was developed for the *Atlas of Stellar Spectra* published in 1943. In this system the spectral type is given a suffix to indicate the luminosity class, as shown in Table 47.

(See also **Stars—spectral classification of.**)

STARS, MAIN-SEQUENCE Stars whose spectral/luminosity classification places them on the main sequence of the **Hertzsprung–Russell diagram.** They comprise stars of all types from *O–M*, and are particularly abundant in classes *B–G*.

(See also **Stars—spectral classification of.**)

STARS—MASSES OF The mass of a star can only be deduced from its gravitational effect upon the motion of another body; thus the binary stars are of great importance as the ratio of the masses of the two components can be determined from observations of their orbital motion. If their parallax is also known the combined mass, and hence the masses of the individual components, can also be obtained.

The mean masses for each spectral class of 343 main-sequence stars are shown in Table 48, together with the number of stars in each sample.

The masses vary with spectral type, in accordance with the **mass–luminosity relationship**; this can therefore be used to estimate the masses of many other

Table 48.   Stellar masses

Spectral class	Mean mass (Sun = 1)	Number of stars
O	27·5	17
B	10·0	111
A	2·2	81
F	1·9	78
G	1·2	39
K	1·1	17

stars of known spectral type, with fair statistical accuracy.

It is of interest that the masses of stars vary over a much smaller range than their diameters; very few stars indeed exceed 30 times the mass of the Sun: even the extremely dense white dwarfs, whilst they do not obey the mass–luminosity relationship, have masses of the same order as that of the Sun. The smallest stellar masses known at present are of the order 0·04 times that of the Sun.

These are important considerations in theories of stellar evolution: it appears that however a star's other physical characteristics may change during its lifetime, its mass is variable only to a very limited extent.

(See also **Stars—diameters of; Stellar evolution.**)

STARS, NAMED Many of the brighter stars are known by the proper names allocated to them in ancient times. Those in the following list are individually described under their proper names in this book.

Achernar	*Alcyone*
Acrux	*Aldebaran*
Adhara	*Algol*
Agena	*Alnilam*
Al Na'ir	*Alnitak*
Albireo	*Altair*
Alcor	*Antares*
	Arcturus

Bellatrix	*Mira*
Betelgeuse	*Mizar*
Canopus	*Polaris*
Capella	*Pollux*
Castor	*Procyon*
Deneb	*Proxima Centauri*
Denebola	
El Nath	*Regulus*
Fomalhaut	*Rigel*
	Rigil Kent
Gacrux	*Saiph*
Hadar	*Shaula*
Hamal	*Sirius*
Miaplacidus	*Spica*
Mimosa	*Vega*

STARS, NEAREST The 25 stars closest to the Earth, excluding the Sun, are listed in Table 49. They are listed in order of decreasing trigonometrical parallax, and the corresponding distance in light years is also shown. The star's positions, spectral classifications and apparent and absolute magnitudes are also tabulated. The components of multiple systems are listed separately.

(See also **Stars, brightest.**)

STARS, PULSATING Variable stars whose fluctuating brightness arises from a

Table 49.   The nearest stars

	Star	Position (1950·0) R.A. hr min	Dec. ° ′	Parallax ″	Distance l.y.	Spectral type	Apparent magnitude	Absolute magnitude
1	*Proxima* Cen	14 26·3	−62 28	0·762	4·3	*M5e*	+10·7	+15·1
2	α Cen A	14 36·2	−60 38	0·751	4·3	*G2*	0·0	4·4
3	α Cen B	14 36·2	−60 38	0·751	4·3	*K1*	1·4	5·8
4	Barnard's star	17 55·4	+04 24	0·545	6·0	*M5*	9·5	13·2
5	Wolf 359	10 54·1	+07 20	0·402	8·1	*M8*	13·5	16·5
6	Lal 21185	11 00·7	+36 18	0·398	8·2	*M2*	7·5	10·5
7	*Sirius* A	06 42·9	−16 39	0·375	8·7	*A1*	−1·5	1·4
8	*Sirius* B	06 42·9	−16 39	0·375	8·7	*wA5*	+8·5	11·4
9	UV Cet A	01 36·4	−18 13	0·369	9·0	*M6e*	12·5	15·3
10	UV Cet B	01 36·4	−18 13	0·369	9·0	*M6e*	13·0	15·8
11	Ross 154	18 46·7	−23 53	0·351	9·3	*M6*	10·6	13·3
12	Ross 248	23 39·5	+43 56	0·316	10·3	*M6*	12·2	14·7
13	ε Eri	03 30·6	−09 38	0·303	10·8	*K2*	3·7	6·1
14	L 789–6	22 35·7	−15 36	0·295	11·1	*M7*	12·2	14·6
15	Ross 128	11 45·3	+01 06	0·294	11·1	*M5*	11·1	13·5
16	61 Cyg A	21 04·7	+38 30	0·292	11·2	*K5*	5·2	7·5
17	61 Cyg B	21 04·7	+38 30	0·292	11·2	*K7*	6·0	8·4
18	*Procyon* A	07 36·7	+05 21	0·288	11·3	*F5*	0·3	2·6
19	*Procyon* B	07 36·7	+05 21	0·288	11·3	*wF*	10·8	13·1
20	ε Ind	21 59·6	−57 00	0·285	11·4	*K3*	4·7	7·0
21	Σ 2398 A	18 42·2	+59 33	0·280	11·6	*M4*	8·9	11·1
22	Σ 2398 B	18 42·2	+59 33	0·280	11·6	*M5*	9·7	11·9
23	Grb 34 A	00 15·5	+43 44	0·278	11·7	*M1*	8·1	10·3
24	Grb 34 B	00 15·6	+43 44	0·278	11·7	*M6*	11·0	13·3
25	Lac 9352	23 02·6	−36 09	0·273	11·9	*M2*	7·4	9·6

regular expansion and contraction of the star. The most important class of pulsating variables are the **Cepheid variables,** *q.v.* It is believed that other types of long-period variables also owe their fluctuations to a pulsating mechanism.

(See also **Variable stars.**)

STARS—ROTATION OF The axial rotation of the Sun can be determined from observations of surface markings such as sunspots; its rotational velocity at the equator is found to be 1·2 miles per second.

The rotation of other stars cannot be determined in the same way, but fortunately the rotation of a star produces a change in the line profiles of its spectrum which varies according to the rotational velocity and is measurable for many stars.

The observed effect is a broadening of the absorption lines; it arises from the **Doppler effect,** since one side of the rotating sphere has an approach velocity, and light from it shows a red-shift, whilst the other side has a recessional velocity and its light has a blue shift. The effect of the combined red- and blue-shifts is to broaden the line by an amount proportional to the rotational velocity.

Determinations of stellar rotation in this way are difficult to make with precision; results obtained to date are summarized in Table 50.

It will be noted that there is a notable discontinuity for main-sequence stars at about spectral type *F3*; this is even more prominent in stars in the *Hyades* and *Præsepe* clusters. The equally prominent discontinuity for main-sequence stars between *A9* and *F0* is however totally absent from the cluster stars. This may prove to be an important difference, especially in studies of the evolution of stars.

The observed velocities (*v*) given in Table 50 are correct only if the axis of rotation of the star is perpendicular to the line of sight; if the axis is inclined to the line of sight by an angle *i*, the true velocity *V* can be obtained from the formula

$$V = \frac{v}{\sin i}.$$

Unfortunately it is not possible to detect rotational velocities less than about 20 miles/sec. from line profiles, and it may be that the tabulated figures are not a true average for all stars. The slow rotation of the Sun may be more common than is suggested by comparison with the table.

Table 50.   Stellar rotational velocities

Spectral class	Observed rotational velocity (miles/sec.)			
	Main-sequence stars	*Hyades* stars	*Præsepe* stars	*Pleiades* stars
Oe, Be	170			
B1–B3	98			
B5–B7	126			
B8–A2	86			
B5–A2	106			120
A3–A9	85	75	70	
F0–F2	40	62	72	
F3–F6	17	21	29	
F7–G0	<15	<19	<28	

STARS—SPECTRAL CLASSIFICATION OF

The majority of stellar spectra comprise an emission continuum crossed by numerous dark absorption lines; some show enhanced emission lines. The study of stellar spectra is the main observational basis of astrophysics, and hence of all theories of stellar and galactic evolution and of cosmology.

Historical background. The science of astronomical spectroscopy sprang, of course, from Newton's classic experiment of 1666 in which he demonstrated that white light was an integration of light of all colours. The first seven absorption lines were discovered by Wollaston in 1802 in the spectrum of the Sun; the solar spectrum was extensively studied by Fraunhofer, who discovered a total of 574 absorption lines and accurately determined the position in the spectrum of 324 of them.

By the middle of the nineteenth century the new technique was being successfully applied by a number of workers, notably Donati—who discovered absorption lines in the spectra of comets and some of the brighter stars—and Huggins, who made some of the first attempts at interpreting stellar spectra as well as making the first positive identifications of absorption lines as being due to specific elements such as hydrogen, iron, sodium, calcium, etc.

The first practicable classification of the various types of stellar spectra was devised by an Italian Jesuit priest, Father Secchi, between 1863 and 1867. Secchi divided the stars into four groups according to their colours. Class I comprised blue and white stars with prominent hydrogen lines, such as *Sirius* and *Vega*. Class II comprised yellow stars with metallic lines, such as *Capella* and the Sun. Classes III and IV contained the red stars with different strong absorption bands, such as *Antares, Betelgeuse,* etc. In 1867 G. Wolf and G. Rayet of the Paris Observatory added a fifth class, V, comprising white stars whose spectra were dominated by numerous enhanced emission lines—the 'Wolf-Rayet stars'.

Secchi's classification system remained in use for a quarter of a century, with only minor modifications.

The Harvard–Draper sequence. A new system was evolved at the Harvard College Observatory by E. C. Pickering, Mrs. W. P. Fleming and Miss A. J. Cannon and used by them in the **Draper catalogue,** published in 1890. The new system comprises a sequence of spectral classes to which stars are allocated according to the prominence or absence of certain lines in their spectra. The sequence became known as the Harvard–Draper sequence, and is still the basis of the systems of spectral classification used today.

The original sequence comprised six classes, termed B, A, F, G, K and M. Later classes W and O were added at one end of the sequence and classes N, R and S at the other, so that the full sequence, arranged in order of descending surface temperature, is:

$$W—O—B—A—F—G—K < \frac{M—S}{R—N} \; .$$

The position in the sequence of classes R, N and S is somewhat arbitrary; it has been suggested that $R—N$ may be a branch sequence from G, and that S may be a branch from K rather than M.

It is conventional to refer to stars at the beginning of the Harvard–Draper sequence, e.g. O and B stars, as 'early-type' stars, and to stars at the end of the sequence, e.g. K and M stars, as 'late-type' stars. It must be emphasized that these terms mean early and late *in the sequence,* and do not refer to any of the possible interpretations of the sequence as a pattern of stellar evolution.

Classes B, A, F, G and K were subdivided on a decimal basis, a numeral being used to indicate the sub-division (e.g. $F2$, $G6$, etc.). Classes O and M were originally sub-divided into fewer parts, which were identified by letters, viz. $Oa–Oe$, $Ma–Md$; numerical designations were later adopted for these sub-classes by the International Astronomical Union.

The principal characteristics of the various classes are as follows:

Class W. The Wolf–Rayet stars; their spectra contain many strong, broad, emission bands due to an abundance of highly ionized helium, carbon, nitrogen and oxygen. Many are spectroscopic binaries, a few are visual eclipsing binaries. Their surface temperatures are extremely high, probably of the order of 80,000° K. The Wolf–Rayet stars were formerly allocated to class *O*, but the separate class *W* was adopted for them by the I.A.U. in 1938.

There are two sub-divisions of the class, the *nitrogen sequence* (sub-class *WN*) and the *carbon sequence* (sub-class *WC*), to take account of the fact that Wolf–Rayet stars had been found to exist in two distinct forms, with nitrogen and carbon emission bands predominating in their spectra. The nitrogen and carbon sequences are sub-divided into four and three parts respectively, designated *WN5–WN8* and *WC6–WC8*. Examples of Wolf–Rayet stars are HD 177230 (*WN8*) and γ Vel (*WC7*).

Class O. These are blue-white stars having a surface temperature of the order of 35,000° K. The continuum is faint, with bright emission lines due to ionized hydrogen, helium, oxygen and nitrogen. Absorption lines due to ionized helium are also present, and in later sub-classes absorption lines of ionized hydrogen also. There are five sub-classes, designated *O5–O9*. Typical examples of *O* stars are ζ Pup (*O5*) and ζ Ori (*O9*).

Class B. Bluish-white (*Bo*) to white (*B9*) stars with surface temperatures ranging from about 25,000° K (*Bo*) to about 12,000° K (*B9*). The spectra of stars in this class show no emission lines; at *Bo* the only absorption lines visible are those of hydrogen and helium. Those due to helium increase in intensity to reach their maximum in class *B2*, thereafter

they become less intense, finally disappearing at *B9*. The hydrogen lines increase in intensity throughout the class. Lines due to some ionized metals, such as iron and magnesium, appear from *B8* onwards. The Fraunhofer H and K lines of calcium are also present, though not prominent. *B*-type stars are sometimes known as 'helium stars' or 'Orion-type stars'. They are very distant, with small proper motions; they are strongly concentrated in the galactic plane. Typical examples are ε Ori (*Bo*) and *Achernar* (*B5*).

Class A. Formerly known as 'Sirian stars' or 'hydrogen stars', these are white stars with surface temperatures ranging from about 10,000° K (*Ao*) to 8,000° K (*A9*). They are the second most numerous class, and tend to be concentrated in and around the galactic plane. The hydrogen absorption lines reach a maximum at *A2* and reduce in intensity thereafter; the lines of ionized magnesium reach their maximum at *Ao*. The calcium lines strengthen throughout the class, and lines due to other ionized metals, such as titanium, appear. Typical examples are *Sirius* (*A1*), *Deneb* (*A2*) and *Altair* (*A7*).

Class F. Yellow-white stars with surface temperatures in the range 7,500–6,000° K. The strongest lines are the calcium H and K lines; lines due to neutral calcium and other neutral metals appear for the first time. The hydrogen stars weaken throughout the class. The lines due to ionized metals are very prominent.

Class *F* stars are sometimes described as 'calcium stars'; they are much less numerous than stars of classes *K* and *A*, and show little evidence of galactic concentration; they include a number of binary systems. Typical *F* stars are *Canopus* (*Fo*) and *Procyon* (*F5*).

Class G. Yellow stars with surface temperatures ranging from 5,500–4,200° K for giants, 6,000–5,000° K in the case of dwarfs. Sometimes formerly referred to as 'solar stars', they show little galactic concentration. The metallic lines are now numerous and prominent, with those of neutral metals outnumbering those of ionized metals. Absorption weakens the violet spectrum notably, and the molecular bands of CN and CH appear. The best known example of the class is the Sun (*G2*); others are β CVn (*Go*) and ξ Leo (*G5*).

Class K. Orange stars, sometimes termed in the past 'Arcturian stars'. Giant stars of this class have surface temperatures of 4,000–3,000° K and the dwarfs 5,000–4,000° K. They are the most numerous class of star, and show some tendency to concentrate in the galactic plane.

The blue continuum is much weakened by absorption; the neutral metal lines are strengthening whilst those of the ionized metals are getting weaker; the hydrogen lines are now almost insignificant. Molecular lines of titanium oxide (TiO) first appear at *K5*. Typical K stars are *Arcturus* (*K1*) and *Aldebaran* (*K5*).

Class M. This class contains orange-red stars with temperatures of about 3,000° K (giants), 3,200° K (dwarfs). They show very broad absorption bands, especially in the violet and blue, due mainly to the radicals CO and CH. TiO bands are very prominent. These stars are very distant, with high mean velocities; the fainter members of the class show some tendency to concentrate near the galactic centre. They were formerly known as 'Antarian stars', after *Antares* (*Mo*); another typical example of the class is *Betelgeuse* (*M2*). In the original notation (*Ma–Mc*) these were classified as *Ma*. A special sub-class *Md* had been formed, comprising the long-period variables in whose spectra the bright emission lines of hydrogen reappear; sub-class *Md* was abolished in 1922 however, when *Ma*, *Mb* and *Mc* became *Mo*, *M3* and *M8* in a decimally sub-divided class, '*e*' being added where necessary to indicate the presence of emission bands. A notable example of a former *Md* star is *Mira Ceti*, now classified *M6e*.

Class R. A small class of orange-red stars with surface temperatures of about 2,500° K, similar to *N* but less red, being brighter in the blue and violet than both *M* and *N* stars. Their spectra show prominent molecular bands due to carbon (C$_2$) and cyanogen (CN); oxygen bands are also quite strong. They are mostly faint stars, a typical example is BD −10° 5057 (class *Ro*).

Class N. A small class of deep red stars with surface temperatures of about 2,500° K, similar to class *R* but deeper in colour. Often termed 'carbon stars', as the spectra show many prominent bands due to carbon compounds. The oxygen bands are less prominent than in class *R*. About 60 per cent of the stars in this class are located in the galactic plane. A typical example is 19 Psc (class *No*).

Class S. A small class of red stars with similar spectra to class *M*, including the hydrogen emission lines, but with strong absorption bands of zirconium oxide (ZrO); the difference between stars in classes *S* and *M* is more probably one of density and temperature than of actual composition. Typical stars in this class, which consists mostly of long-period variables, are R Ori (*S1*) and R And (*S4*).

Further refinements. Miss A. Maury, also at the Harvard College Observatory, devised an extension of the Harvard–Draper system, wherein a star's spectrum was classified firstly by the lines present, and then by the quality of the lines; she found that in some cases the spectral lines were much more sharply defined than in other examples of the same spectral class. This was followed up by Adams and Kohlschütter at Mount Wilson, who demonstrated that a star could be identified directly from its spectrum as a giant or a dwarf. It therefore became the practice to label spectra with a prefix *d* or *g*, as appropriate; thus the giant *Deneb* was classified *gA2*, and the dwarf η Aur as *dB4*, etc. The prefix *c* was also used, to indicate supergiants. The relationship between the luminosity of a star and the characteristics of its spectrum was studied by W. W. Morgan, P. C. Keénan and E. Kellman at the Yerkes Observatory, who devised for their *Atlas of Stellar Spectra*, published in 1943, a system of suffixes to indicate the type of star, as follows:

supergiants	I
bright giants	II
normal giants	III
sub-giants	IV
main sequence stars and dwarfs	V
sub-dwarfs and white dwarfs	VI

Hence we now have classifications such as *Sirius* (*A1* V), *Bellatrix* (*B2* III), *Pollux* (*K0* III) and *Gacrux* (*M3* II). This system is known as the 'MKK system', or 'MK system', after its originators, and sometimes as the 'Yerkes system'.

Other symbols that are used to convey additional information in the spectral classification are:

e	emission lines present
k	interstellar lines present
m	metallic lines present
p	peculiar spectrum
s	sharp lines
n	nebulous lines

(See also **Hertzsprung–Russell diagram; Stars—luminosity of; Stars—spectral distribution of; Stellar evolution.**)

STARS—SPECTRAL DISTRIBUTION OF

The **Draper Catalogue** lists the spectral types of some 225,000 stars distributed over the entire sky; the percentage distribution of these stars among the various spectral classes is shown in Table 51.

The limiting magnitude of the Draper Catalogue is about 8·25; Table 51 may therefore be regarded as showing the

Table 51. *Spectral distribution of stars*

Spectral class	Percentage of stars contained in class
B	10
A	22
F	19
G	14
K	31
M	3
O N R S	1

actual spectral distribution of all stars down to this limit.

(See also **Stars—spectral classification of.**)

STARS, SUB-DWARF Stars whose spectral/luminosity classifications place them 1–2 magnitudes below the main sequence of the **Hertzsprung–Russell diagram.** They are fairly rare; a few are known in spectral classes *O* and *B*, but they are mostly cooler *F*, *G* and *K* stars.

(See also **Stars—spectral classification of.**)

STARS, SUB-GIANT Stars whose spectral/luminosity classification places them just below the giant sequence of the **Hertzsprung–Russell diagram.** Their absolute luminosities are 1–2 magnitudes less than those of giant stars of the same spectral class. They are mostly *G* and *K* stars.

(See also **Stars—spectral classification of.**)

STARS, SUPERGIANT The most luminous stars of all, constituting class I of the Yerkes luminosity classification. Only a few are known, and they are mostly slightly variable and appear to be rather unstable. Many of them are at great distances from us, and their absolute magnitudes are difficult to determine with precision. Class I is usually sub-divided; stars of class Ia are believed to have absolute magnitudes of about -7, those of class Ib about -5. They are believed to be very massive, and are Population I stars found only in the spiral arms of the Galaxy.

Typical supergiants are *Betelgeuse* (class *M2* Ib), *Deneb* (*A2* Ia), *Polaris* (*F8* Ib) and *Rigel* (*B8* Ia).

(See also **Hertzsprung–Russell diagram; Stars—spectral classification of.**)

STARS, VARIABLE See **Variable stars.**

STARS, WHITE DWARF See **White dwarf.**

STATIONARY POINTS The points at which a planet's apparent motion changes from direct to retrograde motion, and vice versa; at these two times the orbital motion of the planet lies in the line of sight and it therefore appears to be stationary.

STEFAN–BOLTZMANN CONSTANT The ratio between the energy emitted by a unit surface area of a black-body radiator and the fourth power of its absolute temperature, in accordance with the Stefan–Boltzmann law. Usually denoted by σ, the value of the Stefan–Boltzmann constant has been determined to be $5 \cdot 67 \times 10^{-5}$ erg/cm^2/sec./($^\circ$ K)^4.

STEFAN–BOLTZMANN LAW A law relating the radiative output of a body and its absolute temperature, deduced from experimental results by C. Stefan and L. Boltzmann in 1879.

The law states that the total energy (E) emitted by a black-body radiator is proportional to the fourth power of its absolute temperature (T). This is usually expressed in the form

$$E = A\sigma T^4,$$

where A is the surface area of the radiator. The proportionality factor σ is known as the Stefan–Boltzmann constant.

STELLAR ASSOCIATION An association is a very large grouping of stars, rather like an open cluster but on a very much larger scale; the diameter of an association is of the order of 100 parsecs—more than ten times that of many open clusters. Stellar associations consist of young stars of Population I, and are therefore considered important in studies of stellar evolution. There are two types, the *O-associations* and the *T-associations*.

O-associations are found in the spiral areas of the Galaxy; they consist mainly of highly luminous supergiants of spectral types *O* and *B*. T-associations consist of T-Tauri type irregular variables, and occur only in regions containing a high concentration of interstellar gas and dust; it has been suggested that these are therefore locations where stars are in the process of formation, by accretion from the gas–dust cloud.

Stellar associations of both types sometimes occur in coincidence—a typical example of this is found in the constellation Orion.

STELLAR EVOLUTION It had long been realized that the observable stars must in fact be a representative collection of stars at all stages of evolution; as the development of observational astrophysics brought to light differences between various kinds of star it was natural to try to place the various types into an evolutionary sequence. Such a proposed sequence, based upon observational evidence, must then be tested by the theoretical astrophysicist who must propose a sequence of physical changes that would lead to the suggested pattern of evolution.

One of the earliest observed differences between the stars was their varying colour; this led to their classification by spectral type. Application of the known laws of radiation then led to the establishment of a relationship between a star's colour (i.e. spectral type) and its temperature: it was suggested by Zöllner in 1865 that a star's colour was an indication of its temperature, red stars being relatively cool and white stars the hottest. A few years later Vogel and others suggested that this was indicative of an evolutionary process, the hot white stars being very young and the cooler, red stars very old. A notable attempt to set up a theoretical basis for such an evolutionary sequence was made by Sir Norman Lockyer in 1887, who suggested that hydrogen atoms in the cooling star broke down to form atoms of heavier elements, with consequent loss of energy as radiation. Although based upon incorrect assumptions Lockyer's suggestion was an important step forward in theoretical astrophysics. The classification by temperature was rationalized by the introduction of the **Harvard–Draper sequence** in the Draper Catalogue published by the Harvard University Observatory in 1890.

The next major step forward was the discovery by E. Hertzsprung in 1905 that whilst the absolute magnitudes of the nearer stars arranged in order of spectral type according to the Harvard–Draper sequence diminished progressively from class B (white) to M (red), the more distant orange and red stars were much more luminous and were more or less constant in absolute magnitude whatever their spectral class. Hertzsprung termed the former type of star *dwarfs* and the latter *giants*; he found that they could be distinguished by means of slight differences in their spectra. The same conclusions were reached independently by H. N. Russell, who in 1913 published the first version of the famous **Hertzsprung–Russell diagram** in which the stars are plotted by spectral type against absolute magnitude (See Fig. 52, p. 172.)

Russell concluded that the giant and dwarf stars differed in density rather than mass; he proposed an evolutionary sequence in which a star would be a comparatively cool giant—say of spectral

type M; it would contract under the effect of its own gravitation and its density would therefore increase. Assuming that it behaved as a perfect gas its temperature would rise in consequence: its increasing temperature would be balanced by its diminishing size, however, so that its total luminosity would remain more or less constant and it would pass through spectral types K, G, F, A and B in turn— i.e. along the giant sequence of the 'H–R diagram' from right to left. At a certain density further contraction would be inhibited and the star would cease to behave as a perfect gas; its total luminosity would then fall as its temperature continued to fall, and the star would slowly pass through the same sequence of spectral classes in the reverse order, but due to the falling luminosity it would now progress down the *main sequence* of the H–R diagram from left to right, and would finally fade out as a very cool red dwarf.

This was a remarkable and far-sighted theory, but in the years that followed it was found to be incompatible with some of the observed data. The obvious break in the giant sequence of the H–R diagram (the *Hertzsprung Gap*), due to the near absence of giant stars of types A and F, was a serious problem; for if Russell's evolutionary theory were correct giant stars must, on reaching class G, accelerate their evolution catastrophically in order to pass through classes A and F to join the main sequence as type B stars. Further, when Eddington discovered the **mass–luminosity relationship** in 1924 he found that it applied to the main-sequence stars as well as the giants, which quite ruled out Russell's premise that the former did not behave as a pefect gas. It thus became clear that the H–R diagram, although invaluable as a 'census' of the present distribution of stars of varying types, could not be interpreted as direct evidence of an evolutionary sequence.

Studies of the stars in the globular clusters by Shapley showed them to have almost the reverse luminosity–spectral class relationship to the main–sequence stars (Fig. 54, p. 173). A further major step was the discovery by Baade that stars exist in two distinct 'populations', Population I stars being mainly blue–white stars of types O and B situated mostly in the arms of spiral galaxies, and Population II stars being the cooler, redder stars found in the nuclei of spiral galaxies and in elliptical galaxies. Globular clusters were found to comprise mainly Population II stars, whereas galactic clusters are found to consist mostly of Population I stars. The study of the intrinsic variable stars of both populations produces some interesting additions to the H–R diagram (Fig. 55, p. 174).

Astrophysicists are still working towards a complete understanding of the processes of star formation and evolution; current ideas of the probable sequence may be very roughly summarized as follows:

A star probably forms by accretion from a mass of gas and dust; this probably takes place in the outer arms of a spiral galaxy, where interstellar gas and dust clouds are abundant. The 'proto-star' collapses under its own gravitational compression, which results in the loss of enormous quantities of energy: it thus becomes a very luminous body—a hot, white star of Population I. Due to the breakdown of hydrogen nuclei in its interior heavier elements are slowly formed, with further loss of radiated energy. When massive stars are first formed they move very rapidly through classes A and F (across the Hertzsprung Gap) and then along the giant sequence. Less massive stars evolve down the main sequence to become, eventually, red dwarfs. The evolutionary sequence is thus, in both cases, from left to right across the H–R diagram, from hot, white stars (Population I) to cooler, red stars (Population II). The latter being found in the nuclei of spiral galaxies, this accords well with theories of galactic evolution, in which the young Population I stars are formed in the outer arms and progress towards the galactic core as they evolve into aged, Population II stars.

This suggested pattern of evolution is both tentative and incomplete: it is believed, for instance, that the oldest stars are the white dwarfs but there is little reliable evidence of the intermediate evolutionary stages between, say, red dwarfs and white dwarfs. It would appear, however, that the broad picture of stellar evolution is emerging from the exciting work of contemporary astrophysicists; it is notable, too, how much this currently proposed sequence owes to the earlier proposals of such pioneers as Lockyer, Hertzsprung and Russell.

(See also **Galactic evolution; Hertzsprung–Russell diagram; Stars— spectral classification of; Stellar populations.**)

STELLAR LIGHT That part of the faint background illumination of the night sky which comprises direct light from stars which are too faint to be individually visible to the naked eye. (See **Night sky— illumination of.**)

STELLAR MAGNITUDE The measured apparent brightness of a star.

(See also **Magnitude**, etc.)

STELLAR MAGNITUDE—DETERMINATION OF The pioneering work in this field, from the days of Hipparchus to modern times, was based, of course, on visual observations; although the advent of astronomical photography enabled magnitude determinations to be made for a far greater number of faint stars, it was found that these were subject to considerable systematic errors. The method now used for accurate determinations is photoelectric photometry. In order to give a complete assessment of the star's magnitude, the measurements are usually made in three separate wavebands. The resulting determinations are compared with a standard sequence of stars for which accurate magnitudes have been determined.

As techniques have developed a number of 'standard' systems have been introduced:

The photovisual system

Photovisual magnitudes are determined from photographs obtained on an iso-chromatic emulsion with a filter transmitting light of wavelength between 5000 and 6000 Ångströms; they correspond closely to visually determined magnitudes. The photovisual system is usually referred to as the 'pv system'. The standard International photovisual system, based upon the work of F. H. Seares in the waveband 4900–5900 Å, is known as the 'Ipv system'.

The 'photoelectric visual' system

This is based upon the work of H. L. Johnson and W. W. Morgan at the Yerkes Observatory, using a photoelectric photometer and a filter confining the determination to the waveband 4800–6500 Å; this system, known as the 'V system', is the photoelectric equivalent of the pv system.

The photographic system

Photographic magnitudes are determined from exposures made on blue-sensitive plates with an ultra-violet cut-off filter; it is referred to as the 'pg system'. The standard is the International photographic system, known as 'Ipg', based upon the work of Seares in the waveband 3420–5170 Å.

The 'B system'

In this system magnitudes are determined by means of a photoelectric photometer and a specified blue filter; it is the photoelectric equivalent of the pg system. The waveband used is 3800–5400 Å.

The 'U system'

In this system photoelectric magnitudes are obtained with a specified ultra-violet filter and a blue-sensitive photocell, the wavelengths used being in the region 3400–4000 Å. U-system magnitudes can also be determined photographically with blue-sensitive plates and the ultra-violet filter.

The 'R system'

Photographic magnitudes obtained with panchromatic plates and a red filter, in the waveband 6100–6700 Å.

The 'G system'

Photographic magnitudes obtained with a green filter transmitting the wavelengths 4500–5000 Å.

The 'I system'

Photoelectric magnitudes obtained in the infra-red spectrum (waveband 7400–10,000 Å).

Standard sequences

In order to reduce magnitude determinations made with diverse instruments in many countries to a common basis, standard sequences of stars have been adopted internationally. The principal standard has been, for many years, the **North Polar Sequence** (NPS), comprising a number of stars close to the north celestial pole whose magnitudes have been determined at many observatories and the mean values adopted. The pg and pv systems are based upon the NPS. Stars in the southern sky which cannot be directly compared with the NPS are compared indirectly by the use of selected intermediate reference stars at Dec. $+15°$. It is likely, however, that the NPS will eventually be superseded by the UBV system (see below).

Colour index

It will be obvious that determinations of stellar magnitudes are affected by the colour of the stars concerned, and therefore by the colour characteristics of the instrument used. As an aid to allowing for this effect the **colour index** was devised; it consists of the difference between the photographic and photovisual magnitudes, i.e.

$$C = m_{pg} - m_{pv}$$

The Ipg and Ipv systems were so defined that the colour index of Ao stars in the NPS was zero; it is now known that when space-reddening has been allowed for the spectral type corresponding to a true colour index of zero is *A4*.

Three-colour determinations

It was found necessary to supplement pg and pv magnitudes with U measurements in order to obviate errors arising from differences in spectral type. This led to the adoption of the principle that magnitudes should be measured in three wavebands as a standard practice. The principle three-colour systems set up were the 'RGU system' devised by W. Becker of Basle, based upon his photographic work in the R, G and U systems, and the photoelectric 'UBV system' of Johnson and Morgan. The UBV system is based upon a standard sequence of some 400 stars distributed over the entire sky; it seems likely that three-colour photometry will become, in due course, the definitive method for determining stellar magnitudes, and that the UBV system will become the universally adopted standard.

STELLAR POPULATIONS It was discovered by Baade in 1944, from observations made with the 100-in. reflector at Mount Wilson, that the stars of the great galaxy in Andromeda, M31, were of two quite different types.

The stars in the spiral arms were mostly bluish stars of very high luminosity, the brighter ones having 4,000–60,000 times the luminosity of the Sun; the stars contained in the core of the galaxy are predominantly of low absolute magnitude and mostly reddish, with luminosities less than 2,000 times that of the Sun.

The hot, bluish stars found in the spiral arms are termed 'Population I' stars; the relationship between their luminosity and spectral type conforms to the classical pattern of the Hertzsprung–Russell diagram. They are mostly *B*- and *O*-type stars and are believed to be comparatively 'young'.

The less luminous, reddish stars found in the core of the galaxy are termed 'Population II' stars; they do not conform

to the classical H–R diagram, their luminosities being unexpectedly low for their spectral types, and are believed to be at an advanced stage of evolution.

A similar distribution of these two stellar populations was later discovered in our own Galaxy and in other spirals; it was also found that the globular clusters and the elliptical galaxies contained only Population II stars. This led to a theory of galactic evolution based upon the suggestion that new and very luminous stars are formed in the peripheral regions, travel down the spiral arms during their lifetimes and reach the nucleus as they fade towards extinction. This theory accorded well with the requirements of the steady-state theories of cosmology, and also with the theory that stars form and develop by a process of **accretion**, for the young Population I stars are found in areas rich in interstellar gas and dust, ideal for this process, whilst the Population II stars are found in regions well-nigh devoid of interstellar material.

(See also **Galactic evolution; Hertzsprung–Russell diagram; Stellar evolution**.)

STELLAR SPECTRA Almost all the data for astrophysical research comes from a study of the light radiated by the stars: comparative studies of stellar spectra are therefore of great importance.

The spectrum of most stars comprises a continuous spectrum, against which many absorption lines (the 'dark-line spectrum') can be seen. In some cases emission lines (the 'bright-line spectrum') are also visible.

The intensity of a star's radiation varies along its spectrum, the maximum being at a point dependent upon the temperature of the star concerned. A rough classification of the stars by colour can thus be made. A more detailed classification can be made by studying the spectrum, noting which lines are present and which absent, and which are enhanced as emission lines (if any). This is the broad basis of spectral classification.

From a detailed study of the absorption and emission lines present in the spectrum of a star we can learn which elements are present in the outer layers of the star, in roughly what proportions and in what state of excitation.

In stellar photometry the integrated amount of light in selected broad wavebands is compared, which leads to an accurate assessment of the star's absolute luminosity and its temperature. Similarly, in spectrophotometry the intensity of radiation is measured at each part of the spectrum, providing a broad spectral 'profile' and, in the case of important lines, the 'line-profiles'. All this provides the raw material of the astrophysicist.

The spectra of intrinsic variable stars, of novae and supernovae, etc., have provided much of the data upon which our knowledge of these objects is based. In the case of the spectroscopic binaries, of course, their detection and their subsequent study is entirely dependent upon observations of their spectra.

(See also **Stars—spectral classification of**.)

STJERNEBORG An underground observatory built on the island of Hven in Copenhagen Sound by Tycho Brahe, to supplement **Uraniborg.**

STÖFLER Lunar surface feature, co-ordinates $\xi + 075$, $\eta - 655$. A large walled plain in the very mountainous southern region of the Moon; approximately 100 miles in diameter. Stöfler is an old formation with massive rugged walls, the south-west quadrant of which have been completely annihilated by the intrusion of Faraday. The floor has some dark patches similar to those of Alphonsus and Grimaldi, the largest being a triangular one under the eastern rampart. The east wall contains peaks between 8,000 and 12,000 feet.

STOP See **Lens stop.**

STOP WATCH A watch equipped with a second hand (sometimes two) which can be stopped at a particular instant by pressing a button; it can therefore be used for the accurate measurement of time intervals whilst observing. If, for instance, a particular phenomenon is to be timed with its aid, the watch is started at a broadcast time-signal or in synchronization with an observatory clock, and stopped as the phenomenon is observed. The interval recorded by the watch may then be added to the known time at which it was started and the time of the phenomenon deduced.

The method is useful for certain kinds of observation, especially in the field, but a **chronograph** provides much greater accuracy.

STORM, GEOMAGNETIC The Earth's magnetic field is constantly undergoing small fluctuations in intensity; it is also subject to sudden, intense variations from time to time—these are termed *geomagnetic storms*, or, commonly, *magnetic storms*. They are not a local phenomenon, the sudden variation in field intensity (termed a *sudden commencement*) is usually recorded at stations throughout the world within minutes. Many of the less severe magnetic storms show a tendency to recur after an interval of 27 days. The average incidence of magnetic storms varies over a cycle of 11 years; this fact led E. W. Maunder of the Royal Observatory, Greenwich, to suggest that the magnetic storms were due to solar activity. It was later shown by H. W. Newton, also of the Royal Observatory, that intense solar flares in the central area of the Sun's disk are followed about a day after their central meridian passage by a severe magnetic storm. It is therefore believed that the mild, recurrent storms are due to active regions on the solar surface (which often persist for several solar rotations), the synodic rotation period of the Sun being about 27 days, and the severe storms to flares. The time lag of a day or more indicates that the medium by which solar activity disturbs the Earth's magnetic field cannot be electromagnetic radiation (heat, light, etc.) as this would require a journey time of only about 8 minutes; it must therefore be a stream of ionized particles, often loosely termed corpuscular 'radiation'. This is probably composed largely of hydrogen; eruptions of gaseous material are a well known event on the Sun, being observed as prominences, coronal streamers, etc. The name usually adopted for the corpuscular material ejected by the Sun is the *solar wind*.

STRAIGHT RANGE Lunar surface feature. A prominent and very straight range of mountains in the northern part of the Mare Imbrium, about half-way between Plato and the Promontarium Laplace. The range stretches for about 40 miles, approximately from $(\xi - 203, \eta + 755)$ to $(\xi - 245, \eta + 753)$.

STRAIGHT WALL Lunar surface feature. A prominent fault line running almost north–south across the south-west corner of the Mare Nubium, about 10 miles west of Birt and some 60 miles east of Thebit. It runs for about 60 miles, from approximately $(\xi - 120, \eta - 400)$ to $(\xi - 136, \eta - 337)$. It is in fact a cliff, the surface of the mare being some 800 ft. higher to the west of the Straight Wall than to the east. The southern end adjoins the prominent Stag's Horn Mountain, and there is a small craterlet just to the west of the northern end.

STRATOSPHERE The stratum of the Earth's atmosphere between about 7 and 48 miles in height above the surface. The upper part of the stratosphere, above about 33 miles, is sometimes termed the *mesosphere*.

(See also **Atmosphere, terrestrial; Ionosphere**.)

STRATTON, F. J. M. (**1881–1960**) One of the foremost among English astronomers for more than half a century. Educated at Gonville and Caius College, Cambridge, where he graduated as 3rd Wrangler in 1904, Stratton remained there for the rest of his life.

In 1913 he was appointed Assistant Director of the Solar Physics Observatory on its removal from London to Cambridge, but his career was interrupted by the First World War. He had a distinguished military career, achieving the rank of Lieutenant-Colonel and being awarded the Distinguished Service Order (D.S.O.) in 1917. On his return to Cambridge in 1919 he became a Tutor in his old college and therefore resigned his appointment in the Observatory. In 1928 he was appointed Professor of Astrophysics and Director of the Solar Physics Observatory, which post he held until his retirement in 1947.

Stratton made notable contributions in many fields of astronomy and astrophysics. He took part in a number of eclipse expeditions, notably that to Sumatra for the eclipse of 1926 January 14, when with C. R. Davidson he obtained superb spectra of the chromosphere and was subsequently able to positively identify the chromospheric emission lines for the first time. His principal interest was the study of the spectra of novae, which he commenced with Nova Geminorum in 1912 and continued throughout his life.

Not the least of Stratton's contributions to English astronomy was his constant endeavour to stimulate the interest of many generations of Cambridge students and to guide them into careers in astronomy. As Tutor, and later Senior Tutor, of Caius College he encouraged many who were to become astronomers of distinction, among them a future Astronomer Royal and an Astronomer Royal for Scotland.

Stratton was a passionate believer in international co-operation in science, and worked unceasingly for this cause for many years. He was General Secretary of the International Astronomical Union (1925–1935) and the International Council of Scientific Unions (1937–1952). He was a Fellow of the Royal Astronomical Society for 55 years, and its President 1933–1935. He also served the Society as Treasurer (1923–1927) and Foreign Secretary (1945–1955). He was created an Officer of the Order of the British Empire (O.B.E.) in 1929, and elected a Fellow of the Royal Society in 1947. Perhaps the most remarkable tribute paid to Stratton was the unique collaboration of 215 astronomers from 26 countries, which resulted in the publication in 1955 of the first two volumes of *Vistas in Astronomy*: more than 1700 pages summarizing the latest developments in almost all branches of the science, which were dedicated to Stratton 'by his friends and admirers everywhere'.

STRUVE, Friedrich Georg Wilhelm (1793–1864) One of the greatest practical astronomers of the nineteenth century—indeed of all time—Wilhelm Struve played an incalculable part in the development of observing techniques and instrumentation; *inter alia*, his pioneering work provided the sure foundation upon which the entire study of double stars has been based.

Born in Altona, near Hamburg, Struve became Director of the Dorpat Observatory in Estonia in 1813, and brought the famous 'Dorpat refractor' into use there in 1824. For some years this superb instrument, constructed by Fraunhofer with an aperture of 9·6 inches and the first practicable clock-driven equatorial mounting, was to remain the largest refractor in the world. With the aid of a simple ring micrometer Struve commenced the great series of double-star observations that was to engage him for the rest of his life. In 1827 he published his first catalogue (*Catalogus Novus Stellarum Duplicium et Multiplicium*)—the 'Dorpat catalogue' in which all Struve's discoveries were given the numbers with the prefix Σ by which they are still known.

In 1835 Struve was appointed by the Tsar Nicholas to found a Russian national observatory; he thus became the first Director of the great Pulkowa Observatory thirteen miles from Leningrad. Despite the tremendous administrative burden involved in the construction and equipping of a large observatory and the development of its observing programmes, Struve continued to be a prolific observer himself. He continued his double-star work, initially with the Dorpat instrument which he had brought with him, and then with a new refractor of 15-in. aperture constructed in 1839. He surveyed the entire heavens from the north celestial pole to Dec. $-15°$, examining some 120,000 stars. He measured more than 3,000 doubles, more than three-quarters of which were new discoveries. His extended catalogue was published in 1837 as the *Stellarum Duplicium et Multiplicium Mensuræ Micrometricæ*.

Struve had obtained, with the Dorpat refractor in 1838, one of the earliest determinations of a stellar parallax—that of *Vega*; his value (0″·262) was rather more than double the correct value (0″·123), but the measurement of parallactic shifts of less than a tenth of a second of arc was a supreme achievement at that time.

Struve is notable as the first of six members of one family to achieve distinction as astronomers—surely a unique record. He retired from Pulkowa in 1861 and was succeeded by his son Otto; he died in Pulkowa three years later, little knowing that both of his grandsons and two great-grandsons were also to follow in his pioneering footsteps.

Wilhelm Struve had been honoured by the award of the Gold Medal of the Royal Astronomical Society in 1826; the same honour was accorded to his son in 1850, a grandson in 1903 and a great-grandson in 1944!

STRUVE, Georg (1886–1933) Born in Pulkowa, the son of Hermann Struve and great-grandson of the great Wilhelm, he joined his father's staff at the new Berlin–Babelsberg Observatory in 1919, where he specialized in planetary studies. His work was cut short by his death at the early age of 47.

STRUVE, Karl Hermann (1854–1920) Born at Pulkowa, the elder son of Otto and grandson of Wilhelm Struve, Hermann Struve did not become an astronomer at the start of his career; after leaving university he was engaged in optical research. The prospect of the arrival of the great 30-in. refractor proved too tempting, however, and he joined the staff at Pulkowa in 1883. Much of his early effort was directed to the study of the satellite system of Saturn, a subject that interested him for the rest of his life; from his observations he calculated the best determination of the mass of Saturn then made. He studied the dynamics of the other difficult satellite systems, especially those of Mars and Neptune. He made long studies of the motion of Eros and Titan, and redetermined the parallax of 61 Cyg.

In 1895 Hermann Struve became Director of the Königsberg Observatory. In 1904 he was appointed Professor of Astronomy in the University of Berlin and Director of the Berlin Observatory; there his special task was the foundation of the new observatory at Neubabelsberg, known as the Berlin–Babelsberg Observatory. This was completed in 1913 with the erection of a new 26-in. Zeiss refractor.

In 1903 he was awarded the Gold Medal of the Royal Astronomical Society, the third member of the family to be so honoured. He died in harness, suddenly, in Herrenalb in the Schwarzwald district of south-west Germany.

STRUVE, Ludwig (1858–1920) Born at Pulkowa, the younger son of Otto Struve and grandson of Wilhelm, Ludwig Struve became Professor of Astronomy and Geodesy in the University of Kharkov, in the Ukraine. He made many contributions to 'classical' astronomical theory, particularly the determination of the constant of precession. He died, together with a son and daughter, during the Russian Revolution. He was, however, survived by a son, Otto, who became one of the most progressive and successful of twentieth-century astrophysicists.

STRUVE, Otto Wilhelm (1819–1905) Born in Dorpat, Estonia, where his father F. G. W. Struve was Director of the Observatory staff in 1837. He followed his father to Pulkowa, where he regularly observed with the new 15-in. refractor. His work on double stars was second only to that of his father, which he continued and extended. In the *Revised Pulkowa Catalogue* published in 1850, he emulated his father in adopting the Greek form of his initials ($O\Sigma$) as the prefix for his own discoveries (more than 500 in number); additional discoveries in Part II of the same catalogue were prefixed $O\Sigma\Sigma$.

Otto Struve also made a study of the solar motion and from an examination of the motions of some 400 stars he was able to demonstrate that the solar system was moving in space as Sir William Herschel had postulated, a fact which had not hitherto been generally accepted.

In 1850 Otto Struve was awarded the Gold Medal of the Royal Astronomical Society in recognition of his contribution to double-star astronomy, an honour which must have pleased his father, who had been similarly honoured 24 years previously, almost as much as Otto himself.

In 1861 Otto succeeded his father as Director of the Pulkowa Observatory. Among his observational achievements during the later part of his career was the discovery of a number of very faint, close, companions to bright stars, notably *Procyon* in 1873. In 1879 he visited Alvan Clark in the U.S.A., and ordered from him the fine 30-in. refractor which was erected at Pulkowa in 1884, thus achieving for Pulkowa the distinction of housing the world's largest refractor for the third time in little more than half a century.

Otto Struve retired in 1890 to Karlsruhe, where he lived to the age of 86, with the satisfaction of knowing that he had proved a worthy successor to his illustrious father and that both of his sons were Directors of important observatories (in Berlin and Kharkov).

STRUVE, Otto (1897–1963) The great-grandson of Wilhelm Struve, and grandson of the first Otto, Otto Struve (II) was born in Kharkov in the Ukraine where his father Ludwig was Professor of Astronomy. His early career was interrupted by service in the Russian army, but he managed to graduate at Kharkov in 1919, between periods of military service. He arrived in western Europe as a refugee from the Russian Revolution, and was brought to the U.S.A., where he was appointed to the staff of the Yerkes Observatory. He obtained a Ph.D. from the University of Chicago in 1923 and became an American citizen in 1927.

In 1932 he became Director of the Yerkes Observatory, and was the architect of the foundation of the sister establishment—the McDonald Observatory—which he also directed from its opening in 1939 to 1947 when he retired from the Directorships of both establishments and became Chairman of the Department of Astronomy of the University of Chicago. In 1950 he took up a similar post in the University of California, and in 1959 became the first Director of the National Radio Astronomy Observatory at Green Bank, West Virginia. He was forced by ill-health to resign three years later.

Otto Struve was predominantly a stellar spectroscopist, and spent many years studying the spectra of binaries and early-type stars. He published pioneering papers in many branches of astrophysics, including the rotation of stars, dynamics of binary systems, stellar evolution, gaseous nebulae, interstellar gas, etc. His output of observational and interpretative work was prodigious, despite the time consumed by his superb administration of the vast instrumental resources and observing programmes under his control.

He was also a leader in the development of international co-operation in astronomy, serving the International Astronomical Union as Vice-President (1946–1952) and as a most successful President (1952–1955). He was not only a worthy descendant of a great line of astronomers, but one of the greatest; his contributions to astronomical knowledge were at least the equal of those of his great-grandfather Wilhelm. In 1944 he was awarded the Gold Medal of the Royal Astronomical Society—the fourth such award to successive generations of the Struve family. He also delivered the George Darwin Lecture to the Society in 1949.

STYLE The shadow-forming component of a **sundial**, also known as a **gnomon**.

STYX Martian surface feature, approximate position Ω 200°, $\Phi + 30°$. Prominent canal radiating north-westwards from Trivium Charontis and forming the north-eastern border of Elysium.

SUB-DWARF A star of luminosity rather less than that of a star of the same spectral type in the main sequence of the Hertzsprung–Russell diagram. They mostly occur in spectral classes F, G and K. (See **Stars, sub-dwarf.**)

SUB-GIANT A star of luminosity rather less than that of a star of the same spectral type in the giant sequence of the Hertzsprung–Russell diagram. They mostly occur in spectral classes G and K. (See **Stars, sub-giant.**)

SUB-SOLAR POINT The point on the Earth's surface from which, at a given instant, the Sun is exactly in the zenith.

SUB-STELLAR POINT The point on the Earth's surface from which, at a given instant, a specified star is exactly in the zenith.

SUMMER SOLSTICE The date on which the Sun reaches its greatest northern declination; also applied to the point on the Ecliptic then occupied by the Sun. It falls on or about June 21.

(See also **Sun—apparent motion of.**)

SUMMIT CRATER A small lunar crater situated at the summit of an eminence, usually the central peak of a ring-structure. (See **Moon—surface features of.**)

SUN The controlling influence of the Sun on all bodies in the solar system, and on all forms of life therein, tends to invest it with an aura of importance—perhaps even uniqueness—that is not really justified. If we ignore its specific importance to ourselves and consider it objectively, we find that it is merely an average dwarf star and a very insignificant component of one of the spiral arms of the Galaxy.

The Sun is situated very close to the galactic plane—about 14 parsecs from it—and about 8,200 parsecs from the galactic centre, i.e. about one third of a radius in from the outer edge of the Galaxy. It shares, of course, in the rotation of the Galaxy, and is revolving about the galactic centre in a period of about 220 million years.

One useful aspect of the Sun's proximity to us is the opportunity this gives us for really detailed physical study; the results obtained by solar physicists are constantly being combined with astrophysical observations of the other—more distant—stars, so as to extend our knowledge of their constitution still further.

The Sun can be usefully studied by amateur and professional astronomers alike, in numerous ways: by optical observation—visual, photographic and positional—and by radio; in both integrated and monochromatic light; with simple, 'classical' telescopes and with highly complex, specially developed equipment; and indirectly, e.g. by the study of solar–terrestrial relationships.

SUN—APPARENT MOTION OF In the course of a year the Sun appears to traverse the entire heavens, its apparent path being termed the **Ecliptic**. The plane of the Ecliptic is inclined to that of the celestial equator by almost 23° 27′ (the 'obliquity of the Ecliptic'). The Ecliptic and the equator are shown in Fig. 140, which represents the celestial sphere with the Earth at the centre. The difference between them in declination is shown in Fig. 141.

At the vernal equinox (♈) the Sun is

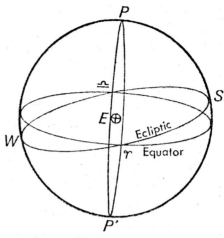

Fig. 140

on the celestial equator, i.e. it will pass through the zenith for an observer on the Earth's equator. For three months the Sun moves northwards, reaching a stationary point in declination at the summer solstice (*S*); it is then at its maximum northern declination, about 23° 27′ N. For the next three months it moves southwards, reaching the equator again at the autumnal equinox (♎). It then passes into southern declination, reaching a maximum of 23° 27′ S at the winter solstice (*W*). The Sun then moves northwards, reaching the equator at the following vernal equinox.

It will be seen that the Right Ascension, Declination and longitude of the Sun at the equinoxes and solstices are as in Table 52, longitude being measured eastward from the First Point of Aries (♈).

It will be noted that at these four points the Right Ascension and the longitude are identical, 1 hour of R.A. being equivalent to 15°; owing to the fact that the Earth's orbit is elliptical, and the Sun's motion is therefore not uniform, this is not the case at any other time.

The vernal equinox (or First Point of Aries) and the autumnal equinox (or First Point of Libra) are together termed the *equinoctial points*; the summer and winter solstices are termed the *solstitial points*.

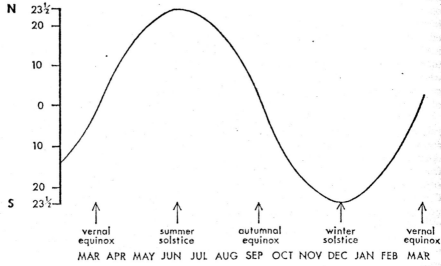

Declination (°)

Fig. 141

The declination circle passing through the equinoctial points ($p\,\Upsilon\ p'\mathrel{\triangle}$) is termed the *equinoctial colure*; that passing through the solstitial points is termed the *solstitial colure*.

(See also **Celestial sphere**.)

SUN—ATMOSPHERE OF The solar atmosphere may be said to consist of the three outermost layers of the Sun, the **photosphere**, the **chromosphere** and the **corona**. The three layers have a similar chemical constitution, and consist largely of hydrogen and helium. Most of the solar radiation originates in the photosphere, as light and heat. There is a steady emission of radio waves from the chromospheric and coronal layers.

SUN—AXIS OF ROTATION OF The Sun rotates about an axis which is inclined to the perpendicular to the plane of the Ecliptic by 7° 15′. The equatorial plane of the Sun cuts the Ecliptic in longitudes 75° and 255° (approximately); the Sun is in these positions on about June 6 and December 8 each year, and at these times the equator is a diameter of the Sun's

Table 52.   *Position of the Sun at the equinoxes and solstices*

	Longitude	Right Ascension	Declination
Vernal equinox:	0°	0 hr	0°
Summer solstice:	90°	6 hr	23° 27′ N
Autumnal equinox:	180°	12 hr	0°
Winter solstice:	270°	18 hr	23° 27′ S

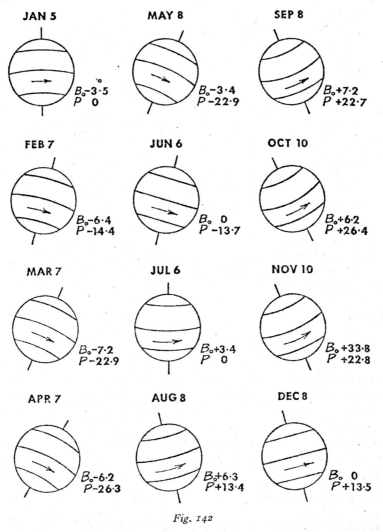

JAN 5

$B_0 -3.5$
$P \quad 0$

MAY 8

$B_0 -3.4$
$P -22.9$

SEP 8

$B_0 +7.2$
$P +22.7$

FEB 7

$B_0 -6.4$
$P -14.4$

JUN 6

$B_0 \quad 0$
$P -13.7$

OCT 10

$B_0 +6.2$
$P +26.4$

MAR 7

$B_0 -7.2$
$P -22.9$

JUL 6

$B_0 +3.4$
$P \quad 0$

NOV 10

$B_0 +33.8$
$P +22.8$

APR 7

$B_0 -6.2$
$P -26.3$

AUG 8

$B_0 +6.3$
$P +13.4$

DEC 8

$B_0 \quad 0$
$P +13.5$

Fig. 142

apparent disk. At other times it appears as a semi-ellipse, north of the centre of the disk between December and June and south of it between June and the following December, reaching the maximum values of 7° 15′ north and south of the disk-centre on March 7 and September 8 respectively.

This effect is measured by the use of the quantity B_0—the heliographic latitude of the centre of the disk. This is tabulated for each day of the year in *The Astronomical Ephemeris*. B_0 varies from $-7°.25$ on March 7 through zero on June 6 to $+7°.25$ on September 8, reducing to zero again on December 8.

The equatorial plane of the Earth is also inclined to the plane of the Ecliptic— by 23° 27′—and the Sun's axis of rotation may therefore be inclined to the vertical bisector of the apparent disk by an angle which is the combined effect of this *obliquity of the Ecliptic* and the inclination of the Sun's axis to the Ecliptic. The maximum value of this apparent tilting from the vertical of the Sun's axis of rotation is 26°·35, west of the vertical on about April 7 and east of it on about October 10. The axis coincides with the vertical on about January 5 and July 6 each year.

This effect is measured by the use of the quantity P—the position angle of the north pole of rotation relative to the north point of the observed disk. This quantity is also tabulated in *The Astronomical Ephemeris*. It has a value of zero on January 5, decreases to $-26°·35$ on April 7, then increases through zero on July 6 to $+26°·35$ on October 10.

The combined result of these effects is illustrated in Fig. 142. It will be appreciated that if the position of sunspots and other features are recorded with respect to the apparent disk, these effects must be allowed for—in addition to the longitude of the central meridian at the time of observation—in order to calculate their heliographic latitude and longitude.

(See also **Sun—rotation of.**)

SUN—BRIGHTNESS OF

The Sun is a normal main-sequence star of spectral type $G2$, having a surface temperature of approximately 5,800° K; it is therefore a predominantly yellow star. Due to absorption the limb regions appear very much less bright than the centre of the disk.

The apparent magnitude (visual) is $-26·7$, corresponding to an absolute magnitude of $+4·85$.

The corona is much fainter than the photosphere, its luminosity being about half that of the Full Moon. It cannot therefore be observed under normal conditions, being lost in the glare of the photosphere. For many years it could only be studied when the photosphere was obscured during a total solar eclipse; the development of the **coronagraph** by Lyot has made it possible to photograph even

the outer corona, which is much fainter still; with long exposures the corona has been photographed out to a 'height' of two solar diameters.

SUN—DIMENSIONS AND PHYSICAL DATA

The apparent equatorial diameter of the Sun at mean distance from the Earth is $31'\ 59''·26$, corresponding to an actual equatorial diameter of 864,950 miles. The surface area is therefore about $2\frac{1}{2}$ billion square miles, and the volume 1,303,800 times that of the Earth.

The mass of the Sun can be determined, assuming the value of the Constant of Gravitation, from the angular velocity of the Earth and its distance from the Sun; it is found to be $1·96 \times 10^{27}$ tons, or approximately 332,958 times the mass of the Earth.

From the mass and volume a value can be derived for the mean density; it is equivalent to $1·409$ times the density of water, i.e. slightly over a quarter the density of the Earth.

The acceleration due to gravity at the surface of the Sun is $27·9$ times that at the surface of the Earth; the velocity of escape is consequently very high indeed—almost 384 miles/sec.

The Sun is a fairly typical main-sequence star of spectral type $G2v$; its effective temperature is about 5,800° K. The radiation per unit mass emitted by the Sun is $1·94$ ergs per gram per second.

The mean visual apparent magnitude is $-26·8$, equivalent to an absolute magnitude of $+4·71$. The colour index ($m_{pg} - m_{pv}$) is $+0·45$.

SUN—MOTION IN SPACE

Although regarded as a fixed reference point for studies of all the bodies in the solar system, the Sun has a motion in space which can, with difficulty, be determined from an analysis of the observed proper motions of stars throughout the Galaxy. The so-called *solar motion*—the motion of the Sun relative to nearby stars, more properly termed *local solar motion*—is comparatively easy to determine; it is found that the Sun is travelling towards the *solar apex* in Hercules at a velocity of about 12 miles per second. The solar motion due to the rotation of the Galaxy is much more difficult to determine, but radial-velocity studies of the globular clusters indicate that the Sun's velocity of rotation about the galactic centre is of the order 125–155 miles per second.

SUN—OBSERVATION OF

Really valuable work is largely carried out with highly complex and sophisticated equipment at many of the world's major observatories, several of which are devoted entirely to solar observation. Even routine observation is now conducted with the refined photoheliographs and spectroheliographs at such observatories, and there is perhaps little scope for amateur observers to contribute substantially to our detailed knowledge of the Sun.

There is, however, a great deal of interest and enjoyment to be obtained from regular solar observation; for visual observers the simplest and safest method is to project the telescopic image of the Sun on to a white screen, so that the position and structure of any sunspots present can be recorded. A number of amateur observers have perfected techniques for photographing the Sun's disk, notably W. M. Baxter of Acton whose sunspot photographs are of a quite remarkable standard, and others record prominences with the aid of small spectroscopes.

The monitoring of solar radio emission has also been undertaken by amateur radio observers.

SUN—PHYSICAL CONSTITUTION OF

The Sun is a spheroid of gases which are maintained at very high temperatures by the nuclear processes which give rise to the solar radiation—thermonuclear radiation liberated by the breakdown of hydrogen nuclei and their transmutation into helium nuclei. The core is believed to be in a state of stable equilibrium, and hence it is possible to calculate the temperature and pressure gradients. The temperature and the percentage of the total mass contained at various levels are shown in Table 53.

The visible 'surface' of the Sun is the *photosphere*; this is a very thin layer, or

Table 53.   Solar mass and temperature gradients

Fraction of radius (r)	Fraction of mass contained by radius r	Temperature (°K. $\times 10^6$)
0·00 (centre of Sun)	0·000	13·6
0·04	0·006	13·1
0·1	0·062	11·6
0·2	0·35	8·5
0·3	0·64	6·0
0·4	0·84	4·2
0·5	0·942	2·8
0·6	0·984	1·9
0·7	0·995	1·2
0·8	0·999	0·68
0·9	~1·000	0·31
0·95	~1·000	0·16
0·99	~1·000	0·042
0·995	~1·000	0·027
1·000 (photosphere)	1·000	0·006

shell, at an effective temperature of about 5,800° K. The solar material is very highly absorbent, even in the tenuous outer regions, and therefore almost all the radiation we receive originates in this one thin layer. [Plate 1(a).]

The temperature gradient is so steep just below the photosphere that there is at this level a region of instability—the *convective zone*. Convection currents are set up, the hot tops of which are seen as bright *flocculi* with darker interstices. The photosphere consequently displays a mottled appearance, termed granulation; this is particularly obvious in spectro-heliograms obtained in monochromatic light, especially that of calcium. The granulation pattern (i.e. the distribution of the flocculi) is constantly changing.

The solar material extends for some distance above the photospheric level, but is much more tenuous. The photosphere is surrounded by a gaseous shell some 5,000 miles in depth whose luminosity is so much less than that of the photosphere that it is normally invisible from Earth; it is, however, seen for a few moments as the Sun passes into the total phase of an eclipse, the last visible portion of the Sun's disk before totality, and is visible again for a few moments at the end of totality. Its appearance is that of a thin bright crescent of a beautiful rose-pink hue, from which derives its name, the chromosphere, meaning 'colour-sphere'. The red hue arises from the strength of radiation in the **hydrogen-alpha line**; the chromosphere consists largely of hydrogen in a high state of excitation. The spectrum of the upper chromosphere can be photographed at these two moments during a total eclipse (termed the *flash spectrum*); it comprises a number of bright emission lines, some of the brightest of which are visible in the normal solar spectrum. [Plate 1(e).]

The lower portion of the chromosphere absorbs and re-emits the radiation from lower levels, and is therefore termed the *reversing layer*; it is here that the solar absorption lines are formed.

Outside the chromosphere there is a vast envelope of very tenuous material which is only very faintly luminescent—the *corona*. This was formerly only observable during the total phase of a solar eclipse, but Lyot's invention of the **coronagraph** has made it possible to observe it at other times, at least from high-altitude observatories. The brighter portion of the corona extends for some 2–3 solar radii above the surface; the very faint outer corona has been detected at very considerable distances.

The form of the corona is found to vary with the **solar cycle**; at sunspot maximum it is more or less uniform in shape, but at sunspot minimum it adopts the characteristic shape of the Sun's magnetic field [see Plates 2(a, b)]. One of the most remarkable features of the corona is its temperature—this is of the order of 1,000,000° K. All the light received from the corona is scattered light.

(See also **Solar activity; Sunspots.**)

SUN—RADIATION OF The Sun does not radiate as a simple 'black body'; the visible surface (the *photosphere*) has a temperature of 5–6,000° K, but the core is believed to have a temperature of the order of 14,000,000° K. The *corona*, through which the photosphere is seen, has a temperature of about 1,000,000° K.

As the opacity of the various levels of the solar 'atmosphere' varies with the wavelength of the radiation transmitted, the emission temperature also varies with wavelength.

The radiation incident upon the Earth is therefore an integration of the varying emissions at all wavelengths; its actual value is known as the **solar constant**, *q.v.* It is, of course, affected by atmospheric extinction as it passes through the Earth's atmosphere.

SUN—ROTATION OF The observed surface of the Sun, i.e. of the photosphere, is of course gaseous and is therefore capable of rotating differentially in different latitudes. From observations of sunspots

Table 54. Variations of solar rotation with latitude

Heliographic latitude of feature (°)	Average synodic rotation period (days)
0	24·6
10	24·9
20	25·2
30	25·8
40	27·5
50	29·2
60	30·9
70	32·4
80	33·7
90	34·0

and other surface markings this is in fact found to be the case, the rotation period of the spots being shortest at the equator and lengthening progressively at higher latitudes. The mean synodic period is 27·2753 days; the rotation periods of spots in approximate latitude 39° N and S average about this figure. The variation in average rotation period with latitude is tabulated in Table 54, and depicted schematically in Fig. 143: the position of a hypothetical line of spots is shown in Fig. 143(a), their position after 29 days

in Fig. 143(b). No adequate explanation of this phenomenon has been forthcoming to date.

In order to facilitate identification of specific rotations of the Sun, a numbered series of rotations was introduced by R. C. Carrington, commencing on 1853 November 9. The mean synodic rotation of 27·2753 days was assumed, and the rotations have been counted ever since; the date and time of commencement of every new rotation are tabulated in *The Astronomical Ephemeris* each year. Rotation number 1500 commenced on 1965 October 19·45.

(See also **Sun—axis of rotation of.**)

SUN—SPECTRUM OF The solar spectrum consists of a bright continuum with some thousands of absorption lines superimposed upon it. The solar continuum was first examined by Newton in his classic experiment of 1666, and the first seven absorption lines by Wollaston in 1802. The first to study the absorption lines and to 'map' them was Fraunhofer, who in 1814 and subsequent years mapped 324 of them, having observed a total of 574. The solar absorption lines are usually known as the *Fraunhofer lines* in commemoration of his pioneering work.

The solar continuum is formed by the

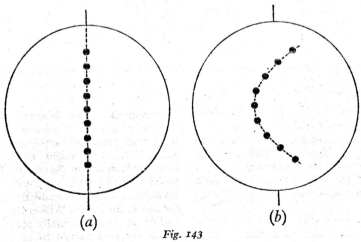

(a)   *(b)*

Fig. 143

Table 55. *Elements detected in the solar spectrum*

Element	Symbol	Atomic number	Element	Symbol	Atomic number
Hydrogen	H	1	Niobium	Nb	41
Helium	He	2	Molybdenum	Mo	42
Lithium	Li	3	Ruthenium	Ru	44
Beryllium	Be	4	Rhodium	Rh	45
Boron	B	5	Palladium	Pd	46
Carbon	C	6	Silver	Ag	47
Nitrogen	N	7	Cadmium	Cd	48
Oxygen	O	8	Indium	In	49
Fluorine	F	9	Tin	Sn	50
Sodium	Na	11	Antimony	Sb	51
Magnesium	Mg	12	Barium	Ba	56
Aluminium	Al	13	Lanthanum	La	57
Silicon	Si	14	Cerium	Ce	58
Phosphorus	P	15	Praesodymium	Pr	59
Sulphur	S	16	Neodymium	Nd	60
Argon	A	18	Samarium	Sm	62
Potassium	K	19	Europium	Eu	63
Calcium	Ca	20	Gadolinium	Gd	64
Scandium	Sc	21	Terbium	Tb	65
Titanium	Ti	22	Dysprosium	Dy	66
Vanadium	V	23	Erbium	Er	68
Chromium	Cr	24	Thulium	Tm	69
Manganese	Mn	25	Ytterbium	Yb	70
Iron	Fe	26	Lutecium	Lu	71
Cobalt	Co	27	Hafnium	Hf	72
Nickel	Ni	28	Tantalum	Ta	73
Copper	Cu	29	Tungsten	W	74
Zinc	Zn	30	Osmium	Os	76
Gallium	Ga	31	Iridium	Ir	77
Germanium	Ge	32	Platinum	Pt	78
Rubidium	Rb	37	Gold	Au	79
Strontium	Sr	38	Lead	Pb	82
Yttrium	Y	39	Thorium	Th	90
Zirconium	Z	40			

radiation from the Sun's core, i.e. from the photosphere; the absorption spectrum is formed in the lower region of the cooler chromosphere. Here the radiation of a given element in the hotter region below is absorbed by cooler atoms of the same element, in accordance with Kirchhoff's laws.

There are more than 20,000 lines in the solar spectrum, and their identification by comparison with laboratory-obtained spectra is a difficult process; there are more than 3,000 lines attributable to iron alone. The first major catalogue was made by Rowland in 1895–1897; Rowland positively identified 39 elements. This catalogue has been constantly extended, notably at the Mount Wilson Observatory, and 67 of the 92 naturally occurring elements are now known to be present in the Sun. Of the remaining 25, seven are relatively unstable and unlikely to exist in solar conditions and the lines of another thirteen would be almost impossible to detect owing to their lying outside the **optical window** of the Earth's atmosphere; there are thus only five elements (Cs, Re, Tl, Bi, U) whose lines should be detectable but which have not been discovered to date.

It is memorable that in 1868 Lockyer discovered a prominent yellow line not identifiable with any known terrestrial element; it was assumed that the line must be due to an element present in the Sun but not the Earth. The name *helium* was given to this hypothetical element, from the Greek ἥλιοσ ('helios'—the Sun); it was several years before helium was discovered on Earth by Ramsay, occluded in the mineral uranite.

The 67 elements known to be present in the Sun are listed in Table 55; both boron and fluorine have only been detected in the form of compounds, and the presence of lithium, boron, rubidium and indium has been detected only in the spectra of sunspots.

(See also **Chemical elements.**)

SUNDIAL A primitive instrument used to determine the time of day from the apparent altitude of the Sun. In its earliest form it consisted of a stake driven vertically into the ground; noon could then be determined by observing the moment when the shadow of the stake cast by the Sun reached its minimum length. This arrangement did not permit the determination of other times of day with any certainty, as the movement of the shadow varies throughout the year.

It was later discovered that if the stake was inclined in the plane of the meridian, so that the angle between it and the horizontal was equal to the latitude of the place (i.e. so that it was parallel to the Earth's axis of rotation) this difficulty was removed and the shadow fell in approximately the same direction at the same apparent time throughout the year. Thus

a dial could be provided on which the directions of the shadow for each hour of the day were marked, with sub-divisions so that the exact time could be read off. Such an instrument is termed an *equatorial sundial.*

The stake of the primitive sundial was known as a *gnomon*; its counterpart in later instruments was also known by this name, and also as the *style*. In the primitive instrument it was the practice to drive pegs into the ground to mark the positions of the shadow at desired times. Later instruments were usually much smaller, and constructed of metal. The hours and their sub-divisions were engraved on a metal plate, the gnomon frequently taking the form of a suitably inclined edge of a second metal plate. The whole was normally mounted on a pillar of stone or other rigid material.

A vertical form of sundial can be constructed, in which the 'dial-plate' is fastened onto a south-facing wall (the dial must be aligned exactly east–west). This form was widely used on medieval churches and other prominent buildings.

It should be noted that the time indicated by a sundial, however accurately constructed and mounted, is not correct on most days of the year until a correction has been applied for the **equation of time,** *q.v.*

SUNRISE The instant at which the upper limb of the Sun appears above the horizon.

The semi-diameter of the Sun is 16', and therefore the upper limb would be expected to appear when the Sun's zenith distance is 90° 16', assuming a true horizon, but the effect of atmospheric refraction is to reduce the apparent zenith distance of the Sun by 34' at the horizon. Sunrise is therefore defined as the moment when the Sun has a zenith distance of 90° 50'.

SUNSET The instant at which the upper limb of the Sun disappears below the horizon.

With allowance for the Sun's semi-diameter (16') and atmospheric refraction (34'), this is the moment when the Sun reaches a zenith distance of 90° 50'.

SUNSHINE RECORDER A simple instrument used in most meteorological stations to record the periods of each day during which the Sun was visible. It consists of a glass sphere, 4 in. in diameter, which focuses the Sun's light on to a specially prepared card on which the times of day are marked. When the Sun is visible its rays burn a trace on the card, from which the hours of sunshine can be read off.

SUNSPOT CYCLE Popular name for the solar cycle, the 22-year cycle of solar activity which was first discovered in the form of the 11-year cycle during which the frequency and distribution of sunspots underwent a periodic variation. (See **Solar cycle; Sunspots.**)

SUNSPOTS Photographs of the Sun's surface reveal a mottled appearance, known as *granulation*; the bright 'granules' are the apices of hot convection currents in the sub-photospheric layer (often termed the *convective zone*), and are of the order of 1,000 miles in diameter. Sometimes a group of granules is seen to separate to reveal a dark pore, and often such *pores* merge to form the larger dark area known as a *sunspot*. [Plate 1(a).]

Form and development. A simple sunspot comprises two quite clearly defined parts, the *umbra* and the *penumbra*. The umbra is usually elliptical or circular in shape, and uniformly dark; it usually represents up to 25 per cent of the total area of the spot. The surrounding penumbra has a much lighter, greyish appearance; its outline tends to follow that of the umbra.

There is a tendency for several simple spots to develop in the same area of the photosphere, and for these to accrete as they grow to form a larger, more complex spot or *spot-group*. Also, small, appendant spots frequently detach themselves from the main spot and become separate members of the group. [Plate 3.]

Sunspots are often formed in pairs; the westernmost member of a pair is termed the 'leading' and the easternmost the 'following' spot. It is usual for the component spots of a pair to increase in size and to move rapidly apart in longitude during the first few days of their existence; the separation usually ceases to increase when they are about 100,000 miles apart. When the spots have reached their maximum size the following spot usually deteriorates rapidly, the leading spot normally taking three or four times as long to fade away.

Larger, more complex spots usually have multiple umbrae, and penumbrae of much more irregular outline, than those of simple spots. Complex spots also sometimes have *bridges*—intensely luminous filaments which cross the umbra; they often span some thousands of miles, and usually undergo rapid changes in form. Bridges are more frequently observed in the following spots of a group.

If the penumbra is examined with a high power, it is seen to have a striated appearance, the fine luminous stria being approximately radial to the umbra. The disturbed area surrounding a spot-group usually exceeds the spots in both area and lifetime. When seen close to the limb brilliant white areas (*faculae*) are observed over much of the disturbed region. In monochromatic light the surrounding photosphere is seen to have a pronounced 'whirlpool' appearance which agrees with the vortical structure that sunspots are generally believed to have.

Temperature and spectrum. The temperature of the umbra is of the order 4,500–5,000° K—about 1,000° less than the temperature of the surrounding photosphere. The spot appears dark purely by contrast, due to this difference in temperature, of course; if seen otherwise than against the brilliant photosphere it would

A

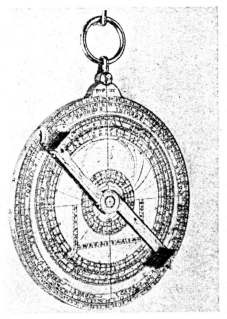

C

D

Plate 25 EARLY ASTRONOMICAL INSTRUMENTS

A A fine 16th century German astrolabe; **B** a 16th century brass armillary sphere; **C** Galileo's refracting telescopes, 1610; **D** mural quadrant installed by Bradley at Greenwich, c. 1750; **E** Sir Isaac Newton's reflecting telescope, 1671

Plate 26 TWO HISTORIC INSTRUMENTS

Lord Rosse's 6 ft. reflector, erected at Birr Castle, Ireland: **A** newly completed in 1845, and **B** a c
temporary photograph, 1966. **C** The Repsold $7\frac{1}{2}$-in. heliometer, installed at the Oxford Univer
Observatory in 1848

Plate 27 MERIDIAN INSTRUMENTS

A The 5-in. transit instrument by Troughton, erected at Greenwich in 1816; **B** The Airy Transit Circle installed at Greenwich in 1851 where it remains, defining the Prime Meridian of longitude; **C** The Troughton mural circle, erected at Greenwich in 1812; **D** A modern 'broken' transit telescope, in use at the Tashkent Observatory, U.S.S.R.; **E** The Cooke Reversible Transit Circle, erected at Greenwich in 1936 and removed to Herstmonceux in 1955

Plate 28 GREENWICH EQUATORIALS

A The 30-in. Thompson reflector, erected at Greenwich in 1897, transferred to Herstmonceux in 1959; **B** the 26-in. Thompson refractor, here seen as erected on the same mounting as the 30-in. reflector at Greenwich in 1897, since re-erected on a separate mounting at Herstmonceux, 1959; **C** the 28-in. 'Great Equatorial' refractor, erected at Greenwich in 1894, transferred to Herstmonceux in 1958; **D** the 36-in. Yapp reflector, erected at Greenwich in 1934, transferred to Herstmonceux in 1959 appear intensely bright.

The spectrum of a sunspot shows a number of important differences from that of the photosphere generally; as is to be expected the enhanced lines present in the normal solar spectrum are much weaker in that of the cooler sunspot. The relative intensities of the absorption lines are quite different, some being weaker and others stronger, again as a result of the lower temperature. Bands due to certain compounds are present which are not found in the normal solar spectrum.

Frequency and distribution. It was first pointed out by Heinrich Schwabe of Dessau, in 1843, that there is a clear periodic variation in the occurrence of sunspots. He had been recording sunspots daily with the aid of a small telescope since 1826, and postulated a period of about ten years. His suggestion met with little support, but he continued his observations and in 1851 was able to prepare a table demonstrating the periodicity beyond all doubt. Thus was the vitally important **solar cycle** discovered. In 1857 Schwabe was awarded the Gold Medal of the Royal Astronomical Society for his patient and valuable work.

Among the astronomers particularly interested by Schwabe's results was R. C. Carrington, an English amateur who had his own observatory at Redhill, Surrey. From his observations Carrington discovered that the latitudes of new sunspots tended to decrease as the solar cycle progressed, the first spots of a cycle occurring some 35° from the equator, the last ones almost on it. Unfortunately the direction of his family's brewing business devolved upon Carrington and put an end to his astronomical studies, and his part in this important discovery was largely overlooked. The phenomenon was studied in detail by Gustav Spörer, and the latitude drift is frequently referred to as 'Spörer's Law'.

The combined effect of the solar cycle (sometimes loosely referred to as the 'sunspot cycle') and the latitude drift was

beautifully demonstrated by Maunder in his famous 'butterfly diagram', in which the latitudes of all spots observed at the Royal Observatory, Greenwich, are plotted against date (Fig. 144).

The first spots of a new cycle are observed in high latitudes, 30–40° N or S of the equator; as the cycle proceeds, spots occur more frequently and their mean latitudes lessen. The maximum occurrence of spots usually takes place 3–5 years after minimum, when the spots are appearing 10–20° N and S. For the next five or six years spots occur at still lower latitudes, but less and less frequently. At the next minimum the spots may be within 5° of the equator, or even on it, and may occur after the first high-latitude spots of the new cycle have been observed. The average length of a cycle is 11·1 years.

In 1852 R. Wolf of Zurich introduced a system of 'sunspot numbers' as an index of sunspot activity. The Wolf sunspot number, R, is derived from

$$R = k(10g + f),$$

where g is the number of disturbed regions, f is the total number of spots and k is a constant depending upon the instrument used. (It should be noted that f is the total number of spots irrespective of whether they are members of a group or isolated spots, whereas g is the number of groups plus the number of isolated spots.) This is of course an arbitrary system, but the Wolf numbers—still compiled in Zurich from the reports of observers all over the world—do provide a useful record of sunspot activity (Fig. 132, p. 399).

A rather different system has been used for many years by the Solar Department of the Royal Greenwich Observatory: the total area of sunspots is measured on the daily photoheliograph plates, and recorded as a fraction of the Sun's visible disk. If the mean values over a reasonable period—e.g. a month—are used, there is a good correlation between the mean spotted area (A) (measured in millionths

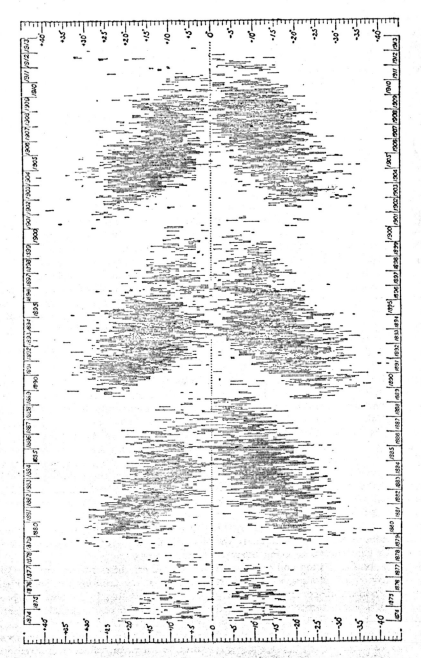

Fig. 144

of the visible disk) and the Wolf number (R), of the form

$$A = 16 \cdot 7 R.$$

The Zurich mean sunspot numbers (R_Z) and the Greenwich mean daily areas (A) are given in Table 56 for the years 1889–1958, almost six complete cycles.

Structure. It was observed by A. Wilson of Glasgow, as long ago as 1769, that the

penumbra appeared to vary in width depending upon the spot's position on the visible disk: when close to a limb, the penumbra on the limbward side appeared very wide and that on the side farthest from the limb very narrow, or even non-existent. As the spot moved across the disk this disparity gradually disappeared until the penumbra appeared of uniform width. As the spot approached the other limb, however, the effect reappeared, this

Table 56.   Zurich mean sunspot numbers (R_Z) and Greenwich mean daily areas (A_G)

Year	R_Z	A_G	Year	R_Z	A_G
1889	6·3	78	1924	16·7	276
1890	7·1	97	1925	44·3	830
1891	35·6	421	1926	63·9	1262
1892	73·0	1214	1927	69·0	1058
1893	84·9	1458	1928	77·8	1390
1894	78·0	1282	1929	65·0	1242
1895	64·0	974	1930	35·7	516
1896	41·8	543	1931	21·2	275
1897	26·2	514	1932	11·1	163
1898	26·7	376	1933	5·6	88
1899	12·1	111	1934	8·7	119
1900	9·5	75	1935	36·0	624
1901	2·7	29	1936	79·7	1141
1902	5·0	63	1937	114·4	2074
1903	24·4	339	1938	109·6	2019
1904	42·0	488	1939	88·8	1579
1905	63·5	1191	1940	67·8	1039
1906	53·8	778	1941	47·5	658
1907	62·0	1082	1942	30·6	423
1908	48·5	697	1943	16·3	295
1909	43·9	692	1944	9·6	126
1910	18·6	264	1945	33·1	429
1911	5·7	64	1946	92·5	1817
1912	3·6	37	1947	151·5	2637
1913	1·4	7	1948	136·2	1977
1914	9·6	152	1949	134·7	2129
1915	47·4	697	1950	83·9	1222
1916	57·1	724	1951	69·4	1136
1917	103·9	1532	1952	31·5	404
1918	5	1118	1953	13·9	146
1919	6	1052	1954	4·4	35
1920	6	618	1955	38·0	553
1921	26·1	420	1956	141·7	2393
1922	14·2	252	1957	190·2	3057
1923	5·8	55	1958	184·6	2950

time in reverse so that the side farthest from the limb grew narrower and that nearest the limb broadened. This was a remarkable discovery, and became known as the *Wilson effect*. Wilson deduced that sunspots must have a saucer-like profile, an interpretation that has been widely supported for two centuries; recently, however, it has been suggested that the effect is due to high transparency of the umbra compared with that of the penumbra, rather than to an actual effect of physical shape. [Plate 3(b).]

The motion of the gases in sunspot penumbra is radially outwards; this was first demonstrated by Evershed at the Kodaikanal Observatory. Evershed set the slit of his spectroheliograph across a spot-group and along a solar radius. The relative motions of the gases could then be determined from Doppler displacements of the spectral lines. The *Evershed effect*, as it became known, was found to be undetectable in spots near the centre of the disk, but was well defined for spots closer to the solar limb. Evershed later found that the gases of the upper chromosphere show a similar motion in the reverse direction, i.e. radially inwards.

It is generally accepted that sunspots have a vortical form, the (comparatively) dark umbra being produced by adiabatic cooling of an ascending, expanding mass of gas, and the penumbra by the mixing of this cooled gas with the hotter gases of the surrounding surface. Photographs in hydrogen light clearly show the vortical form of the photospheric gases surrounding the spot. It is usual for the direction of the vortical rotation to be anti-clockwise for spots in the northern hemisphere and clockwise in the southern hemisphere.

In 1908 Hale demonstrated the presence of a strong **Zeeman effect**, indicating that sunspots have powerful magnetic fields. The leading and following spots of a northern-hemisphere pair were found to have opposite magnetic polarity, whereas the reverse polarities obtained for a pair in the southern hemisphere.

Hale sought to explain these effects by postulating a U-shaped vortex below the photosphere, of which the leading and following spots of a pair were the ends; Bjerknes proposed an annular vortex, running around the Sun meridionally just below the photosphere and breaking through it at these points. Many further theories have been developed but there is no evidence at present that any of them are necessarily correct.

Hale also discovered that the magnetic polarities are reversed each solar cycle, which suggests that the full cycle is in fact one of 22 years.

(See also **Solar activity; Sun—physical constitution of.**)

SUPERGIANT A very massive star of the highest luminosity known. (See **Stars, supergiant.**)

SUPERIOR CONJUNCTION That position of an inferior planet where its geocentric longitude is the same as that of the Sun and the Sun lies between the planet and the Earth. (See **Planetary motion.**)

SUPERIOR PLANET Term used to describe the group of planets more distant from the Sun than the Earth—i.e. Mars, Jupiter, Saturn, Uranus, Neptune and Pluto.

SUPERNOVA This term was originally applied to those novae whose increase in absolute luminosity was very much greater than normal—the distinction being purely a quantitative one. It is now realized however that there are qualitative differences between the novae and the supernovae also. The 'explosion' of a supernova, although similar in general form to that of a typical nova, may be of the order of ten thousand times the radiative output. The radiation emitted by a supernova during its outburst is equal to 5 to 10 per cent of the total radiation of the galactic system in which it is situated. An outburst on this scale must represent a partial disruption of the star concerned: indeed, some cases of known

Table 57. Galactic and extragalactic supernovae

Galactic system	Integrated magnitude of galaxy	Supernova date; designation		Observed apparent magnitude of supernova at maximum
Galaxy	—	1054	Crab nebula	?
Galaxy	—	1572	Tycho's nova	−3·5
Galaxy	—	1604	Kepler's nova	−2·5
N.G.C. 224 (M 31)	5	1885	S And	6·5
N.G.C. 4424	12·6	1895	VW Vir	10·5
N.G.C. 5253	10·8	1895	Z Cen	8·0
N.G.C. 5457 (M 101)	9·0	1910	SS UMa	10·8
I.C. 4182	13	1937	—	8·4

supernovae are surrounded by an expanding shell of nebulosity—no doubt material thrown off by the star during its outburst.

Only three supernovae have been identified in our own Galaxy, and then only by means of careful analysis of ancient records. The earliest of these occurred in A.D. 1054, when it was recorded by Chinese observers. The remains of this cosmic explosion can be seen today as the Crab Nebula in Taurus, a vast complex envelope of nebulosity three light years in diameter which is also a very strong radio force. The second supernova was observed by Tycho Brahe in 1572 in the constellation Cassiopeia; this is the brightest nova on record, having reached an apparent magnitude of −3·5; it cannot now be identified and must have a magnitude fainter than +18, indicating that its outburst must have been through a range of at least 22 magnitudes. The third galactic supernova, and the second brightest nova on record, is Nova Ophiuchi which was observed by Kepler in 1604. This supernova reached a maximum of −2·5; it too is now fainter than the eighteenth magnitude.

Perhaps the most famous of all supernovae was that observed in the central region of the great spiral galaxy in Andromeda in 1885; this star, now known as S And, attained an apparent magnitude of ·5—an individual brightness of about a tenth of the integrated light of the whole galaxy. By careful surveys of thousands of distant galaxies some fifty extragalactic supernovae have since been detected. Some of the brightest are listed, together with the three known galactic supernovae, in Table 57.

Studies of the light curves of the extragalactic supernovae have shown that there are two distinct types, known as Type I and Type II supernovae. Type I supernovae undergo an outburst of astonishing brilliance, attaining absolute luminosities of up 200 million times that of the Sun. Their light curves are very smooth and are all very similar, showing a decrease in luminosity of 50 per cent in a period of 55 days following the maximum; the rate of fading then slows significantly. Their spectra are notable for extremely broad emission bands which are very difficult to identify but should certainly include 'forbidden lines' of neutral oxygen. The supernova observed in the faint galaxy I.C. 4182 in 1937 was of Type I, it attained a luminosity 100 times that of the entire galaxy.

Type II supernovae occur much more frequently than those of Type I, but are much less bright at maximum and consequently more difficult to detect. They attain, at maximum, luminosities equivalent to 10 to 20 million times that of the Sun. Their fading after maximum is much

Table 58.   Surveyor Moon-probe vehicles

Vehicle	Date launched	Result
Surveyor 1	1966 May	Soft landing; obtained many successful photographs of the lunar surface.
Surveyor 2	1966 September 20	Failure—hard landing.
Surveyor 3	1967 April 17	Soft landing; many photographs, also sampled surface material by mechanical grab.
Surveyor 4	1967 July 14	Failed—signals lost before impact.
Surveyor 5	1967 September 8	Soft landing; first chemical analysis of lunar 'soil', by radioactive reflection technique.
Surveyor 6		Soft landing; further photographs and soil analysis.
Surveyor 7	1968 January	Soft landing; photographs from mountainous area near Tycho.

slower than that of the Type I supernovae, especially during the first few months. Their spectra are continuous for a few days following maximum, and particularly intense in the ultra-violet; then broad emission bands and some absorption lines begin to appear. The general spectral characterisitics are very similar to those of the novae.

Little is known of the physical processes causing a supernova outburst; it seems possible that the Type II supernova is simply what its name suggests, an ordinary nova but on a grand scale: if so, it may be a normal event in the life-pattern of a certain type of star. It is difficult to believe that the Type I supernovae, however, are anything but the spectacular results of a very special and rather rare combination of physical circumstances. (See also **Nova; Variable stars.**)

SURGE A type of eruptive solar prominence, usually associated with a spotgroup or flare. It is a brilliant jet of luminous material which shoots out into the corona with a velocity of the order of 200 miles/sec.; surges reach heights of the order of 60,000 miles above the solar surface before falling back, usually over the same path as they ascended.

SURVEYOR Name given to a series of space-probe vehicles launched from the United States to make 'soft' landings on the Moon. The *Surveyor* vehicles launched at the time of writing are listed in Table 58.

SYMBOLS,   ASTRONOMICAL A number of special symbols have been used by astronomers for many generations past; many of them are of great antiquity. The most common ones are the symbols used to represent the Sun, Moon and planets, and the zodiacal constellations. The use of these symbols constitutes a very convenient shorthand for use in reports, diagrams and tabulated data; they can also be used as annotative indices—e.g. ⊙ can be used to denote the Sun *per se*, and also in such forms as $\mathscr{M}_\odot$ (mass of the Sun), $\mathscr{R}_\odot$ (solar radius), etc.

A number of the general symbols have also been utilized for specific purposes, e.g. ♈ is used to denote the **First Point of Aries** as well as being the symbol for the constellation Aries.

Some commonly used symbols are listed in Table 59; where alternatives are accepted the preferred version is shown first.

Many Roman, italic, Greek and other characters are recognized as the symbol denoting various physical quantities, an

Table 59. *Common astronomical symbols*

Symbol	Alternative form(s)	Meaning
☉		Sun
☾		Moon
○		Full Moon
●		New Moon
◐	○	Gibbous Moon
☽	◐	Moon, First Quarter
☽	◑	Moon, Last Quarter
☿		Mercury
♀		Venus
⊕	♁	Earth
♂		Mars
♃		Jupiter
♄		Saturn
♅	⛢	Uranus
♆	♆	Neptune
♇		Pluto
⑮		Minor planet (with appropriate number)
☄		Comet
★	☆ ✳ etc.	Star
☍		Opposition
☌		Conjunction
□		Quadrature
☊		Ascending node (also longitude of)
☋		Descending node (also longitude of)
♈		First Point of Aries
♎		First Point of Libra
♈		Aries
♉		Taurus
♊		Gemini
♋		Cancer
♌		Leo
♍		Virgo
♎		Libra
♏		Scorpio
♐		Sagittarius
♑		Capricornus
♒		Aquarius
♓		Pisces

are given under the appropriate headings in this book.

(See also **Comets—nomenclature of; Constants, astronomical; Constella-tion names and abbreviations; Notation; Star catalogue designations; Star nomenclature.**)

SYNODIC MONTH Term sometimes used for the **synodic period** of the Moon, *q.v.* It is equal to 29·53 mean solar days.

SYNODIC PERIOD The period of apparent revolution of a body as observed from the Earth, measured from opposition to opposition. It therefore differs from the sidereal period by an amount equal to the apparent annual motion of the Sun during the period.

SYRIA Martian surface feature, approximate position $\Omega\ 100°$, $\Phi - 20°$. Name given to a bright area in the north-western part of Thaumasia, between the Solis Lacus and Phoenicis Lacus and bounded by the canali Tithonius and Claritas.

SYRTIS MAJOR Martian surface feature, approximate position $\Omega\ 290°$, $\Phi + 10°$. The most prominent feature of the planet's surface, first drawn by Huyghens in 1659. Formerly known as the Kaiser Sea, it is a vast triangular dark area, with a well defined western border sweeping north-eastwards from the Mare Serpentis, and spreading also from the northern ends of the Mare Hadriacum and Mare Tyrrhenum. Its prominence is emphasized by the light areas by which it is surrounded—Æria to the west, Meroe Insula and Isidis Regio to the north and Libya to the east. The tip runs into the great canal Nilosyrtis, swinging northwards across some 20° of latitude, and at times as prominent as the Syrtis Major itself.

The Syrtis Major and surrounding features are subject to changes which largely seem to be seasonal. The Syrtis Major is fairly wide during much of the Martian year, but during summer the lighter area in its eastern part lightens and merges into Libya, so that the Syrtis Major itself appears to narrow very considerably.

SYRTIS MINOR Martian surface feature, approximate position $\Omega\ 260°$, $\Phi - 5°$. A fairly prominent dark triangular feature on the northern edge of the Mare Tyrrhenum, very similar in form to the larger Syrtis Major just to the West. The prominent canal Pallas runs north-westwards across Libya from the Syrtis Minor to Mœris Lacus, where it connects with the great Nepenthes–Thoth canal.

SYZYGY The Moon is said to be in syzygy when at conjunction (New Moon) or opposition (Full Moon).

T

T TAURI STARS A class of extrinsic variables whose variation in luminosity appears to be stimulated by the effects of associated nebulosity. Their light variation is similar to that of the **R Coronae Borealis stars**. The type-star, T Tau, is an irregular variable situated in the variable nebula N.G.C. 1555. Other notable examples are RY Tau, associated with the nebula Barnard 214, and R Mon, associated with N.G.C. 2261. The latter two are examples of a type of star–nebula combination of which a number of examples are known; they consist of a star at the tip of a fan- or funnel-shaped variable nebula, giving a general appearance similar to that of a comet with its tail. The exact nature of these systems, and the cause of their variability, is not known.

TAIL, COMET'S An appendage developed by most comets as they approach perihelion and which fades away as they recede from it. It always points radically away from the Sun, and is caused by matter being ejected from the head of the comet by the radiation pressure of the Sun. (See **Comets—structure of.**)

TANAÏS Martian surface feature, approximate position Ω 70°, Φ + 50°. Dark condensation north of Tempe, close to the north-western corner of the Mare Acidalium.

TANGENTIAL VELOCITY The component of the actual velocity of a star, measured perpendicularly to the line of sight. The tangential velocity T is determined from the relation
$$T = 4 \cdot 74 \ \mu/d \ \text{km/sec},$$
where μ is the observed annual proper motion of the star in seconds of arc and d is the distance of the star in parsecs.

If the radial velocity V is also known it is possible to calculate the true space velocity v by means of the formula
$$v = \sqrt{(V^2 + T^2)}$$
(See also **Proper motion.**)

TAURIDS A meteor shower of exceptionally long duration, activity usually lasting from about October 26 to November 16 and reaching a maximum during the first week in November. The radiant is almost between the *Hyades* and *Pleiades* clusters, a few degrees west of *Aldebaran*.

There is evidence that, like the associated daylight stream, the β-Taurids, the Taurids may have a common origin with Encke's Comet.

TAURUS (The Bull. *Genitive* Tauri, *I.A.U. abbreviation* Tau.) Large northern circumpolar constellation which reaches midnight culmination in late November. Situated between Aries and Cetus to the west and Gemini and Orion to the east, and stretching southwards from the boundaries of Auriga and Perseus to join Eridanus at the equator.

The constellation contains some notable star fields, especially in the two great open clusters, the **Hyades** and the **Pleiades**. The principle stars are *Aldebaran* (α Tau), a first-magnitude orange giant of spectral type $K5$, and β Tau which has a magnitude of $+ 1 \cdot 8$ and lies almost on the boundary with Auriga (it has in fact been erroneously designated γ Aur). λ Tau is an eclipsing binary of the same type as **Algol**.

One of the most important objects in the constellation is the **Crab nebula**, situated near ζ Tau, designated M1 in the **Messier catalogue**. Originally discovered in 1731, this supernova remnant was rediscovered by Messier in 1758; this stimulated him to compile his famous catalogue of nebulous objects, in order to facilitate the identification of new comets.

TAURUS A A strong discrete radio source, number 05N2A in the I.A.U. catalogue. Situated at R.A. 05 hr 31 min, Dec. 21° 59′ N, it is associated with the **Crab Nebula**, *q.v.* [Plate 23(e).]

(See also **Radio astronomy.**)

TEKTITE Name given to a special class of silicaceous meteorite. The first tektite was discovered by Charles Darwin in Australia—hence their earlier designation 'australite'. They are not randomly distributed upon the Earth's surface, being confined to certain specific areas; they are found mainly in Australia, Moldavia, Java, Malaya, Indo-China and the Sahara Desert.

They are small objects, usually pear-shaped. They consist largely of silica (SiO_2)—up to 80 per cent, hence their characteristic 'glassy' appearance. They also contain small quantities of metallic oxides such as Al_2O_3, FeO, Fe_2O_3, Na_2O, K_2O, etc. It can be deduced from their constitution that they originated at a high temperature, of the order of 1500 °C, and then solidified; their surface layers show evidence of a later melting, presumably due to the heating effect of their descent through the Earth's atmosphere.

Tektites have been the subject of much speculation as to their origin; it has been suggested that they originate on the Moon, or from interplanetary dust, or in comets' tails; to date, however, the problem remains in the realm of speculation.

(See also **Meteorite.**)

TELESCOPE The telescope is the principal instrumental aid of the astronomer. It occurs in many forms, but all of these comprise an objective to gather the greatest possible amount of light and bring it to a focus, and an eyepiece to produce a magnified version of this image.

The eyepiece may be a single lens or may be a compound one composed of two or more lenses. The various forms are discussed elsewhere in this book.

There are two basic types of telescope,

the refractor (in which the objective takes the form of a lens) and the reflector (in which it is a mirror). Many different forms have been devised, mostly to meet special requirements; some of the main ones are described in the following entries. Owing to limitations of space it has not been possible to do more than point out the principle differences between the various types; more exhaustive discussion can be found in more specialized works.

TELESCOPE, ALTAZIMUTH A telescope provided with an **altazimuth mounting**, *q.v.*

The term is also used to denote an instrument formerly used to supplement meridian-transit observations, especially of the Moon, which cannot be observed on the meridian when close to the Sun in the sky, i.e. for a period before and after New Moon. It consisted of a transit circle so mounted that it could be rotated about a vertical axis into any selected azimuth. (See also **Meridian astronomy.**)

TELESCOPE, APLANATIC A telescope whose objective is so designed that the image of a very distant object is free from both **spherical aberration** and **coma**. The term was invented by Sir John Herschel. (See also **Aplanatic lens.**)

TELESCOPE, ASTROGRAPHIC See **Astrographic telescope.**

TELESCOPE, ASTRONOMICAL Although purely a general description, this term is also used, especially by physicists, to denote the simple form of refractor which is non-erecting, as opposed to the terrestrial telescope, which gives an erect image. This instrument is fully described under **Telescope, refracting.**

TELESCOPE, BAKER–SCHMIDT A number of forms of Schmidt camera have been designed by J. G. Baker, mostly high-performance instruments designed to be anastigmatic and distortion-free, such as the system shown in Fig. 145, which makes

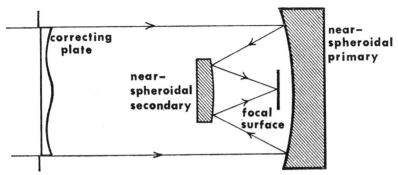

Fig. 145

use of two spherical mirrors and has a flat field. (See also **Telescope, Schmidt; Telescope, Super-Schmidt.**)

TELESCOPE, CASSEGRAIN A form of reflecting telescope announced in 1672 as the work of an otherwise unknown Frenchman, believed to be Sieur Guillaume Cassegrain. The Cassegrain is the most compact form of reflector in use, and is the form in which a great many large observatory reflectors have been made. All modern large reflectors are made with provision for working at the Cassegrain focus. It has proved less popular with amateurs, no doubt due to the difficulties of figuring the secondary mirror and piercing the primary.

It comprises a concave paraboloidal primary and a convex hyperboloidal secondary mounted on the same axis, inside the prime focus; the separation is very roughly the difference in the focal lengths of the two mirrors (Fig. 146). The image is formed just behind the primary mirror, which is centrally pierced; the instrument produces a rather small field

(with correspondingly large image size), and is comparatively free from spherical aberration. Astigmatism is rather more severe than in the Newtonian reflector, and the field is slightly curved.

The location of the eyepiece when observing at high altitudes is inconveniently near the floor, and necessitates the use of a diagonal. In the case of large instruments visual observing is largely restricted to finder and guiding telescopes, the main instrument being used for photographic or spectrographic observation. Most Cassegrain systems operate at focal ratios between $f/7$ and $f/12$.

TELESCOPE, CASSEGRAIN–NEWTONIAN A reflecting telescope so designed as to be usable at both the Cassegrain and Newtonian foci; this refinement is usually found only in large instruments.

TELESCOPE, CHRÉTIEN An aplanatic form of Cassegrain reflector, usually known as the Ritchey–Chrétien telescope (*q.v.*).

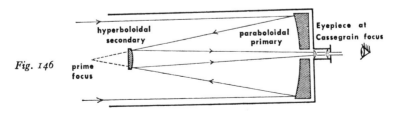

Fig. 146

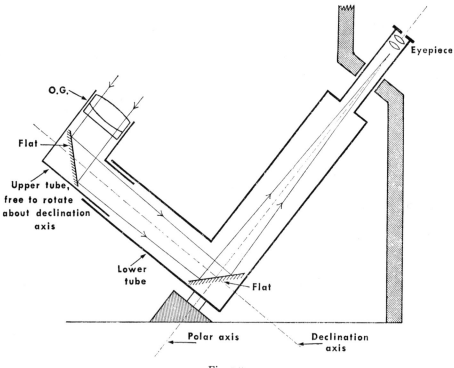

O.G.

Flat

Upper tube,
free to rotate
about declination
axis

Lower
tube

Flat

Eyepiece

Polar axis

Declination
axis

Fig. 147

TELESCOPE, COUDÉ An instrument in a form of polar mounting in which the tube is of 'elbow' form, so arranged that the light is passed along the polar axis to an eyepiece whose position is, therefore, fixed. The best-known example is the 23½-in. photographic refractor erected by Loewy at the Paris Observatory. Two typical forms of coudé arrangement are shown in Figs. 147 (a coudé refractor) and 148 (a coudé–Cassegrain reflector). It will be noted how the use of these designs permits the observer to remain inside a closed room in the observatory; the comparative comfort of this greatly increases the observer's ability to work accurately and at length. It is also possible to mount very heavy or very delicate ancillary equipment at the coudé focus, which would be impossible or undesirable at one of the moving foci.

Most modern reflecting telescopes are designed to operate at more than one focus, usually some combination of the prime, Newtonian, Cassegrain and coudé foci. They are sometimes given explanatory descriptions such as coudé–Newtonian–Cassegrain, etc.

TELESCOPE, COUDÉ–NEWTONIAN–CASSEGRAIN A reflecting telescope so designed as to be usable at the coudé, Newtonian or Cassegrain focus, as required. This refinement is usually confined to large instruments; it is a design feature of most really modern reflectors.

TELESCOPE, COUDER A variant of the Schwartzschild reflector—designed by A. Couder of the Paris Observatory—in which the astigmatism is also removed, but at the expense of a curved field surface,

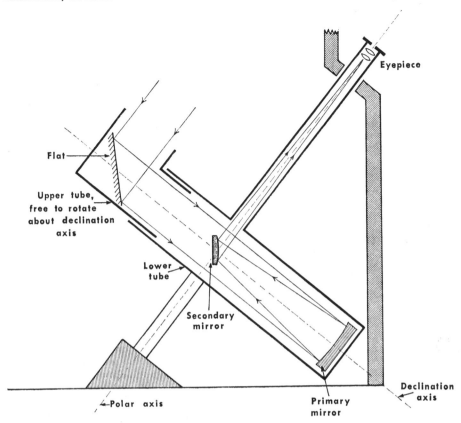

Fig. 148

thus necessitating the use of deformed plates or a field-flattener. Its design requires an even longer tube-length than the Schwartzschild, although a shorter extension is needed to combat sky-fog (Fig. 149). It is thus a cumbersome instrument to construct and mount successfully,

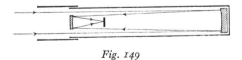

Fig. 149

and despite its optical advantages has not been widely used. It operates at a focal ratio of about $f/3$.

(See also **Telescope, Schwartzschild.**)

TELESCOPE, EQUATORIAL A telescope provided with an **equatorial mounting,** *q.v.*

TELESCOPE, GALILEAN The form of telescope used by **Galileo** comprised two single lenses mounted at opposite ends of a tube, a plano-convex object glass and a plano-concave eyepiece (Fig. 150). It is probable that this or a similar combination was used by the discoverer, Lippershey, and by the other early developers.

The name 'Galilean' is now applied to any system comprising a convex objective and concave eyepiece, although these may be bi-curved, and even compound, lenses; the principle of the Galilean telescope is

467

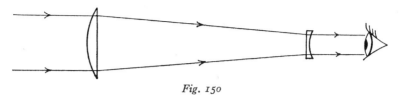

Fig. 150

that utilized in opera-glasses and toy telescopes, its advantages being cheapness and the formation of an erect image. The Galilean telescope suffers from its small field of view and unsuitability for high magnifications, and it is of course subject to considerable chromatic aberration.

TELESCOPE, GREGORIAN A form of reflecting telescope, the principle of which was published by James Gregory in 1663, some five years before Newton constructed his first reflector. The figuring of the mirrors for a Gregorian was difficult, however, and after several unsuccessful attempts Gregory abandoned the task. Gregorian reflectors were successfully constructed by other workers (after Newton had produced his first Newtonian instruments), notably by John Hadley, inventor of the marine octant, and James Short.

The Gregorian comprises a concave paraboloid primary and a concave ellipsoidal secondary, mounted on the same axis and separated by approximately the sum of their focal lengths (Fig. 151). The image is formed just behind the primary mirror which has a central hole for the purpose. Although the concave secondary is easier to construct than the convex one

of the Cassegrain reflector, the Gregorian is subject to greater aberrations and is longer and therefore more difficult to mount and to handle, and has gradually fallen into disuse. A considerable number were made in the past, however, and are still obtainable on the secondhand market; they are very popular with the general public, no doubt because they produce an erect image and are therefore quite satisfactory for normal terrestrial uses.

TELESCOPE, HERSCHEL–CASSEGRAIN A variant of the Herschelian reflector, in which the primary is tilted but a Cassegrain-type secondary is introduced; as this secondary is off-axis, however, it is not necessary to perforate the primary as in the conventional Cassegrain instrument. The primary is a concave spheroid and the secondary a convex oblate spheroid (Fig. 152). This design offers many advantages over the classical Cassegrain and Newtonian reflectors, but owing to its difficulties of construction and adjustment it has not been in common use for many years. The principle has been utilized to some extent in recent years, however, for certain specialized fields of observation.

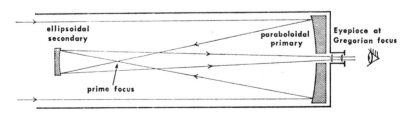

ellipsoidal secondary

paraboloidal primary

Eyepiece at Gregorian focus

prime focus

Fig. 151

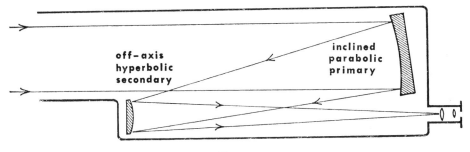

Fig. 152

TELESCOPE, HERSCHELIAN Before the introduction of silvered glass mirrors, the second reflection (usually from a speculum surface) in a Newtonian or Cassegrain reflector involved a loss of light of some 40%; in an effort to avoid this Sir William Herschel devised this instrument in which the primary (paraboloidal) mirror is slightly inclined to the axis, thus permitting the eyepiece to be located at the prime focus (Fig. 153). The Herschelian reflector suffers from a number of disadvantages, notably reversal of the image,

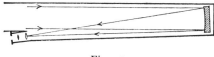

Fig. 153

astigmatism and image-distortion. Instruments of this type have not been manufactured for many years.

TELESCOPE, MAKSUTOV A variant of the Schmidt camera devised by D. D. Maksutov, in which the aspherical corrector plate of the conventional Schmidt camera is replaced by a weakly negative meniscus. Usually known as the **Maksutov camera**, *q.v.* [Plate 29(c).]

TELESCOPE, MAKSUTOV–SCHMIDT See **Telescope, Schmidt–Maksutov**.

TELESCOPE, MENISCUS–SCHMIDT A form of Schmidt camera which consists of a Maksutov camera in which the meniscus is supplemented by a Schmidt-type aspherical corrector. Sometimes described as a Schmidt–Maksutov telescope. (See **Telescope, Schmidt.**)

TELESCOPE, MERIDIAN An instrument used in meridian astronomy, usually the transit instrument or meridian circle, but the term might more generally be applied to such instruments as the prismatic astrolabe, P.Z.T., etc. (See **Meridian astronomy; Transit circle.**)

TELESCOPE, NEWTONIAN The first type of reflecting telescope ever to be made and used, by Isaac Newton in 1668. It is the simplest form and one of the most effective. Owing to its ease of manufacture it is the design used by most amateurs, and all modern large observatory reflectors have provision for working at the Newtonian focus.

The Newtonian reflector consists of a concave paraboloidal primary, and a diagonal flat mounted on the same axis, just inside the prime focus, to turn the convergent beam through 90° and divert it through the side of the tube to the eyepiece (Fig. 154). The diagonal is sometimes replaced by a right-angled prism. Although Newtonians exist in a vast range of dimensions they are mostly made to operate at focal ratios between $f/4$ and $f/8$.

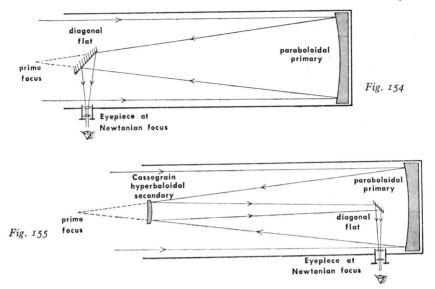

Fig. 154

Fig. 155

TELESCOPE, NEWTONIAN CASSE-GRAIN

A modified form of the Cassegrain reflector, in which the light rays, after reflection by the Cassegrain secondary, are deflected to an eyepiece position at the side of the tube by a Newtonian-type diagonal flat (Fig. 155); this avoids the need to pierce the primary mirror, and also renders the eyepiece position more accessible.

Also known as the Nasmyth focus, after James Nasmyth who used this focus in his 20-in. reflector.

TELESCOPE, NEWTONIAN–CASSE-GRAIN

A reflecting telescope designed in such a way that it can be used as a Newtonian or a Cassegrain reflector at will; this is a refinement normally confined to large instruments.

TELESCOPE, OFF-AXIS

A variant of the Newtonian reflector, in which only a

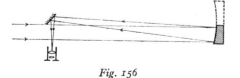

Fig. 156

portion of the normal primary mirror is in fact used; this has the effect of removing the flat outside the tube, which is thereby rendered obstruction-free (Fig. 156). This design avoids the astigmatism and distortion present in the Herschelian reflector, but owing to the difficulty of figuring the off-axis primary paraboloid mirror it has not been widely used.

TELESCOPE, POLAR

A telescope designed to provide a fixed observing position, with consequent advantages to the observer not only in that he can observe from the comparative comfort of an adjoining closed room, but also in that he can use equipment which would be too delicate, or too heavy and cumbersome, to be attached to the moving tube of the telescope.

A simple form of polar telescope is that designed by Grubb (Fig. 157). It comprises a simple refractor built as the polar axis of an equatorial mounting. Below the object-glass there is an equatorially mounted cœlostat-type flat, which permits any region of the sky to be fed into the telescope. The flat is usually clock-driven, so that it can be set to counteract the

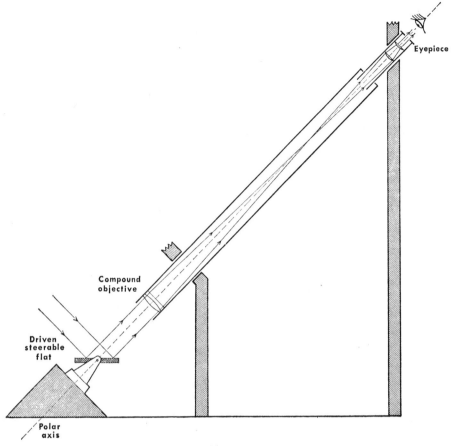

Fig. 157

rotation of the Earth and hence keep the same area of the sky in the field.

(See also **Telescope, coudé**.)

TELESCOPE, PREDICTOR A form of refracting telescope originally designed for military purposes which has been widely distributed through the government surplus market. Its main feature is an unusual form of roof prism (Fig. 158 (a)) which serves as an image erector as well as to turn the light rays through 90° to an eyepiece perpendicular to the tube; this arrangement was particularly suitable for the original purpose for which the

instrument was designed, in which the observer looked down into the eyepiece to observe distant airborne targets. The arrangement also explains the alternative name sometimes given to the instrument—'elbow telescope'.

The most common version of the instrument comprises a compound achromatic objective of 48 mm aperture, or slightly less than 2 inches, and a focal length of 6 inches; there is a compound eyepiece of which the field lens is cemented to the upper surface of the prism and the compound eye lens is in an adjustable focusing mount (see Fig. 158 (b)). This

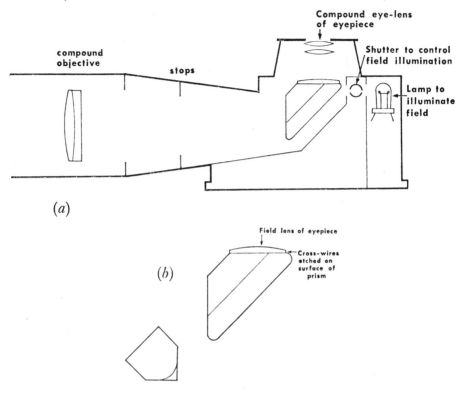

(a)

(b)

Fig. *158*

eye-piece gives a linear magnification of approximately ×7 and a field of 8°.

The focal ratio of this incredible instrument is *f*/3. It is ideal for work requiring a good performance over a wide field, where magnification is relatively unimportant. Its light-grasp is remarkable, and with it many of the open clusters and other interesting star-fields are a splendid sight. It is ideal for regularly following the motions of Uranus and Neptune and the Galilean satellites of Jupiter; it is also ideal for studying the structure of comets sufficiently bright to be observed with this aperture.

This instrument is essentially a 7×50 monocular; its performance is vastly superior, however, as the use of the roof prism obviates the need for a number of glass–air surfaces and the transmission is consequently much greater.

There is also a smaller predictor telescope available, approximately 5×25, and giving the same high performance. Properly mounted and adjusted on larger instruments they make excellent finders—especially, thanks to their 'elbow' form, for Newtonian reflectors.

TELESCOPE, RADIO See **Radio telescope.**

TELESCOPE, REFLECTING The first telescopes, constructed in 1609, were refractors; during the years that followed it was suggested more than once that a telescope might be designed utilizing mirrors instead of lenses, but it was left to Isaac Newton to construct the first reflector, in 1668. Newton—who was then a Fellow of his Cambridge college, having graduated in 1665—sought no publicity for his feat, but news of it gradually spread and in due course he was invited to send a paper on his invention to the Royal Society. Newton made a second instrument in 1671, which was eagerly examined by the assembled Fellows of the Royal Society, who in the same day elected Newton one of their number.

Newton's principle was the simplest and most effective form of reflector; owing to its effectiveness, and its simplicity and economy of construction, it is the form most popular with amateur observers. A great number of Newtonian reflectors are in constant use. Many modern large reflectors incorporate provision for working at the Newtonian focus.

Before Newton constructed his first instrument, James Gregory had proposed a two-mirror telescope system, in 1663; it called for the figuring of aspherical surfaces, however, a concave paraboloidal primary and a concave ellipsoidal secondary, and Gregory abandoned his attempts to manufacture the instrument he had designed. His name was, however, given to the system he proposed—the Gregorian reflector—which was successfully developed by Hadley, Short and others.

In 1672 a Frenchman named Cassegrain invented a reflecting telescope very similar to the Gregorian in principle, except that the concave secondary is replaced by a convex one. The Cassegrain is a much superior instrument to the Gregorian, being shorter and consequently easier to handle, and much less subject to aberrations.

Until the advent of the Schmidt camera and similar rapid photographic telescopes, all new reflectors have been based upon one or more of these principles. Since the turn of the century all new large instruments have been reflectors, and it would not be an exaggeration to say that the development of the reflecting telescope

made possible the whole science of astrophysics.

(See also **Telescope, Cassegrain; Telescope, Gregorian; Telescope, Newtonian; Telescopes, large reflecting.**)

TELESCOPE, REFRACTING The earliest telescopes were refractors, and for about 60 years no other form was available. The Galilean instrument was limited by its small field and low powers, however, and by extreme chromatic and spherical aberration. Many efforts were made to improve these faults.

It is necessary to substitute a positive lens for the negative eyepiece of the Galilean instrument in order to increase the field of view for a given magnification, and the earliest record of this suggestion is in the *Dioptrice* by Kepler, published in 1611. Kepler was not a practical man, however, and did not make such an instrument, and its invention is generally attributed to A. M. Schyrle, a Bohemian, more than 30 years later. Schyrle is also reputed to have invented both the terrestrial telescope and the compound eyepiece, for he proposed the addition of both a field lens and an additional erecting lens.

For astronomical purposes it is not necessary to produce an erect image, and since to do so necessitates the use of an additional lens, with a consequent additional loss of light transmitted, instruments designed specifically for astronomical purposes are normally inverting.

One of the most important improvements in the astronomical refractor was the invention of the achromatic object glass; originally devised by Chester Moor Hall in 1729 and developed by Dolland. Hall's principle was to combine two lenses, appropriately curved, manufactured from two types of glass of different refractive indexes; the effect of this was to reduce the chromatic aberration considerably, by bringing light of two wavelengths at opposite ends of the spectrum to a common focus, and thus bringing the foci of rays of all the intermediate wavelengths closer together. A great advance in the design of achromatic objectives was made in the early nineteenth century by Fraunhofer, who made some of the most highly corrected objectives then produced.

Apart from the need to reduce the aberrations produced by the object-glass, the development of good compound eye-pieces, to make the fullest possible use of the image formed by the objective, was essential; the development of the Huyghenian and, later, the Ramsden eye-piece, largely met this need.

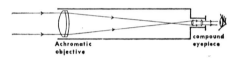

Fig. 159

The astronomical refractor is thus still basically a simple instrument (Fig. 159); further refinements are necessary only to fit it for specific kinds of observational work. Most of the development during the present century has been devoted to the latter task; improvements in light-gathering power by manufacturing larger and larger objectives appeared to reach a limit at the turn of the century. (It is notable that the nine largest refractors in the world were all completed between 1895 and 1915.) Despite the magnificent performance of the two giants made by the Warner & Swasey Company with optics by Alvan Clark (the 40-in. at the Yerkes Observatory and the 36-in. at Lick) we are unlikely ever to see the construction of a larger refractor attempted; the economics of production, inch for inch of useful aperture, are entirely in favour of the building of reflectors. Most astronomical refractors are designed to operate at focal ratios between $f/12$ and $f/15$.

(See also **Telescope, terrestrial**.)

TELESCOPE, RITCHEY–CHRÉTIEN A highly corrected instrument, being a

variant of the Schwartzschild reflector developed by G. W. Ritchey of Mount Wilson and Henri Chrétien of the Paris Optical Institute; it is a form of aplanatic Cassegrain reflector, operating at focal

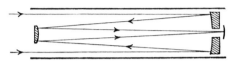

Fig. 160

ratios of $f/6$–$f/8$, and is a much more compact and practicable instrument than the Schwartzschild (Fig. 160). It produces a wide—albeit curved—field, and is free from spherical aberration and coma; it is, however, subject to astigmatism. The primary mirror is near-paraboloidal and the secondary near-hyperboloidal.

(See also: **Telescope, Schwartzschild**.)

TELESCOPE, SCHMIDT One of the most important developments in the history of the astronomical telescope was the invention by Bernhard Schmidt of the instrument which bears his name. Schmidt was an observer and instrument-maker of Estonian birth, who spent the latter part of his life as a voluntary assistant at the Bergedorf Observatory near Hamburg. In 1930 Schmidt produced the prototype of his telescope, a photographic instrument having a spherical primary mirror with a glass correcting plate situated at its centre of curvature. The correcting plate was so figured as to remove the spherical aberration without introducing further aberrations; it comprised a plate of optical glass which was almost plane-parallel but figured on one surface so as to make its central area slightly convex and its peripheral region slightly concave (Fig. 161); the effect of this was to converge slightly the near-axial rays and to diverge slightly those farther from the axis, thus bringing them all to a common focus. It will be noted that off-axis rays are also brought to a focus in the same

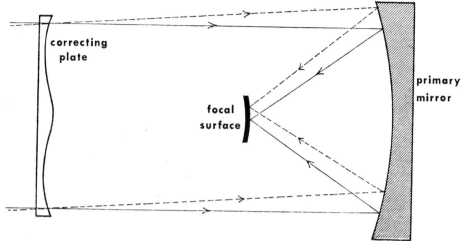

Fig. 161

(curved) focal surface. The figure of the corrector plate shown in Fig. 161 is exaggerated about 100 times. The first Schmidt camera (as these instruments are usually known) was constructed by Schmidt himself and comprised a spherical mirror 44 cm in diameter and a corrector of 36 cm, giving an aperture ratio of $f/1\cdot7$. These dimensions are usually indicated by describing the instrument as, e.g., a 36×44cm Schmidt.

By enabling cameras to be constructed giving sharp definition over huge fields, and operating at very low focal ratios, Schmidt's invention made a tremendous contribution to the development of astronomical photography; instruments with focal ratios as low as $f/0\cdot6$ have been constructed.

The principal disadvantages of the Schmidt camera are its relatively long tube-length (approximately twice that of a conventional reflector of similar focal ratio), some chromatic aberration and a curved field—necessitating the use of plates constrained to a curved form in a special plateholder during exposure.

A great number of modified designs of Schmidt camera have been evolved in attempts to remove these defects, to improve the performance still further and to utilize the principle for special purposes.

An early development (due to D. O. Hendrix) was the use of a very thick primary mirror (Fig. 162) in order to reduce the chromatic aberration in very fast Schmidt systems ($f/1$ and less); this led to the concept of the solid-Schmidt in which the entire optics are formed from one piece of glass (Fig. 163); for compact-

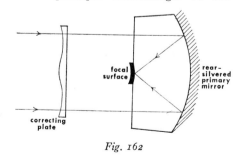

Fig. 162

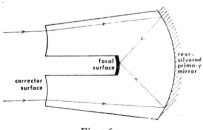

Fig. 163

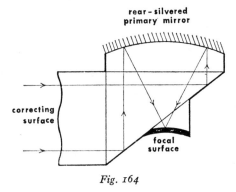

Fig. 164

rear-silvered
primary mirror

correcting
surface

focal
surface

ness and ease of access to the focal surface the solid-Schmidt is sometimes constructed in a 'folded' form, also invented by Hendrix (Fig. 164).

An interesting variation was evolved by F. B. Wright, who replaced the spheroidal mirror with an ellipsoidal one, amending the figure of the correcting plate accordingly; this arrangement halves

the tube-length, and may be used at a Newtonian focus (Fig. 165). A further convenience of the Wright telescope is that it produces a flat field; chromatic aberration and astigmatism become troublesome, however, if the system is used at focal ratios lower than $f/3$.

An important advance was made in 1944 by D. D. Maksutov, who substituted a weakly negative meniscus for the normal Schmidt correcting plate; this instrument is virtually free from chromatic aberration and, having no aspherical surfaces, is easy to manufacture. It has been widely used in photographic (down to about $f/2$) and visual (to about $f/8$) forms. The basic form is shown in Fig. 166; some of the numerous variants are shown in Figs. 77 and 78. The use of a meniscus, also discovered independently by A. Bouwers in Holland, led to a new generation of Schmidt-type instruments, the so-called Meniscus–Schmidt cameras. In these a weaker form of corrector plate is used in

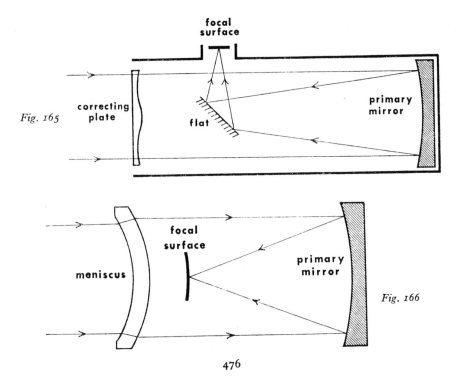

focal
surface

Fig. 165

correcting
plate

flat

primary
mirror

meniscus

focal
surface

primary
mirror

Fig. 166

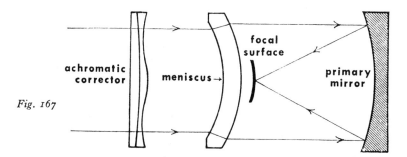

Fig. 167

addition to the meniscus (see Fig. 167).

A further development, the double-meniscus system of C. G. Wynne, gave a performance almost as good as that of the Meniscus–Schmidt cameras but with no aspherical surfaces (Fig. 168). A similar system, one of the 'super-Schmidts' designed by Baker for meteor photography, incorporated an achromatizing doublet between the concentric meniscus lenses (Fig. 169). Another family of Schmidt instruments are the Schmidt–Cassegrain cameras (Fig. 170), in which a Schmidt corrector is combined with a pair of mirrors in Cassegrain arrangement, giving an extremely accessible plate-position and a compact form. Where the two mirrors are spheroidal the field is curved, but a flat field can be obtained if both mirrors are suitably aspherized.

One of the most successful Schmidt telescopes is the 'A.D.H.' telescope at the Boyden Station (Bloemfontein) of the Armagh, Dunsink and Harvard observatories; this $32 \times 35\frac{1}{2}$-in. $f/3.75$ Schmidt–Cassegrain has produced some magnificent

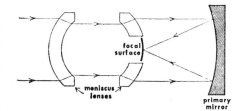

Fig. 168

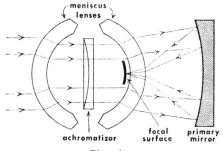

Fig. 169

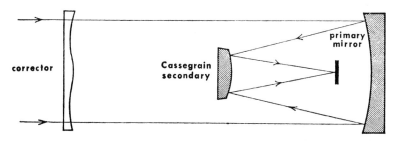

Fig. 170

plates of the southern sky, notably of the Magellanic Clouds, which have been used in important astrophysical investigations.

Perhaps the best known Schmidt is the 48 × 72-in. $f/2\cdot5$ instrument on Mount Palomar, used to produce the most comprehensive photographic atlas of the northern and equatorial sky ever undertaken. [Plate 29(b).]

TELESCOPE, SCHMIDT–CASSEGRAIN
A variant of the Schmidt camera, combining a Schmidt correcting plate with a pair of spheroidal or slightly aspherical mirrors in Cassegrain arrangement. This system has the advantages of compactness and accessibility of the image position. (See also **Telescope, Schmidt.**)

TELESCOPE, SCHMIDT–MAKSUTOV
A form of Maksutov camera in which the meniscus is supplemented by a Schmidt-type aspherical corrector. Usually known as a Meniscus–Schmidt camera. (See **Telescope, Schmidt.**)

TELESCOPE, SCHWARTZSCHILD
A highly corrected form of reflector devised in 1905 by Karl Schwartzschild; it produces a photographic image free from both spherical aberration and coma, and

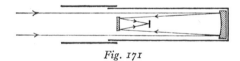

Fig. 171

is the only possible two-mirror system that can be designed to achieve this. It has a flat field, but is unfortunately subject to astigmatism.

Both the primary and secondary mirrors are concave and almost spheroidal in form; they are thus separated by the sum of their focal lengths, resulting in a rather long tube (Fig. 171). The plate must be situated well towards the mouth of the tube, which must therefore be fitted with a light-weight extension to prevent the spoiling of the plate by sky-fog. For these

reasons the Schwartzschild reflector is a very cumbersome instrument to mount, to house and to handle; its adjustments are also highly critical. Only two of these instruments have been constructed and brought into observatory use. They operate at focal ratios of about $f/3$. (See also **Telescope, Couder; Telescope, Ritchey–Chrétien.**)

TELESCOPE, SOLID SCHMIDT
A form of Schmidt camera designed to operate at very small aperture ratios—as little as $f/0\cdot3$ in some cases. The optical system is constructed from a single block of glass, the correcting plate and mirror surfaces being worked on its faces. (See **Telescope, Schmidt.**)

TELESCOPE, SUPER-SCHMIDT
A type of Schmidt camera devised by J. G. Baker which operates at a very small aperture ratio. A series of these instruments was designed by Baker for a programme of meteor photography; they utilized a compound corrector, consisting of a pair of opposing meniscus lenses and an achromatic doublet. (See also **Telescope, Schmidt.**)

TELESCOPE, TERRESTRIAL
The normal refracting telescope used for terrestrial purposes; i.e. the mariner's telescope, the instrument used for target-spotting on the rifle range, for watching yacht-races, etc., etc. For these purposes a telescope must obviously produce an erect image. The original (Galilean) instrument did, indeed, do this, and the small telescopes found in toyshops are usually of this form; to achieve wide fields with high powers, however, it is necessary to use a positive eyepiece, which inverts the image. This is of no consequence for astronomical purposes, and so observatory instruments are normally non-erecting, this being preferable to the acceptance of the loss of light that would accrue from the inclusion of an erector. The loss of light is of less consequence for most terrestrial purposes, and a single or

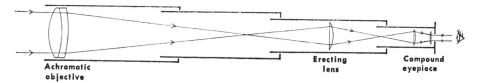

Achromatic objective

Erecting lens

Compound eyepiece

Fig. 172

compound erecting lens is therefore built in to 'terrestrial' instruments (Fig. 172).

Some observers favour the use of a small terrestrial telescope as an additional low-power finder; its erect image corresponding to the view of the heavens obtained by the observer's unaided eye which greatly facilitates rough setting of his instrument. In such cases it is usual to have a conventional astronomical telescope also fitted as a higher-power finder/guider.

TELESCOPE, TOWER A special installation devised for the furtherance of research in solar physics; there are a number of these instruments at the major solar physics observatories throughout the world, and each has been tailored to the particular requirements of the observatory concerned. They are, however, basically similar. They comprise a tall inner tower, which supports a large cœlostat, and an outer tower, on separate foundations and quite detached from the inner one, which supports the observer's platform and the walls and dome of the cœlostat housing. This arrangement ensures the maximum freedom from vibration in the cœlostat mounting.

The light from the Sun is fed, via the cœlostat, vertically down the tower; it is then fed into a spectroheliograph or other apparatus, as required. Many tower telescopes provide a range of alternative ancillary instruments.

The use of a tower enables very long focal length equipment to be used without the use of too great a ground area; it has the additional advantage of gathering the Sun's light at a position well above the disturbed air found near ground level. The objective of any ancillary equipment

which requires one can be located well up the tower, and a large paraboloidal primary mirror is usually situated at the foot of a deep well beneath the tower, thus providing an even greater vertical operating distance. Sometimes flats are also introduced so as to increase the vertical operating distance still further.

The original concept of the tower telescope is due to G. E. Hale, who designed the first, the 65-ft tower erected at Mount Wilson in 1907. To this he shortly afterwards added a more refined instrument on a 150-ft. tower. [Plate 29(a).]

There are many difficulties associated with the successful construction of a solar tower, but those that have been erected have contributed greatly to our knowledge of solar physics. Particularly notable has been the work done at the McMath–Hulbert Observatory of the University of Michigan, which has two towers, of 50 ft and 70 ft; the use of cinephotography to record the development of solar activity has been a speciality at this observatory since its foundation nearly forty years ago, and has proved to be a most important tool to the solar physicist.

TELESCOPE, WRIGHT A development of the Schmidt camera devised by F. B. Wright, in which the spherical primary mirror is replaced by an ellipsoid, and the figure of the correcting plate modified accordingly; this system gives the advantage of a flat field and a tube-length approximately half that of the classical Schmidt. (See **Telescope, Schmidt.**)

TELESCOPE, ZENITH See **Zenith telescope.**

479

TELESCOPES—LARGE REFLECTING

The locations of reflecting telescopes with apertures of 30-in. and over are listed in Table 60. The foci at which they can be used are also given. Telescopes with the same aperture are listed in order of age.

Key: P—Prime
N—Newtonian
C—Cassegrain
G—Gregorian
cdé—coudé
Nas—Nasmyth

Table 60. Large reflecting telescopes

	Aperture (in.)	Foci used	Location	Date of Construction
1.	236		U.S.S.R.	Under construction
2.	200	P C cdé	Mount Palomar Observatory, California, U.S.A. [Plate 31(d).]	1948
3.	152		Queen Elizabeth II Observatory, British Columbia, Canada.	Planned
4.	150		Siding Spring, New South Wales, Australia. [Proposed joint British/Australian instrument.]	Planned
5.	144		La Silla mountain, Chile. [Proposed European Southern Observatory.]	Under construction
6.	120	P cdé	Lick Observatory, Mt. Hamilton, California, U.S.A. [Plate 31(a).]	1959
7.	102	P C cdé Nas	Crimean Astrophysical Observatory, Nauchny, Crimea, U.S.S.R. [Plate 31(c).]	1960
8.	100	N C cdé	Mount Wilson Observatory, Pasadena, California, U.S.A. [Plate 30(d).]	1917
9.	98	P C cdé	[Isaac Newton Telescope], Royal Greenwich Observatory, Herstmonceux Castle, Sussex, England. [Plate 31(b).]	1967
10.	84	C cdé	Kitt Peak Observatory, Tucson, Arizona, U.S.A.	1961
11.	82	P C cdé	McDonald Observatory, Fort Davis, Texas, U.S.A. [Plate 30(b).]	1939
12.	77	N C cdé	Observatoire de Haute Provence, Saint Michel l'Observatoire, (Basses Alpes), France.	1958
13.	74	N C	David Dunlap Observatory, Richmond Hill, Ontario, Canada.	1935
14.	74	N C cdé	Radcliffe Observatory, Pretoria, South Africa.	1948
15.	74	N C cdé	Commonwealth Astronomical Observatory, Mt. Stromlo, Canberra, Australia.	1955
16.	74	N C cdé	Helwan Observatory, Helwan, Egypt.	1960
17.	74	N C cdé	Okayama Astrophysical Observatory, Kamogata, Okayama-ken, Japan.	1960
18.	73	N C	Dominion Astrophysical Observatory, Victoria, British Columbia, Canada	1918
19.	69	N C	Perkins Observatory, Delaware, Ohio, U.S.A.	1932
20.	61	N C cdé	G. R. Agassiz Station, Harvard College Observatory, Cambridge, Massachusetts, U.S.A.	1934

Table 60.   Large reflecting telescopes (continued)

	Aperture (in.)	Foci used	Location	Date of construction
21.	61	N C	National Observatory, Bosque Alegre Station, Argentina.	1942
22.	60	N C	Mount Wilson Observatory, Pasadena, California, U.S.A. [Plate 30(c).]	1908
23.	60	N	Boyden Observatory, Bloemfontein, South Africa.	1930
24.	50	Gr	Commonwealth Astronomical Observatory, Mt. Stromlo, Canberra, Australia.	1868 (Rebuilt 1954)
25.	50	N C	Osservatorio Astronomica, Merate, Como, Italy.	1926
26.	50	P N C	Sternberg Astronomical Institute, Southern Station, Crimea, U.S.S.R.	1960
27.	48	N C	Astrophysical Observatory of Padua University, Asiago, Italy.	1942
28.	48	N	Observatoire de Haute Provence, Saint Michel l'Observatoire, (Basses Alpes), France.	1943
29.	48	C	Crimean Astrophysical Observatory, Nauchny, Crimea, U.S.S.R.	1952
30.		P C cdé	Dominion Astrophysical Observatory, Victoria, British Columbia, Canada.	1961
31.		N C cdé	Nizamiah Observatory, Osmania University, Hyderabad, India.	1962
32.		N C	Hamburg–Bergedorf Sternwarte, Hamburg, Germany.	1910
33.	42	C	Lowell Observatory, Flagstaff, Arizona, U.S.A.	1910
34.	40	N C	Osservatorio Astronomica, Merate, Como, Italy.	1926
35.	40	C	Observatoire de Geneve, Geneva, Switzerland.	1927
36.	40	P N C	Stockholm Observatory, Saltsjöbaden, Sweden.	1931
37.	40	C	U.S. Naval Observatory, Flagstaff Station, Flagstaff, Arizona, U.S.A.	1955
38.	40	P C	Royal Observatory, Cape of Good Hope, South Africa.	1964
39.	39	N	Observatoire de Paris, Meudon, France.	1893
40.	38·5	P C cdé	IRSAC Observatory, Lubumbashi, Congo. [Can also be used as Schmidt with 26·3-in. correcting plate.]	1960
41.	37·5	P C	University Observatory, Ann Arbor, Michigan, U.S.A.	1911
42.	36	P	Lick Observatory, Mt. Hamilton, California, U.S.A.	1898
43.	36	N C cdé	Steward Observatory, Tucson, Arizona, U.S.A.	1922
44.	36	P C	Royal Observatory, Edinburgh, Scotland.	1928

Table 60.   Large reflecting telescopes (continued)

	Aperture (in.)	Foci used	Location	Date of construction
45.	36	P C	Royal Greenwich Observatory, Herstmonceux Castle, Sussex, England. [Formerly at Greenwich.] Plate 28(d).	1934
46.	36	P N	Goethe Link Observatory of Indiana University, Brooklyn, Indiana, U.S.A.	1939
47.	36	P C cdé	University Observatory, Cambridge, England.	1955
48.	36	C	Warner and Swasey Observatory, Cleveland, Ohio, U.S.A.	1957
49.	36	C	McDonald Observatory, Fort Texas, U.S.A.	1957
50.	36	C	Washburn Observatory, University of Wisconsin, Madison, Wisconsin, U.S.A.	1958
51.	36	C	Universitats-Sternwarte, Astrophyikalisches Institut, Jena, Germany.	1960
52.	36	C	Kitt Peak Observatory, Tucson, Arizona, U.S.A.	1960
53.	36	C	Okayama Astrophysical Observatory, Kamogata, Okayama-ken, Japan.	1960
54.	36	P C	Tokyo Astronomical Observatory, Mitaka, Tokyo-to, Japan.	1961
55.	33	C	La Plata Observatory, La Plata, Argentina.	1896
56.	33	N	Observatoire de Toulouse, Toulouse, France.	1895
57.	32	N C	Perkins Observatory, Delaware, Ohio, U.S.A.	1958
58.	32	N C	Observatoire de Haute Provence, Saint Michel l'Observatoire, (Basses Alpes), France.	1932
59.	31·5	N	National Observatory, Marseilles, France.	1864
60.	31	C	Allegheny Observatory, Pittsburgh, Pennsylvania, U.S.A.	1906
61.	30	P C	Royal Greenwich Observatory, Herstmonceux Castle, Sussex, England. [Formerly at Greenwich.] Plate 28(a).	1897 (Cass. focus 1957)
62.	30	N	Helwan Observatory, Helwan, Egypt.	1905
63.	30	N C	Commonwealth Astronomical Observatory, Mt. Stromlo, Canberra, Australia.	1930
64.	30	[N] C	Royal Observatory, Cape of Good Hope, South Africa. [Reconstructed as folded Cassegrain on transfer from Cambridge, England, to the Cape in 1960.]	1939 (Cass. focus 1960)

TELESCOPES—LARGE REFRACTING

The present locations of refracting telescopes with apertures of 20-in. and over are listed in Table 61. Telescopes of the same aperture are listed in order of age.

It is unlikely that object glasses larger than the Yerkes 40-in. will ever be constructed. Larger lenses would have to be made so thick in relation to their diameters —in order to prevent them flexing under their own weight—that the consequent loss of transmitted light would outweigh the increase in light-gathering power due to the larger diameter.

Table 61.   Large refracting telescopes

	Aperture (in.)	Location	Date of construction
1.	40	Yerkes Observatory, Williams Bay, Wis., U.S.A. [Plate 30(a).]	1897
2.	36	Lick Observatory, Mt. Hamilton, California, U.S.A.	1888
3.	32·7	Observatoire de Paris, Meudon, France. [Same mounting as no. 17.]	1893
4.	32	Astrophysikalisches Observatorium, Potsdam, Germany. [Same mounting as no. 30.]	1899
5.	30	Allegheny Observatory, Pittsburgh, Pennsylvania, U.S.A.	1914
6.	28	Royal Greenwich Observatory, Herstmonceux Castle, Sussex, England [Plate 28(c)].	1894
7.	26·5	Universitäts-Sternwarte, Vienna, Austria.	1878
8.	26·5	Union Observatory, Johannesburg, South Africa.	1925
9.	26	U. S. Naval Observatory, Washington, D.C., U.S.A.	1873
10.	26	Leander McCormick Observatory, Charlottesville, Virginia, U.S.A.	1883
11.	26	Royal Greenwich Observatory, Herstmonceux Castle, Sussex, England [Plate 28(b)].	1897
12.	26	Sternwarte Berlin–Babelsberg, Berlin, Germany.	1912
13.	26	Astronomical Observatory, Belgrade, Yugoslavia.	1929
14.	26	Tokyo Astronomical Observatory, Mitaka, Tokyo-to, Japan.	1930
15.	26	Commonwealth Astronomical Observatory, Mt. Stromlo, Canberra, Australia.	1953
16.	26	Astronomical Observatory of the Academy of Sciences, U.S.S.R.	1957
17.	24·4	Observatoire de Paris, Meudon, France. [Same mounting as no. 3.]	1893
18.	24	Lowell Observatory, Flagstaff, Arizona, U.S.A.	1896
19.	24	Royal Observatory, Cape of Good Hope, South Africa.	1901
20.	24	Hamburg–Bergedorf Sternwarte, Hamburg, Germany.	1908
21.	24	Sproul Observatory, Swarthmore, Pennsylvania, U.S.A.	1911
22.	24	Stockholm, Observatory, Saltsjöbaden, Sweden. [Same mounting as no. 32.]	1931
23.	24	London University Observatory, Mill Hill, London, England.	1939
24.	24	Observatoire du Pic du Midi, Bagnères de Bigorre, France.	1943
25.	24	Observatorio Astronomico Nacional Universidad de Chile, Santiago, Chile.	1956
26.	23·6 (twin)	Bosscha Observatory, Lembang, Java, Indonesia. (Twin visual and photographic refractors in combined mounting.)	1928
27.	23	University Observatory, Princeton, New Jersey, U.S.A.	1882
28.	20	Osservatorio Astronomica, Merate, Como, Italy.	1890
29.	20	Chamberlin Observatory, University of Denver, Denver, Colorado, U.S.A.	1894
30.	20	Astrophysikalisches Observatorium, Potsdam, Germany. [Same mounting as no. 4.]	1899
31.	20	Van Vleck Observatory, Middletown, Connecticut, U.S.A.	1922
32.	20	Stockholm Observatory, Saltsjöbaden, Sweden. [Same mounting as no. 22.]	1931
33.	20	Lick Observatory, Mt. Hamilton, California, U.S.A.	1940

TELESCOPES—LARGE SCHMIDT, ETC.

The present locations of the largest Schmidt and other short-focus astronomical cameras are given in Table 62. Telescopes of the same aperture are listed in order of age.

Key: S—Schmidt
　　BS—Baker–Schmidt
　　MS—Meniscus–Schmidt
　　Mak—Maksutov

Table 62.　Large Schmidt-type instruments

	Aperture (in.) (corrector)	(mirror)	Type	Location	Date of construction
1.	54	80	S	Observatorium der Deutschen Akademie der Wissenschaften, Tautenburg, Thurigen, Germany.	1960
2.	48	72	S	Mount Palomar Observatory, California, U.S.A. [Plate 29(b).]	1948
3.	40	54	S	Kvistaberg Observatory, Uppsala Observatory, Bro, Sweden.	1962
4.	33	46	S	Royal Observatory, Uccle, Belgium.	1958
5.	32	48	S	Hamburg–Bergedorf Sternwarte, Hamburg, Germany.	1955
6.	32	36	BS	Boyden Observatory, Bloemfontein, South Africa.	1950
7.	28	38	MS	Abastumani Astrophysical Observatory, Mt. Konobili, Georgia, U.S.S.R.	1956
8.	26·3	38·5	S	IRSAC Observatory, Lubumbashi, Congo.	1960
9.	26	40	S	Stockholm Observatory, Saltsjöbaden, Sweden.	1960
10.	26	37	S	Osservatorio Astronomico di Roma, Stazione di alta montagna sul Gran, Sasso, L'Aquila, Italy.	1959
11.	26	32	S	Tonantzintla Observatory, Tonantzintla, Mexico.	1948
12.	25·5		MS	Crimean Astrophysical Observatory (Simeis Branch), Simeis, U.S.S.R.	1951
13.	25·5		MS	Crimean Astrophysical Observatory, Nauchny, Crimea, U.S.S.R.	1951
14.	25	38·5	S	Vatican Observatory, Castel Gandolfo, Italy.	1959
15.	25		MS	Ondrejov Observatory, Czechoslovakia.	1959
16.	24	36	S	G. R. Agassiz Station, Harvard College Observatory, Cambridge, Massachusetts, U.S.A.	1941
17.	24	36	S	Nassau Astronomical Station of the Warner and Swasey Observatory, Ohio, U.S.A.	1941

Table 62.   Large Schmidt-type instruments (continued)

	Aperture (in.) (corrector)	(mirror)	Type	Location	Date of construction
18.	24	36	S	Portage Lake Observatory, Dexter, Michigan, U.S.A.	1950
19.	21	21	S	Burakan Astrophysical Observatory, Burakan, Armenia, U.S.S.R.	1954
20.	20	28	S	Bosscha Observatory, Lembang, Java, Indonesia.	1958
21.	20	28	Mak	Sternberg Astronomical Institute (Southern Station), Crimea, U.S.S.R. [Plate 29(c).]	1958
22.	20	27	S	Astrophysikalisches Observatorium, Potsdam, Germany.	1952
23	20	26·5	Mak	Astrophysical Institute of the K.S.S.R. Academy of Science, Kamenskoje Plato, Alma-Ata, U.S.S.R.	1950
24.	20	26	S	Commonwealth Astronomical Observatory, Mt. Stromlo, Canberra, Australia.	1956

TELESCOPIUM (The Telescope. *Genitive* Telescopii, *I.A.U. abbreviation* Tel.) Small southern constellation containing only three fourth-magnitude stars and a few fainter ones.

TEMPE Martian surface feature, approximate position Ω 70°, $\Phi+40°$. Prominent light area in the north temperate region of the planet, north of Lunæ Lacus. Bounded by the Mare Acidalium to the east, Tanaïs to the north and Ceraunius to the west.

TEMPERATURE, ABSOLUTE Temperature measured in a scale whose lowest point is the **absolute zero**; that commonly used is the International Kelvin scale (° K), in which temperatures are equivalent to the Celsius (Centigrade) scale $+273\cdot15°$.

TEMPERATURE, STELLAR It is difficult to define the temperature of a star exactly, since the observable radiation received from a star is the integrated radiation emitted from a number of levels in the star's outer layers. For comparative purposes the **effective temperature** is used, which assumes that each star behaves as a black-body radiator. The temperature may also be defined in terms of the wavelength in which the star's intensity is a maximum, or from a comparison of the intensity at a number of selected wavelengths. Astrophysicists also use a theoretical concept—the **bolometric magnitude**—which attempts to evaluate the total radiation from the star.

TEMPERATURE OF SPACE It is virtually impossible to give an accurate numerical value for the absolute temperature of interstellar space. It is above the absolute zero, as space is not empty but contains a very low concentration of dust and gas particles. The temperature measured in terms of black-body radiation is only about 3° K, but if measured in terms of the atomic activity in the particles it does contain it would probably be between 10,000 and 20,000° K.

TEMPERATURE SCALES Temperatures are measured in a number of scales, according to need. The scales most commonly encountered in astronomy are the International Kelvin and the Celsius scales. The Fahrenheit scale is widely used for terrestrial purposes in many English-speaking countries, but is rightly being superseded by the Celsius (Centigrade) scale as decimal and metric systems are adopted in order to simplify and rationalize the everyday use of numerical and statistical data.

The International Kelvin scale is the scale for measuring absolute temperatures, and is based upon the **absolute zero**; its degrees have the same magnitude as those of the Celsius scale. Temperatures measured in this scale are expressed as ° K; thus the freezing point of water (0° C) is 273·15° K.

The Celsius scale was formerly known as the Centigrade scale and is still widely referred to as such; it is based upon a fundamental interval, between the freezing and boiling points of water, of 100 degrees. Temperatures measured in this scale are expressed as ° C; the freezing point of water in this scale is 0° C and the boiling point 100° C.

The Fahrenheit scale has a degree of smaller magnitude than the Celsius scale, having a fundamental interval of 180°; it is illogical in form and complex in use, since its zero is not coincident with either of the fundamental fixed points. It has been widely used in many English-speaking countries, however, and only in recent years has there been a welcome trend to replace it with the more rational Celsius scale. Temperatures measured in this scale are expressed as ° F; the freezing point of water (0° C) is 32° F and the boiling point (100° C) is 212° F. The absolute zero is equivalent to −459·7° F.

The Rankine scale is a scale of absolute temperature, measured in the degree Fahrenheit; in view of the unsuitability of the latter for scientific purposes its use is not advised, the International Kelvin scale being preferred. Temperatures measured in this scale are expressed as ° R; its zero point is, of course, the absolute zero. The freezing point of water is 491·7° R and the boiling point 671·7° R.

TERMINATOR In the case of a planet or satellite subject to a phase effect (e.g. the Moon or Venus), the edge of the illuminated hemisphere as seen from the Earth; i.e. the line separating the visible and invisible parts of the disk.

TERRESTRIAL Description indicating that the feature or object so described pertains to the Earth.

TERRESTRIAL PLANET Arbitrary description given to members of the group of planets Mercury, Venus, Earth and Mars.

TETHYS Satellite III of Saturn, *q.v.*

THALES (624–548 B.C.) A merchant of Miletus in Ionia who was one of the great natural philosophers of his day; he is often termed the Founder of Greek Astronomy. From a study of Mesopotamian records he learnt of the **Saros** and used it to predict the solar eclipse of B.C. 585 May 28.

THARSIS Martian surface feature, approximate position Ω 100°, Φ + 5°. Lightly shaded region sometimes detectable in the southern portion of the Tractus Albus.

THAUMASIA Martian surface feature, approximate position Ω 85°, Φ − 35°. A vast diamond-shaped ochre tract between Auroræ Sinus and the Mare Sirenum, in the centre of which is found the prominent Solis Lacus from which several canali radiate.

THEBIT Lunar surface feature, co-ordinates ξ − 065, η − 375. A most interesting multiple crater at the south-west corner of the Mare Nubium. It consists of a deep, well-defined, circular crater some 30 miles in diameter, with a central ring-mountain; the north-east wall is broken by an equally sharply defined, newer ring 12 miles in diameter, also with a central peak; the north-eastern wall of this ring, in turn, is itself broken by a craterlet about 5 miles in diameter.

It is notable that in the immediate vicinity of Thebit, just on the other side of the Straight Wall, is another multiple crater, Birt.

THEMIS The supposed satellite X of Saturn, discovered by W. H. Pickering in 1898 but never subsequently confirmed. (See **Saturn—satellites of.**)

THEODOLITE A surveying instrument used for the accurate measurement of angles in both the horizontal and vertical planes. It consists of a small telescope free to rotate about a horizontal axis, the whole being mounted on a turntable free to rotate about the vertical axis. Divided circles are provided to read off angular settings of the telescope in both co-ordinates, and also means of accurately levelling the instrument before use.

THEOPHILUS Lunar surface feature, co-ordinates $\xi + 435$, $\eta - 199$. Perhaps the most perfectly formed formation on the Moon, this magnificent 65-mile diameter ring plain is the northernmost of a fine chain with Cyrillus and Catherina. Its continuous and perfectly circular rampart has a sharp crest and much terracing on the lower slopes, and rises 18,000 ft above the floor. There is a superb multi-peaked central mountain mass rising to over 10,000 ft.

THERMOCOUPLE An instrument used for the detection and measurement of very small quantities of long-wavelength radiation—especially infra-red radiation (heat). In its simplest form it consists of a closed circuit composed of two wires joined at their ends, the wires being made of two different metals. Combinations commonly

encountered are iron–constantin, copper–iron, antimony–bismuth, etc.

If there is a difference in temperature between the two junctions an electrical current will flow around the circuit; if a simple voltmeter is inserted in either wire, between the junctions, this current can be measured. The voltage recorded will be a direct measure of the temperature gradient between the two junctions, one of which is normally maintained at a standard temperature such as that of melting ice.

Thermocouples are used in astronomy to measure the surface temperature of astronomical bodies; one junction is maintained at a standard temperature for reference and the other has a small, black disk attached, upon which the telescopic image of the body under study is focused. In view of the small radiation available in astronomical temperature measurements, a **thermopile** is often used in preference to a single thermocouple element.

THERMOPILE A sensitive instrument for the measurement of extremely small quantities of long-wavelength radiation, i.e. heat radiation. It consists of a battery of **thermocouples**, the alternate junctions being maintained at a standard temperature and the remainder being used collectively as the radiation-detecting element.

THOTH The scribe of the Gods in ancient Egyptian mythology, corresponding to 'Hermes' in Greek and 'Mercury' in Roman mythology.

THOTH Martian surface feature, approximate position Ω 255°, $\Phi + 30°$. A darkish canal running northwards from Tritonius Lacus, being an extension of Nepenthes-Thoth.

THREE-BODY PROBLEM A dynamical problem of fundamental importance in celestial mechanics, comprising the study of the motions of three bodies resulting from their mutual gravitational influence. There is no general solution; partial solutions have been found in cases where one or more of the bodies is of negligible mass compared with the others.

(See also **Many-body problem; Two-body problem.**)

THYLE I Martian surface feature, approximate position Ω 180°, Φ − 70°. Light area in the south sub-polar region, west of the Mare Australe.

THYLE II Martian surface feature, approximate position Ω 230°, Φ − 70°. Light area in the south sub-polar region, west of Thyle I and south of the Mare Chronium.

THYMIAMATA Martian surface feature, approximate position Ω 10°, Φ + 10°. Lightish region between the Sinus Meridiani and Margaritifer Sinus.

TIDAL FRICTION An effect due to the tides: the daily movement of large masses of water creates friction along the shores and on the seabeds; a small amount of energy is dissipated and the Earth's rate of rotation is slowed. This effect is extremely small—about one millisecond per century.

TIDAL THEORIES A group of theories postulating that the component members of the solar system were formed by tidal forces arising from the close approach of two stars. (See **Cosmogony—theories of.**)

TIDES The familiar tidal effects in large masses of water are due to the gravitational attraction of the Moon, which acts upon the oceans and causes a large volume of the water to move in the apparent direction of the Moon. Thus a tidal 'bulge' of water is raised on that part of the Earth's surface facing the Moon at the time; there is also a corresponding 'bulge' formed on the opposite face of the Earth.

Successive tides at a given point are not equal; this is shown in Fig. 173. If an observer at *A* experiences a high tide, twelve hours later he will have been

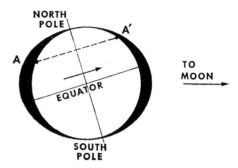

Fig. 173

carried (by the Earth's axial rotation) to *A'*, which although at the same latitude is experiencing a lower tide.

This effect arises, of course, solely from the fact that the Earth's axis of rotation is inclined to the plane of its orbit, and is known as the *diurnal inequality*.

Although at a much greater distance, the Sun also raises tides on the Earth; this gives rise to variations in the size of the tides, depending upon the relative positions of the Sun and Moon from the Earth. When both exert a pull from the same direction their tide-raising effects are added and a particularly high tide—the 'spring' tide—results (Fig. 174 (a)). This situation occurs at New Moon and Full Moon. When the Sun and Moon are 90° or so apart, as at First or Last Quarter, the resultant tidal effect is much smaller (Fig. 174 (b))—the 'neap' tide.'

Due to friction caused by the uneven nature of the ocean floor there is a lag between the Moon's passage over a given area and the resulting high tide; this lag may be as much as 6 hours.

The friction between tidal waters and the Earth's solid surface causes energy to be dissipated and thus reduces the Earth's angular momentum; its rate of axial rotation is therefore being constantly slowed (see **Tidal friction**).

It is obvious that the Earth must also exert a tidal influence on the Moon, although the Moon's lack of water or other fluid masses will render the effects less

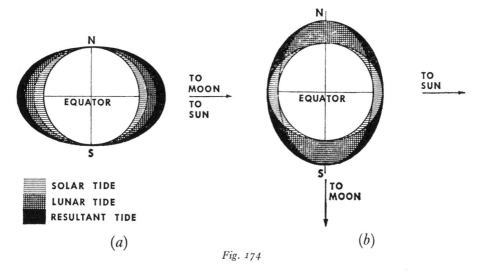

SOLAR TIDE
LUNAR TIDE
RESULTANT TIDE

(a)

(b)

Fig. 174

obvious; the fact that the Moon constantly presents one face towards the Earth suggests that its figure has been deformed by the Earth's tidal pull, and that there is a permanent 'bulge' towards the Earth. The continued tidal influence of the two bodies will eventually result in the Earth's rotation slowing until it too presents the same face towards the Moon; the day will then equal the month, which will then equal about 47 of our present days. This process will, however, take many millions of years.

TIME—DETERMINATION OF The normal method of recording the continuous passage of time is by means of a clock. Clocks, however, are subject to errors which have a cumulative effect, and so must be subjected to regular checks to ensure that the time as recorded is kept in step with its theoretical basis.

The theoretical basis of time measurement is, of course, astronomical: the year is based upon the period of orbital revolution of the Earth, the day upon its period of axial rotation; in antiquity the month was related to the period of the Moon's apparent revolution around the Earth, although it has now ceased to be a unit of

time measurement and is merely a convenient sub-division of the calendar.

It is usual for the maintenance of standard civil time in each country to be the responsibility of a leading observatory —e.g. the Royal Greenwich Observatory in the United Kingdom, the Paris Observatory for France, etc. At these national observatories a bank of clocks are maintained and regularly intercompared; they normally operate dials registering both local sidereal time and mean solar time. The former are regularly compared with sidereal time as redetermined by astronomical observation. For many years the clocks used for this purpose were pendulum clocks of ever-increasing sophistication and complexity; this type of clock undoubtedly reached its ultimate performance in the **Shortt clock,** *q.v.* Shortt clocks were installed at the Royal Observatory, Greenwich, in 1924; as a result of an analysis of their performance and reliability carried out at Greenwich they were adopted by observatories throughout the world, and in many of them are still in use, although they are no longer responsible for the maintenance of the national time services. The distribution of accurate time made a great step forward with the introduction of broadcast time signals: in the United Kingdom the regular broadcasting of the well known 'six pips' signals regulated by the clocks of the Royal Observatory commenced in 1924. A centre for the international co-ordination of time services, the Bureau International de l'Heure, was set up at the Paris Observatory and adopted by the International Astronomical Union in 1920. Since 1927 Greenwich Mean Time signals have been transmitted twice daily on international frequencies, to facilitate international clock-comparisons and to aid navigators at sea, etc.

The Shortt clocks have now been superseded as the national time standard by the **quartz clock,** *q.v*, the first of which were installed at the Royal Observatory's war-time time-service station at Abinger in 1943.

The zero of the mean sidereal day is the transit over the local meridian of the First Point of Aries, or vernal equinox; this is determined by the observation of the times of meridian transit of fundamental stars— i.e. stars selected for the purpose because their positions are known to high accuracy and can be assumed. Their observed Right Ascensions can therefore be compared with their calculated R.A.s. to obtain the error of the clock. A series of observations of fundamental stars made on one night is averaged to give the mean clock error for the night: a series of determinations of the mean clock error enables the clock's mean rate to be determined.

The instrument used for the observations of the R.A.s. of the fundamental stars has for many years been the **transit circle.** The principal transit circle of the observatory (e.g. the Airy transit circle at Greenwich) was normally used to provide the time-determinations as well as to carry out its major programmes of positional work. In 1927 the Airy instrument was replaced for time-determination work by a small (3-in. aperture) reversible transit circle, owing to its greater freedom from troublesome instrumental errors. During the past few years the 'small transit' has been replaced by the **photographic zenith tube** at Herstmonceux, which is producing time-determinations based upon transits of zenithal stars to a high degree of accuracy. P.Z.T.s are also in operation at Washington, Canberra, Neuchâtel and elsewhere.

TIME SIGNALS Signals used to communicate precisely defined instants of time for the regulation of clocks and watches. These took various forms in earlier times (see, e.g. **Time-ball**), but today they consist of radio transmissions of time-pulses from an observatory clock whose errors have been established by astronomical observation.

(See also **Time, determination of; Wireless time signals.**)

TIME SYSTEMS A number of time systems are in use, each being the most practicable for certain purposes. Astronomers are both producers and consumers, it being part of their function to provide the astronomical control of the clocks of the national time services (see **Time— determination of**) and time being also an essential element in most of their other observational work.

In antiquity the system of time recording was developed using units based upon readily observable astronomical phenomena whose effects were a controlling factor in man's environment: thus, the year was based upon the period of the Earth's revolution around the Sun, with its repeating cycle of the seasons; the month was based upon the synodic period of the Moon; the day, upon the period of the Earth's axial rotation and the consequent diurnal motion of the Sun and stars.

As methods of time recording improved it became necessary to draw up several systems of time measurement which could be directly related to such observations, for it soon became clear than no single system could satisfy all requirements.

Probably the first time system to evolve was that now known as *solar time*, in which the day is the interval between successive meridian transits of the Sun; unfortunately this interval is not constant, due to the eccentricity of the Earth's orbit and the obliquity of the Ecliptic. It therefore became necessary to introduce the concept of *mean* solar time, based upon the apparent motion of a hypothetical 'mean Sun'—i.e. one which coincides with the true Sun at perigee but moves around the Ecliptic at a uniform rate.

When meridian transits of stars became regularly observed it was clear that the mean solar day was not a suitable interval for such work, the sidereal day, or interval between successive transits of a star, being some four minutes shorter. Thus the system of *sidereal time* emerged, having the advantage that a star of a given Right Ascension would be on the meridian at the same (sidereal) time each day. Unfortunately the length of the apparent sidereal day is not constant, due to the effects of nutation, and so a system of *mean* sidereal time was developed in which the effects of nutation are averaged out.

The length of the mean sidereal day, expressed in mean solar time, is 23 hr 56 min 04·09054 sec; the mean solar day expressed in mean sidereal time is 24 hr 03 min 56·55536 sec. Conversion tables can be used to convert intervals of time from one system to another very simply. It is usual for mean sidereal time to be used for the preparation of observing schedules and for most time-determination and positional work; mean solar time is used as the basis of civil time for everyday purposes.

Three time systems are now used in the observatory: mean sidereal time, universal time and ephemeris time.

Universal time (U.T.) is the adopted basis of civil time; it is based upon a dynamical extrapolation to take account of the fact that the Earth's rotation is variable, but to a very close approximation is synonymous with mean solar time.

Ephemeris time (E.T.) is a system devised to facilitate the production of astronomical ephemerides well in advance, whose accuracy will not be impaired by unpredictable variations in the rate of rotation of the Earth. It is therefore not based upon the period of the Earth's axial rotation, but its period of orbital revolution in the form of the Tropical Year, and is therefore independent of the fluctuating rotation of the Earth. The system was adopted by the International Astronomical Union with effect from 1960. The unit adopted was the *Ephemeris second*, defined as 1/31,556,925·9747 of the Tropical Year for 1900 January 1 at 12 noon. The Ephemeris Time of any instant is obtained by calculating the number of ephemeris seconds that have elapsed by that instant since a moment defined as 'the instant, near the beginning of the calendar year A.D. 1900, when the geometric mean longitude of the Sun was 279° 41′ 48″.04, at which instant the measure of Ephemeris Time was 1900 January 0 d 12 hr precisely'.

TIME—UNITS OF The basic units of time are the year, based upon the Earth's period of orbital revolution, and the day, based upon its period of axial rotation. Larger and smaller units are obtained by sub-dividing these basic units. In using these units it is usual to specify the system in which they are being used. In the three time systems used in current observatory practice the basic units are as follows: in Ephemeris Time, the Tropical Year; in Universal Time, the mean solar day (to a very close approximation); in Sidereal Time, the mean sidereal day. Table 63 (overleaf) includes a selection of useful values and conversion factors.

(See also **Time—determination of; Time systems.**)

TIME-BALL A means of communicating a given time, precisely determined at an observatory, to enable interested parties to regulate their clocks and watches; a relic of the days preceding the invention of radio and the development of wireless time signals. The apparatus consisted of a large ball which would be hoisted to the top of a tall mast and released at a given

Table 63.   Units of time and conversion factors

Year	days	d	hr	min	sec
Julian	365·25	365	06	00	00
Sidereal	365·25636	365	06	09	10
Tropical	365·24220	365	05	48	46
Month					
Sidereal	27·32166	27	07	43	12
Synodic	29·53059	29	12	44	03

Day

1 mean solar day = 1·0027379093 mean sidereal days,
                 = 24 hr 03 min 56·55536 sec (mean sidereal time),
                 = 86,636·55536 mean sidereal seconds.

1 mean sidereal day = 0·9972695664 mean solar days,
                    = 23 hr 56 min 04·09054 sec (mean solar time),
                    = 86,164·09054 mean solar seconds.

General

1 Julian year = 365·25 days = 31,557,600 seconds.
1 day = 24 hours = 1440 minutes = 86,400 seconds.

time each day. Originally the ball was released by hand, later it was released by an electrical impulse from an observatory clock.

Among the few remaining time-balls is perhaps the best-known—that at the old Royal Observatory at Greenwich. This was erected in 1833, when John Pond was Astronomer Royal. It consisted of a 5-ft copper sphere on a mast erected over the east turret of the original Wren building. In an Admiralty announcement it was stated that the ball would 'be hoisted half-way up the pole, at five minutes before one o'clock, as a preparatory signal, and close up, at two minutes before one'. Then, 'by observing the first instant of its downward movement, all vessels in the adjacent Reaches of the river, as well as in most of the Docks, will thereby have an opportunity of regulating and rating their chronometers'. Thus began the first public time-signal. The use of the Greenwich time-ball ceased during the Second World War, but has otherwise continued right up to the present day, although for many years it has had no scientific value and has been continued for sentimental reasons, and as a working reminder of the great and valuable past of the Royal Observatory.

TIMOCHARIS Lunar surface feature, co-ordinates $\xi - 202$, $\eta + 449$. A prominent crater of perfect form, a little south of the centre of the Mare Imbrium. The diameter is 25 miles, the walls are terraced and rugged on the inner slopes and rise 7,000 ft above the floor. There is a very prominent central crater-peak. The crater is the centre of a faint but extensive ray-system.

TITAN Satellite VI of Saturn, *q.v.*

TITANIA Satellite III of Uranus, *q.v.*

TITHONIUS Martian surface feature, approximate position Ω 95°, $\Phi - 15°$. Sinuous canal radiating northwards from Solis Lacus to Tithonius Lacus.

TITHONIUS LACUS Martian surface feature, approximate position Ω 85°, $\Phi - 5°$. Dark feature on the northern border of Thaumasia, due south of the

Solis Lacus to which it is connected by the canal Tithonius. Connected to Auroræ Sinus by Agathodæmon and to Phœnicis Lacus by Nox, these canali forming the northern boundary of Thaumasia.

TITIUS, J. B. (1729–1796) A professor from Wittenberg, of whom it has been claimed that he should be credited, together with J. E. Bode, with the formulation of Bode's Law.

TORQUETUM A medieval instrument devised by Arabian astronomers which may be regarded as the forerunner of the modern **transit circle**. It consisted of a base, hinged to which was another plate which could be set at an inclination appropriate to the observer's latitude. Perpendicular to the inclined plate was a polar axis, on which there were two engraved circles; the first, graduated in Right Ascension, was parallel to the inclined plane and was provided with an alidade free to rotate around the polar axis. Mounted on the alidade was a support carrying a vertical circle graduated in Declination; this too was provided with a sighting alidade.

By rotating both alidades until the star could be sighted along the upper one, its R.A. and Dec. could be read off the lower and upper circles respectively.

TOTALITY Name given to the central phase of an eclipse, during which the eclipsed body is wholly within the umbra of the eclipsing body.

TRACTUS ALBUS Martian surface feature, approximate position Ω 80°, Φ + 30°. Light area running south-westwards from Tempe and across the equator to the northern edge of Phœnicis Lacus; bounded by Lunæ Lacus and Tithonius Lacus to the east and Ceraunius to the west. The southern part (Tharsis) is sometimes seen lightly shaded.

TRANSIT Literally meaning 'crossing' the word transit is used in a number of ways in astronomy. It is used to denote the passage of a body between the Sun and the Earth (see, e.g. **Transit of inner planet**). It is also used to denote the passage of an observed feature across the apparent disk of a body due to its axial rotation (see, e.g. **Central meridian transit**). The term is also used to denote the passage of a body across the observer's meridian due to the Earth's axial rotation (**Meridian transit**); the telescope used to observe such transits, the **transit instrument**, is also often termed a 'transit'.

TRANSIT CIRCLE The principal instrument used in fundamental astronomy. It is used for two main purposes—the determination of time and the measurement of the positions of celestial objects to a high degree of precision. It was developed by the amalgamation of two earlier instruments, the mural circle used for Declination determinations and the transit instrument used for the measurement of Right Ascensions. The transit circle is sometimes referred to as the meridian circle, but this permits confusion with the older type of circle that was not equipped for the making of transit observations and is not desirable terminology.

The transit circle consists of a refracting telescope (with an aperture of 6–9 in.) having a rigid mechanical axis mounted perpendicularly across its optical axis; at the ends of the mechanical axis are accurately machined cylindrical pivots which are supported in Y-bearings mounted on solid piers (see Fig. 175). The instrument is mounted with its mechanical axis East–West, so that the telescope is free to rotate in the plane of the meridian, around the mechanical axis. One or (more usually) two large, finely divided circles are mounted on the mechanical axis; these permit the angle of the telescope to be determined, and hence the Zenith Distance of the object under observation, from which its Declination can be computed. The Right Ascension is obtained by recording the sidereal time of transit of the

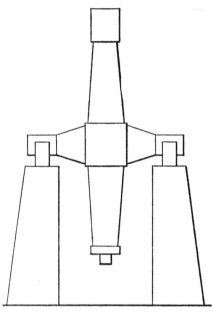

Fig. 175

object across the meridian.

Very rigid construction is essential; the axis and tube of modern instruments are usually built from heavy steel mouldings. The usual mode of construction is a hollow central 'cube' with two sections of tube bolted onto opposing faces of the cube and two conical axis-sections bolted onto two more faces. The two remaining faces of the cube are usually pierced and provided with covers, to facilitate collimation determinations (see **Transit circle—errors of.**) The pivots are usually machined from stainless steel, and the piers upon which they are supported, formerly constructed of stone, are now usually built up from iron castings and filled with oil or glycol to reduce vibration and prevent rapid expansion due to sudden temperature changes. Despite these precautions, and the highest precision in manufacture, no transit circle can be built free of instrumental error; it is necessary therefore to minimize the errors and then to correct the observations for the effects

caused by them. The determination of the errors must be carried out at frequent intervals—in some cases several times during an observing session—as their effects vary with the ambient temperature and other factors.

Determination of Right Ascension

The recording of a transit involves the timing of the passage of the body concerned past selected 'wires' symmetrically placed in the field of the eyepiece. Originally this was done by listening to the beats of an observatory clock, interpolating mentally. In 1854, three years after the Airy transit circle—perhaps the best known of all such instruments—was erected at the Royal Observatory, Greenwich, it was provided with a 'galvanic' chronograph also designed by Airy: this incorporated a paper-covered drum, revolving at a constant rate, with a pen making a continuous helical trace on it; the pen was deflected by pulses from the observatory clock every two seconds, and could also be deflected by the observer by means of a hand tapper. The observer was thus enabled to record the moments at which the star passed each wire in the field, for subsequent measurement and reduction. In 1915 the instrument was fitted with an impersonal micrometer, with which the observer had only to keep the object under observation bisected with a moveable wire, the times of its passage across selected points in the field being automatically recorded on the chronograph drum. After the Second World War the Airy instrument was fitted with a modern two-pen chronograph producing a record on paper tape, Airy's drum chronograph being retained as a stand-by. Thus, in its century-long span of useful life, the 'Airy T.C.' had bridged the gap from the 'eye-and-ear' method of recording transits used by Halley to the refinements of modern electrical recording.

It is now common for the moving wire to be motor-driven, the observer keeping the observed object bisected by means of a remote control for the motor speed. Instruments at the great national observatories are now equipped to record their observations automatically on punched cards or magnetic tapes for subsequent reduction by computer. [Plate 27(b, e).]

Determination of Declination

The Declination of an object observed with the transit circle is obtained from a measurement of its North Polar Distance (South Polar Distance in the Southern Hemisphere), usually abbreviated to N.P.D. [S.P.D.]. The Declination may be obtained from the relation Dec. $= 90° -$ N.[S.]P.D.

The circles of a transit instrument are normally adjusted to read zero when the telescope is pointing to the zenith, so that the observation of a body usually gives its Zenith Distance (Z.D.) The Z.D. of the pole having been obtained (by observing the Z.D. of a circumpolar star at both upper and lower culminations and taking the mean of the two values) the Z.D.s can readily be converted to N.P.D.s.

The observation of a Z.D. is usually made in two parts: the angle at which the instrument is set is determined, by means of the circle-reading microscopes, and the position of the object in the field of the telescope is also recorded. The latter part is carried out at two or more points in the field, preferably symmetrical about the centre of the field (= the meridian), by means of a moving horizontal wire coupled to a micrometer. It used to be the practice to have an assistant to read the microscopes, thus permitting the observer to remain at the eyepiece to carry out the other parts of the observation during the very short time available. In modern instruments the circle-reading microscopes are replaced by cameras which can be exposed by the observer so that the position of the circle is recorded on 35-mm film for subsequent measurement. Zenith Distance observations require corrections to be applied for latitude variation and atmospheric refraction.

Observing programmes

The use of the transit circle to control a

time-service is becoming increasingly rare, most of the national observatories concerned having introduced small transit instruments (of about 3-in. aperture) custom-built for the purpose during the last quarter of a century. In recent years this function has been assumed by more sophisticated instruments such as the **photographic zenith tube** (P.Z.T.).

The regulation of a time service with a transit circle involves the observation of the sidereal time of meridian transit of stars whose Right Ascension is assumed for the purpose; they must therefore be selected from among the *fundamental stars* whose positions and proper motions are known with great accuracy. The observation is thus the converse of that used to determine the position, in which the clock-time is assumed.

Positional observations made with transit circles have traditionally been used in two ways: in the compilation of catalogues of star positions and for the improvement of the ephemerides of members of the solar system. When making a catalogue a large number of selected stars are observed at every opportunity over a period of some years; the observations are reduced to a common epoch and the mean position published in the catalogue. By comparison of the positions of a star from catalogues made, say, 50 years apart the proper motion may be derived.

Observations for the improvement of their ephemerides are made of the Sun, Moon, planets and minor planets. It is usual to observe four limbs—the preceding and following limbs in R.A., the north and south limbs in Z.D.—where the phase permits. In the case of the Moon this is possible only at or very near to Full Moon; at most times only one limb each in R.A. and Z.D. can be observed. The motion of the Moon is by far the most complex and difficult to predict of all the members of the solar system, and so to extend the limited number of possible observations a small crater very close to the centre of the disk—Mösting A—is also observed whenever possible.

Future developments

Despite the advent of the photographic zenith tube, the prismatic astrolabe and other positional instruments of high precision, transit circles continue to play an important role in fundamental astronomy. The transit circle itself is still the subject of new developments, such as the mirror transit circle.

(See also **Airy transit circle; Transit circle—errors of; Transit circle, mirror.**)

TRANSIT CIRCLE—ERRORS OF As the function of the transit circle is to make positional observations of the highest possible accuracy it is essential to ascertain all small errors in the manufacture and installation of the instrument, to calculate their effect upon the observations and to allow for this when the observations are reduced. The determination and correction of instrumental errors comprises a major part of transit-circle observation.

The errors which affect the observed times of transit, and thus the determined Right Ascensions, are the level error, azimuth error, collimation error and pivot

errors; those which affect observations of Zenith Distance, and hence the determined Declinations, are zenith-point error, division errors and flexure of the telescope tube.

Errors affecting observed times of transit

Of these only the pivot errors do not require constant redetermination, as the level, azimuth and collimation errors vary continually with the prevailing conditions and must be measured at intervals throughout every watch at the telescope.

In the discussion which follows each type of error is considered separately, assuming for the purpose that the other errors are nil. It is conventional to regard a correction as positive when it must be added to the observed value in order to obtain the correct value. The latitude of the instrument is signified by ϕ and the Declination of the observed body by δ throughout.

Level error. This is caused by the mechanical axis of the instrument being inclined to the horizontal by an angle l, as shown in Fig. 176 (a); the effect of this is

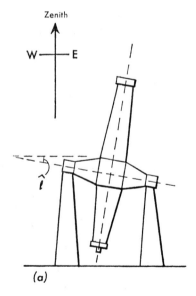

(a)

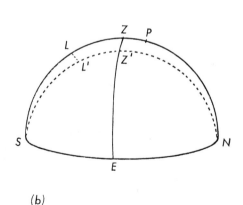

(b)

Fig. 176

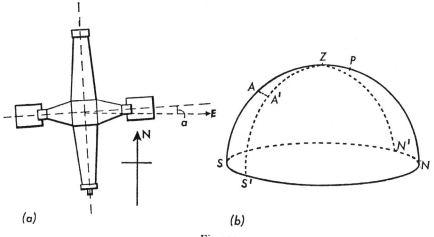

Fig. 177

shown in Fig. 176(*b*)—the telescope, instead of tracing out the meridian *NPZS* when rotated, traces out the arc of a great circle *NZ'S*. From this it will be seen that the effect of level error is nil at the North and South Points, *N* and *S*, and has its maximum value in the zenith (*Z*). The correction for the level error (shown as *LL'* for a typical latitude) is

$$LL' = l \cos (\phi - \delta) \sec \delta,$$

which must be added to the observed time of transit.

Determination of level error. In the case of small transit instruments this is effected by means of a striding level placed across the pivots; a reading of the departure from horizontal is taken and the level is then reversed and a further reading taken; the mean of the two values is used. This method would be both impractical and insufficiently sensitive for large instruments, however, and the following procedure is used.

The instrument is set vertical, O.G. downwards, and a bath of mercury (forming a horizontal reflecting surface) is placed beneath it. Using a Bohnenberger eyepiece the moving ('vertical') wire is set to coincide with its own image reflected by the mercury surface. At this setting the light path 'wire–mercury–wire's image' must be vertical. The micrometer reading for this setting is taken; the difference between this setting and that for the line of collimation at the same time (see below) is a measure of the level error.

Azimuth error. This is caused by the mechanical axis being inclined to the true *E–W* line by a small angle *a*, as shown in Fig. 177 (*a*); the effect of this is shown in Fig. 177 (*b*)—the instrument, instead of tracing out the meridian *NPZS* when rotated, traces out the arc of a great circle *N'ZS'*. The effect of azimuth error is nil in the zenith (*Z*) and maximal at the North and South Points, *N* and *S*. The correction for the azimuth error *AA'* is

$$AA' = a \sin (\phi - \delta) \sec \delta,$$

which must be added to the observed time of transit.

Determination of azimuth error. The azimuth error cannot be directly measured, but must be derived from observations of circumpolar stars. It is necessary for this purpose that the level error has already been reduced to a small amount and the error and rate of the clock must be known. When the corrected clock time is equal to the Right Ascension of the star, the star must be on the meridian; the difference

497

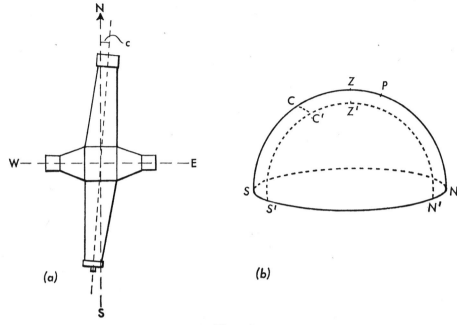

Fig. 178

between the micrometer reading for the star's position in the field at that moment and the setting for the line of collimation gives a measure of the azimuth error.

In practice it is much more difficult to disentangle the azimuth error from the level error; fortunately the former affects stars of low altitude to the greatest extent whereas the latter principally affects high-altitude stars, so that they can be separated. There are three methods of determining the error: by combining 'above-pole' and 'below-pole' observations of the same star made twelve hours (or multiples thereof) apart; by combining above-pole and below-pole observations of different stars made during the same watch; and by combining an observation of a very close circumpolar star with one of a 'clock star' (i.e. a star culminating south of the zenith, normally observed for the purpose of obtaining the clock error).

Collimation error. This is caused by failure of the optical axis to be perpendi-

cular to the mechanical axis; if the mechanical axis is assumed to be exactly East–West this will cause the plane in which the optical axis rotates to be inclined to the plane of the meridian by a small angle c, as shown in Fig. 178(a). The effect of this is shown in Fig. 178(b)—the instrument, instead of tracing out the meridian $NPZS$ when rotated traces out the arc of a small circle $N'Z'S'$. The correction for the collimation error CC' is

$$CC' = c \sec \delta,$$

which must be added to the observed time of transit.

Determination of collimation error. A transit circle is provided with two fixed 'collimating' telescopes in the plane of the meridian, both with their O.G.s toward the transit circle, one due North and the other due South of it. The transit circle is first set vertical, and shutters covering openings in the sides of its central cube are opened; this permits a fixed, illuminated wire in one of the collimators to be observed with the other, in which a moving wire is set coincident with the image of the other wire. This defines the *line of collimation*. The transit-circle telescope is then set on the illuminated wire in each collimator in turn. The difference between the micrometer settings on the line of collimation and at the centre of the field is a measure of the collimation error.

Combined correction for level, azimuth and collimation errors. If all three are present as defined above, the resulting correction Δt required to the observed time of transit is given by:

$$\Delta t = l \cos (\phi - \delta) \sec \delta + a \sin (\phi - \delta) \sec \delta + c \sec \delta.$$

This is often expressed in the form

$$\Delta t = m + n \tan \delta + c \sec \delta,$$

where $m = l \cos \phi + a \sin \phi$, and $n = l \sin \phi - a \sin \phi$.

In this form the variation with Declination of the effects of these errors on the time of transit is more readily seen—for stars with values of δ close to $+90°$ or $-90°$, i.e. close to the poles, the effect on the transit times due to instrumental errors is very pronounced.

Pivot errors. The pivots must be machined and polished with great care when constructed, so as to ensure that they are as near possible truly cylindrical, of the same radius and co-axial. They must therefore be maintained with scrupulous care, both in use and on the frequent occasions when they must be cleaned and oiled. The small residual errors are determined by a special programme in which the exact orientation of the telescope at different settings is measured. Once determined the pivot errors are virtually constant, however, and need be redetermined only at rare intervals to check for the effects of wear, etc.

Errors affecting observed Zenith Distances

Zenith point. The circles are set, in theory, to read $0°$ $0'$ $0.''00$ when the instrument is pointing exactly towards the zenith; in practice the reading will differ slightly from this value, by an amount which will vary with prevailing conditions: a correction equal to the angle by which the circle reading for the zenith differs from the zero must, of course, be applied to the observed Zenith Distances.

The zenith-point reading is obtained by taking a reading of the nadir setting and subtracting $180°$ therefrom; this is done at the same time as the level error is measured, with the instrument set vertically over a bath of mercury. With the Bohnenberger eyepiece the 'horizontal' wire is set coincident with its own image reflected in the mercury surface; in this situation the light path 'wire–mercury–wire's image' must be vertical and hence the telescope must be pointing to the nadir. The micrometer setting is taken and the circle reading recorded.

Division errors. Errors in the positions of the circle divisions (which are usually incised, in the case of a large transit circle, at $5'$ intervals) are determined by a lengthy programme of micrometer readings at each of the settings, entailing many thousands of readings in all. Once determined they are virtually constant.

Flexure of the telescope tube. This defect, which may be described as a 'sagging' of the two halves of the telescope tube under their own weight, can only be measured with the instrument in the horizontal position, by means of the collimators; its effect at other settings must be calculated on the basis of an assumption as to its variation with the Zenith Distance of the object observed.

TRANSIT CIRCLE, MIRROR A development from the conventional **transit circle**, *q.v.*, the mirror transit circle was originally suggested by H. H. Turner and developed by R. d'E. Atkinson. In it the cumbersome transit telescope is replaced by a plane mirror attached to a divided circle and mounted on an East–West axis in the usual way; the mirror is set at an appropriate angle to direct the light from the object observed into one or other of the

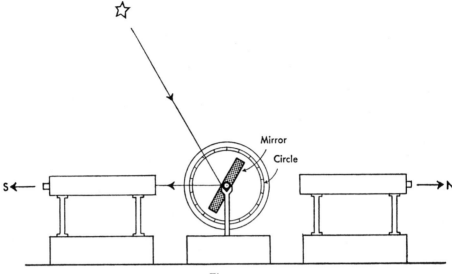

Fig. 179

collimating telescopes, through which the observations are made (Fig. 179). The principal advantage of this design is the avoidance of the complex errors caused by flexure of the telescope tube, etc., in the conventional form.

TRANSIT CIRCLE, REVERSIBLE It is now common practice for transit circles to be so constructed that they can be lifted out of their bearings, turned through 180° and replaced. This enables systematic errors inherent in the particular instrument to be determined in both orientations: it is then usual for the instrument to be used in one orientation for a period and then in the reverse orientation for a corresponding period, so that observations from both periods may be combined.

In the case of small transit circles used for time determination it is usual for them to be reversed mid-way through the observation of each star, whereby the collimation error is cancelled out. (See **Transit circle; Transit circle—errors of.**)

TRANSIT INSTRUMENT A refracting telescope having a mechanical axis fixed

perpendicularly across its optical axis, bearing a pivot at each end. The pivots are supported on Y-bearings and the instrument mounted with its mechanical axis orientated East–West, thus constraining the telescope to rotate only in the plane of the meridian. It is then used to obtain the sidereal time of meridian passage of stars, planets, etc., from which their Right Ascensions can be determined.

The development of the transit instrument is attributed to Römer, who erected one in Copenhagen in 1684. A famous example of the type was that constructed by Graham in 1721 for the use of Halley at the Royal Observatory, Greenwich, where it is still preserved. It had an aperture of 1¾-in. and a focal length of 5 ft.

The transit instrument was, with the meridian circle, the precursor of the **transit circle,** *q.v.* It has also been widely used in a modern form, usually with an aperture of about 3-in. and about 3 ft. focal length, for the regulation of time-services by transit observations of fundamental stars.

TRANSIT INSTRUMENT, BROKEN A variant of the small transit instrument used for time determinations, in which a right-angled prism is mounted at the intersection of the optical and mechanical axes, to direct the image-forming rays to an eyepiece position at the end of the hollow mechanical axis [Plate 27(d)]. (See **Transit instrument, small.**)

TRANSIT INSTRUMENT, SMALL Most transit circles used for positional observations are relatively large instruments, with apertures of 6–9 inches. For time-determination observations a small transit instrument was adopted, at Greenwich in 1927 and subsequently at other national observatories. The 'small transits' used for this purpose are usually reversible instruments with O.G.s of about 3 inches aperture. By reversing the instrument midway through the transit observation the effect of collimation error is cancelled out and can be ignored in reducing the observation. An interesting variant of the small reversible transit instrument is the so-called 'broken transit', in which a right-angled prism is mounted at the intersection of the optical and mechanical axes and diverts the light rays from the objective out along the (hollow) mechanical axis to a fixed eyepiece position at the side of the instrument. The 'eye-end' half of the tube is not required, of course, and is replaced by a counterweight. An instrument of this type has been successfully used for many years in the Time Department of the Royal Greenwich Observatory.

(See also **Transit circle; Transit circle—errors of.**)

TRANSIT, LOWER See **Culmination, lower.**

TRANSIT OF INNER PLANET From time to time the inner planets, Mercury and Venus, pass between the Sun and the Earth at inferior conjunction, and may therefore be seen in silhouette traversing the Sun's disk. (See **Mercury—transits of; Venus—transits of**).

TRANSIT, UPPER See **Culmination, upper.**

TRANS-NEPTUNIAN PLANET SEARCH A tremendous programme carried out by Clyde Tombaugh at the Lowell Observatory between 1929 and 1945, based upon the earlier searches for a planet beyond Neptune instigated by Percival Lowell.

Within a year of the commencement of the search the planet **Pluto** was discovered, very close to the position predicted by Lowell's analysis of the perturbations of the orbits of Uranus and the other planets.

The search when completed established that no other planets could exist unless they were very insignificant ones. (See **Pluto—discovery of.**)

TRANSURANIC ELEMENTS Name given to the elements having atomic numbers between and including 93 and 102; these elements do not occur naturally but can be synthesized by nuclear processes. (See **Chemical elements.**)

TRIANGULATION Surveyor's method of determining the distance of a body by measuring the angle subtended at the body by a baseline of known length. Adapted by the astronomer for the determination of the parallax of astronomical bodies.

(See **Parallax, stellar—determination of.**)

TRIANGULUM (The Triangle. *Genitive* Trianguli, *I.A.U. abbreviation* Tri.) A small constellation south of the westward extension of Andromeda and north of Aries; reaches midnight culmination in late October. Contains two third-magnitude stars and a few fainter ones, including R Tri, a long-period variable with a variation of more than six magnitudes.

The most important object is the fine spiral galaxy, M33, which can be faintly seen on a moonless night using a low-power eyepiece.

TRIANGULUM AUSTRALE (The Southern Triangle. *Genitive* Triangulis Australis, *I.A.U. abbreviation* TrA.) Small southern circumpolar constellation containing a number of naked-eye stars, the brightest (a TrA) having a magnitude of 1·9. At the northern boundary of the constellation there is a fine open cluster (N.G.C. 6025).

TRIESNECKER Lunar surface feature, co-ordinates $\xi + 063$, $\eta + 073$. A circular crater some 14 miles in diameter; it is crossed by a fault and the western side is higher than the eastern. There is a remarkable associated cleft system.

TRIESNECKER CLEFTS The area immediately to the west of the lunar crater Triesnecker is covered by a complex network of clefts or rilles. A 3-in. refractor will show the principal members of the system, but a powerful instrument is necessary to show the many very fine, criss-crossing rilles that make up this remarkable fault-area. Just to the west are the major clefts associated with Hyginus and Ariadæus, making the whole area one of the most important in studies of the lunar surface.

TRIGONOMETRIC PARALLAX The annual parallax of a star determined by positional observations. (See **Parallax, stellar—determination of.**)

TRIGONOMETRY Branch of mathematics dealing with the properties of a triangle. The study of the normal triangle, consisting of three points in a plane connected by three straight lines, is termed *plane trigonometry*; the study of the **spherical triangle**, which has wide applications in astronomy, is termed *spherical trigonometry*.

TRINACRIA Martian surface feature, approximate position $\Omega\ 268°$, $\Phi - 25°$. Greyish area between the Mare Tyrrhenum and the Mare Hadriacum, a pair of dark parallel bands running SE–NW through some 40° of latitude. It is a northern extension of Ausonia and has sometimes been mapped as Ausonia Borealis. It is separated from Ausonia (sometimes termed Ausonia Australis) by the canal Euripus II.

TRIPLET A compound lens having three components, which may or may not be cemented, or may comprise a cemented doublet and a separate, single lens.

TRITON Satellite I of Neptune, *q.v.*

TRITONIS LACUS Martian surface feature, approximate position $\Omega\ 260°$, $\Phi + 20°$. Prominent oasis at eastern border of the Isidis Regio; Nepenthes-Thoth curves south-west towards the Mœris Lacus and Syrtis Major, and the extension Thoth runs due north.

TRITONIS SINUS Martian surface feature, approximate position $\Omega\ 245°$, $\Phi - 5°$. Light bay in north-western end of the Mare Cimmerum.

TRIVIUM CHARONTIS Martian surface feature, approximate position $\Omega\ 198°$, $\Phi + 20°$. Prominent dark feature on southeast border of Elysium. A number of important canali radiate from it, notably Cerberus, Styx, Hades, Orcus and Læstrygon.

TROJAN ASTEROIDS Two groups of asteroids whose mean distance from the Sun is the same as that of Jupiter—483 million miles; the groups are thus located in the planet's orbit, one group 60° ahead and the other 60° behind the planet. The asteroids have no doubt been captured by the gravitational pull of Jupiter; it is notable that the positions they maintain relative to the planet are in accordance with a solution of the three-body problem propounded by Lagrange.
(See also **Minor planets.**)

TROPICAL YEAR The unit of time measurement derived from observation, being the interval between successive similar equinoxes or solstices; it is usually defined as the interval between successive passages of the Sun through the First Point of Aries, and is equivalent to 365·2422 mean solar days.

TROPOPAUSE The upper surface of the

troposphere, and its boundary with the stratosphere. The height at which temperature ceases to fall progressively with increasing altitude.

TROPOSPHERE The lowest layer of the Earth's atmosphere, from surface level to a height which varies in different latitudes but is about 7 miles on average. The upper surface of the troposphere is termed the **tropopause**, and is the lower boundary of the **stratosphere**.

Temperature decreases with height in the troposphere, but this effect ceases at the tropopause.

Most of the clouds, dust and other weather-making ingredients are found in the troposphere.

TRUE ANOMALY A term used in celestial mechanics, relating to the orbit of a planet. It is a quantity which is constantly varying as the planet travels around its orbit. It is, at a given moment, the angular distance between the planet and perihelion, measured at the Sun. It may also be expressed as the angle swept out by the radius vector of the planet since the most recent perihelion passage. It is usually denoted by the symbol v.

(See **Planetary motion**.)

TRUE PLACE The true position of a star on the celestial sphere as it would be seen from the centre of the Sun, referred to the true equator and equinox of the moment of observation. (See also **Star places**.)

TRUMPLER STARS Certain stars contained in open clusters, and found by Trumpler to have extremely high densities.

TSIOLKOVSKII Lunar surface feature, located on the far side of the Moon and discovered on photographs taken by the Soviet 'interplanetary station' *Lunik III*. It appears to be a large but uneven crater-ring with a dark floor and central peak. The name, adopted by the U.S.S.R. Academy of Sciences, is after the Russian teacher who first suggested the use of rocket power for interplanetary flight [Plate 7(a, c)]. (See also **Moon, far side of**.)

TUCANA (The Toucan. *Genitive* Tucanæ, *I.A.U. abbreviation* Tuc.) A southern circumpolar constellation containing very few stars, and none brighter than third magnitude. Notable objects are the **Nubecula Minor** and two magnificent globular clusters adjoining it.

TURNER, H. H. (**1861–1930**) Very distinguished English astronomer. Second Wrangler at Trinity College, Cambridge, in 1882, Turner became Chief Assistant at the Royal Observatory, Greenwich, in 1884 and made many contributions to the fundamental work of that establishment (notably the production of the Greenwich zone of the Astrographic Catalogue) and took part in several eclipse expeditions.

In 1893 Turner was appointed Savilian Professor of Astronomy at Oxford and Director of the University Observatory, which posts he held for the remainder of his life. Turner naturally took great pride in the completion of the Oxford zone of the Astrographic Catalogue, and also took over the completion of the work on other zones to assist the observatories to whom they had been allocated. Turner was also responsible for the collation and analysis of seismological observations from the entire world, and established the Oxford observatory as an international data centre in this field. Much of Turner's theoretical work was based upon his studies of the seismological records, and he was also one of the leading interpreters of variable-star observations.

Turner was President of the Royal Astronomical Society (1903–1905) and its Secretary (1892–1899) and Foreign Secretary (1919–1930). In 1930 he suggested the name 'Pluto' which was subsequently adopted for the newly discovered planet.

TWENTY-ONE CENTIMETRE LINE The 'line' of the radio spectrum due to hydrogen radiation at a wavelength of 21 cm, the principal radiation from interstellar hydrogen clouds. (See **Hydrogen radiation, 21 centimetre**.)

TWILIGHT If the Earth were entirely devoid of an atmosphere, total darkness would be experienced in the instants immediately before sunrise and immediately after sunset; in practice, however, the light rays from the Sun are scattered by air molecules and dust particles in the atmosphere. The effect of this is to produce an intermediate period during which the illumination of the sky slowly increases (before sunrise) or decreases (after sunset). The level of illumination is determined principally by the depression of the Sun below the horizon, but there are a number of factors affecting the duration of twilight.

In equatorial regions where the Sun's apparent path is approximately perpendicular to the equator, the duration is much shorter than in temperate latitudes; there is also a seasonal effect at higher latitudes, the duration of twilight being much greater at the summer solstice than at the equinoxes.

It has been found convenient to consider three forms of twilight: civil, nautical and astronomical; their times of commencement before sunrise and after sunset are tabulated in annual publications, astronomical twilight in *The Astronomical Ephemeris*, civil and nautical twilight in *The Nautical Almanac*.

Civil twilight. This is the period when normal daytime activities are not possible; its limit is taken to be when the zenith distance of the Sun is 96°—i.e. its centre is depressed 6° below the theoretical horizon.

Nautical twilight. During this period the horizon at sea can still be seen and the brightest stars become visible; it is thus possible to make altitude observations. The limit of nautical twilight is taken to be the instant when the Sun has a zenith distance of 102°—i.e. its centre is 12° below the horizon; at this point the marine horizon can no longer be seen.

Astronomical twilight. The limit of astronomical twilight is total darkness, and is taken to be the moment when the Sun's zenith distance reaches 108°—i.e. when its centre is 18° below the horizon.

TWIN RING-STRUCTURES Type of lunar surface feature, being a special case of **consanguineous ring-structures** whose component craters are equal in size as well as similar in form. (See **Moon—surface features of**.)

TWO-BODY PROBLEM A dynamical problem of fundamental importance in celestial mechanics, consisting of the study of the motions of two bodies in space, resulting from their mutual gravitational attraction and independent of any other bodies in space. This is the only form of the many-body problem for which there is an exact solution.

(See also **Many-body problem; Three-body problem**.)

TYCHO Lunar surface feature, co-ordinates $\xi - 142$, $\eta - 684$. One of the best-known of all lunar ring-structures, and certainly the most prominent, especially at or near Full Moon. It is situated in the very rugged southern hemisphere of the Moon, some 500 miles from the lunar South Pole. It has a magnificent rampart 56 miles in diameter, rising 12,000 ft. above the interior with some peaks of 17,000 ft.; when the structure of the rampart is examined in detail it is found to be polygonal rather than circular. The inner slopes are terraced, especially in the south-east. There is a splendid central mountain mass, about 5,000 ft. in height; on its north-western side there is a lower peak with a summit crater. A spur runs northwards from the eastern end of the central massif and curves round to form a shallow ring-structure. A great many crater-pits, mostly occurring in chains, radiate in all directions from the northern rampart of the formation [Plates 5(a); 7(b)].

The most notable feature of Tycho is its magnificent ray system, by far the most extensive on the Moon. A great many narrow, linear streaks radiate from the area of Tycho, and stretch for huge distances— in some cases more than 1,000 miles. One of the most conspicuous rays from Tycho crosses the Mare Serenitatis, passing right across the crater Bessel. The rays are so bright under high illumination that quite prominent features crossed by them virtually disappear around Full Moon— e.g. Maginus [Plate 4(a)].

It is noticeable that the rays do not commence at the rampart of Tycho, but are separated from it by a dark annular area.

TYPE I SUPERNOVA A rare type of **supernova** (*q.v.*), notable for its extremely bright maximum (of the order of 100–200 million times the luminosity of the Sun) and for a comparatively rapid decline.

TYPE II CEPHEIDS The **W Virginis stars**, *q.v.*

TYPE II SUPERNOVA The more common form of **supernova** (*q.v.*), attaining a maximum luminosity 10–20 million times that of the Sun and otherwise showing many similarities to the fainter novae.

U

U GEMINORUM STARS A division of the class of variables known as **dwarf novae**. Their light-curves are similar in form to those of novae, but the range of variation in brightness is about four magnitudes. U Gem and SS Cyg are the best-known examples; the class is sometimes termed the 'SS Cygni stars'.
(See also **Novae; Variable stars**.)

UBV SYSTEM The system of three-colour photometry for the determination of stellar magnitudes, devised by H. L. Johnson and W. W. Morgan of the Yerkes Observatory. It is based upon a standard sequence of some 400 stars distributed over the entire heavens.
(See also **Stellar magnitude—determination of**.)

UV CETI STARS The class of intrinsic variables better known as **flare stars**. The name derives from the type-star UV Cet.

UCHRONIA Martian surface feature, approximate position Ω 260°, $\Phi + 70°$. Dusky area in north polar region.

ULTRA-VIOLET SPECTRA Spectrograms obtained with the aid of a suitable filter or other means of selecting a part of the ultra-violet region of the spectrum, i.e. in the range of wavelengths between, approximately, 3,600Å and 200 Å. This technique is widely used in astrophysical research.

UMBRA The central part of a shadow where the light is totally cut off—e.g. the shadow-cone of the Moon during a solar eclipse, from any point within which the eclipse appears total.
The term is also used to denote the dense central area of a sunspot.
(See also **Eclipse, lunar; Eclipse, solar; Penumbra; Sunspot**.)

UMBRA Martian surface feature, approximate position Ω 290°, $\Phi + 50°$. Ochre area between Nilosyrtis and Boreosyrtis.

UMBRIEL Satellite II of Uranus, *q.v.*

UNITED STATES NAVAL OBSERVATORY, WASHINGTON The national observatory of the U.S.A., principally devoted to positional astronomy. For this purpose there are two transit-circles and a photographic zenith tube.
There are also a fine 26-in. refractor, erected in 1873, and a 40-in. Ritchey–Chrétien reflector. The 26-in. is noted for its remarkable light-gathering power, which was demonstrated by Hall in 1877 when he discovered the two tiny satellites of Mars with its aid.
There is also an out-station at Flagstaff, Arizona, equipped with a 40-in. Cassegrain reflector erected in 1955.

UNIVERSAL TIME (U.T.) Mean solar time for the meridian of Greenwich, reckoned from midnight; it is in fact synonymous with Greenwich Mean Time, but is now referred to as U.T. on the recommendation of the International Astronomical Union, to avoid confusion arising from the fact that until 1925 G.M.T. was reckoned from midday.
(See also **Ephemeris time; Time systems**.)

URANIA The Muse of Astronomy in Greek mythology.

URANIBORG The magnificent observatory erected by Tycho Brahe on the island of Hven in Copenhagen Sound in 1576 at the expense of King Frederick II of Denmark. The establishment was later supplemented by the construction of the underground observatory **Stjerneborg**.

URANOMETRIA A star atlas compiled by Bayer and published in 1603. (See **Bayer letters**.)

URANUS The seventh planet in order of distance from the Sun and the third of the major planets; the first planet ever to be discovered. Although visible to the unaided eye as a very faint star, observations of Uranus show little detail and are of little use unless carried out with large telescopes.

URANUS — APPEARANCE AND OBSERVATION OF Uranus is visible as a starlike object with the unaided eye, and the disk (apparent diameter at mean opposition distance 3″58) is resolvable with quite small apertures; it usually appears to be a pale, greenish-blue. An aperture of 10 or 12 in. is required to detect any detail, and comparatively little has been recorded even with much larger apertures. The general appearance is essentially similar to that of Jupiter and Saturn, with a broad, bright equatorial zone bounded by dusky belts. Spots or other condensations have rarely been seen, but those that have indicate an axial rotation period of 10 hr 49 min. [Plate 14(a, b).]

Uranus is unique among the planets in that its axis of rotation is inclined to the perpendicular to the plane of its orbit by more than a right angle; identifying the 'north' pole by the direction of rotation, the inclination is found to be 97° 53′. The effect of this is to give the planet an appearance of retrograde rotation.

URANUS—DIMENSIONS AND PHYSICAL DATA The apparent equatorial diameter at mean opposition distance is 3″58, corresponding to an actual equatorial diameter of 29,300 miles, almost four times that of the Earth. The volume is 47 times that of the Earth, but as the density is very low—1·71 times that of water—the mass of Uranus is only 14·6

times that of the Earth.

The gravitational acceleration at the surface is only 1·12 times that of the Earth —slightly less than Saturn and the lowest among the major planets; the velocity of escape is also low, 14·0 miles per second.

Like the other major planets Uranus has a very high albedo, suggesting a predominantly gaseous constitution; the actual value, 0·93, is in fact the highest of all the planets.

URANUS—DISCOVERY OF The discovery of Uranus by Sir William Herschel in 1781 was a very important event in the hsitory of astronomy. Never before had a planet been discovered, all the others having been known from antiquity; Herschel's discovery doubled the size of the known planetary system and stimulated a new era of thorough and painstaking observation. Herschel's feat was all the more noteworthy as it was accomplished with the aid of a telescope of his own making—a very fine 7-ft. equatorial reflector of 6·2-in. aperture.

On 1781 March 13, Herschel was engaged in studying a star-field on the borders of Taurus and Gemini, contained in the triangle formed by β Tau, ζ Tau and η Gem; noticing a rather bright object a little to the south of 132 Tau he carefully compared it with neighbouring stars and with his charts, and owing to its rather large, fuzzy image decided that it must be a comet. Herschel continued to observe the object and record its changing position for some weeks, still under the impression that it was a comet; eventually Herschel and other observers had amassed sufficient observations to enable the body's orbit to be determined, which proved it to be not a comet but a planet.

In recognition of his great discovery King George III granted Herschel an income for life of £200 per annum, thus enabling him to devote himself solely to astronomical research. In gratitude he wished to name the new planet *Georgium Sidus* (the Georgian star), but after some discussion Bode's suggestion of the name

Uranus was adopted, thus preserving the practice of naming the planets after Greek and Roman deities.

Some astronomers had wished to call the planet *Herschel*, and although this suggestion was not adopted Herschel's initial was incorporated in the symbol devised for the planet (♅).

It was later found that Uranus had been recorded by a number of observers, the earliest observation being one made by Flamsteed in 1690, the first of six occasions on which he observed the planet but took it to be a star. There are records of nineteen such observations made prior to the date of discovery, a fact which underlines the magnitude of Herschel's achievement, the superb quality of his instrument, and his diligence and outstanding ability as an observer.

URANUS—ORBITAL DATA

The orbit of Uranus has a semi-major axis of 19·181910 A.U., equivalent to a mean distance from the Sun of 1,782 million miles. The eccentricity of the orbit is 0·0472, very similar to that of Jupiter; the actual distance from the Sun can therefore vary from about 1,700 million miles at perihelion to nearly 1,870 million miles at aphelion.

The orbit is inclined to the plane of the Ecliptic by 0° 46′ 23″·1, the smallest value for any of the planets. The mean orbital velocity is 4·2 miles per second, resulting in a sidereal period of 30,685·1 days—about 84·01 years.

URANUS—SATELLITES OF

Having discovered the planet Herschel was anxious to discover its satellites, if any, as well, and during the years following the discovery of Uranus he constantly examined the star-field surrounding it hoping to find a 'star' which did not share the apparent motion of the background stars but displayed its own motion relative to Uranus. For six years Herschel met with no success, but following the making of some improvements to his telescope he did detect two faint 'stars' close to the planet on 1787 January 11, which were not visible on the following night. With characteristic caution Herschel continued to observe the objects nightly, and after a week or so was quite convinced that he

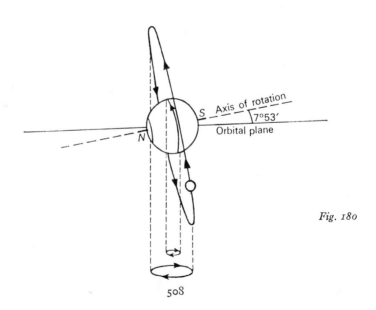

Fig. 180

had discovered one, and perhaps two, satellites of Uranus. On the night of 1787 February 7–8, he kept watch from 6 p.m. to 3 a.m., and during this nine-hour vigil was able to detect the motion of one of the suspected satellites around the primary. The following evening Herschel was able to confirm the nature of the second satellite. The first satellite, now numbered IV and bearing the name *Oberon*, orbits the planet at a mean distance of about 364,400 miles in a synodic period of 13 days $11\frac{1}{4}$ hours, and the second (III, *Titania*) orbits at a mean distance of 272,500 miles in a period of 8 days 17 hours.

In 1851 Lassell, observing with his 24-in. reflector, discovered two further satellites, both closer to the primary than *Titania*: satellite II (*Umbriel*), orbiting 166,100 miles above the planet in a little under 4 days $3\frac{1}{2}$ hours, and satellite I (*Ariel*), distance 119,200 miles, period 2 days $12\frac{1}{2}$ hours.

Finally, in 1948 February, Kuiper photographed a further satellite (V, *Miranda*) with the 82-in. reflector at the McDonald Observatory. The mean distance of this remarkable body from its primary is only a little more than 76,700 miles; its synodic revolution period is a little under 34 hours [Plate 14(c)].

The satellites of Uranus orbit almost in the equatorial plane of the planet, and therefore appear to have retrograde motion due to the great inclination of the planet's axis of rotation (Fig. 180). Satellites I–IV are all believed to be between 400 and 700 miles in diameter; satellite V is very difficult to measure owing to its proximity to the parent planet, but is believed to be about 200 miles in diameter.

In 1954 it was pointed out by A. E. Roy and M. W. Ovenden that the mean motions of the satellites are commensurable being related by the formula

$$n_I - n_{II} - 2n_{III} + n_{IV} = 0.$$

URANUS—STRUCTURE AND CONSTITUTION

In view of its low mean density Uranus is of great interest to students of the internal constitution of the planets, in common with the other major planets. Wildt suggested in the 1930's that the planet consisted of a core of metal-bearing rocks some 14,000 miles in diameter, covered by a layer of frozen material about 6,000 miles thick and a gaseous 'atmosphere' some 2,000 miles deep. (These figures would need reducing slightly today, as they are based upon an assumed diameter of 32,000 miles, 2,700 greater than the currently adopted figure.)

More recently Ramsey has suggested that each of the major planets may be a homogeneous whole, the increase in density towards the centre being due to phase-changes resulting from the high pressures induced by gravitational compression. On the basis of this theory a large percentage of the constituent matter would be hydrogen, together with helium and other light gases and simple compounds such as carbon dioxide (CO_2), water (H_2O), ammonia (NH_3) and methane (CH_4). The presence of methane is confirmed by the existence of its very strong absorption bands in the spectrum of Uranus; most of the other constituents suggested would be frozen out of the upper layers and consequently undetectable by this means [Plate 13(f)].

(See also **Planets, major—constitution of**.)

URANUS—VISIBILITY FROM EARTH

The synodic period is 369·66 days; hence, oppositions occur about four days later each year. The planet moves between declination limits 24° N and 24° S.

The magnitude at opposition is 6·0; the planet is therefore visible with the unaided eye but is much easier to locate with the aid of binoculars or a small telescope, using a low-power eyepiece. A chart to assist location of the planet is published each year in the *Handbook of the British Astronomical Association*.

UREY, H. C.

Contemporary American astronomer; a leading theorist, especially in studies of the chemical composition of celestial bodies.

URSA MAJOR (The Great Bear. *Genitive* Ursae Majoris, *I.A.U. abbreviation* UMa.) Prominent northern circumpolar constellation reaching midnight culmination in March. Seven stars in a prominent configuration are known as **The Plough,** six of these being first- and second-magnitude stars; two of them (α and β UMa) are used to locate the direction of the north celestial pole and are hence termed 'the Pointers'. *Mizar* (ζ UMa) is a naked-eye double with its companion *Alcor*, and is itself a binary.

In the United States the Plough is better known as 'the Big Dipper'.

There are two long-period variables having a wide variation in magnitude, R and T UMa. The constellation also contains a considerable number of nebulae and clusters, notably the spiral galaxies M81 and M82 and the **Owl nebula** (M97).

URSA MINOR (The Lesser Bear. *Genitive* Ursae Minoris, *I.A.U. abbreviation* UMi.) The constellation containing the north celestial pole. The brightest star, *Polaris* (α UMi) is within one degree of the pole. There are only two other stars brighter than the fourth magnitude in this small constellation, which is in the form of a wedge cut into Draco.

URSIDS A meteor shower occurring about December 22, from a radiant in Ursa Minor close to the Pointers. The stream is associated with Comet 1926 IV P/Tuttle; it was discovered visually by Bečvář in 1945 and confirmed by radar observations.

UTOPIA Martian surface feature, approximate position Ω 250°, Φ + 50°. Lightish area in the otherwise dark north temperate region.

V

VAN ALLEN BELTS Zones of charged particles surrounding the Earth, discovered by J. Van Allen with the aid of radiation counters carried on board the artificial Earth satellites *Explorer 1* and *Pioneer 3*, launched from the United States in 1958 and 1959 respectively.

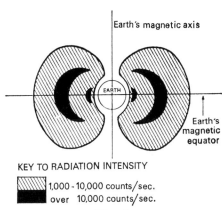

Earth's magnetic axis

Earth's magnetic equator

KEY TO RADIATION INTENSITY

1,000 - 10,000 counts/sec.

over 10,000 counts/sec.

Fig. 181

The cross-section of the belts, their normal intensity and their usual height above the Earth's surface, are shown in Fig. 181.

VARIABLE NEBULA Emission nebulosity centred on a variable star. A particularly good example is NGC 2261, a fan-shaped nebula whose very complex filamentary structure is subject to considerable variations; the nebula is energized by the variable star R Mon. A number of these nebulae are found in association with variable stars of the T Tauri type.

VARIABLE STARS Generally, all stars whose apparent magnitudes are observed to vary. A great many variable stars are

known—the *General Catalogue of Variable Stars* published in Moscow in 1958 lists 14,700.

The light variation is usually studied in the form of a light curve, in which the magnitude of the star, observed on numerous occasions, is plotted against a time-scale. For many years light curves were based upon the large numbers of magnitude estimations made by visual observers, many of them amateur; amateur observers still undertake an important share of the work of recording the light variation of many stars, but their work is today supplemented—especially for the fainter variables—by photometric observations made by professional observers.

Nomenclature

The system used for naming variable stars is somewhat complicated, having evolved over a lengthy period; when first devised it catered quite satisfactorily for the few variables then known, but as time passed and more variables were discovered the necessary extensions to the system of nomenclature rendered it rather more cumbersome.

The designations originally adapted for variable stars comprised the constellation name (usually abbreviated) together with a prefix consisting of one or two letters. In many constellations so many variables are now known, however, that a numbered sequence is now in use. Thus the first variable discovered in a constellation is denoted by R, the next by S, then T, and so on to Z. The next discovery after Z was designated RR, then RS, RT, etc., to RZ. The sequences SS–SZ, TT–TZ, etc., to ZZ are then used, followed by AA–AZ, BB–BZ, etc., to QQ–QZ, excluding all combinations involving the letter J.

511

Where the number of known variables exceeds the 334 prefixes provided in this way the additional variables are numbered in the sequence V335, V336, etc., which permits an unlimited number of designations. Where bright stars are known to be variable they often retain their normal designation and are not allocated a specific designation as a variable—e.g. α Ori and β Per, both of which are variable. The designation of variable stars is undertaken by the International Astronomical Union.

Classification of variable stars

Variable stars may be sub-divided into classes in a number of different ways: perhaps the most obvious differentiation is between *regular variables*, whose light variation repeats in predictable cycles, and *irregular variables*, whose light-variation is non-cyclic and unpredictable. There are also many variables whose light-variation is approximately cyclic, but whose period and characteristic light-curve vary from one cycle to another; these are termed *semi-regular variables*.

A more fundamental division is between *intrinsic variables*, whose light-variation represents an actual change in the star's radiative output, and the *extrinsic variables* whose light-variation is due to an external circumstance and does not indicate any change in the star's actual radiation.

Extrinsic variables

The extrinsic variables principally comprise the *eclipsing binary stars*; in the case of these the light observed is the integrated light of the two or more component stars and varies according to whether the components are observed 'side by side' or when one is occulting the other. The eclipsing binaries are described under **binary system** (*q.v.*) and need not concern us here.

Nebula variables. Another group of extrinsic variables, sometimes known as the *T Tauri stars*. The nebula variables, as the name suggests, are located inside patches of nebulosity. Examples are found in both emission and absorption nebulae.

The type-star, T Tau, is situated inside the nebula N.G.C. 1555 which is itself slightly variable. Many of them, such as R CrA, R Mon and RY Tau, are situated at the tip of small fan-shaped emission nebulae.

The T Tauri stars are irregular variables of spectral classes *F*, *G*, *K* and *M*, and all have emission spectra showing features peculiar to the type. They are rather brighter than main-sequence stars of the corresponding spectral types, by up to two magnitudes, and appear to be stars of approximately the same mass as the Sun. They are obviously subject to a strong interaction with their surrounding nebula, and are believed by some astrophysicists to be in the process of being formed from it.

A number of nebulous regions with associated variable stars are known, notably in Orion, Taurus, Cassiopeia, Monoceros, Aquarius, Carina and Corona Austrinus. Some of the best-known nebula variables are listed in Table 64.

Table 64. Nebula variables

Star	Associated nebula
T Tau	N.G.C. 1555
T Ori, RZ Ori, etc.	N.G.C. 1976, 1982, etc.
R Mon	N.G.C. 2261
η Car	N.G.C. 3372
R CrA	N.G.C. 6726
TY CrA	N.G.C. 6729
α Cyg	N.G.C. 7000

Intrinsic variables

The intrinsic variables include both regular and semi-regular, and irregular, variables. Among the regular variables are the pulsating variables, including the very important Cepheids and the long-period variables; the irregular variables include the novae and other types of explosive variable.

Table 65. RR Lyrae stars

Star	Period (days)	Magnitude range (min) (max)	Spectral type
SW And	0·442	10·3– 9·3	*A3–F8*
RS Boo	0·377	10·6– 9·5	*A3–F4*
RV Cap	0·448	10·5– 9·2	*A8*
RW Dra	0·443	11·1–10·1	*A5*
RR Lyr	0·567	8·0– 7·2	*B9–F2*
AR Per	0·426	10·7– 9·8	*Go*

Pulsating variables. The existence of intrinsic variables with regular cycles of light variation puzzled many astronomers, who sought a mechanism which would explain this remarkable feature; in 1914 Shapley suggested that these stars were physically pulsating, that is to say alternately expanding and contracting in regular cycles. Spectroscopic investigations later provided evidence confirming this theory. Little is known of the energy-forming processes deep in the interior of a star, and it is still largely a matter of conjecture what causes a star to pulsate in this manner; possibly there is a periodical transformation of gravitational energy into thermal energy and back again.

The most important group of pulsating variables are the *Cepheid variables*: the widespread incidence of these fairly short-period variables with their characteristic light-curves, coupled with the discovery of the period–luminosity law, has made them one of the most useful types of celestial object, invaluable in the determination of distances on a galactic scale.

The classical Cepheids are Population I stars occurring mostly in the galactic plane; they have periods ranging from 1–50 days and light variations of the order of one magnitude. Some typical Cepheids are listed in Table 7 on p. 58. The light curve of δ Cephei, the type-star, is shown in Fig. 19 on p. 58.

There are several groups of pulsating variables with somewhat similar characteristics to the Cepheids. Foremost among these are the *RR Lyrae stars*, which are Population II stars occurring at all galactic latitudes and especially common in the globular clusters; for this reason they are sometimes termed *cluster variables*. They have very short periods, less than 1 day, and are mostly stars of spectral class *A*. They have larger proper motions than the classical Cepheids. Some typical cluster variables are listed in Table 65.

The *W Virginis stars*, sometimes known as *Type II Cepheids*, are pulsating stars with periods of 1–50 days which are some two magnitudes fainter than classical Cepheids of corresponding period. The metallic lines in the spectra of some of them have been found to be temporarily doubled during the rise to maximum; this is believed to be due to the pulsating star emitting two distinct bursts of radiation.

Another group of pulsating variables are the *RV Tauri stars*, which have periods between about 50 and 150 days. Their light curves have alternate deep and shallow minima, but the 'depths' of the minima are subject to change over long periods of time, so that the order of occurrence of deep and shallow minima may be reversed from time to time. The range of apparent brightness is 2–3 magnitudes. There is also a long-term component in the light variation having a period of 3½ years in the case of RV Tau itself. Some fairly typical members of this class are listed in Table 66.

The RV Tauri stars are orange super-

Table 66. RV Tauri stars

Star	Period(s) (days)		Magnitude range (approx.) (primary (secondary (min) max) max)			Spectral type
	(1)	(2)				
AC Her	75·2	—	8·4	– 8·3,	8·0	F8–K4
TT Oph	61·1	—	11·0	– 8·8,	10·5	F8
R Sge	70·8	—	10·4	– 8·6,	9·1	G7
RV Tau	78·6	1360	12·5	– 9·4,	10·5	K0–M
V Vul	76·0	—	10·0	– 8·2,	8·6	G7–K0

giants of spectral classes *G* and *K*. More than 90 stars of this type are known.

The light curve of R Sge, an RV Tauri star, is shown in Fig. 182.

Long-period variables. This group is generally defined as comprising those variables with periods exceeding 100 days. Most of those known have periods of 100–400 days; about 40 per cent have periods between 200 and 300 days. They are red giant stars of Population I; their spectra normally show bright emission lines of metallic oxides and carbon compounds. Nearly 90 per cent are of spectral class *M*, the remainder are mostly of classes *N* and *S*, with a very few in classes *K* and *R*.

The long-period variables display a large variation in magnitude, the amplitude of which appears to be related to the period, from an average range of about three magnitudes for a period of 100 days to five magnitudes for a period of 500 days, and so on. There is also evidence that the period increases with redness, the average period for *N*-type stars being about double that of classes *K–M5*. The details of their spectra tend to vary during the cycle and the periods are also not constant to within small limits (unlike the Cepheids whose periods are very regular indeed).

Probably the best known long-period variable is *Mira* (o Cet); it was also the first variable star to be discovered, its variability having been recorded by Fabricius in 1596. *Mira* has a period of nearly 332 days and a light variation of almost six magnitudes; its spectrum varies from *M6* at maximum to *M8* at minimum. *Mira* is one of the few stars having a measurable angular diameter, 0″·056, equivalent to an actual diameter 300 times that of the Sun.

The light curves of many of the long-period variables show irregularities which are difficult to reconcile with the concept of pulsation, and it is believed that other mechanisms must contribute, at least in some measure, to their variability. A

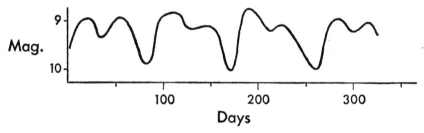

Fig. 182

Table 67. Long-period variables

Star	Period (days)	Magnitude range (min) (max)	Spectral type
R And	409	13·3–6·9	S4
R Boo	223	12·3–7·1	M3
S Cam	328	10·6–8·3	R8
R CVn	325	11·9–7·6	M8–M5
o Cet (Mira)	332	9·2–3·4	M8–M6
RS Cyg	413	8·9–7·2	N3
R Lep	440	10·4–6·0	N6

selection of long-period variables is listed in Table 67.

Semi-regular variables. More than 1,600 variable stars are known whose periodicity is less consistent than that of the long-period variables, whilst averaging about 100 days; they display light-variations of some two magnitudes. Their periods, and the general form of their light curves, vary considerably from one cycle to another; they are giant stars, mostly of spectral classes *G*, *K* and *M*. Notable semi-regular variables of longer period are α Ori (*Betelgeuse*) and α Sco (*Antares*).

It is, of course, difficult to designate individual variables as 'semi-regular': the period of a regular long-period variable can only be established precisely if hundreds of observations are available for analysis; consequently, in the various tabulations there is probably a measure of overlap between the stars listed as semi-regulars, regular long-period variables and irregular variables.

Irregular variables. Nearly 1,400 of the known variable stars show no evidence of periodicity in their light variation; probably a proportion of these are in fact regular variables of which too few observations have been obtained to permit the period to be ascertained.

A few of these irregular variables are of spectral class *K*; most of them are late-type stars, however, principally of classes *M* and *N* with a few of types *S* and *R*.

Some typical irregular variables are listed in Table 68.

Table 68. Irregular variables

Star	Magnitude range (min) (max)	Spectral type
RS And	9·0–7·0	Mc
α Cas	2·6–2·1	G8
α Her	3·9–3·1	M5
R Lyr	4·5–4·0	M5
κ Oph	5·0–4·1	Ko
ρ Per	4·1–3·2	Mb

Explosive variables. An important group of stars usually regarded as a form of irregular variable are the *novae*—stars which suddenly increase in luminosity, usually by several magnitudes, and then fade more slowly until a steady minimum is reached. They are more fully described under **nova** and **supernova**. Together with the *dwarf novae* they form the group usually termed 'explosive' or 'cataclysmic' variables.

The dwarf novae, usually termed *SS Cygni stars* or *U Geminorum stars*, are a remarkable form of recurrent variable whose light curves show a marked resemblance to the non-recurrent one of a nova. They remain steady at a minimum for intervals which range from about 20 to 150 days, then undergo a sudden rise through some 2–4 magnitudes, then almost immediately commence a steady fading to the former minimum. The fade to minimum is usually less rapid than the rise to maximum. The maxima appear at roughly periodic intervals. The SS Cygni stars are dwarfs, a fact ascertained by an examination of their proper motions. More than a hundred SS Cygni stars are known. The light curve of SS Cyg, the type star is shown in Fig. 183, and some members of this important group are listed in Table 69.

Some of the dwarf novae show an alternating pattern of maxima of different dimensions, e.g. U Gem, which displays alternate maxima lasting for approximately 20 days and 12 days (Fig. 184). The 'period' of U Gem varies between 62 and 257 days.

The *Z Camelopardalis stars* are a sub-group of the SS Gygni stars, of which 15 are known. Some typical examples are listed in Table 70. Their light curves are very similar to those of the SS Cygni stars, but are characterized by an occasional discontinuity—always in the form of a break in the fall towards minimum, when the star oscillates about a magnitude intermediate between its maximum and minimum for an interval which may last many months (Fig. 185).

Table 69. *SS Cygni stars*

Star	Magnitude range (min) (max)	Spectral type
UU Aql	16·8–11·0	?
SS Aur	14·7–10·5	B
SS Cyg	12·0– 8·1	B
U Gem	13·8– 8·8	O
RU Peg	13·1– 9·0	?
SU UMa	13·3–11·1	?

Table 70. *Z Camelopardalis stars*

Star	Magnitude range (min) (max)	Spectral type
RX And	13·9–10·3	?
Z Cam	13·3– 9·6	G
CN Ori	14·7–11·0	?
TZ Per	15·3–12·4	?

RW Aurigae stars. The stars in this class are typified by light variations of extreme rapidity, occurring at irregular intervals. Nearly 600 of the known variable stars behave in this manner.

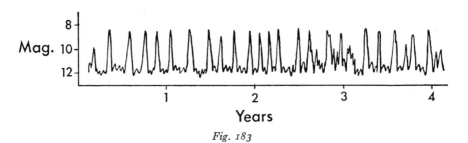

Fig. *183*

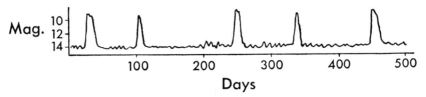

Fig. *184*

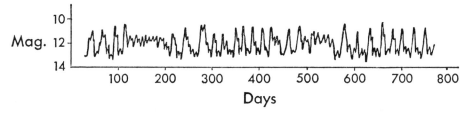

Fig. 185

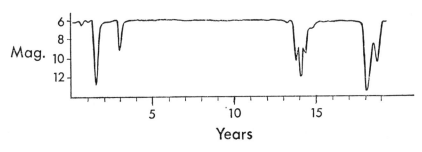

Fig. 186

UV Ceti stars. Another group of explosive variables of much interest to artrophysicists, otherwise known as *flare stars.* Their variability occurs as a very sudden surge of radiation, increasing the luminosity by several magnitudes, but of very short duration, seldom exceeding a few minutes. The spectrum indicates that very high surface temperatures are attained during the surge, which has been likened to a solar flare—hence the name given to these stars. It is possible to identify potential flare stars between their outbreaks of activity, as their spectra often show characteristic emission lines of hydrogen and ionized calcium. The outbreaks are at irregular intervals however and are thus quite unpredictable.

R Coronae Borealis stars. Another type of irregular variable which can be considered as a special case of an explosive variable. These are giant stars, mostly of spectral classes *G* and *R*, which remain at a steady *maximum* brightness for very long periods, and then suddenly decrease in brightness by three or more magnitudes,

the decrease being extremely rapid. Within a few days the star is increasing in brightness, rather more slowly, towards its normal brightness. The light curve of R CrB itself is shown in Fig. 186; some typical R Coronae Borealis stars are listed in Table 71.

Abundance of variable stars

The relative abundance of the different types of variable star is demonstrated in Table 72, showing the breakdown of the 14,708 stars listed in the *General Catalogue*

Table 71.   *R Coronae Borealis stars*

Star	Magnitude range (max) (min)	Spectral type
S Aps	10·0–15·2	*R3*
WX CrA	12·2–16·2	*R5*
R CrB	5·8–13·8	*G0*
RY Sgr	6·1–14·0	*G0*
SU Tau	9·5–15·4	*G0*
RS Tel	9·3–13·3	*R8*

Table 72.   *Abundance of variable stars*

Eclipsing variables		2763
Pulsating variables		
classical Cepheids	610	
RR Lyrae stars	2426	
RV Tauri stars	92	
Mira-type long-period variables	3657	
semi-regular variables	1675	
irregular variables	1370	
others	25	
	——	9855
Explosive variables		
novae	146	
supernovae	7	
nova-like variables	35	
RW Aurigae stars	590	
SS Cygni stars	112	
Z Camelopardalis stars	15	
R Coronae Borealis stars	39	
UV Ceti stars	15	
	——	959
Others		
unique variables	10	
unstudied variables	982	
suspect variables	142	
	——	1134
Total:		14,711

of Variable Stars (three stars being listed twice in different categories, hence the apparent total of 14,711).

(See also **Binary system; Cepheid variables; Nova; Supernova.**)

VARIABLE STARS — OBSERVATION OF A single observation of a variable star consists of determining its apparent magnitude by comparison with non-variable stars close by, which are selected for their proximity to the variable and for their similarity of apparent magnitude (ideally they should be within half a magnitude of the variable's average brightness). A series of such observations is plotted against a time-scale, producing a light curve for the star.

The value of such observations lies in quantity, for the more observations are made of a variable the more accurate its derived light curve will be. Even very regular variables show minor variations in the form of the light curve from one cycle to another, and so must be continually monitored; in the case of irregular variables the need for constant observation is obvious. Explosive variables in particular require very frequent observation, so that any outbreak of activity is detected early and recorded in detail.

The estimation of the magnitude of a variable star could for very many years be made only by eye; now magnitudes are determined by photometric measurement and from photographic plates. So great is the number of observations required, however, that they cannot be obtained at the professional observatories engaging in variable-star astronomy, and much of this routine but nonetheless important work is still carried out by amateurs. In no other branch of astronomy is it possible for the amateur observer to make a more valuable contribution to scientific knowledge. There are a number of active groups of skilled and experienced amateur observers, notably the Variable Star Section of the British Astronomical Association, and the American Association of Variable Star Observers. Such groups provide their regular observers with charts showing the stars in their observing programme and the comparison stars to be used. A telescope is normally required for serious work, although quite a modest one (e.g. a 3-in. refractor) is quite adequate for some of the brighter variables. A very low-power eyepiece is needed.

The normal procedure is to select two comparison stars, one slightly brighter and one slightly fainter than the variable, and to estimate the brightness of the variable relative to these. There are two methods by which this may be done.

(i) The 'Fractional Method'. In this method the observer mentally sub-divides the interval of brightness between the two comparison stars into several equal parts, and then estimates the correct position of the variable along this scale. Thus, if m_A and m_B are the apparent magnitudes of the brighter and fainter comparison stars respectively and m_V is that of the variable, the observer might take the brightness scale $m_A - m_B = 5$, and decide that m_V lies $\frac{2}{5}$ of the distance along this scale. This would normally be recorded in the form m_A, 2, m_V, 3, m_B. The magnitudes of the comparison stars being known, they can be substituted and the magnitude of the variable determined. For instance, if $m_A = 4\cdot5$ and $m_B = 6\cdot0$, the unit of one-fifth of the interval would be $0\cdot3$, and hence $m_V = m_A + (2 \times 0\cdot3) = 4\cdot5 + 0\cdot6 = 5\cdot1$.

(ii) Pogson's Step Method. This method requires much more skill and experience, but is preferred by most experienced observers. In this case the observer must train himself to recognize specific differences of brightness in units of one-tenth of a magnitude; this is done by constant observation of pairs of stars with known differences in magnitude. When sufficiently skilled the observer can then relate the magnitude of his variable, m_V, to those of the comparison stars, m_A and m_B, in tenths of a magnitude; thus, his observation might be in the form $m_V = m_A + 0\cdot4$; $m_V = m_B - 0\cdot3$. This would mean that comparison star *A* appeared to be four-tenths of a magnitude brighter than the variable, which in turn looked three-tenths of a magnitude brighter than comparison star *B*. Thus, if $m_A = 4\cdot7$ and $m_B = 5\cdot4$, m_V must be $5\cdot1$.

VEGA The Northern star α Lyr.; a brilliant blue-white star of type *Ao*, *Vega* is a magnificent sight with a small or moderate-sized telescope, appearing very blue and diffuse. *Vega* is the fifth brightest star in the heavens, with an apparent magnitude of $+0\cdot1$; it is actually an optical double, having a tenth-magnitude companion at a separation of 56 seconds of arc.

VELA (The sails; a modern constellation, part of that originally designated **Argo**, *q.v. Genitive* Velorum, *I.A.U. abbreviation* Vel.) A moderately large constellation in the southern sky, containing eight stars brighter than fourth magnitude.

VELOCITY, ANGULAR The rate at which a body is changing its angular separation from a fixed point or direction—i.e. the rate of change of direction. Angular velocity is usually measured in radians per second. It is usually applied to the angular movement of an orbiting body around a focus of the orbit, or the angular movement of a body measured against the background sky from a fixed point of observation.

VELOCITY, AREAL The area of the segment traversed in a unit of time by the **radius vector** of an orbiting body obeying the **law of equal areas**.

VELOCITY CURVE A plot against a time scale of the line-of-sight velocity of a component of an eclipsing binary system, from which the nature of the system can be deduced. (See **Binary system**.)

VELOCITY, ORBITAL The linear velocity of a planet in its orbit—strictly speaking its tangential velocity at a given instant. It is normally used, however, in the form of the mean orbital velocity, which is of course a constant figure not subject to the variations arising from the eccentricity of an elliptical orbit.

The mean orbital velocities of the planets are as follows, expressed in miles per second:

Mercury	29·8	Jupiter	8·1
Venus	21·8	Saturn	6·0
Earth	18·5	Uranus	4·2
Mars	15·0	Neptune	3·4
		Pluto	2·9

VELOCITY, RADIAL The velocity of a body in the line of sight of the observer, i.e. the rate at which the body is approaching or receding. It is of course usually only one component of the body's actual motion, except when this happens to be exactly in the line of sight. Observed radial velocities must be corrected for the effects of the rotation and revolution of the Earth.

VELOCITY OF LIGHT The finite speed at which light travels, first demonstrated by Römer in 1675 by timing the phenomena of Jupiter's satellites.

Highly refined experiments have been carried out to determine this fundamental quantity as precisely as possible; the figure adopted for general purposes is 299,792 kilometres per second, about 186,282 miles per second. (See also **Light year**.)

VENDELINUS (Lunar surface feature, co-ordinates $\xi + 850$, $\eta - 275$); a vast

formation with rather broken walls, situated on the western edge of the Mare Fœcunditatis. It is over 100 miles in diameter, and part of a great meridional chain of formations including Furnerius, Petavius, Langrenus, Cleomedes and Endymion. Has a rather dark floor, in contrast to its neighbour, the very prominent Langrenus. There are several intruding craters in its walls, notably Lohse and the larger but older and less well preserved Vendelinus C.

VENUS The second known planet (in order of increasing distance from the Sun), whose orbit lies between those of Mercury and the Earth. Owing to its greater distance from the Sun, it is much more readily observable than Mercury. At favourable elongations it is so bright that it will cast shadows, and is the brightest of all the planets.

To the unaided eye it appears as a brilliant star-like object shining with a steady, white light.

Venus was known to the ancients, but as in the case of Mercury, its appearances as a 'morning star' and an 'evening star' were for a long time taken to be two separate objects—these were named **Lucifer** (the morning star) and **Hesperus** (the evening star). The planet is now, of course, named after the Goddess of Love.

VENUS—DIMENSIONS AND PHYSICAL DATA The apparent diameter of Venus, at a mean distance for inferior conjunctions, is 1′ 1″3; which corresponds to a true equatorial diameter of 7,650 miles (only 276 miles less than the diameter of the Earth). There is no detectable polar flattening. The mass is difficult to determine accurately, Venus having no satellite, but the perturbations of the orbits of the other planets due to Venus enable its mass to be fixed rather more precisely than that of Mercury, the resulting value of the mass being 0·815 that of the Earth. This corresponds to a mean density of 4·99 that of water—slightly less than that of Mercury and about $\frac{9}{10}$ that of the Earth.

The volume is 0·902 that of the Earth. The gravitational attraction at the surface of Venus is 0·87 that at the Earth's surface; a space-traveller from Earth would not, therefore, feel significantly lighter on Venus.

The velocity of escape for gases is 6·4 miles per second, thus enabling Venus to retain a substantial atmosphere. The albedo is 0·76—much higher than for any of the other inner planets, due no doubt to the reflecting surface being formed by the dense gaseous atmosphere, and not by an irregular, solid surface.

VENUS—NATURE AND ATMOSPHERE

The mean density of Venus (4·89 times that of water) suggests that, like Mercury and the Earth, it is a spheroid of rocky constitution, but has a much more extensive gaseous mantle, or atmosphere, than either. This is borne out by visual observations, which show only the bright, diffuse, highly reflecting surface of a dense layer of gases or dust. At the time of a transit of Venus, the atmosphere can be clearly seen as a bright annulus or ring of light surrounding the black disk of the planet's silhouette against the bright surface of the Sun. Measurements made at these transits suggest that the atmosphere must have a depth of fifty miles or more, but such estimates are necessarily very tentative. At the early crescent phase, shortly after inferior conjunction, Venus can sometimes be observed with the cusps of the crescent considerably extended; occasionally they may be seen to merge into a thin ring of light surrounding the entire planet. These refraction effects provide obvious and cogent evidence of the presence of a deep atmosphere.

A great deal of effort has been expended in attempts to determine the composition of the atmosphere. Spectroscopic observations have shown that there are no appreciable amounts of oxygen or water vapour present. Infra-red spectrograms made at the Mount Wilson Observatory have shown that carbon dioxide (CO_2) is present in very large quantities; this is the only constituent of the planet's atmosphere to have been identified with reasonable certainty. The presence of large amounts of CO_2 in the atmosphere render it chemically unlikely that any quantity of water vapour can exist in the atmosphere. Various other possible constituents have been suggested from time to time on theoretical grounds, but no spectroscopic evidence has been obtained to confirm them [Plate 9(e, f)].

The 'surface' temperature—that is, the temperature at the upper surface of the cloud layer—was determined by Pettit and Nicholson using thermocouples attached to the 100-in. reflector at the Mount Wilson Observatory, who gave a temperature of $-38°C$ for the sunlit hemisphere and $-33°C$ for the unlit hemisphere; if these figures seem surprisingly low for a planet so near to the Sun, it must be remembered that they are for the 'top' of the atmosphere, far above the solid surface of the planet. Considerable doubt remains regarding the correct values, as various other conflicting determinations have been made—notably by Kozyrev at the Crimean Astrophysical Observatory, who obtained a value of $-90°C$ for the sunlit side.

VENUS—OBSERVATION OF

Owing to its proximity to the Sun, Venus can only be observed at rather low altitudes, and rarely against a dark sky; it is not therefore a very rewarding object for observation.

One of the most useful observations that can be made by the amateur is a careful determination of the times of observed dichotomy; these may differ from the calculated times by several days (Schröter's Effect).

It is also valuable to record any peculiarities in the apparent shape of the cusps or the terminator, and to watch for any appearance of the Ashen Light [Plate 9(c)].

Any faint grey markings should be carefully drawn, provided that this can be done with certainty; unfortunately such markings are rarely obvious, and as they are atmospheric in origin, observations of them are of very limited value unless they are obtained in large numbers over a period by a reliable observer. The bright cusp caps should be watched for, and also any suggestion for a dark 'collar' surrounding them [Plate 9(d)].

Observations should, of course, bear the usual details of date, time, location, instrument and eyepiece used, etc. The use of grey or other glare-reducing filters may sometimes be found helpful.

VENUS—ORBITAL DATA The orbit of Venus has a semi-major axis of 0·723332 A.U., corresponding to a mean distance from the Sun of 67·2 million miles; the actual distance varies by less than one million miles from perihelion to aphelion, due to the very small orbital eccentricity of 0·0068.

The orbit of Venus is second only to that of Mercury in inclination to the Ecliptic, although the figure for Venus is less than half that for Mercury: 3° 23′ 39″·5.

A further result of the small eccentricity is that the planet's velocity in orbit is almost constant, varying only minutely from the mean value of 21·8 miles per second. The resulting sidereal period is 224·701 days.

VENUS—TELESCOPIC APPEARANCE Venus appears in the telescope as a bright diffuse object, with no obvious surface detail. Numerous observations of very faint dusky grey markings have been made, both visually and by ultra-violet photography. They are almost certainly atmospheric; it is probable that the atmosphere is so dense that no feature of the solid surface can even be seen. There are many cases, however, where markings of similar shape and arrangement have been observed; this could be an indication of features of the solid surface being seen 'through the cloud', but it is equally possibly due to repetitive atmospheric movement producing similar cloud formations under given circumstances.

Because of this difficulty, it has not been possible to establish with any certainty either the direction of the axis of rotation of the planet or the period of axial rotation. Many attempts to do so have been made, but no reliable evidence has been procured. The earliest known attempt is that of J.-D. Cassini, who in 1667 announced a rotation period of 23 hr 21 min. For more than 200 years the rotation period was believed to be of the order of 24 hours, but in 1890 Schiaparelli made the startling announcement that his observations over a period of thirteen years indicated that the rotation period was equal to the sidereal period—224 d 16 hr 48 min; in other words, that the day and the year on Venus were equal, and the planet, like Mercury, always presented the same face to the Sun.

Since then, estimates have been made by amateur and professional astronomers the world over, using methods involving the techniques of spectroscopy and radio astronomy as well as visual observations; the resulting rotation periods suggested range from 15 hours to 225 days.

Bright patches are sometimes seen at the cusps during the crescent phase, and series of bright oval areas along the terminator, bounded by grey markings, are also frequently recorded (especially during the gibbous phase).

Also occasionally observed is the so-called **Ashen Light**, a very faint luminous glow from the unlit part of the disk during crescent phases; the most likely explanation of this is that the luminescence is due to electrical disturbance in an ionospheric layer of the planet's atmosphere—similar to the aurorae observed in high latitudes on Earth [Plate 9(c)].

VENUS—TRANSITS OF If Venus is at or near one of its nodes when at inferior conjunction, it may be seen to pass across the disk of the Sun. For this to occur, the date of inferior conjunction must be within a few days of June 7 or December 8.

Five synodic periods of Venus are almost equal to 8 years, and so transits normally occur in pairs eight years apart;

as a much more precise relation, 152 synodic periods are approximately equal to 243 years. After a pair of transits 8 years apart, no further transit will occur at the same node for at least 235 years; a pair will occur at the other node in the meantime, however. The intervals between pairs of transits are alternately $105\frac{1}{2}$ years and $121\frac{1}{2}$ years; thus we are experiencing a series of December transits in 1631 and 1639; 1874 and 1882; 2117 and 2125, and a series of June transits in 1761 and 1769; 2004 and 2012, etc.

The transit of 1631 December 6 was predicted by Kepler, and Gassendi (who had made the first observation of a transit of Mercury) observed the planet at every possible moment on December 4, 5, 6 and 7, but did not see a transit. This is now known to be due to the transit having occurred during the night of December 6/7, when the Sun was invisible from Europe. Kepler had foretold only a 'near miss' for 1639, but the remarkable calculations of Jeremiah Horrocks, a young but very competent and enthusiastic amateur astronomer, who was curate of Hoole in Lancashire, suggested that this was erroneous, and that a transit would in fact occur on 1639 December 4. In the moments when his clerical duties would permit, Horrocks watched for the event, and in mid-afternoon he was rewarded with the first recorded observation of a transit of Venus. Horrocks had informed a friend—William Crabtree of Manchester—of his prediction, and shortly before sunset he too saw the transit in progress. No other observations of this transit are known.

In 1716 Halley pointed out that accurate observations of the times of the contacts of transits of Venus could be used to obtain a more accurate determination of the **solar parallax**; for this reason the next four transits (1761 June 5, 1769 June 3, 1874 December 8 and 1882 December 6) were widely observed. Future transits are unlikely to be used for the determination of the solar parallax, as the method has been superseded by more accurate procedures, and is in any case

subject to several difficulties. Not least among these is the so-called **black drop**— an optical illusion whereby the gap between the limit of Venus and the limit of the Sun, just after second and before third contact, appears to be bridged momentarily by a black spot; although this effect lasts for only a few seconds it renders accurate determination of the time of these contacts extremely difficult. Transits of Venus will still be widely observed, however, not only for their rarity but also for the additional information they give about the orbit of Venus. The next four transits are due to take place on 2004 June 7, 2012 June 5, 2117 December 10 and 2125 December 8.

VENUS—VISIBILITY FROM EARTH

Venus cannot, of course, be observed when at or close to its conjunctions, being lost in the glare of the Sun. The angular distance of Venus from the Sun at its elongations varies between 45° and 47°. The planet is visible in the western sky in the evening at eastern elongations and in the east in the early morning at western elongations. The mean synodic period (the interval between inferior conjunctions) is 583·92 days. Greatest elongation occurs about 72 days before and after inferior conjunction; hence greatest elongation west occurs about $20\frac{1}{2}$ weeks after greatest elongation east, and greatest elongation east 63 weeks (about 1 year and $2\frac{1}{2}$ months) after greatest elongation west.

Venus reaches its maximum brightness about 36 days before and after inferior conjunction, that is to say about 5 weeks after greatest elongation east and 5 weeks before greatest elongation west; at these times the phase resembles that of a five-day-old Moon. The maximum stellar magnitude attained by the planet is $-4\cdot4$; its apparent brightness is then more than twelve times that of **Sirius,** the brightest of the 'fixed' stars [Plate 9(a)].

As with Mercury, the angle made by the planet's apparent path when rising or setting, and the horizon, is such that morning elongations in spring and evening

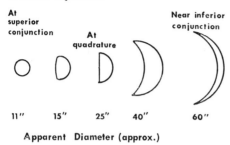

At superior conjunction   At quadrature   Near inferior conjunction

11"   15"   25"   40"   60"

Apparent Diameter (approx.)

Fig. 187

elongations in the autumn are the most favourable for observers in the northern hemisphere.

The apparent diameter of Venus, seen from the Earth, varies from 67" to 11", according to its distance. Its orbit lying within that of the Earth, the planet undergoes a complete cycle of phases similar to those of Mercury (see **Phase of inferior planet**). The comparative size of the apparent disk at the various phases is shown in Fig. 187.

VERNAL EQUINOX The date at which the Sun lies in the direction of the **First Point of Aries**; also the name given to this point, which is the point of intersection of the Ecliptic and the celestial equator.

The Sun reaches the vernal equinox on or about March 21; it should be remembered that this date should strictly be termed the northern hemisphere vernal equinox, it being autumn in the southern hemisphere at this time.

VERNIER A measuring device invented by Pierre Vernier of Ornans, Burgundy, in 1631, which enables the position of a movable scale to be read to a higher order of accuracy than is otherwise possible. The vernier is a fixed reference scale which replaces the single fiducial mark, and comprises n graduations in a length occupied by $n-1$ graduations of the movable scale. Thus, Fig. 188 (a) shows a

vernier with ten divisions occupying a space equivalent to nine divisions on the moving scale.

For simplicity, we shall consider only this (decimal) case, but the same principle applies with any number of divisions of the vernier. When taking a reading, the zero mark on the vernier indicates the first decimal place, and the second is given by the division of the vernier scale which coincides with a division of the moving scale. Thus, in Fig. 188 (b), the zero mark lies between the divisions 10·3 and 10·4, whilst the vernier mark ·07 coincides with a division of the moving scale (11·0); the reading is therefore 10·37.

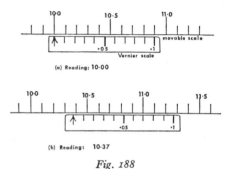

10·0   10·5   11·0

movable scale
·05   ·1
Vernier scale

(a) Reading: 10·00

10·0   10·5   11·0   11·5

·05   ·1

(b) Reading: 10·37

Fig. 188

VERTICAL, ANGLE OF Angle on the celestial sphere between the **prime vertical** and any other vertical circle. (See also **Celestial sphere**.)

VERTICAL CIRCLE A great circle on the celestial sphere which passes through both the **zenith** and the **nadir**, and is therefore perpendicular to the horizon. (See also **Celestial sphere**.)

VESTA Minor planet number 4, discovered in 1807 by Olbers—within five years of his discovery of Pallas. Has a diameter of only 243 miles, but a high apparent magnitude (approximately +6)—indicating a highly reflective surface. (See also **Minor planets**.)

524

VINCI, Leonardo da (1452–1519) The famous artist, scientist and man of letters. He had a considerable interest in astronomical matters, and was the first person to explain correctly the phenomenon of **Earthshine**. He also produced reasoned evidence in favour of the hypothesis that the Earth was in rotation, which was not generally accepted at the time.

VIOLET LAYER A layer of particles in the upper atmosphere of Mars, which scatter and absorb short-wavelength radiation, rendering the atmosphere opaque to, and the surface of the planet invisible in, blue or violet light. Although normally present this layer has been observed to be absent at times. (See also **Wright's phenomenon**.)

VIRGO (The Virgin, *Genitive* Virginis, *I.A.U. abbreviation* Vir.) A zodiacal constellation reaching midnight culmination at the beginning of April. The northern portion of the constellation, adjoining Coma Berenices, contains like that constellation a considerable number of nebulae. The principal star is the first-magnitude *Spica*.

The star γ Vir is of much interest, being a long-period binary; the components are almost equal in magnitude (+3·6, +3·7), and separated by about 4 seconds of arc. The period is 180 years and owing to the very eccentric orbit the two stars appear to merge, in all but the largest instruments, for about half a century each cycle; they are now converging and will appear to merge again about 2015.

VIRGO A. A strong discrete radio source, number 12N1A in the I.A.U. catalogue, position R.A. 12 hr 28 min, Dec. 12°40′N. It is associated with the peculiar galaxy M 87 (N.G.C. 4486). This is a large elliptical galaxy with a blue 'jet' protruding from the nucleus [Plate 23(f)].

(See also **Radio astronomy**.)

VISIBLE SPECTRUM That part of the frequency range of electromagnetic radiation to which the human eye is sensitive—in general terms 'light'. The visible spectrum is usually said to comprise light of seven distinct, albeit merged, colours: red, orange, yellow, green, blue, indigo and violet. It consists of radiation with wavelengths ranging from approximately $7 \cdot 2 \times 10^{-5}$ cm (red) to 4×10^{-5} cm (violet).

VISUAL BINARY Name given to that type of binary system that can be observed optically as a double star. (See **Binary systems**.)

VOLANS (The Flying Fish, *Genitive* Volantis; *I.A.U. abbreviation* Vol.) A small southern circumpolar constellation, containing no stars brighter than the fourth magnitude.

VOLCANIC THEORY A theory that the majority of the lunar surface features were formed by volcanic activity. (See **Moon—origin of surface features**.)

VOSKHOD Name given to a series of manned artificial Earth satellites launched from the Soviet Union. A development from the *Vostok* programme, *Voskhod 1* (launched on 1964 October 12 and landed the following day after a flight lasting 1·01 days) made history by being the first spacecraft to carry three astronauts. Moreover, the spacecraft's design was such as to enable the three crew-members to wear ordinary track-suits instead of the customary space-suits.

Voskhod 2 was launched on 1965 March 18 and landed on March 19 after a flight of 1·09 days.

VOSTOK Name given to a series of manned artificial Earth satellites launched from the Soviet Union as part of the programme for developing spacecraft techniques. Six *Vostok* vehicles were launched, as listed in Table 73 overleaf.

Table 73. Vostok satellite vehicles

Vehicle	Launched	Descended	Duration of flight
Vostok 1	1961 Apr. 12	Apr. 12	1 hr 48 min
Vostok 2	1961 Aug. 6	Aug. 7	25 hr 18 min
Vostok 3	1962 Aug. 11	Aug. 15	3·95 days
Vostok 4	1962 Aug. 12	Aug. 15	2·96 days
Vostok 5	1963 Jun. 14	Jun. 19	4·96 days
Vostok 6	1963 Jun. 16	Jun. 19	2·95 days

VULCAN This was the name given to a supposed inferior planet having its orbit within that of Mercury. Belief in the existence of this planet was quite widespread at one time, and arose from an observation made by M. Lescarbault, a French physician. On 1859 March 26, Lescarbault observed a small dark body in transit across the Sun's disk, and attempted to record its movements with much care. A study of his observations suggested that the body was a planet some 14 million miles from the Sun (rather less than half the mean distance of Mercury), with a revolution period of about 20 days in an orbit inclined to the Ecliptic by about 12°.

No confirming observations were made by other observers, and frequent searches were made at major observatories during the next few years, at times when it had been calculated that the 'planet' should once again be in transit. Despite the fact that no less a person than Le Verrier had examined Lescarbault's work and satisfied himself of his good faith and competence, no trace has since been seen of Vulcan, and it has long been regarded as non-existent.

VULCANI PELAGUS Martian surface feature, approximate position, $\Omega\ 15°$, $\Phi - 35°$. Dusky area on the northern border of Argyre, south of the Mare Erythræum.

VULPECULA (The Fox; *formerly* Vulpecula et Anser, the Fox and Goose. *Genitive* Vulpeculæ, *I.A.U. abbreviation* Vul.) A fairly small northern constellation to the south of Cygnus. Contains M 27, a diffuse nebula known as the 'Dumb-bell' nebula.

W

W STARS Stars of spectral class *W*, also known as the **Wolf–Rayet stars,** *q.v.*

W URSAE MAJORIS STARS A class of eclipsing variable stars whose components are very close together and hence highly ellipsoidal, and also of almost equal brightness.
(See **Variable stars.**)

W VIRGINIS STARS A group of pulsating variable stars, also known as Type II Cepheids. About forty of these stars are known, with periods between 10 and 30 days. They are characterized by an unusual doubling of their spectral lines during the rise to maximum, not due to two component stars as in the case of a spectroscopic binary, but to two independent 'surges' or outbursts of activity from the same star. Thus, during the rise to maximum the existing spectral lines slowly fade, finally disappearing altogether; simultaneously, a new set of lines appears, faint at first but gradually strengthening, until at maximum it alone remains, and lasts until it too fades at the beginning of a new cycle. The W Virginis stars also display bright (emission) lines due to hydrogen during the rise to maximum. W Vir, the type-star, has a period of $17\frac{1}{4}$ days and is farther from the galactic plane than any other Cepheid-type variable known (galactic latitude $+61°$).
(See also **Variable stars.**)

WALTER Lunar surface feature, co-ordinates $\xi+010$, $\eta-548$. A prominent walled plain in the heart of the mountainous southern region of the Moon, about 90 miles in diameter. Its walls are wide and rugged, and rise to 10,000 ft in places; there are many craterlets and mountain ridges. The eastern rampart is more broken than the others, and contains a lozenge-shaped low-walled formation which also intrudes into the floor of the adjoining ruined walled plain Hörbiger.

Walter is one of a magnificent north-south chain of formations consisting of Ptolemæus, Alphonsus, Arzachel, Purbach and Regiomontanus to the north and Stöfler to the south.

WARGENTIN Lunar surface feature, co-ordinates $\xi-565$, $\eta-761$. A most unusual and interesting formation close to the south-eastern limb of the Moon. Although approximately circular (when due allowance is made for limb foreshortening), it is not a crater-type formation but a plateau raised some 1,500 ft above the surrounding surface; there is however a vestigial wall at the south-west corner, about 500 ft above the 'floor'. The surface of the formation appears smooth with moderate apertures but a great deal of fine detail is revealed with a large aperture.

WAVELENGTH All astronomical observations comprise the analysis of some form of electromagnetic radiation received from the body concerned through the Earth's atmosphere by means of the **optical window** or the **radio window**. The wavelength is therefore an important indication to the exact nature of the radiation used, especially as many programmes involve the comparison of observations made in two or more different wavebands.

Wavelengths are normally expressed in metric units; in radio astronomy they are usually quoted in metres (m) or centimetres (cm), but the frequency in cycles per second (c/s) or Hertz (Hz) is often used; in optical astronomy the wavelength is quoted, usually in Ångström units (Å).

The units commonly encountered, and their centimetre equivalents, are as follows:

Ångström unit (Å)	1×10^{-8} cm
micron (μ)	1×10^{-4} cm
millimicron ($\mu\mu$)	1×10^{-7} cm

The limiting wavelengths of the main parts of the electromagnetic spectrum are as follows:

long-wave radio	30,000–1,000 m
medium-wave radio	1,000–100 m
short-wave radio	100–10 m
television	10 m–10 cm
radar	10 cm–0·1 cm
infra-red radiation	20,000–7,700 Å
red light	7,700–6,500 Å
orange light	6,500–6,000 Å
yellow light	6,000–5,500 Å
green light	5,500–5,000 Å
blue light	5,000–4,500 Å
violet light	4,500–3,600 Å
ultra-violet radiation	3,600–200 Å
X-rays	200–1·0 Å
γ-rays	1·0–0·1 Å
cosmic rays	0·001–0·00001 Å

In 1907 the International Solar Union adopted the red cadmium line at a wavelength of 6438·3696 Å as the fundamental reference point of the solar spectrum, to which all other measured wavelengths are referred.

(See also **Electromagnetic spectrum; Light; Sun—spectrum of.**)

WEB The fiducial mark(s) in the field of a telescope eyepiece, so-called owing to the frequent use of a stretched strand of spider's web for the purpose. Although often not of metal they are now more commonly termed 'wires'.

WEBB'S ATLAS OF THE STARS A most useful atlas by H. B. Webb privately published as the *Atlas of the Stars* (2nd Edition, New York, 1945) containing 110 charts which cover the entire sky north of Dec. $-23°$ to a Scale of 1 cm per degree. The limiting magnitude is about 9·5. It is of considerable value to observers of comets, minor planets, etc., and is widely used by them for identification/ position-estimating purposes.

WEDGE, OPTICAL A plate, usually of glass or similar substance, bearing an obscuring film whose density increases uniformly from one end to the other, so that the transmission of light through the wedge is maximal at one end and nil at the other, being uniformly and progressively reduced in intermediate positions. Optical wedges are used to dim the telescopic images of very bright objects, and for many other purposes in connection with the use of telescopes and other optical apparatus.

WERNER Lunar surface feature, co-ordinates $\xi+052$, $\eta-470$. A prominent and well-formed crater 45 miles in diameter in the very mountainous southern region of the Moon, just to the west of Regiomontanus. Its walls are terraced and sharp-crested, and rise 15,000 ft above the interior; there is a central peak of about 5,000 ft.

WEST POINT The point on the **celestial sphere,** due west of the observer, at which the Equator intersects the horizon.

WHIPPLE, F. L. Contemporary American astronomer, who has made many important contributions to studies of comets and the planets.

WHITE DWARF A type of star, of which many are known, having very small diameters and extremely high densities. They are far less luminous than normal stars of similar spectral type, and so appear well below the main sequence in the Hertzsprung–Russell diagram. Their ultra-high densities were explained by Eddington as arising from almost total ionization of all their atoms, and account for their very small size (mostly smaller than the planet

Uranus). They are believed to be the oldest stars visible, in the final, decaying stage of their evolution.

(See also **Stellar evolution**.)

WILDT, Rupert Contemporary American theorist who has played a leading role in studies of the constitution of the planets. In the 1930's he published proposed models for the internal constitution of the planets which formed the basis of further thinking for many years.

WILHELM HUMBOLDT Lunar surface feature, co-ordinates $\xi + 878$, $\eta - 457$. A magnificent walled plain 120 miles in diameter, on the south-west limb of the Moon. The walls rise to 16,000 ft in places.

WILLIAMS, A. STANLEY (1861–1938) A solicitor by profession, Stanley Williams was one of the most outstanding of English amateur astronomers and one of the leading planetary observers of his time. He devised the technique of timing the central-meridian transits of the surface features of Jupiter, and thus laid the foundations of the invaluable series of observations upon which our knowledge of the behaviour of the surface layers of the outer planets is based. Williams himself made many important contributions; from an analysis of his observations from 1877–1896 he discovered the first nine of the atmospheric currents of Jupiter. Williams' observations of the bright and dark equatorial spots of 1891–1894 played an important part in the confirmation of the rotation period of Saturn.

Stanley Williams was a Founder Member of the British Astronomical Association; in 1923 he was awarded the Jackson–Gwilt Medal and Gift of the Royal Astronomical Society for his pioneering work.

WILSON EFFECT Phenomenon discovered in 1769 by Alexander Wilson, Professor of Astronomy in the University of Glasgow. Wilson noticed that as a large sunspot approached the western limb of the Sun the penumbra on its eastern side gradually contracted and finally disappeared altogether. When the spot reappeared at the eastern limb of the Sun, however, it had a full penumbra at its eastern edge but none at the other; as it moved onto the disk the western penumbra appeared and gradually broadened until it attained normal width [Plate 3(b)].

Wilson explained this disappearance of the penumbra on the side farthest from the limb of a spot close to the limb by suggesting that sunspots were saucer-shaped depressions. It is now accepted, however, that the phenomenon is due to the greater transparency of the sunspot penumbra and umbra compared with that of the surrounding photosphere—the umbra being especially transparent.

WINTER SOLSTICE The date on which the Sun reaches its greatest southern declination; also applied to the point on the Ecliptic then occupied by the Sun. It falls on or about December 22.

(See also **Sun—apparent motion of**.)

WIRE Term used by observers to denote the fiducial webs used in a telescopic eyepiece, especially those of a transit-circle or filar micrometer. They are occasionally constructed from fine wire, but a stretched strand of spider's web is still the most frequently used material.

WIRELESS TIME SIGNALS In order to relate the time measured by ordinary clocks to that maintained by the standard clocks of the national observatories (which are controlled by astronomical observation) to facilitate intercomparison of the latter, and also to provide a time reference for astronomical observations, it is necessary for time signals to be regularly transmitted by wireless. This is done in two forms: (i) time signals for the domestic consumer, broadcast at convenient times over the ordinary broadcasting networks, and (ii) precise transmissions on specially allocated frequencies, for the use of observatories and other establishments who need to

Table 74. Principal wireless time-signals

Country	Time-keeping authority	Call-sign of transmission	Frequency of transmission (kc/s)	Times of transmission (hr, U.T.)
France	Paris Observatory	FYP	91·15	0800 0900 0930 1300 2000 2100 2230
Federal German Republic	German Hydrographic Institute, Hamburg	DAM	4265 } 6475·5 } 8638·5	0000 0000 1200
Switzerland	Cantonal Observatory, Neuchâtel	HBB	96·5	0815
U.S.S.R.	Central Scientific Investigation Institute, Moscow	ROR	25	0000 0400 0800 1200 1600 2000
United Kingdom	Royal Greenwich Observatory, Herstmonceux	GBR GBZ	16·0 19·6	1000 1800
U.S.A.	United States Naval Observatory, Washington	NSS	121·95 5870 9425 13575 17050 23650	0000 0200 0600 0800 1200 1400 1800 2000

maintain very accurate time.

The principal transmissions in the latter category are listed in Table 74.

WOLF, Max (1863–1932) German astronomer who pioneered many fields of astronomical photography. In 1891 he made the first photographic discovery of a minor planet (No. 323); by the end of the nineteenth century he had discovered more than a hundred, and in his career discovered 582, for 228 of which precise orbits were determined.

Wolf was also a pioneer in the photographic discovery of nebulae; among his discoveries were the North America nebula (N.G.C. 7000) and the nebulosity surrounding the Pleiades. He photographed many of the dark, absorption nebulae and discovered about 5,000 distant galaxies; for the latter achievement he was awarded the Gold Medal of the Royal Astronomical Society in 1914.

Wolf was one of the first to obtain spectrograms of the nebulae, using the 28-in. reflector of the Heidelberg Observatory; in 1901 he discovered the first cluster of galaxies, that in Coma Berenices, and later discovered the Virgo cluster.

WOLF, Rudolf (1816–1893) Swiss astronomer, notable for his contributions to the study of solar activity; discoverer of the 11-year sunspot cycle, and inventor of the **Wolf relative sunspot numbers** which are still widely used as a general index of the level of sunspot activity.

WOLF–RAYET STARS The stars comprising spectral class W; they are intensely hot and pose many problems to the astrophysicist. Their spectra contain numerous enhanced lines and show an abundance of highly ionized elements such as He, C, N and O. Most of them are spectroscopic binaries and some are known to be eclipsing binaries. Their surface temperatures are probably in the range $50,000–100,000°K$, the highest stellar temperatures known to us. About 200 Wolf–Rayet stars are known, the brightest being γ Vel.

There are many resemblances between the Wolf–Rayet stars and the stars at the centres of the planetary nebulae, which lead to speculations that the two types may be related—such a relationship, if confirmed, will be a most important factor in theories of stellar evolution.

WOLF RELATIVE SUNSPOT NUMBERS System invented by R. Wolf of Zurich in the mid-nineteenth century, to record the varying amount of sunspot activity. The Wolf relative number for a given day is calculated from the number

of individual spots visible on the day (f), each counting 1 towards the total, and also the number of spot-groups (g), each group adding a further 10 towards the total. In order to permit observations made with different instruments at a number of observatories to be compared, Wolf multiplied the total by a special factor (k); k is constant for a given instrument at a given observatory, and is calculated on the basis $k=1$ for observations made with the 10-cm refractor at Zurich with a power of $\times 64$. The Wolf relative number for the day (R) may therefore be expressed as:

$$R=(10g+f)k.$$

The Wolf numbers are averaged for the year to provide a convenient guide to the sunspot activity occurring during the year; typical mean Wolf numbers for a year range from 5 or less at sunspot minimum to 150 at a high sunspot maximum.

(See also **Sunspots**.)

WOOLLEY, Sir Richard van der Riet The eleventh, and present, Astronomer Royal. A leading astrophysicist, he was Commonwealth Astronomer at the Commonwealth Observatory, Mount Stromlo, Australia, for eleven years before his appointment as Astronomer Royal in 1956.

WRIGHT'S PHENOMENON Name given to the discovery reported by W. H. Wright of the Lick Observatory in 1925, that the diameter of Mars was greater on plates exposed in ultra-violet light than on plates exposed in infra-red light, the excess amounting to 3 per cent. Further experiments by F. E. Ross in 1926 showed an excess of 6 per cent. The phenomenon was attributed to the fact that the Martian atmosphere is opaque to radiation of wavelength shorter than about 4,500 Å. The phenomenon was utilized to determine the depth of the Martian atmosphere, a figure of some 60 miles being obtained. More recently, however, it has been suggested that the phenomenon arises from the fact that there is extreme limb-darkening in infra-red and red-light photographs of Mars, whereas the image in ultra-violet and blue-light photographs is extremely bright at the limb. If this is the case it is probable that the depth of the atmosphere below the top of the violet layer, as previously determined (i.e. 60 miles), exceeds the true figure [Plate 10(e)].

WRINKLE RIDGE A type of lunar surface feature found only in the dark lunabase of the maria. They are well-defined, often sinuous ridges with gently sloping slides, seldom higher than some 500 ft. above the surrounding terrain. Some are continued as rilles, suggesting that they had a common origin during the cooling and faulting of the lunar crust. They are often concentric with the walls of large ring-structures. A notable example is the great 'serpentine' ridge in the eastern part of the Mare Serenitatis, discovered by Schröter.

X

XANTHE Martian surface feature, approximate position Ω 50°, Φ + 10°. Ochre area north of Auroræ Sinus, bounded by Ganges and the Lunæ Lacus to the west, Nilokeras to the north and Jamuna to the east.

Y

YALE CATALOGUES Catalogues of all but the brightest stars, published in sections in the *Yale Observatory Transactions*; they give proper motions for all stars listed, as well as their places, magnitudes, etc. They have been completed for declination zones +90° to +85°; +60° to +50° and +30° to −30°.

(See also **Star catalogues**.)

YAONIS REGIO Martian surface feature, approximate position Ω 320°, Φ − 40°. Dusky streak branching southward from Hellespontus.

YEAR A unit of time measurement defined by the period of orbital revolution of the Earth around the Sun; to a terrestrial observer this may be regarded as the time taken by the Sun to complete one circuit of the Ecliptic.

For accurate work it is necessary to define the starting point carefully, from which three forms of year arise. The interval required for the Sun to return to the same point relative to the background stars is known as the *sidereal year*; the period between successive passages of the Sun through the First Point of Aries (i.e. between successive vernal equinoxes) is known as the *tropical year* and is some 20 minutes shorter than the sidereal year; the period between successive perigees is known as the *anomalistic year* and is about 4½ minutes longer than the sidereal year.

(See also **Calendar**.)

YERKES OBSERVATORY The observatory endowed by C. T. Yerkes, a Chicago businessman, for the University of Chicago; it is situated at Williams Bay, Wisconsin, on the shores of Lake Geneva, some 80 miles north-west of Chicago, and commenced work in 1897 under the direction of G. E. Hale.

The principal instrument is the great 40-in. refractor provided by Yerkes, still the largest refractor ever constructed [Plate 30(a)].

YERKES SYSTEM OF LUMINOSITY CLASSIFICATION The system devised by Morgan, Keénan and Kellman of the Yerkes Observatory for their *Atlas of Stellar Spectra*, to define the luminosity class of a star from characteristic features of its spectrum; also known as the 'MKK' or 'MK System'. (See **Stars—luminosity of; Stars—spectral classification of**.)

533

Z

Z CAMELOPARDALIS STARS A division of the class of variables known as **dwarf novae**, similar to the U Geminorum stars but with a smaller range of variation in brightness (about three magnitudes) and with frequent, and sometimes very protracted, halts in the decline from maximum to minimum. (See also **Novae; Variable stars.**)

Z.D. Usual abbreviation for **Zenith distance**, *q.v.*

ZAGUT Lunar surface feature, co-ordinates $\xi + 317$, $\eta - 530$. An irregular formation in the south-west quadrant of the Moon, situated inside the triangle formed by Rabbi Levi, Lindenau and Wilkins. About 50 miles in diameter, its western wall is broken by a ring formation some 20 miles in diameter and having a small central mountain. The floor is broken by a number of craterlets and crater-pits and a ridge or spur running northwards from the south wall.

ZEEMAN EFFECT The Dutch physicist P. Zeeman discovered in 1896 that absorption lines in a laboratory spectrum were multiplied if the source was placed in a magnetic field. It was shown by **G. E. Hale** in 1908 that the absorption lines in the solar spectrum were split into two or three components in the neighbourhood of sunspots, thus establishing that sunspots have a strong magnetic field; this is termed the Zeeman effect.

Hale also showed that pairs of sunspots have opposite magnetic polarities, related to their opposite vortical motions.
(See also **Sunspots.**)

ZENITH The point on the celestial sphere vertically above the observer; it is the opposite point to the **nadir**. The zenith and nadir are the poles of the great circle known as the celestial horizon.
(See also **Celestial sphere; Horizon, celestial.**)

ZENITH DISTANCE The angular distance, measured in the meridian, between an object and the zenith. It is usually abbreviated 'Z.D.' and is equivalent to 90° minus the **altitude** of the object.
(See also **Celestial sphere.**)

ZENITH TELESCOPE A telescope fixed in the vertical or permitted to move only a limited amount from it, used to obtain positional measurements of stars passing close to the zenith. Such instruments were used very early in the history of the telescope; a 36-ft fixed zenith telescope was used by Hooke in 1669 in an attempt to determine the **annual parallax** of the star γ Dra.

Zenith sectors, in which the telescope is pivoted at its upper end and can be set in positions up to several degrees from the vertical, were made by George Graham for both Molyneux (a 24-ft instrument erected at Kew) and Bradley. Bradley's instrument was a $12\frac{1}{2}$-ft tube with a range of angular movement of 12° 30′; it was erected at Wanstead in 1727. Its large range of angular movement permitted Bradley to make observations of nearly 200 stars; his observations with this instrument led Bradley to his discoveries of the aberration of light and nutation. Following Bradley's appointment as Astronomer Royal his zenith sector was purchased for the Royal Observatory, Greenwich, with a government grant in 1749.

A more recent form of zenith telescope, developed for the purpose of measuring

latitude variation, takes the form of a reversible transit instrument, with an accurate level attached to the telescope tube in the plane of the meridian and a declination micrometer.

In order to obviate the necessity for the difficult-to-determine level corrections an improved form was devised by Brian Cookson in about 1900, in which the Y-bearings carrying the telescope axis are mounted on an iron annulus which is floating in an annular trough of mercury. This arrangement enables the telescope to be reversed between two observations, the mean of which will be automatically referred to the true vertical. The **Cookson floating zenith tube** was used by him at Cambridge from 1903–1908, and following his death was loaned to the Royal Observatory, Greenwich, in 1911, where it was in continuous use for some 40 years. It has now been replaced by the photographic zenith tube at Herstmonceux [Plate 29(d, e)].

(See also **Photographic zenith tube.**)

ZENITHAL HOURLY RATE Statistical datum for comparing the numbers of meteors observed in meteor showers; it is derived from the observed hourly rate by the application of a factor correcting for the zenith distance of the radiant; a secondary correction is also made to take account of any moonlight. (See **Meteors.**)

ZENOCENTRIC CO-ORDINATES A system of co-ordinates referred to the centre of Jupiter; the co-ordinate usually encountered is the zenocentric latitude, there being no significant difference between zenocentric longitude and zenographic longitude. The zenocentric latitude is the angle between a line joining the point concerned to the centre of Jupiter and the equatorial plane of the planet.

(See also **Co-ordinate systems; Zenographical co-ordinates.**)

ZENOGRAPHICAL CO-ORDINATES A system of co-ordinates referred to the surface of Jupiter. Jupiter being an oblate spheroid there is no significant difference between zenographical and zenocentric longitude, but the maximum difference between zenographical and zenocentric latitude is $3° \, 48' \, 38''$; it is therefore significant in the analysis of observations of belt latitudes.

The zenographical latitude may be regarded as the angle between the plane tangential to the surface of the planet at the point concerned and the planet's axis.

It is conventional to record belt-latitude determinations in the form of zenographical latitudes; this is rather regrettable as the zenocentric latitude is the more fundamental quantity and is much more appropriate for analysis; it would be undesirable to change the adopted system, however, and as the two systems can be easily inter-converted no great disadvantage accrues from the continued use of the zenographical system.

(See also **Co-ordinate systems; Zenocentric co-ordinates.**)

ZEPHYRIA Martian surface feature, approximate position $\Omega \, 195°$, $\Phi \, 0°$. Large ochre area in the equatorial region of the planet, north-west of the Mare Sirenum and south of Trivium Charontis; separated from Æolis to the west by Læstrygon.

ZETA GEMINORUM STARS A group of Cepheid variables having an atypically symmetrical light curve; that for the type-star ζ Gem is shown in Fig. 189.

(See also **Cepheid variables; Variable stars.**)

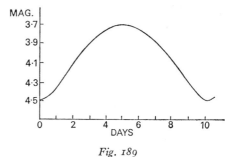

Fig. 189

ZEUS Name of the King of the Gods in Greek mythology (*Jupiter* in Roman mythology); root of words used in astronomical terminology such as *zenocentric*, *zenographical*, etc.

ZODIAC The zone centred on the Ecliptic and extending for 8° on either side of it. It is the zone in which the Moon and the planets are always found, whatever their orbital position may be.

The zodiac comprises twelve sections, each 30° long, known as the *signs of the zodiac*. These were named after the constellations that they contained in the time of Hipparchus, and the names have been retained although, due to the precession of the equinoxes, they do not now contain the same constellations.

Table 75.   Signs of the Zodiac

Constellation	Conventional sign
Aries	♈
Taurus	♉
Gemini	♊
Cancer	♋
Leo	♌
Virgo	♍
Libra	♎
Scorpio	♏
Sagittarius	♐
Capricornus	♑
Aquarius	♒
Pisces	♓

The first sign of the zodiac, Aries, commences at the **vernal equinox**, also termed the *First Point of Aries*. The names of the signs of the zodiac, and their conventional signs, are given in Table 75.

The zodiacal constellations remain the same, but are now located further along the Ecliptic, as explained; thus, the First Point of Aries is located in the constellation Pisces, etc.

ZODIACAL BAND A faint, parallel-sided glowing band around the Ecliptic,

joining the apices of the cones of the **zodiacal light**, of which it is an extension. Its intensity fades until about 135° from the Sun, then increases until the band merges with the **gegenschein**.

ZODIACAL LIGHT This comprises two cones of faint luminosity, centred on the Sun and lying along the Ecliptic. They are very difficult to observe, and are rarely seen outside the tropics. Under tropical observing conditions they can be seen to within as little as 20° of the Sun, and extend for about 100° around the Ecliptic. There are two associated phenomena, the *zodiacal band* and the *gegenschein*.

The zodiacal band is a very faint continuation of the zodiacal light, consisting of a narrow, parallel-sided band of luminosity along the Ecliptic, joining the apices of the cones; it fades in intensity to about 135° from the Sun, then brightens again until it merges with the gegenschein about 170° from the Sun; this pattern is repeated between the gegenschein and the other cone.

The gegenschein is an oval patch of luminosity, usually about 20° × 10°, along the Ecliptic and centred on the anti-solar point (180° from the Sun); it is brighter than the zodiacal band but fainter than the cones of zodiacal light.

The zodiacal light and associated phenomena are believed to be due to the presence of meteoric dust in the plane of the Earth's orbit, which shines by reflected sunlight.

ZODIACAL STARS CATALOGUE The **Catalogue of Zodiacal Stars**, *q.v.*

ZOND Name given to a series of Russian space-probe vehicles. *Zond 1* was launched on 1964 April 2 and was stated to be for the purpose of 'further developing a space system for distant interplanetary flights'. It was believed, however, to have been intended to make a close approach to the planet Venus. It was tracked by the Russian observers for more than six weeks, during which time it travelled more than 8 million miles from the Earth, but contact with the vehicle was then lost. It is believed that it may have impacted with Venus on 1964 July 25.

Zond 2 was launched into a parking orbit on 1964 November 30, and then propelled into a trajectory towards the planet Mars. It was stated to have pioneered the use in space of electric jet plasma engines. Radio contact was lost before the vehicle reached Mars.

Zond 3 was launched on 1965 July 18. It obtained photographs of the far side of the Moon before entering a solar orbit.

Zond 4 was launched on 1968 March 2 and was stated to be intended to study 'near-Earth space'.

ZONE Term used in describing planetary surface features, especially those of the major planets, where it denotes the light bands between the darker, parallel, longitudinal belts.

ZONE-TIME A system of differential time reckoning adopted for the whole world at the Washington conference in 1884, to facilitate the adoption of Greenwich Mean Time as the international standard and obviate the difficulties of using actual Local Time. At this conference the meridian of Greenwich was adopted as the zero of longitude, and zones of longitude, each 15° in width, were set up. Throughout each zone a common time is used, there being 24 zones in all. In the Greenwich zone ($7\frac{1}{2}°$E–$7\frac{1}{2}°$W) the standard time is, of course, G.M.T.; the standard time in each successive zone eastwards is one hour fast on the previous zone, and in each successive zone westwards one hour slow. The resulting discrepancy at longitude 180° (the International Date Line) is taken care of by omitting one day from the calendar if crossing west–east or repeating one day if crossing east–west.